Physics
A First Course
Second Edition

Tom Hsu, Ph.D.

School Specialty
Science

cpo)science

Physics A First Course
Second Edition
Copyright©2012 CPO Science, a member of School Specialty Science

ISBN: 978-1-60431-203-4
Part Number: 492-3860
Printing 6— August, 2017
Printed by Webcrafters, Madison, WI

CPO Science
80 Northwest Boulevard
Nashua, New Hampshire 03063
(866)588-6951
http://www.cposcience.com
Printed and Bound in the United States of America

Author

Thomas C. Hsu, Ph.D.

Nationally-recognized innovator in science and math education and the founder of CPO Science. Holds a Ph.D. in Applied Plasma Physics from the Massachusetts Institute of Technology (MIT), and has taught students from elementary, secondary, and college levels. Tom has worked with numerous K–12 teachers and administrators and is well known as a consultant, workshop leader, and developer of curriculum and equipment for inquiry-based learning in science and math.

Contributors

Mary Beth Abel – Principal Writer

B.S., Marine Biology, College of Charleston; M.S., Biological Sciences, University of Rhode Island

Taught science and math at an innovative high school and at the college level. Has expertise in scientific research, inquiry-based teaching methods, and science curriculum development. Mary Beth has been a principal writer with CPO Science since 2000.

Erik Benton – Principal Investigation Writer

B.F.A., University of Massachusetts with minor in Physics

Taught for eight years in public and private schools, focusing on inquiry and experiential learning. Erik brings extensive teaching and technical expertise, ranging from elementary and adult education to wildlife research. Currently he is involved in bird population studies in Massachusetts. Erik is the CPO Science investigation writer and conducts national content presentations.

Scott Eddleman – Project Manager and Writer

B.S., Biology, Southern Illinois University; M.Ed., Harvard University

Taught for 13 years in urban and rural settings. Developed two successful science-based school-to-career programs. Participated in a fellowship at Brown University where he conducted research on the coral reefs of Belize. Worked on National Science Foundation–funded projects at TERC. Scott has been a principal writer and curriculum developer for CPO Science since 1999.

Patsy Eldridge – Principal Writer

B.S., Biology, Grove City College; M.Ed., Tufts University

Experienced science teacher and national hands-on science trainer and presenter. Develops and teaches content-intensive graduate courses for science educators. Worked as a research scientist in the medical device industry. Patsy has developed curriculum and training materials with CPO Science since 2000.

Sonja Taylor – Principal Teacher's Guide Writer

B.S., Chemistry, Stephen F. Austin State University; M.Ed., Divergent Learning, Columbia College

Worked as an analytical chemist and has taught high school chemistry, biology, and physical science. While teaching in an innovative academy-based high school, Sonja was an academy team leader with responsibilities that included overseeing cross-curricular integration and serving as the liaison between students, faculty and members of the corporate advisory board. She enjoys developing lessons focused on engaging learners at all levels. Sonja has been a writer for CPO Science since 2003.

Laine Ives – Connection and Ancillary Writer

B.A., Gordon College and graduate coursework at Washington University, Cornell University, and Wheelock College

Taught elementary and middle school science at an independent school and an environmental education center in New England. Taught middle and high school English overseas. Laine has worked in curriculum development at CPO Science since 2000.

Senior Editor

Lynda Pennell – Executive Vice President

B.A., English; M.Ed., Administration, Reading Disabilities, Northeastern University; CAGS Media, University of Massachusetts, Boston

Nationally known in high school restructuring and for integrating academic and career education. Served as the director of an urban school for 5 years and has 17 years teaching/administrative experience in the Boston Public Schools. Lynda has led the development for CPO Science for the past eight years. She has also been recognized for her media production work.

Art and Illustration

Polly Crisman – Graphics Manager/Illustrator

B.F.A., University of New Hampshire

Worked as a designer and illustrator in marketing and advertising departments for a variety of industries. Polly has worked in the CPO Science design department since 2001, and is responsible for organizing workflow of graphics and file management. She created the CPO Science logo and supervises the graphic design image for CPO publications and media products.

Jesse Van Valkenburgh – Designer/Illustrator

B.F.A. Illustration, Rochester Institute of Technology

Worked in prepress and design. Was responsible for creative design and prepress film production for computer catalogs, brochures, and various marketing materials. Jesse completes photography and illustrations as a graphic designer for CPO Science book and media products.

Bruce Holloway – Senior Designer/Illustrator

Pratt Institute, New York, Boston Museum of Fine Arts

Expertise in illustration, advertising graphics, exhibits and product design. Commissioned throughout his career by The National Wildlife Federation's Conservation Stamp Campaign. Other commissions include the New Hampshire State Duck Stamp campaigns for 1999 and 2003. Bruce creates the cover art for the CPO Science textbooks.

Assessment

Mary Ann Erickson

B.S., Naval Architecture and Marine Engineering, Massachusetts Institute of Technology

Ran a technical writing consulting business, writing process control manuals for water treatment plants, software design documentation for simulation software, and operator manuals for mining equipment.

David H. Bliss

B.S., Science, Cornell University; M.Ed., Zoology

Taught for 39 years in the science field: biology, chemistry, earth science, and physics. Served as science department chair of Mohawk Central School District in Mohawk, New York.

Jane Fisher

B.S. Economics, Massachusetts Institute of Technology; Associate of the Society of Actuaries

Taught science for 39 years.

Editorial Consultant

Alan Hull

B.S., Emery University, Atlanta, Georgia; M.S., Georgia State University

Former high school physics and math teacher in Atlanta, Georgia. After teaching, Alan entered the school textbook publishing business where he held a variety of positions, including as a national secondary math-science consultant for major publishing companies.

Project and Technical Support

Susan Gioia – Educational CPO Science Administrator

Expertise in office management. Oversees all functions necessary for the smooth product development of CPO products, including print and media.

Sara Desharnais – Electronic Production Specialist

B.A., Creative Writing, Chester College of New England

Has worked in the publishing industry since 2004 and joined CPO Science in 2010.

Equipment Design

Thomas Narro – Senior Vice President

B.S., Mechanical Engineering, Rensselaer Polytechnic Institute

Accomplished design and manufacturing engineer; experienced consultant in corporate reengineering and industrial-environmental acoustics.

Marise Evans – Industrial Designer

M.S., Industrial Design, Auburn University, B.S., Interior Design and Environmental Design, Auburn University

Works with mechanical engineers to design new CPO products and improve the design of current products.

Dr. Darren Garnier – Research Physicist, Columbia University/MIT

Material Support

Kathryn Gavin – Purchasing and Quality Control Manager

Responsible for all functions related to purchasing raw materials and quality control of finished goods. Works closely with product development and design.

Matthew Connor – Product Quality Specialist

B.A., Philosophy, University of Toronto.

Responsible for production quality assurance, product testing and troubleshooting, creating and editing product documents and experiment testing.

Science Content Consultants

Dr. Jeffrey Williams – Bridgewater State College, Bridgewater, Massachusetts - Professor of Physics

Stacy Kissel – Physics Teacher, Brookline High School, Brookline, Massachusetts

Dr. David Guerra – Associate Professor, Department Chair Physics, St. Anselm College, Manchester, New Hampshire

Dr. Mitch Crosswait – Nuclear Engineer/Physicist, United States Government, Alexandria, Virginia

Science Content Reviewers

Dr. Jeff Schechter – Physicist, Boston, Massachusetts

Dr. Tim Daponte – Physics Teacher, Houston ISD, Houston, Texas

Wanda Pagonis – Physics Teacher, Our Lady of the Lake University, San Antonio, Texas

Kurt Lichtenwald – Physics/Robotics Teacher, Gloucester High School, Gloucester, MA

Dr. Willa Ramsay – Science Education Consultant

DaMarcus Wright – Physics Teacher, Grand Prairie ISD, Grand Prairie, Texas

Beverly T. Cannon – Physics Teacher, Highland Park High School, Dallas, Texas

Betsy Nahas – Physics Teacher, Chelmsford High School, Westford, Massachusetts

Neri Giovanni – Physics Teacher, Kennedy High School, San Antonio, Texas

Scott Hanes – Physics Teacher, Liberty-Eylau High School, Hooks, Texas

Bruce Ward – Nuclear Medical Technician, Boston, Massachusetts

Lee DeWitt – Physics Teacher, NEISD, San Antonio, Texas

Steve Heady – Physics Teacher, Houston High School, Houston, Texas

Dr. Michael Saulnier –Physicist, Boston, Massachusetts

Gigi Nevils – Physics Teacher, Bellaire High School, Houston, Texas

Lebee Meehan – Physicist, National Aeronautics and Space Administration, Houston, Texas

Dr. Manos Chaniotakis – Physicist, Massachusetts Institute of Technology, Cambridge, Massachusetts

Jay Kurima – Physics Teacher, Fort Worth ISD, Fort Worth, Texas

James DeHart – Physics Teacher, West Brook High School, Beaumont, Texas

David Binette – Engineering Student, Cornell University, Ithaca, New York

Rebecca DeLozier – Physics Teacher, Lewisville ISD, Shady Shores, Texas

Valerie Felger – Physics Teacher, North East ISD, New Braunfels, Texas

George Whittemore – Physics Instructor, Leominster High School, Leominster, MA

Ken Rideout – Physical Science Teacher, Swampscott High School, Swampscott, MA

Brett Malas – National Board Certified Science Teacher, Naperville North High School, IL

William G. Fleischmann – Science Teacher, Wood Hill Middle School, MA

Ruby Ashley – Project Coordinator, Georgia Southern Museum Outreach Programs, GA

Mary Jo Carabatsos PhD – Science Teacher, Andover High School, Andover, MA

Angela Benjamin – AP Physics Instructor, Woodrow Wilson Senior High School, DC

Richard Famiglietti – Science Teacher, Lynn Classical High School, Lynn, MA

Elizabeth A. Jensen – Science Teacher, James Blair Middle School, VA

Colleen M O'Shell – Chemistry Teacher, Cambridge Rindge and Latin School, MA

Ian Smith – Physics Teacher, Bellows Free Academy, VT

Jean Lifford – Reading Coach, Boston Public Schools, MA

Ed Wiser – Physics Teacher, Brookline High School, MA

David Harris – Head of Science Department, Hackley School, NY

Sarah Segreti – Science Teacher, Naperville North High School, IL

Nick Nicastro – Physics Teacher, Wachusett Regional High School, MA

Cecilia A. Cherill – Physical Science Teacher, Churchill Junior High School, NJ

Kristy Beauvais – Physics Teacher, Concord-Carlisle Regional High School, MA

Special Thanks

for their time and contributions:

Lotfi Merabet, OD PhD – Research Scientist, The Boston Retinal Implant Project, Boston, Massachusetts

Dr. Joseph F. Rizzo III, MD – Director, Center for Innovative Visual Rehabilitation, Boston VA Medical Center, Professor, Massachusetts Eye and Ear Infirmary, Harvard Medical School, Boston, Massachusetts

Dr. Juris Zarins – Professor, Department of Sociology and Anthropology, Missouri State University Springfield, Missouri

Ronald G. Blom, Ph.D. – Lead Scientist, Terrestrial Science Research Element, Discipline Program Manager, Solid Earth Science and Natural Hazards, NASA Jet Propulsion Laboratory, Pasadena, California

Laura Ort – Lesson Organizer, B.A., Cornell College.

Physics
A First Course

table of contents

ELECTRICITY

POSITIVE

Measurement & motion

Mechanical advantage

QWERT
ASDF
ZXC

Van de Graaff

Unit 3: Energy and Systems   166

Unit 4: Matter and Energy   214

Unit 5: Electricity   292

Unit 1 MOTION

Gravity

Collisions

Acceleration

Position vs. Time

Describing the Physical Universe

On June 21, 2004, SpaceShipOne became the first private aircraft to leave Earth's atmosphere and enter space. What is the future of this technology? Private companies are hoping to sell tickets to adventurous people who want to take a trip beyond Earth's atmosphere. Our study of physics can help us understand how such a trip is possible.

Many people, when asked the question "What is physics?" respond with "Oh, physics is all about complicated math equations and confusing laws to memorize." This is not the physics of the world around us, and it is definitely not the physics that you will study in this course! In this chapter, you will be introduced to what studying physics is really all about, and you will begin your physics journey by studying motion and speed.

VOCABULARY

accuracy	independent variable	scientific method
constant speed	length	second
control variable	mass	SI
dependent variable	model	significant digits
distance	natural law	speed
energy	objective	system
English System	physics	theory
experiment	precision	time interval
experimental variable	repeatable	variable
hypothesis	resolution	

KEY QUESTIONS

✓ *How can an accident or a mistake lead to a scientific discovery?*

✓ *If someone is 2-meters tall, what is their height in feet and inches?*

✓ *What is the fastest speed in the universe?*

1.1 The Science of Physics

Imagine you are slowly riding up the highest hill of a roller coaster. Soon, there will be a fast, exciting ride down the hill. Why does a motor pull you up that hill and why isn't it needed for the rest of the ride? Physics can answer these questions. You might think physics is a complicated set of rules, equations to memorize, and confusing laws and theories. In fact, physics is about finding the simplest and least-complicated explanation for why things happen the way they do.

Important ideas in physics

Energy and matter are important in physics
Physics is a type of science that studies matter and energy. Everything in the universe is believed to be either matter or energy (Figure 1.1). Matter is anything that has mass and takes up space. **Mass** is the measure of the amount of matter that makes up an object. A car has more mass than a bicycle. Steel, plastic, and rubber are different forms of matter, and the car has a lot more than the bicycle, so the car has more mass than the bicycle. **Energy** is a measure of a system's ability to change or create change in other systems. Energy flows any time something gets hotter, colder, faster, slower, or changes, such as when an ice cube melts.

Understanding natural laws
A **natural law** is a rule that describes an action or set of actions in the universe. Physics is concerned with understanding natural laws related to matter and energy. For example, if you apply a force to a cart, you might change its motion. Newton's second law of motion is the natural law that describes how much force you will need to cause a certain amount of change in motion. Sometimes a natural law, like Newton's second law of motion, can be expressed by a mathematical equation. You will learn about this law and its mathematical equation in Chapter 3.

Discovering the natural laws
Unfortunately, no one is born knowing any of the natural laws. By clever thinking and observations, over thousands of years, humans have deduced many of the natural laws. An important part of physics is understanding natural laws. This part of physics includes observation and experiments, and you will review those activities in this section. We do not know all of the natural laws, so there is a lot left for students like you to discover!

> **physics** - a branch of science concerned with understanding the natural laws that relate to matter and energy
>
> **mass** - the amount of matter an object has and a measure of its inertia
>
> **energy** - a measure of a system's ability to change or create change in other systems
>
> **natural law** - a rule that describes an action or set of actions in the universe

Matter
Material that has mass and takes up space

Solid
Liquid
Gas

Energy
The ability to cause changes in factors like temperature, height, or speed

Figure 1.1: *The universe contains matter and energy.*

Systems and variables

Defining a system
The universe is huge and complex. One way to make sense of it is to think about a small part at a time. If you want to understand a car rolling down a ramp, you don't need to confuse yourself with the Sun, or the Milky Way galaxy, or even the room next door. When you want to understand something, you focus your attention on a group of factors called a **system**. A system is a group of objects, effects, and variables that are related. You choose the system to include the things you wish to investigate. You exclude the things you think are not relevant.

Variables
A **variable** is a factor that affects the behavior of the system. When you are trying to find out how a system works, you look for relationships between the important variables of the system. For example, imagine you are doing an experiment with a car rolling down a ramp. The car and the ramp are the system. The car's speed is one important variable. Time, position, and mass are other variables.

system - a collection of related factors that you identify to help answer a question or solve a problem

variable - a factor that affects the results of an experiment and which can have different values under different conditions

Some important variables in this system

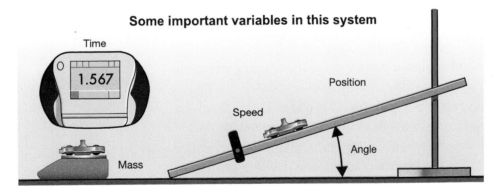

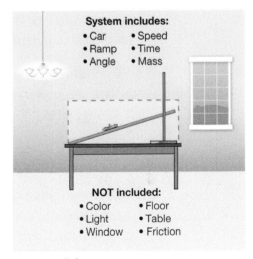

System includes:
- Car
- Ramp
- Angle
- Speed
- Time
- Mass

NOT included:
- Color
- Light
- Window
- Floor
- Table
- Friction

Figure 1.2: *Choose variables that are relevant to your investigation.*

What's in a system?
The ideal system includes all the objects, effects, and variables that affect what you are trying to understand (Figure 1.2). To understand the motion of a car on a ramp, you might include the mass of the car, the angle of the ramp, and the speed of the car. The fewer the number of variables, the easier it is to find important relationships among them. You can always add more variables, like friction from the wheels, after you understand how the most basic variables are related.

The scientific method

Learning by chance
Once you have defined a system, you can start to learn about it. One way to learn about a system is by chance. For example, think of how you might try to open a jar that has a stuck lid. After trying many techniques, you will eventually be able to open the jar. By chance, you will have learned a technique that works.

Learning by the scientific method
Learning by chance is one way to learn. However, you don't always end up with information that might be helpful to others since your method might not be documented or thoroughly tested. The **scientific method** is a much more dependable way to learn and gather information. Key parts of the scientific method include the hypothesis and the experiment. A **hypothesis** is a tentative, testable statement that tries to explain a set of scientific observations. An **experiment** is a situation specifically set up to test or investigate a hypothesis.

> **scientific method** - a process of learning that begins with a hypothesis and proceeds to prove or change a hypothesis by comparing it with scientific evidence
>
> **hypothesis** - a tentative statement that can be tested by comparison with scientific evidence
>
> **experiment** - a situation created to test or investigate a hypothesis

The Scientific Method

1. Scientists observe nature, then develop or revise hypotheses about how things work.
2. The hypotheses are tested against evidence collected from observations and experiments.
3. Any hypothesis that correctly accounts for *all* of the evidence from the observations and experiments is a potentially-correct theory.
4. A theory is continually tested by collecting new and different evidence. Even one single piece of evidence that does not agree with a theory will force scientists to return to the first step.

Theories start out as hypotheses
Theories in science start out as hypotheses (Figure 1.3). For example, the early explanations of heat were all incorrect hypotheses. But, in 1842, the hypothesis that heat is a form of energy was made by a German doctor, Julius Mayer. Then, this hypothesis was confirmed by experiments done by James Joule in 1843. Energy has no weight, so Mayer's hypothesis explained why an object's weight remained unchanged whether it was hot or cold. After many experiments, Mayer's hypothesis that heat is a form of energy became the theory of heat that we accept today.

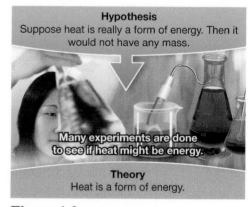

Figure 1.3: *A theory begins as a hypothesis.*

Scientific theories

What is a scientific theory? In everyday language, the word *theory* means a vague idea that may or may not be right. You might say "I have a theory to explain why my dog hides when I get out the vacuum cleaner." In this statement, you are using the everyday meaning of theory. In science, the word *theory* is used differently. A scientific **theory** is a comprehensive, well-tested description of how and why a process in nature works the way it does. Usually, one or more natural laws fit into a single comprehensive theory. For example, the classical theory of motion includes Newton's three laws, as well as conservation laws for energy and momentum. It is a common mistake for someone to carry the everyday meaning of theory into a discussion of scientific theory. Be careful not to make this mistake.

The nature of scientific research The purpose of scientific research is to do experiments which show that existing theories do *not* give the right prediction. A theory that correctly explains 1,000 experiments but fails to explain the 1,001st cannot be wholly complete. An unexplained experiment points out where a theory is lacking, and is a tip to a scientist that something new may be undiscovered.

Science versus pseudoscience Professor Rory Coker of the Physics Department at the University of Texas offers an entire college course devoted to distinguishing science from pseudoscience. "The word *pseudo* means fake," says professor Coker, "and the surest way to spot a fake is to know as much as possible about the real thing, in this case science itself." People sometimes confuse the terms *astronomy* and *astrology*, much to the dismay of scientists. Astronomy is the scientific study of objects in space like stars, planets, comets, and galaxies. Astrology is completely different. Astrology is *not* a scientific field of study. Astrology is a group of traditions and beliefs that say the positions of objects in space can provide information about human personalities, events, and daily life. Astrologers create and use horoscopes. Horoscopes contain very general statements that could be true and helpful for almost anyone, not just the reader, and the particular "star" a person is "born under." Astrology is not a science, it is a *pseudoscience*. It is important to be able to distinguish between pseudoscience and science. Beware of such "science knowledge" you find on the Internet. Some of it is correct, but much of it is not.

theory - a scientific explanation supported by a lot of evidence collected over a long period of time

Theory

A self-consistent and comprehensive explanation that is supported by a large body of scientific evidence

Example

The classical theory of motion

Newton's 1st law

Newton's 2nd law

Newton's 3rd law

The law of conservation of energy

The law of conservation of momentum

Investigating systems

Experiments   Observation and experimentation are key processes in science. An experiment investigates the relationship between variables in a system. Experiments usually have a question associated with them. An example would be "How does the steepness of a ramp affect the speed of a ball?" A stepwise way to conduct your experiment using the scientific method is described below.

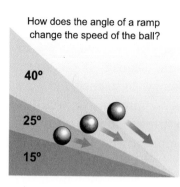

How does the angle of a ramp change the speed of the ball?

40°
25°
15°

> **independent variable** - the variable in an experiment that is manipulated by the experimenter and that causes changes in the dependent variable in the experiment
>
> **dependent variable** - the variable in an experiment that changes in response to choices made by the experimenter
>
> **control variable** - a variable in an experiment that is kept the same throughout the experiment
>
> **experimental variable** - a variable in an experiment that is changed by the experimenter

Types of variables   To answer the question, you do an experiment. In this experiment, you will measure the cause-and-effect relationship between the ramp's angle and the speed of the ball. The variable causing the change in the system is called the **independent variable**. This is the variable that you change in an experiment. The angle of the ramp is the independent variable in this example. The variable that may show the effect of those changes is called the **dependent variable**. The speed of the ball is the dependent variable.

Making a hypothesis   You can think of a hypothesis as an educated guess that predicts the relationship between the independent and dependent variables in an experiment. Coming up with a good hypothesis means you must have some experience with the system you are investigating. However, you may be unsure about what will happen in an experiment. Scientists often make hypotheses that they end up proving to be incorrect. The first hypothesis is just a *starting point* for developing a correct understanding.

Designing experiments   In an ideal experiment, you change only one variable at a time. You keep *all* of the other variables the same. This means that any change you see in the system must be associated with the one variable you changed. A variable that is kept the same is called a **control variable**. The variable that is changed is called the **experimental variable**. In the ball-and-ramp experiment, the ramp angle, the mass of the ball, and the starting point are all important variables that affect the speed. In a well-designed experiment, you change only one variable at a time and keep the others constant.

Scientific evidence

What counts as scientific evidence? The goal of an experiment is to produce scientific evidence. But what types of evidence qualify as *scientific* evidence? Do feelings or opinions count as scientific evidence? Does what other people think qualify as scientific evidence? The answer to both questions is no. Because evidence is so important in science, there are exacting rules defining what counts as scientific evidence.

An example of scientific evidence Scientific evidence might include numbers, tables, graphs, words, pictures, sound recordings, or other information. The important thing is that the evidence accurately describes what happens in the real world (Figure 1.4). Scientific evidence might be collected without doing experiments in a laboratory. For example, Galileo used his telescope to look at the Moon. He recorded what he saw by sketching in his notebook. Galileo's sketches are considered scientific evidence.

When is evidence scientific? Scientific evidence must be objective and repeatable. **Objective** means the evidence should describe *only what actually happened* as exactly as possible. **Repeatable** means that others who look the same way at the same thing will observe the same results. Galileo's sketches describe in detail what he actually saw through the telescope. That means the sketches are *objective*. Others who looked through his telescope saw the same thing. That makes the sketches *repeatable*. Galileo's sketches are good scientific evidence because they are both objective and repeatable. Galileo's sketches helped make the case that the Moon is actually a world like Earth, with mountains and valleys. This is not what was believed in Galileo's time.

Communicating scientific evidence with exact definitions It is important that scientific evidence be clear, with no room for confusion or misunderstanding. For this reason, scientists define concepts like *force* and *weight* very clearly. Usually, the scientific definition is similar to the everyday meaning of the word, but more exact. For example, when you talk about your weight in everyday terms, you're talking about the number of pounds that your body weighs. In science, your weight is the force of gravity pulling on the mass of your body.

objective - describes evidence that documents only what actually happens and is observed as exactly as possible

repeatable - describes evidence that can be seen independently by others if they repeat the same experiment or observation in the same way

Examples of Scientific Evidence

Pictures or sketches that show actual observations

MOON DATA FOR 9/9-11/08
(LONGITUDE 71.1 W, LATITUDE 42.3 N)

EVENT	TIME (EDT)
MOONRISE	4:07 PM ON 9/9/08
MOONSET	12:58 AM
MOONRISE	4:44 PM
MOON TRANSIT	9:20 PM
MOONSET	2:03 AM 9/11/08

Measurements and data

Figure 1.4: *Some examples of scientific evidence.*

Models

An example of a system   Consider the following system: A rubber band is used to launch a car along a track that turns uphill. If the rubber band is stretched more, the car has more speed. If the car has more speed, it goes higher up the hill. How do we explain the relationship between height and speed?

What is a model?   Explanations in physics often come in the form of models. In physics, a **model** links the variables in a system through cause-and-effect relationships.

An example of a model   The top diagram in Figure 1.5 shows a real-world model of the car-and-track system. Launching the car gives it energy that shows up as its speed. Climbing the hill takes energy. The car climbs only so high because it has only so much energy. Making the car go faster gives it more energy, so it goes higher. This model links the height and speed through the idea of energy. This model is known as the *law of conservation of energy*. It is one of the natural laws of physics. The bottom diagram in Figure 1.5 shows a *conceptual model*. It is not precise enough to predict exactly how high the car goes at a given speed. Later, you will study a more detailed version of the law of conservation of energy.

> **model** - a method of representing a relationship between variables

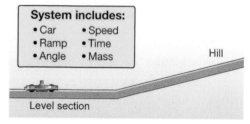

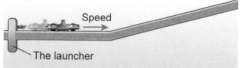

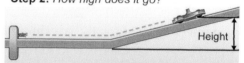

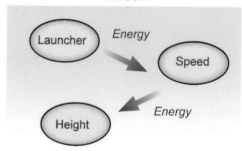

Figure 1.5: *The two models of the car-and-track system.*

1.1 Section Review

1. What are the main activities involved in studying physics?
2. You are doing an experiment to find out if expensive batteries will run your radio longer than cheaper batteries. List a question, a hypothesis, the independent and dependent variables, and the control variable(s) for this experiment. Then, write a step-by-step procedure to test your hypothesis.
3. Compare and contrast natural law, hypothesis, and scientific theory.

1.2 **Distance, Time, and Measurement**

In science, you need a precise way to describe the natural world. In physics, many things are described with measurements. For example, 2 meters is a measurement of length that is a little more than the height of an average person. Measurements such as length, mass, speed, and temperature are important in science. They are a language that allows us to communicate information. In this section, you will learn about measuring distance and time.

> **distance** - a measure of the space between two points
>
> **length** - a measured distance that uses a specific measurement system's units

Measuring distance

Measurements A measurement is a precise value that tells how much. How much *what*, you ask? That depends on what you are measuring. A measurement communicates the amount in a way that can be understood by others. For example, 2 meters is a measurement because it has a *quantity,* 2, and a *unit,* meters.

Units All measurements must have units. Without a unit, a measurement cannot be understood. For example, if you asked someone to walk 10, she would not know how far to go: 10 feet, 10 meters, 10 miles, and 10 kilometers are all 10. However, the units are different and the distances are, too. Units communicate amounts. Physics uses a set of units that have been agreed upon around the world.

What is distance? **Distance** is the amount of separation between two unique points. You can also think of distance as how far apart two objects are. You probably have a good understanding of distance from everyday experiences. The concept of distance in physics is the same. However, the actual distances may be larger or smaller than what you normally refer to as a distance. For example, think about the shortest distance between two points on the floor and the shortest distance between two points on a basketball (Figure 1.6).

Distance is measured in units of length Distance is measured in units of **length**. Some of the commonly-used units of length include inches, miles, centimeters, kilometers, and meters. It is important to always specify which length unit you are using for a measurement.

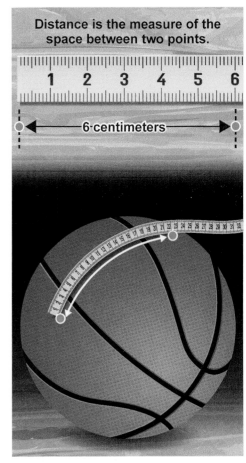

Distance is the measure of the space between two points.

6 centimeters

Figure 1.6: *The shortest distance between two points on the floor (top) and on a basketball.*

Two systems of measurement

English System measurements The **English System** is used for everyday measurements in the United States. Miles, yards, feet, inches, pounds, pints, quarts, gallons, cups, and teaspoons are all English System units. However, only one or two countries other than the United States still use this system of measurement today.

Measuring with SI units During the 1800s, a new system of measurement—the Metric System—was developed in France and was quickly adopted by other European and South American countries. The goal of this system was for all units of measurement to be related, and for the units to form a base-10, or decimal system. In 1960, the Metric System was revised and simplified, and a new name was adopted—the International System of Units, or **SI** for short. The acronym SI comes from the French name *Le Système International d'Unités*. Today, the United States is the only industrialized nation that has not switched completely to SI.

Scientists use SI Almost all fields of science worldwide use SI units because they are so much easier to work with. In the English System, there are 12 inches in a foot, 3 feet in a yard, and 5,280 feet in a mile. These are not easy numbers to remember or to compute with. In SI, there are 10 millimeters in a centimeter, 100 centimeters in a meter, and 1,000 meters in a kilometer. Factors of 10 are easier to remember and work with, mathematically, than 12, 3, and 5,280. The illustration gives a sense of how SI units of length compare. Figure 1.7 shows some SI prefixes and their values.

> **English System** - the measurement system used for everyday measurements in the United States
>
> **SI** - the International System of Units (SI) used by most countries for everyday measurement and used by the scientific community worldwide

Prefix	Meaning	Value
giga (G)	1 billion	1,000,000,000
mega (M)	1 million	1,000,000
kilo (k)	1 thousand	1,000
centi (c)	1-hundredth	0.01
milli (m)	1-thousandth	0.001
micro (µ)	1-millionth	0.000001

Figure 1.7: *SI prefixes and their values.*

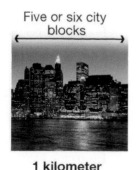

Five or six city blocks — 1 kilometer

Height of a first grade student — 1 meter

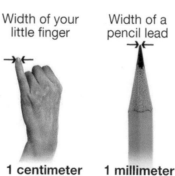

Width of your little finger — 1 centimeter

Width of a pencil lead — 1 millimeter

Measuring time

Time in science   We often want to know how things change over time. For example, a car rolls down a hill over time. A hot cup of coffee cools down over time. Many laws of physics tell us how things change over time.

What time is it?   Time is used two ways (Figure 1.8). One way is to identify a particular moment in the past or in the future. For example, saying your 18th birthday party will be on January 1, 2014, at 2:00 p.m. identifies a particular moment in the future for your party to start. This is the way "time" is usually used in everyday conversation.

How much time?   The second way is to describe a *quantity* of time. The question "How much time?" is asking for a quantity of time. A quantity of time is also called a **time interval**. Any calculation involving time that you do in physics will use time intervals, *not time of day*. Any exceptions will be explained.

Time in seconds

Hours   Minutes   Seconds

2 : 30 : 45

Many problems in science use time in seconds. For calculations, you may need to convert hours and minutes into seconds. For example, this timer shows 2 hours, 30 minutes, and 45 seconds.

How many total seconds does this time interval represent? There are 60 seconds in a minute, so multiply 30 minutes by 60 to get 1,800 seconds. There are 3,600 seconds in an hour, so multiply 2 hours by 3,600 to get 7,200 seconds. Add up all the seconds to get your answer: 45 + 1,800 + 7,200 = 9,045, or 9,045 seconds.

> **time interval** - a quantity of time separating two events

What time is it?

11:52 a.m. March 12, 2012

How much time?

2 hours, 22 minutes, 42 seconds

Figure 1.8: *There are two different ways to understand time.*

Time scales in physics

One second The **second** (s) is the basic unit of time in both the SI and English systems. One second is about the time it takes to say "thousand." There are 60 seconds in a minute and 3,600 seconds in an hour. The second was originally defined in terms of one day: There are 86,400 seconds in an average day of 24 hours (24 h × 3,600 s/h).

Time in physics Events in the universe happen over a huge range of time intervals. Figure 1.9 gives a few examples of time scales that are studied in physics. The average life span of a human being is 2.2 billion seconds. The time it takes a mosquito to beat its wings once is 0.0005 seconds. The time it takes light to get from this page to your eyes is 0.000000002 seconds.

Time in experiments In many experiments, you will observe how things change with time. For example, when you drop a ball, it falls to the ground. You can make a graph of the height of the ball versus the time for it to fall. The *time* is the time interval measured from when the ball was released. This graph shows how the height of the ball changes with time. The graph shows that it takes the ball about 0.45 seconds to fall a distance of 1 meter. Many of the experiments you will do involve measuring times between 0.0001 seconds and a few seconds. When making graphs of results from experiments, the time almost always goes on the horizontal or *x*-axis.

second - the basic unit of time in both the English and SI systems of measurement

An experiment involving time

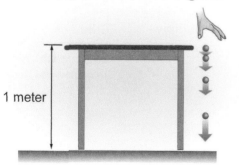

1 meter

Height vs. Time

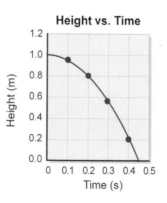

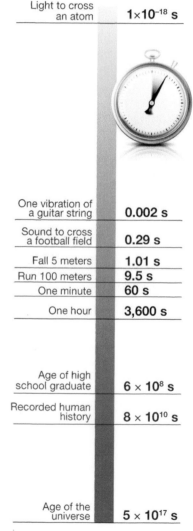

Light to cross an atom	1×10^{-18} s
One vibration of a guitar string	0.002 s
Sound to cross a football field	0.29 s
Fall 5 meters	1.01 s
Run 100 meters	9.5 s
One minute	60 s
One hour	3,600 s
Age of high school graduate	6×10^{8} s
Recorded human history	8×10^{10} s
Age of the universe	5×10^{17} s

Figure 1.9: *Time intervals in physics.* (Note: *The timeline is not drawn to scale.*)

Accuracy, precision, and resolution

Accuracy The words *accuracy* and *precision* have special meanings in science that are different from how people use these words in daily conversation (Figure 1.10). **Accuracy** is how close a measurement is to its accepted or "true" value. An accurate clock or watch will give a time reading that is the same as or extremely close to the official time from a government time standard. An accurate golf putt is one that falls in the hole. A very accurate golf drive would be a hole-in-one!

Precision Precision does not have the same meaning as accuracy. **Precision** describes how close together several repeated measurements or events are to one another. Precise clocks throughout a school would all read the same time at any given moment. School clocks can be precise without being accurate. Can you explain how this could be true? If three different golf balls are hit off of the same tee, and each one of them goes into the same sand trap, this represents good precision, but poor accuracy.

Resolution **Resolution** is another important term to understand when you are working with measured quantities. Resolution refers to the smallest interval that can be measured (Figure 1.10). The resolution of a metric ruler is 0.5 millimeters. This is because resolution is often defined as one half of the smallest measurement possible. With some metric rulers, like the meter stick, the smallest unit is the millimeter; therefore, 0.5 millimeters is its resolution.

Resolution in images The word *resolution* often appears in connection with digital cameras or high-definition televisions (HDTV). A high-resolution image is very sharp and of high quality. For example, an HDTV image can have 1,980 dots in the horizontal direction. A standard TV image has only 640 dots. A feature that is two dots wide in an HDTV image is just a blur on a standard TV. You can think of resolution as the "sharpness" of a measurement. A measurement with lots of resolution is a very "sharp" measurement. A timer that measures seconds to four decimal places has a resolution of one ten-thousandth of a second (0.0001 s). A stopwatch that measures seconds to two decimal places has a lower resolution of one-hundredth of a second (0.01 s).

accuracy - how close a measurement is to an accepted or "true" value

precision - describes how close together or reproducible repeated measurements are

resolution - refers to the smallest interval that can be measured

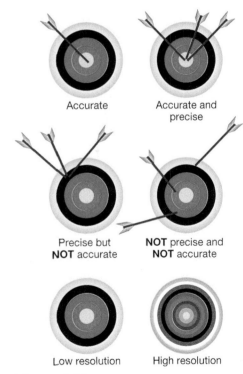

Accurate

Accurate and precise

Precise but **NOT** accurate

NOT precise and **NOT** accurate

Low resolution

High resolution

Figure 1.10: *Accuracy, precision, and resolution.*

Working with Measurements

Uncertainty in measurement   All measurements involve a degree of uncertainty. The object in Figure 1.11 is definitely longer than 2.6 centimeters. But how much longer? Not everyone would agree on the third digit of the measurement. One person might read the measurement as 2.63 centimeters. Another might argue it is closer to 2.65 centimeters. It is *impossible* to make a measurement of the exact true value of anything, except when counting "things." Using the ruler in Figure 1.11, the best answer for the length of the paper clip is 2.65 centimeters. To a scientist this number means "between 2.6 and 2.7 centimeters." The last digit, 5, represents the smallest amount, 0.05 cm, and it is uncertain.

Significant digits   **Significant digits** are the meaningful digits in a measured quantity. The third digit in the measurement 2.65 centimeters is meaningful even though it is uncertain. The third digit tells someone the object is about halfway between 2.6 and 2.7 centimeters in length. Therefore, we say there are three useful or significant digits in this length measurement.

Using significant digits in math problems   What happens when you use measured quantities with *different numbers of significant digits* in a math problem? A shoe is 38 centimeters long and you want to convert the length to inches:

$$38 \text{ cm} \times \left(\frac{1 \text{ inch}}{2.54 \text{ cm}} \right) = ?$$

To find the answer, divide 38 by 2.54 and you get 14.960629. This answer has a large number of digits. An answer involving measured quantities should have no more significant digits than the starting measurement with the *least* number of significant digits. The correct answer to this problem is rounded up to 15 inches, since 38 centimeters has two significant digits.

> **significant digits** - meaningful digits in a measured quantity

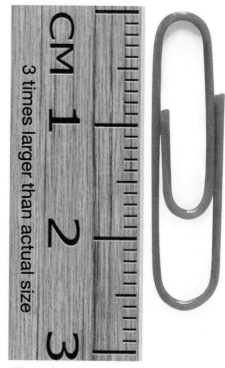

Figure 1.11: *Find the length of the object in centimeters. How many digits should your answer have?*

1.2 Section Review

1. List two common systems of units and give examples of distance measurements for each.
2. What are significant digits, and how are they used when working with measured quantities?
3. Study Figure 1.10. Explain why each target-and-arrow example was chosen for each of the labeled situations.

1.3 Speed

Nothing in the universe stays still. A book on a table appears to be sitting still. However, Earth is moving in its orbit around the Sun at a speed of 66,000 miles per hour. You and the book move with Earth. Speed is an important concept in physics. Saying that something is "fast" is not enough to describe its speed. A race car is fast compared with other cars, but it is slow compared with a jet airplane. In this section, you will learn a precise definition of speed.

speed - the rate at which an object's distance changes over time

constant speed - an unchanging speed of a moving object that covers the same distance each second

Speed

An example of speed   Consider a bicycle moving along the road. The diagram shows the positions of two bicycles at different times. To understand the concept of speed, think about these two questions:

- How many meters does the bicycle move each second?
- Does the bicycle move the same number of meters every second?

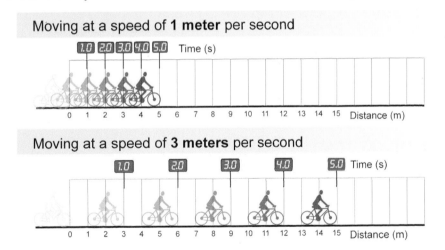

The speed limit of the universe

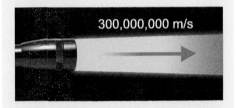

The fastest speed in the universe is the speed of light. Light moves at 300 million meters per second (3×10^8 m/s). If you could make light travel in a circle, it would go around Earth 7½ times in 1 second!

The precise meaning of speed   The **speed** of a bicycle is the distance it travels divided by the time it takes. At 1 m/s, a bicycle travels 1 meter each second. At 3 m/s, it travels 3 meters each second. Both bicycles are moving at **constant speed**. Constant speed means the same distance is traveled every second.

Calculating speed

Speed is distance divided by time

Speed is a measure of the *distance* traveled in a given amount of *time*. To calculate the speed of an object, you need to know two things:

- the distance traveled by the object
- the time it took to travel the distance

Average speed

Speed is calculated by dividing the distance traveled by the time taken. For example, if you drive 150 kilometers in 1.5 hours (Figure 1.12), then the average speed of the car is 150 kilometers divided by 1.5 hours, or 100 kilometers per hour.

What does *per* mean?

The word *per* means "for every" or "for each." The speed of 100 kilometers per hour is short for saying 100 kilometers *for each* hour. You can also think of *per* as meaning "divided by." The quantity before the word *per* is divided by the quantity after it. For example, 150 kilometers divided by 1.5 hours equals 100 kilometers per hour.

Units for speed

Speed is also a ratio of distance to time. Therefore, the units for speed are distance units divided by time units. In SI, distance is measured in centimeters, meters, or kilometers. If distance is in kilometers and time in hours, then speed is expressed in kilometers per hour (km/h or kph). Other metric units for speed are centimeters per second (cm/s) and meters per second (m/s). Speed is also commonly expressed in miles per hour (mph). Table 1.1 shows different units commonly used for speed.

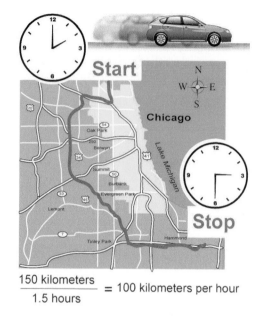

$$\frac{150 \text{ kilometers}}{1.5 \text{ hours}} = 100 \text{ kilometers per hour}$$

Figure 1.12: *A driving trip with an average speed of 100 km/h.*

Table 1.1: Common units for speed

Distance	Time	Speed	Abbreviation
meters	seconds	meters per second	m/s
kilometers	hours	kilometers per hour	km/h
centimeters	seconds	centimeters per second	cm/s
miles	hours	miles per hour	mph
inches	seconds	inches per second	in/s
feet	minutes	feet per minute	ft/min

Relationships between distance, speed, and time

Distance, speed, and time A common question in physics is "How far do you go if you drive for 2 hours at a speed of 100 km/h?" You know how to get speed from time and distance. How do you get distance from speed and time? The answer is the reason mathematics is the language of physics.

Calculating speed Let the letter v stand for "speed," the letter d stand for "distance traveled," and the letter t stand for "time taken." If we remember that the letters stand for those words, we can write a precise definition of speed.

$$\textbf{SPEED}$$

$$\text{Speed (m/s)} \ \ v = \frac{d \ \ \text{Distance traveled (m)}}{t \ \ \text{Time taken (s)}}$$

There are three ways to arrange the letters, or *variables*, that relate distance, time, and speed. You can get any one of the three variables if you know the other two (Figure 1.13).

Using formulas Remember that the words or letters stand for the values of the variables. For example, the letter t will be replaced by the actual time. Think of each letter as a box that will hold a number. Once we get everything arranged according to the rules, we can fill the boxes with the numbers that belong in each one. The last box left will be the answer. The letters, or variables, are the labels that tell us which numbers belong in which boxes.

Why *v* is used to represent speed

When we represent speed in a formula, we use the letter *v*. If this seems confusing, remember that *v* stands for *velocity*.

It is not important for this chapter, but there is a technical difference between speed and velocity. Speed is a single measurement that tells how fast you are going, such as 80 kilometers per hour.

Velocity means you know both your speed and the *direction* you are going. If you tell someone you are going 80 km/h directly south, you are telling them your velocity. If you say only that you are going 60 mph, you are telling them your speed.

Equation	gives you	if you know
$v = d \div t$	speed	distance and time
$d = vt$	distance	speed and time
$t = d \div v$	time	distance and speed

Figure 1.13: *Different forms of the speed equation.*

How to solve physics problems

Physics problems
In physics, you will be asked to analyze and solve problems. In fact, learning physics will make you a better problem solver. This skill is important in all careers. For example, financial analysts are expected to look at information about businesses. Doctors collect information about patients. Mechanics gather information about a car to troubleshoot what is causing a malfunction and how to fix it. All of these examples use problem-solving skills.

A four-step technique
The technique for solving problems in this book has four steps. Follow these steps and you will be able to see a way to the answer most of the time. Figure 1.14 illustrates these steps, and Table 1.2 explains them.

Table 1.2: Steps to solving physics problems

Step	What to do
1	Identify what the problem is asking. If you can, identify what variables or quantities need to be in the answer.
2	Identify the information you are given. Sometimes this includes numbers or values. Other times, it includes written information you must interpret. Look for words like *constant* or *at rest*. In a physics problem, saying something is *constant* means it does not change. The words *at rest* in physics mean the speed is zero. You may need conversion factors to change units.
3	Identify any relationships that involve the information you are asked to find and what is given. For example, suppose you are given a speed and a time, and are asked to find a distance. The relationship $d = vt$ relates what you are asked to find to what is given.
4	Combine the relationships with what you know and what you are trying to find. Once you complete steps 1–3, you will be able to see how to solve most problems.

1. Looking for

What do you want to find?

2. Given

What do you know?

3. Relationships

Identify useful relationships.

4. Solution

Solve the problem!

Figure 1.14: *Follow these steps and you will be able to see a way to the answer most of the time.*

Example problems

Throughout this book, you will find example problems that have been solved for you. Following each solved example, there are one or more practice problems. The answers to these practice problems appear at the end of the chapter so you can check your work. Always remember to write out the steps when you are solving problems. If you make a mistake, you will be able to look at your work to find your errors. Here is the format for example problems:

 Calculating speed

An airplane flies 450 meters in 3 seconds. What is its speed in meters per second?

1. Looking for:	You are asked for the speed in meters/second.
2. Given:	You are given the distance in meters and the time in seconds.
3. Relationships:	Use this version of the speed equation:
	$v = d \div t$
4. Solution:	$v = 450 \text{ m} \div 3 \text{ s} = 150 \text{ m/s}$

Your Turn:

a. A snake moves 20 meters in 5 seconds. What is the speed of the snake in meters per second?

b. A train is moving at a speed of 50 kilometers per hour. How many hours will it take the train to travel 600 kilometers?

(Answers are listed at the end of the chapter.)

1.3 Section Review

1. List three commonly-used units for speed.
2. State the steps used to solve physics problems.
3. Calculate the average speed of a car that drives 140 kilometers in 2 hours.
4. How long will it take you to swim 100 meters if you swim at a speed of 1.25 m/s?
5. How far will a dog travel if he runs for 1 minute at a constant speed of 5 m/s?

Scientific Method and Serendipity

Have you ever made a mistake that resulted in an unexpected positive outcome? Usually, we try to avoid mistakes. However, sometimes making a mistake—like taking a wrong turn—leads to a place you would have never seen if you had taken the correct turn.

Serendipity is a term used to describe an event that happens by accident and results in an unexpected discovery. An example of an accident might be losing your keys. An example of a serendipitous event would be that looking for your keys causes you to find the watch you lost a week ago.

Scientists tend to follow the scientific method or some version of it to "do science." However, researchers tell us that while they are searching for answers to nature's mysteries or looking for a cure to a disease, many important discoveries come about unexpectedly. Sometimes, small-chance events are just enough for a curious and observant person to unravel an important mystery.

A scientist made famous by serendipity

In 1928, Alexander Fleming, a British bacteriologist, was investigating the influenza virus as well as his own interests in the antibacterial properties of mucus. He was working at St. Mary's Hospital in London. In one experiment, Fleming smeared mucus in a petri dish that contained a culture of a harmful strain of bacteria called *staphylococcus*, or "staph" for short. Staph infections could spread uncontrollably, and often caused the death of the infected person.

An important observation brings fame and saves lives

At one point in his research, Fleming took a two-week vacation. He happened by chance to leave a petri dish containing staphylococcus on his laboratory bench. What happened next is a good example of serendipity. When Fleming returned from his vacation he noticed that mold had grown on the plate of the petri dish. The growth was a simple mold that appears as green and white fuzzy masses on food that is left out too long and exposed to air. In Fleming's case, a mold spore had entered his lab from another lab in his building. This mold spore had traveled through the air and had landed by chance on the petri dish. When Fleming examined the petri dish plate, he saw that the staphylococcus was growing, but it was not growing near the mold. At this point, Fleming came up with a hypothesis that brought him great fame and helped save the lives of many people. His hypothesis was that a substance produced by the mold could kill harmful bacteria.

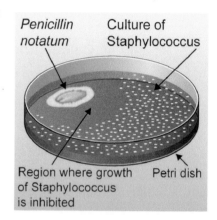

Penicillin notatum Culture of Staphylococcus

Region where growth of Staphylococcus is inhibited Petri dish

A miracle drug

After Fleming made his important hypothesis that mold has antibiotic properties, he investigated the mold on the petri dish. He grew a pure sample of the mold and learned that it produced a substance that stopped some of the bacteria from growing. Fleming named the substance *penicillin* after the mold that was growing in the plate, *Penicillin notatum*. You may be familiar with the drug penicillin. It is a very common and effective antibiotic.

Although Fleming was not able to purify penicillin enough for use as an antibiotic, he published his findings so others could. In 1945, Fleming received the Nobel Prize along with two other scientists (Ernst B. Chain and Sir Howard Florey) who helped develop penicillin. Chain and Florey were important in developing the techniques needed to make large quantities of penicillin. During World War II, penicillin saved the lives of thousands of injured soldiers and civilians. Not surprisingly, penicillin became known as a "miracle drug."

More discoveries

Alexander Fleming made an important discovery by recognizing the importance of mold in a petri dish. He took advantage of a serendipitous event and opened the door to a lifesaving medical breakthrough!

It is through education and a strong sense of curiosity, tempered with a bit of creativity (and yes, sometimes a little luck), that people can make great scientific discoveries. So, the next time you make a mistake or something does not seem to be working as you think it should, be patient and think about it. You may discover something yourself!

Here are some other serendipitous events that resulted in scientific breakthroughs. Take the time to research these important events and get inspired.

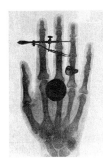

Wilhelm Röentgen's x-ray photograph of his wife's hand (1896)

- An apple falling from a tree inspired Isaac Newton to develop the idea of gravity.

- An unusual, accidental photograph revealing the bone structure of a hand lead to the discovery of x-rays by Wilhelm Röntgen.

- Two photographs of the same star field, taken a few days apart by astronomy student Clyde Tombaugh, reveals that one of the "stars" moved during that time. The "star" turned out to be a previously undiscovered object in our solar system—Pluto.

- After developing safely-stored photographic film, Henri Becquerel discovered a "ghostly" image on new photographic paper. That something turned out to be coming from uranium salts stored in the same drawer. The accidental exposure of the film led to the pioneering work of Marie and Pierre Curie on "radioactivity"—a term coined by Marie Curie.

- Background radio noise coming from space led technicians Arno Penzias and Robert Wilson to the realization that they were actually listening to the remnants of the Big Bang, an event that formed our universe billions of years ago.

Penzias and Wilson stand in front of the Horn Antenna they used to record cosmic background radiation.

QUESTIONS

1. What serendipitous event led to the discovery of penicillin?

2. Lewis Thomas, a medical research scientist and former president of Memorial Sloan-Kettering Cancer Center, once stated "You create the lucky accidents." What do you think he meant by this statement?

3. Why is it important to follow the scientific method when confirming an accidental discovery?

4. Do some research to find three additional serendipitous events other than the ones on this page that led to important scientific discoveries.

Chapter 1 Review

Understanding Vocabulary

Select the correct term to complete the sentences.

accurate	independent variable	scientific method
constant speed	length	second
control variable	mass	SI
dependent variable	model	significant digits
distance	natural law	speed
energy	objective	system
English system	physics	theory
experiment	precise	time interval
experimental variable	repeatable	variable
hypothesis	resolution	

1. The measure of the inertia of a body is measured as _____.

2. Newton's description of the force needed to change the motion of an object is an example of a(n) _____.

3. In a system designed to measure the acceleration of a car on a ramp, the angle of the ramp would be treated as a(n) _____.

4. Units of inches, feet, centimeters, and meters may be used to measure _____.

5. An archer aiming at the center of a target hits the target with four arrows. If the arrows are 20 cm from the center but within 2 cm of each other, the archer's shooting would be considered _____ but *not* _____.

6. To calculate speed, _____ is divided by _____.

Reviewing Concepts

Section 1.1

1. List and define the two categories we use to classify everything in the universe.

2. How have physicists come to understand the natural laws?

3. Define the term *matter*.

4. Explain why light is not considered to be matter.

5. Define the term *system* as it relates to experiments.

6. When designing an experiment, how do you determine what to include in the system?

7. List the steps of the scientific method.

8. Explain the difference between a hypothesis and a theory.

9. Explain the difference between a control variable and an experimental variable.

10. You wish to do an experiment to determine how a ball's radius affects how fast it rolls down a ramp. List the independent and dependent variables in this experiment.

11. What is the goal of an experiment?

12. What are the characteristics of scientific evidence?

13. Define the term *model* and give three examples.

Section 1.2

14. Why are units important when measuring quantities?

15. What is the current name given to the metric system? Name two reasons for using this system in place of the English System.

16. Define the word *time* as it is used in physics calculations.

17. On which axis of a graph is time generally placed?

18. What are the meanings of the terms *accuracy*, *precision*, and *resolution* as applied to science measurements?

19. How is the correct number of significant figures determined in a science problem?

Section 1.3

20. Write the form of the speed equation that you would use in each of the following scenarios. Let v = speed, t = time, and d = distance.

 a. You know distance and speed and want to find the time.

 b. You know time and distance and want to find the speed.

 c. You know speed and time and want to find the distance.

21. What is the speed of an object that is standing still?

22. Your friend rides her bicycle across town at a constant speed. Describe how you could determine her speed.

23. Fill in the missing information in the table showing common units for speed below:

Distance	Time	Speed	Abbreviation
meters	seconds		
			km/h
		centimeters per second	

24. Summarize the four steps for solving physics problems as described in the text.

Solving Problems

Section 1.1

1. You want to find out whether the birds near your school prefer thistle seed or sunflower seed. You have a bag of thistle seed, a bag of sunflower seed, and two bird feeders. Describe the experiment you would do to see which type of seed birds prefer. Write down your question, your hypothesis, and the procedure you would follow when doing your experiment.

2. You are doing an experiment to determine whether a dropped ball's mass affects the rate at which it falls. Describe the system you are studying. Write down your question, your hypothesis, and the procedure you would follow when doing your experiment.

Section 1.2

3. Order the following lengths from shortest to longest.

 a. 400 mm

 b. 22 km

 c. 170 m

 d. 3.3 cm

4. Convert:

 a. 3 km = _____ m

 b. 1.5 m = _____ cm

 c. 110 cm = _____ m

 d. 2.5 cm = _____ mm

5. Convert:

 a. 3 min = _____ s

 b. 200 s = _____ min, _____ s

 c. 2.00 days = _____ min

 d. 1,000 min = _____ hr

6. Determine your age in each of the following units.

 a. months

 b. days

 c. hours

 d. seconds

7. Luis rides his new bike while his brother records his position and time. They create the data table shown below.

Position (m)	0.00	105	270	400	540	600
Time (s)	0.00	30	60	90	120	150

   a. Name the dependent variable and the independent variable.

   b. On which axis would each variable be placed on a graph?

Section 1.3

8. Use the data from Luis's bike ride in question 7 to answer the following:

   a. What was Luis's speed (in meters per second) for the entire ride from 0 to 150 s?

   b. What was Luis's speed (in meters per second) between 60 and 90 s?

   c. During which 30 s interval did Luis have the greatest speed? Calculate his speed during this interval.

9. A bicyclist, traveling at 22 mph, rides a total of 44 mi. How much time (in hours) did it take?

10. A mouse travels in a straight line at a steady speed of 2 m/s for 10 seconds. How far (in meters) did the mouse travel?

11. The gray wolf is a threatened animal that is native to the United States. A wildlife biologist observes an adult wolf traveling 250 m in 100 s. What is the average speed (in meters per second) of the gray wolf over this interval?

12. It takes Brooke 10 min to walk 1 mi. What is her speed in miles per second?

13. If it takes 500 s for the light from the Sun to reach Earth, what is the distance to the Sun in meters? (*Note*: The speed of light is 300,000,000 m/s.)

Test Practice

Section 1.1

1. Scientific evidence must be

   a. objective.

   b. subjective.

   c. repeatable.

   d. both objective and repeatable.

2. _____ is a measure of a system's ability to change or create change in other systems.

   a. Mmass

   b. A natural law

   c. Energy

   d. An experiment

3. A factor that affects the behavior of a system is known as a

   a. hypothesis.

   b. natural law.

   c. theory.

   d. variable.

Section 1.2

4. A rectangle is measured to be 14.2 cm long by 6.8 cm wide. The area of the rectangle should be reported as

   a. 96.56 cm^2.

   b. 96.5 cm^2.

   c. 96.6 cm^2.

   d. 96 cm^2.

5. The diagram below represents a centimeter scale placed next to a rectangle.

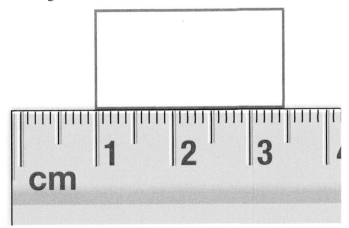

The dimension of the rectangle adjacent to the centimeter scale would be *most* accurately given as

a. 3.40 cm.

b. 3.48 cm.

c. 2.48 cm.

d. 2.5 cm.

The diagram below represents a portion of a centimeter scale. Answer the following two questions about this diagram.

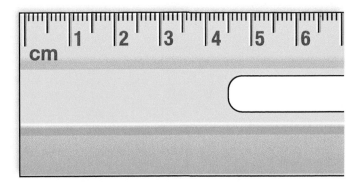

6. The greatest number of significant figures that should be reported when measuring with this scale is

   a. 1.

   b. 3.

   c. 5.

   d. 7.

7. The highest degree of resolution possible using this centimeter scale is

   a. 1.0 mm.

   b. 0.5 mm.

   c. 1.0 cm.

   d. 0.5 cm.

8. The number of seconds represented by an elapsed time of 3 h, 42 min, 3 s is

   a. 13,323 s.

   b. 2,703 s.

   c. 225 s.

   d. 3 s.

9. A 12-inch ruler compares most closely in length to

   a. 1.0 m.

   b. 12 cm.

   c. 300 mm.

   d. 5 μm.

10. On a graph, the _____ variable is normally plotted on the *x*-axis.

   a. control

   b. dependent

   c. experimental

   d. independent

Section 1.3

11. Traveling at an average speed of 55 mph, in 14 hr a driver will travel

   a. 770 mi.

   b. 393 mi.

   c. 69 mi.

   d. 55 mi.

Applying Your Knowledge

Section 1.1

1. Read an article in a science magazine and identify how scientists have used the scientific method in their work.

2. Given a ruler, a stopwatch, a tennis ball, a 1-m long piece of string, a rubber band, tape, and 10 pieces of paper, design an experiment. List a question, a hypothesis, the independent variable, the dependent variable, the control variables, and the procedure for your experiment.

Section 1.2

3. Research the number system and length units of an ancient civilization. What types of things did this ancient group of people need to measure? What were the smallest and largest units of length used? Write a short report on what you learn.

4. Research what the time standard is for the United States. How is the correct time determined? Where is this national clock kept? How can you access this clock for setting your clocks at home? Write a short report on what you learn.

5. Checking in magazines, newspapers, or the Internet, collect pictures or diagrams illustrating models used to represent systems in everyday life.

Section 1.3

6. Research the speeds of many kinds of animals and make a table showing fastest to slowest.

7. Determine your average walking speed. How long would it take you to walk 2,462 mi (3,962 km) from New York to Los Angeles?

8. Prepare a short report on important speeds in your favorite sport.

9. Use the Internet to find the world record times for running races for the following distances: 100 m, 200 m, mile, and marathon. Calculate the speed for each race and compare the results in a table.

 *Your Turn* **Answers**

Calculating speed (Section 1.3, page 21)

   a. 4 m/s

   b. 12 hr

Describing Motion

How long can you stand perfectly still? Ten seconds? A minute? Even if you stand still, things inside your body are moving, like your heart and lungs. Even fast asleep, your body is not really at rest with respect to the universe! The 24-hour rotation of Earth is carrying you around at several hundred miles per hour. Every 365 days, Earth completes a 584-million-mile orbit around the Sun. To make this trip, Earth (with you on its surface) is rushing through space at the astounding speed of 67,000 miles per hour! To understand nature we need to think about motion. How do we describe going from here to there? Whether it is a toy car rolling along a track or Earth rushing through space, the ideas in this chapter apply to all motion. Position, speed, and acceleration are basic ideas we need in order to understand the physical world.

67,000 mph

KEY QUESTIONS

✓ *How do you use position, velocity, and acceleration to describe an object's motion?*

✓ *How can a position vs. time graph tell you something about an object's velocity?*

✓ *Why do some velocity vs. time graphs have negative values on the y-axis?*

VOCABULARY

acceleration	frame of reference	relative velocity
average velocity	instantaneous velocity	slope
constant velocity	origin	velocity
displacement	position	

2.1 **Position, Velocity, and Acceleration**

Where are you right now? How fast are you moving? What direction are you going? Is your motion constant, or is it changing? To answer these questions precisely, you need to use the concepts of position, velocity, and acceleration. These ideas apply to ordinary objects, such as cars, bicycles, and people. They also apply to microscopic objects the size of atoms and to enormous objects like planets and stars. Let's begin our discussion of motion with the concept of position.

> **position** - a variable that tells location relative to an origin
> **origin** - a place where the position has been given a value of zero

The position variable

Position as a variable   You will do an experiment in your class with a car on a track that has an electronic sensor on one end. How do you tell someone exactly where the car is located on the track? The answer is by recording its **position**. Position is a variable. The position of the car describes where the car is relative to the track. In the illustration, the position of the car is 50 centimeters. That means the center of the car is at the 50-centimeter mark on the track.

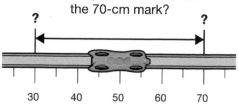

Figure 2.1: *Knowing the car moves 20 centimeters does not tell you its final position. The car could end up at the 70-cm mark or at the 30-cm mark.*

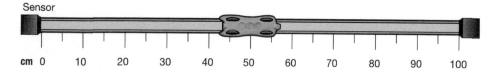

Position versus distance   Position and distance are similar but not the same. Both use units of length. However, position is given relative to an **origin**. The origin is the place where position equals zero, in this case at the sensor-end of the track. Here's an example of the difference between position and distance. Assume the track is 1 meter long. Suppose the car starts at a position of 50 cm and moves a distance of 20 cm. Where is it now? You know a distance (20 cm) but you still don't know where the car is (Figure 2.1). It could have moved 20 cm away from the origin or 20 cm toward the origin. The car could end up at the 70-cm position or the 30-cm position. We need a way to communicate direction as well as position.

Position and displacement

Using positive and negative numbers The distance variable does not indicate direction. If you know the car moves a distance of 20 cm, and it started at the 50-cm mark, you don't know if it ends up at the 70-cm mark or the 30-cm mark. To indicate a direction, you need to use the position variable and allow positive and negative position changes.

Displacement A change in position is called **displacement**. In this car-and-track system, the origin is defined at the sensor-end of the track. When the car moves away from the origin it has a positive displacement. When the car moves toward the origin it has a negative displacement. Suppose the car begins at the 50-cm mark. A displacement of –20 cm means the car leaves the 50-cm mark and moves toward the origin. The negative sign tells you the direction, toward the origin, and the length measurement tells you how far the car moves in that direction, 20 cm. The car ends up at a position of 30 cm.

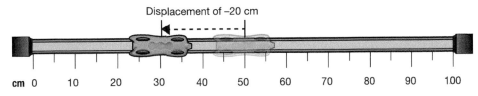

A displacement of 20 cm (positive sign is understood) means the car moves away from the origin. The car leaves the 50-cm mark and ends up at a position of 70 cm.

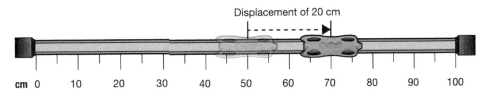

By using positive and negative displacement instead of the distance variable, you now have a way of describing motion in two directions on the track.

> **displacement** - a change in position

The girl walks from **A** to **B** to **C** to **D** and back to **A**

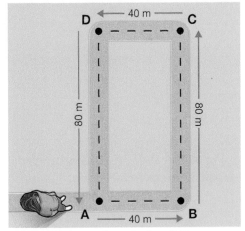

Distance traveled = 240 m
Displacement = 0 m

Figure 2.2: *Distance and displacement are two different variables. In this case, the displacement is zero because the girl returned to the starting point, or origin. The distance she traveled, however, was the perimeter of the rectangle (240 m). Finding the displacement from A to C is a skill you will learn in a later chapter.*

Velocity

Speed in opposite directions
Two cars travel the same route at a speed of 100 km/h in opposite directions, between two cities that are 400 kilometers apart. The cars have the same speed, but their direction is different. How can we show this difference?

Velocity versus speed
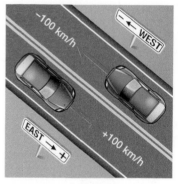
The **velocity** (v) of an object tells you both its speed and its direction of motion. Velocity is an object's change in position (x) over time. Like the position variable, a velocity can be positive or negative. By contrast, speed cannot have a negative value. Speed is what you read on a speedometer, which tells you how fast you are going, but nothing about what direction you are going. Velocity can be positive or negative, so it includes information about the moving object's direction. **Constant velocity** means that both the speed and the direction an object is traveling remains constant.

Positive and negative velocity
In this example, east is in the positive direction and west is in the negative direction. The positive or negative sign for velocity is based on the calculation of a change in position. Velocity is the change in position divided by the change in time. The diagram shows the position for both cars at 1-hour intervals. The change in position is the final position minus the initial position (Figure 2.3). For the east-bound car, the final position is 300 km and the initial position is 200 km. The change is +100 km. For the west-bound car, the final position is 100 km and the initial position is 200 km. The change is –100 km and the velocity is therefore –100 km/h.

velocity - describes an object's change of position over time; can also be defined as speed in a given direction

constant velocity - an unchanging velocity; both speed and direction remain the same

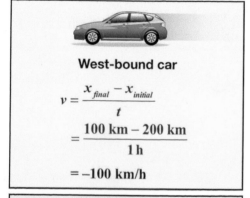

West-bound car

$$v = \frac{x_{final} - x_{initial}}{t}$$

$$= \frac{100 \text{ km} - 200 \text{ km}}{1 \text{ h}}$$

$$= -100 \text{ km/h}$$

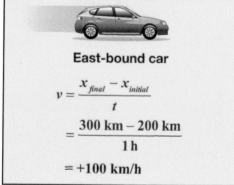

East-bound car

$$v = \frac{x_{final} - x_{initial}}{t}$$

$$= \frac{300 \text{ km} - 200 \text{ km}}{1 \text{ h}}$$

$$= +100 \text{ km/h}$$

Figure 2.3: *You can calculate velocity (v) from changes in position (x).*

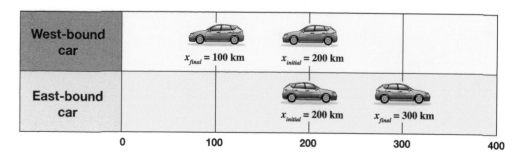

West-bound car		$x_{final} = 100$ km	$x_{initial} = 200$ km		
East-bound car			$x_{initial} = 200$ km	$x_{final} = 300$ km	

0	100	200	300	400

Average and instantaneous velocity

Calculating velocity Let the letter v stand for velocity, the letter x stand for position, and the letter t stand for time taken. The greek letter Δ (delta) stands for "a change in." In the formula for velocity, Δx means "a change in position," or displacement.

VELOCITY

Velocity (m/s) $\quad v = \dfrac{\Delta x}{t} \quad$ **Displacement** (m)

Time taken (s)

average velocity - found by dividing total displacement by total time taken

instantaneous velocity - describes an object's velocity at one moment in time or at one specific point in the object's path

Average velocity The map below shows a hiker's route. The red segments of the map show where the hiker moved the slowest. Orange areas are a little faster, yellow faster still, and green areas show the fastest pace. You can see that the pace changed during the hike. One way to describe the trip is to find the hiker's average velocity. **Average velocity** is the total displacement divided by the total time taken. If the hiker's displacement was 4,000 meters and it took her 50 minutes to complete the hike, her average velocity was 1.3 m/s.

Instantaneous velocity Saying the hiker's average velocity is 1.3 m/s does not mean she walked at a rate of 1.3 m/s for every moment of the trip. In reality, the hiker's velocity changed many times. **Instantaneous velocity** describes the velocity of an object at one specific moment in time or at one specific point in its path. The green areas of the route map show where the hiker moved at 2.5 m/s. Perhaps these were the downhill portions of the hike.

Instantaneous velocity trap

Law enforcement authorities use radar guns to check vehicle speeds. The radar gun transmits a high-frequency electromagnetic wave. The wave bounces off the moving vehicle and returns to a receiver on the radar gun. The radar gun uses information from the receiver to calculate the instantaneous velocity of the vehicle. The police officer wants to know if you are exceeding the speed limit at that moment in time. The officer is not interested in your average velocity!

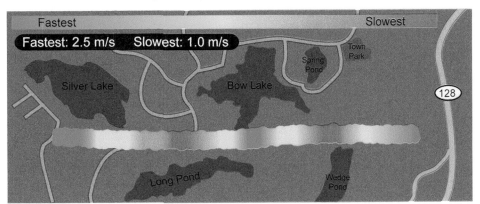

Relative velocity

Frame of reference   The motion of an object can be described by its velocity compared to or *relative* to a frame of reference. In this case, a **frame of reference** is an object or system assumed to be at rest. Earth is usually the frame of reference. If you are sitting in a chair, you are not moving relative to Earth. However, you are moving at about 67,000 mph relative to the Sun! When giving an object's velocity, it is important to consider the frame of reference.

Relative velocity   **Relative velocity** describes the velocity of an object with respect to a frame of reference. Almost all velocities are relative. Consider this example. Many airport terminals have moving sidewalks, or "people movers." Suppose a people mover has a velocity of 1 m/s. You are *standing* on the people mover. If your frame of reference is Earth, then you and the people mover are moving at a velocity of 1 m/s. However, if your frame of reference is the people mover, your relative velocity would be 0 m/s.

Walking on a people mover   Suppose you *walk forward* at a velocity of 2 m/s relative to the people mover. Your velocity relative to Earth would be 3 m/s, because you would add your velocity of 2 m/s to the people mover's velocity of 1 m/s (Figure 2.4). This is the advantage of walking on a people mover instead of just riding.

> **frame of reference** - an object or system assumed to be at rest
> **relative velocity** - describes the velocity of an object with respect to a frame of reference

Figure 2.4: *How can you walk 2 m/s but actually cover 3 m/s? Walk on a people mover that goes 1 m/s.*

   Using relative velocity

A people mover has a velocity of 1 m/s and is 150 m long. If a man walks 2 m/s relative to the people mover, how long will it take him to reach the opposite end if he walks in the direction that the people mover travels?

1. *Looking for:*   You are asked for the time in seconds.

2. *Given:*   You are given the velocity of the people mover, the relative velocity of the walker, and the displacement.

3. *Relationship:*   Use this version of the velocity equation: $t = \Delta x \div v$

4. *Solution:* $t = 150 \text{ m} \div (1 \text{ m/s} + 2 \text{ m/s}) = 150 \text{ m} \div 3 \text{ m/s} = 50 \text{ s}$

Your Turn:

a. How much time will it take the man in the example above if he walks in a direction opposite to the people mover?

(Answers are listed at the end of the chapter.)

Acceleration

Definition of acceleration What happens if you coast on a bicycle down a long hill? At the top of the hill, you move slowly. As you go down the hill, your velocity increases—you accelerate. **Acceleration** is the rate at which your velocity changes. If velocity increases by 1 km/h each second, the acceleration is 1 km/hr per second, or 1 km/h/s.

Time (s)	Speed (km/h)
0 (start)	0 (start)
1	1
2	2
3	3
4	4
5	5

Acceleration = 1 km/h each second

Time (s)	Speed (km/h)
0 (start)	0 (start)
1	2
2	4
3	6
4	8
5	10

Acceleration = 2 km/h each second

Steeper hills Your acceleration depends on the steepness of the hill. If the hill is a gradual incline, you have a small acceleration. If the hill is steeper, your acceleration will be greater. On the gradual hill, your speedometer increases by 1 km/h every second. On the steeper hill, it increases by 2 km/h every second.

Car acceleration Advertisements for some cars often discuss acceleration. An ad might state that a car can go "from 0 to 60 in 10 seconds." This means the speed of the car begins at 0 and reaches 60 miles per hour (96 km/h) after accelerating for 10 seconds. The car's acceleration is therefore 6 miles per hour per second (Figure 2.5).

Acceleration versus velocity Acceleration and velocity are completely different ways to describe an object's motion. Just because an object is moving, doesn't mean it is accelerating. For example, a car moving at a constant velocity of 120 km/h has zero acceleration. Furthermore, an object can be accelerating when its velocity is zero! Suppose you release a toy car on a ramp. The moment you release the car, the car has zero velocity because it is not moving yet. But, it is accelerating because its velocity is already changing the moment it is released.

> **acceleration** - a change in velocity over time

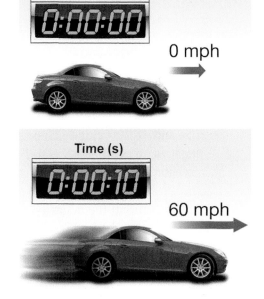

Acceleration of the car is 6 mph/s

Figure 2.5: *It takes 10 seconds for a car to go from 0 to 60 mph if it has an acceleration of 6 mph per second. In SI units, the car goes from 0 to 96 km/h in 10 seconds. The acceleration is 9.6 km/h per second.*

Calculating acceleration

The equation for acceleration To calculate acceleration, you divide the change in velocity by the time over which the velocity changed. To find the change in velocity, subtract the initial velocity from the final velocity. For example, if a bicycle's velocity increases from 2 m/s to 6 m/s, its change in velocity is 4 m/s. Because two velocities are involved, subscripts are used to show the difference. The initial velocity is v_i, and the final velocity is v_f.

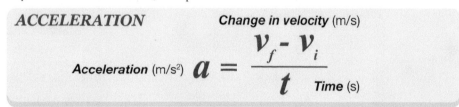

$$ACCELERATION \qquad \text{Change in velocity (m/s)}$$

$$\text{Acceleration (m/s}^2\text{)} \quad a = \frac{v_f - v_i}{t} \quad \text{Time (s)}$$

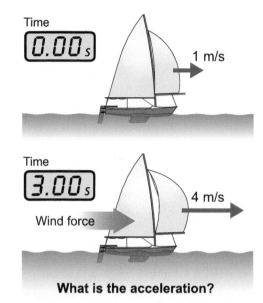

Time **0.00 s**   1 m/s

Time **3.00 s**   4 m/s

Wind force

What is the acceleration?

Figure 2.6: *An example of acceleration with a sailboat.*

Positive and negative acceleration Like velocity, acceleration can be positive or negative. An object will have a positive acceleration if it is speeding up in the positive direction, or if it is slowing down in the negative direction. An object will have a negative acceleration if it is slowing down in the positive direction, or if it is speeding up in the negative direction. If you keep track of the sign on your initial and final velocity, you can use the acceleration formula to get the correct sign for the acceleration every time.

 **Calculating acceleration**

A sailboat moves at 1 m/s. Wind increases its velocity to 4 m/s in 3 seconds (Figure 2.6). Calculate the acceleration.

1. *Looking for:*   You are asked for the acceleration in m/s/s.

2. *Given:*   You are given the initial velocity in m/s (v_i), final velocity in m/s (v_f), and the time change in seconds.

3. *Relationship:*   Use the formula for acceleration: $a = \dfrac{v_f - v_i}{t}$

4. *Solution:* $a = \dfrac{4 \text{ m/s} - 1 \text{ m/s}}{3 \text{ s}} = \dfrac{3 \text{ m/s}}{3 \text{ s}} = 1 \text{ m/s}^2$

Your Turn:

a. Calculate the acceleration of an airplane that starts at rest and reaches a speed of 45 m/s in 9 seconds.

b. Calculate the acceleration of a car that slows from 50 m/s to 30 m/s in 10 seconds.

(Answers are listed at the end of the chapter.)

Units of acceleration

What do units of seconds *squared* mean? An acceleration in m/s/s is often written m/s² or meters per second squared. Apply the rules for simplifying fractions on the units of acceleration, m/s/s. The denominator ends up having units of seconds times seconds, or s². Saying *seconds squared* is math shorthand. In physics, it is better to think about acceleration in units of velocity change per second, such as m/s *per second*.

$$Acceleration = \frac{change\ in\ velocity}{change\ in\ time}$$

How we get units of m/s² ▶

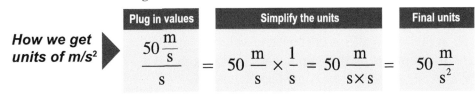

Plug in values	Simplify the units	Final units
$\dfrac{50\frac{m}{s}}{s}$	$= 50\frac{m}{s} \times \frac{1}{s} = 50\frac{m}{s \times s}$	$= 50\frac{m}{s^2}$

Acceleration in m/s² Nearly all physics problems will use acceleration in m/s² because these units are used with newtons, the SI unit of force. If you measure velocity in centimeters per second, you may have to convert to m/s before calculating acceleration that will be used with newtons.

2.1 Section Review

1. How is the position variable different from the distance variable in motion experiments?
2. A runner completes one lap around a 400-m oval track, returning to her starting position. What distance did she cover, and what was her displacement? Explain.
3. Why can velocity be negative, but non-zero speed is always positive?
4. Compare and contrast: constant velocity, average velocity, and instantaneous velocity.
5. Use the term *relative velocity* to explain why it is helpful to paddle a boat downstream.
6. What is the acceleration, in m/s², of a car that can go from 0 mph to 60 mph in 4 seconds? (*Hint*: Remember to convert all necessary units.)

Acceleration and direction

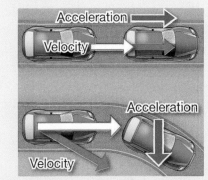

The velocity of an object includes both its speed and the direction it is moving. A car with a velocity of 20 m/s north has a speed of 20 m/s and is moving north. An object accelerates if its velocity changes. This can occur if its speed changes, its direction changes, or both. Therefore, a car traveling at a constant speed of 40 mph around a bend is actually accelerating. The only way a moving object can have an acceleration of zero is to be moving at constant speed in a straight line.

This chapter covers acceleration that involves only changes in speed. In a later chapter, you will learn about the acceleration of moving objects that change direction as well.

2.2 Position vs. Time Graphs

Motion graphs are an important tool used to show the relationships between position, velocity, acceleration, and time. For example, you could make a graph that compares the motion of two race cars that zoom along a straight track at top speed. This graph would help drivers and engineers see how much of the straight track each car covered in equal time intervals. This could help drivers make adjustments in how they operate the cars. A graph like that could also help engineers see where they need to make design adjustments. In this section, you will use graphs of position versus time and speed versus time to represent motion.

slope - ratio of rise to run

The position vs. time graph

Position versus time The position vs. time graph in Figure 2.7 shows the constant-velocity motion of two cars, A and B. Using the numbers on the graph, you see that both cars move for 5 seconds. Car A moves 10 meters while Car B moves only 5 meters. Using the equation $v = \Delta x/t$, the speed of Car A is 2 m/s. The speed of Car B is 1 m/s. Notice that the line for Car A is steeper that of Car B. A steeper slope on a position vs. time graph shows a greater velocity.

The definition of slope The **slope** of a line is the ratio of the "rise," or vertical change, to the "run," or horizontal change. The diagram below shows how to calculate the slope of a line. The rise is equal to the height of the triangle. The run is equal to the length along the base of the triangle. Here, the horizontal run values represent time and the vertical rise values represent position. The slope of a position vs. time graph is a displacement divided by a time, which equals velocity.

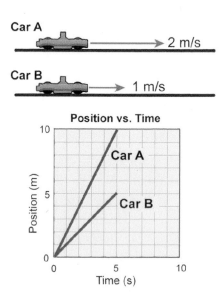

Figure 2.7: *Both cars have constant velocity, but Car A is faster than Car B.*

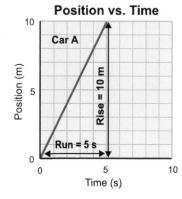
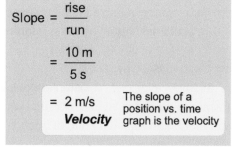

$$Slope = \frac{rise}{run}$$

$$= \frac{10\ m}{5\ s}$$

$$= 2\ m/s$$ *Velocity*   The slope of a position vs. time graph is the velocity

Position vs. time graphs of accelerated motion

Graphing free fall A position vs. time graph can tell you whether an object's velocity is constant or changing. If the velocity is *constant*, the graph is a straight line with a constant slope. If the velocity is changing, the slope changes, so the graph curves. Consider the velocity of an accelerating ball in free fall. As time passes, the velocity of the ball increases. Because the slope represents the velocity, the slope must also increase with time. The graph is a curve that gets steeper as you move along the time axis. A position vs. time graph for a ball in free fall is shown below.

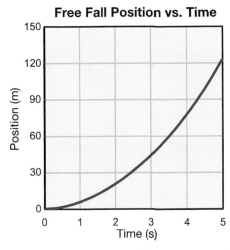

Free Fall Position vs. Time

Time (s)	Position (m)
0	0
1	4.9
2	19.6
3	44.1
4	78.4
5	122.5

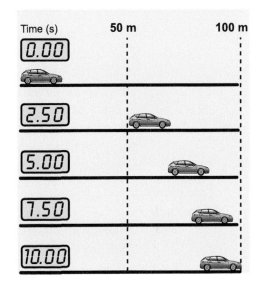

Slowing down The graph of an object slowing down is also curved. An example is a car coming to a gradual stop at a red light. As time passes, the speed of the car decreases. The slope of the graph must also decrease as you trace the line to the right. Figure 2.8 shows the position vs. time graph for a car slowing down before it stops at a red light.

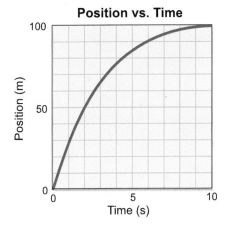

Figure 2.8: *The position vs. time graph for a car coming to a gradual stop at a red light.*

2.2 Section Review

1. Explain how to calculate the slope of a graph.
2. What does the slope of a position vs. time graph represent?
3. Draw the position vs. time graph for an object moving at a constant velocity of 2 m/s.
4. Sketch a position vs. time graph (no number scale needed) for a ball rolling down a ramp.

2.3 Velocity vs. Time Graphs

The velocity vs. time graph
The velocity vs. time graph has velocity on the *y*-axis and time on the *x*-axis. Figure 2.9 shows the velocity vs. time graph for a ball rolling at constant speed on a level floor. On this graph, constant velocity is shown with a straight horizontal line. If you look at the velocity on the *y*-axis, you see that the ball is moving at 1 m/s for the entire 10 seconds. Figure 2.10 is the position vs. time graph for the ball. Both of the graphs in the sidebar show the exact same motion. If you calculate the slope of the lower graph, you will find that it is 1 m/s, the same as the velocity in Figure 2.9.

Calculating displacement
A velocity vs. time graph also can be used to find the object's displacement. Displacement equals the velocity multiplied by the time, $\Delta x = vt$. Suppose we draw a rectangle on the speed vs. time graph between the *x*-axis and the line showing the speed. The area of the rectangle is equal to its length times its height. On the graph, the length is equal to the time and the height is equal to the velocity. Therefore, the area of the graph is the velocity multiplied by the time. This is the displacement of the ball.

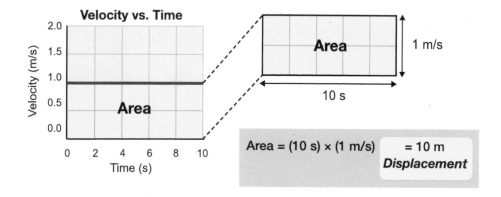

Constant velocity

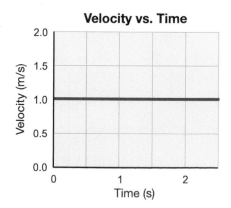

Figure 2.9: *The speed vs. time graph for a ball rolling on a level floor at a constant speed of 1 m/s.*

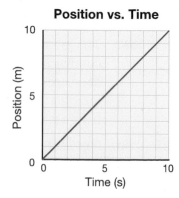

Figure 2.10: *The position vs. time graph that shows the exact same motion as the velocity vs. time graph above.*

Velocity vs. time graphs of accelerated motion

The velocity vs. time graph If an object is accelerating, it is easier to work with the velocity vs. time graph than it is to work with the position vs. time graph. The velocity vs. time graph is the best tool for understanding acceleration. It clearly shows how the velocity of an object changes with time.

Constant acceleration The velocity vs. time graph shown below is for a ball in free fall. The straight line sloping upward shows that the velocity increases by the same amount each second. This means the ball has a *constant acceleration*. Make sure not to confuse constant velocity with constant acceleration. As long as it is moving in one direction, an object at constant speed has zero acceleration (Figure 2.11, bottom). Constant velocity means an object's *position* changes by the same amount each second. Constant acceleration means an object's *velocity* changes by the same amount each second.

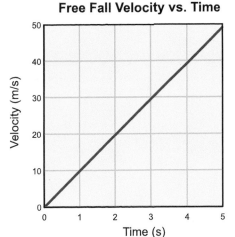

Free Fall Velocity vs. Time

Time (s)	Velocity (m/s)
0	0
1	9.8
2	19.6
3	29.4
4	39.2
5	49.0

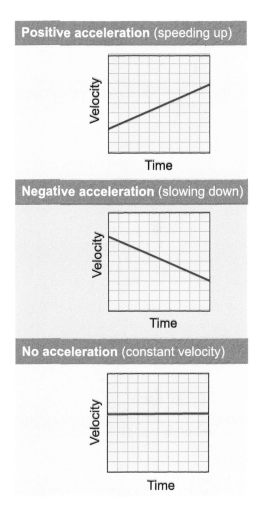

Figure 2.11: *Examples of graphs showing different constant accelerations.*

Calculating acceleration The slope of a velocity vs. time graph represents the acceleration of the object. Figure 2.11 shows some examples of graphs with constant acceleration. Note that there is non-zero acceleration any time the velocity vs. time graph is *not perfectly horizontal*.

Calculating acceleration from the velocity vs. time graph

Slope You know that the slope of a graph is equal to the ratio of *rise* to *run*. On the velocity vs. time graph, the rise and run have special meanings. The *rise* is the amount the *velocity* changes. The *run* is the amount the *time* changes.

Acceleration and slope Remember, acceleration is the change in velocity over the change in time. This is *exactly the same* as the rise over run for the velocity vs. time graph. The slope of the velocity vs. time graph is equal to its acceleration. Figure 2.12 shows how to find the acceleration of a ball in free fall from a velocity vs. time graph.

Make a triangle to get the slope To determine the slope of the velocity vs. time graph, take the change in velocity and divide by the change in time. It is helpful to draw a triangle on the graph to identify the rise and run. The rise is the height of the triangle. The run is the length of the base of the triangle. The graph is for a ball in free fall, so you should not be surprised to find that the slope is 9.8 m/s², the acceleration due to gravity.

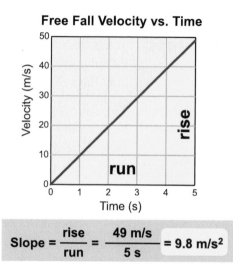

Free Fall Velocity vs. Time

$$\text{Slope} = \frac{\text{rise}}{\text{run}} = \frac{49 \text{ m/s}}{5 \text{ s}} = 9.8 \text{ m/s}^2$$

Figure 2.12: *The slope of a velocity vs. time graph equals the acceleration.*

⊕ ⊖ ⊗ ⊘ Finding acceleration from a velocity vs. time graph

Calculate the acceleration shown by the velocity vs. time graph.

1. **Looking for:**   You are asked for the acceleration in m/s/s.

2. **Given:**   You are given a graph of velocity vs. time.

3. **Relationship:**   The acceleration is equal to the slope of the line.

4. **Solution:**   The rise is 40 m/s, and the run is 10 s. Dividing the rise by the run gives an acceleration of 4 m/s².

Your Turn:

a. Calculate the acceleration shown by the graph in Figure 2.13.

b. Calculate the acceleration shown by the graph in Figure 2.9.

(Answers are listed at the end of the chapter.)

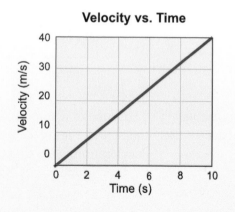

Velocity vs. Time

Displacement on an accelerated-motion graph

A ball rolling downhill Consider an experiment with a ball rolling downhill. The velocity of the ball increases as it rolls downward. The velocity vs. time graph looks like Figure 2.13. This graph shows a velocity that starts at zero. Two seconds later, the velocity is 2 meters per second. A velocity vs. time graph that shows any non-zero slope tells you there is acceleration because the velocity is changing over time.

The distance traveled when velocity is changing The velocity vs. time graph gives us a way to calculate the object's displacement even when its velocity is changing. The displacement is equal to the area on the graph. However, the area is a triangle instead of a rectangle. The area of a triangle is one half the base times the height. The base is equal to the time, just as before. The height is equal to the velocity of the ball at the end of two seconds. For the graph in the example below, the ball's position changes by 2 meters from 0 seconds to 2 seconds.

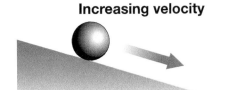

Increasing velocity

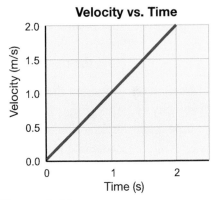

Figure 2.13: *The velocity vs. time graph for a ball rolling down a hill.*

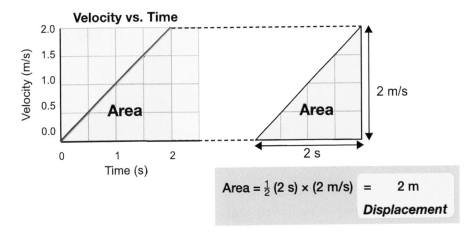

Area = $\frac{1}{2}$ (2 s) × (2 m/s) = 2 m

Displacement

Direction on motion graphs

A car, track, and sensor   Consider a toy car on a track that has an electronic sensor on one end. The sensor can detect changes in the car's position. The sensor-end of the track is the origin.

Direction on a position vs. time graph   A position vs. time graph created from the sensor data easily shows whether the car is moving away from the sensor or toward the sensor (Figure 2.14). If the car is moving away from the sensor, the line on the graph will show that the position increases, since the car moves away from the origin. If the car is moving toward the sensor, the line on the position vs. time graph will show that the position decreases, since the car moves toward the origin.

Direction on a velocity vs. time graph   To show direction on a velocity vs. time graph, we must include a portion of the graph that shows negative velocities. To do this, we will extend the *y*-axis below the zero line to include negative values. When the car moves away from the sensor, the velocity is positive. When the car moves toward the sensor, the velocity is negative.

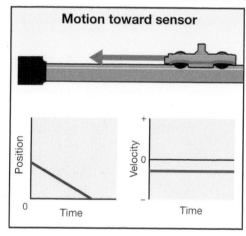

Figure 2.14: *A positive displacement and positive velocity occurs when the car moves away from the sensor. The opposite is true for motion toward the sensor.*

2.3 Section Review

1. Why does the velocity vs. time graph for constant velocity have a horizontal line, when the position vs. time graph for the same motion is a diagonal line?
2. Figure 2.7 shows a position vs. time graph for two cars that have different constant velocities. Sketch a velocity vs. time graph for the same two cars.
3. What does the slope of a velocity vs. time graph represent?
4. How can you determine an object's displacement from its velocity vs. time graph? Is the method the same for both constant velocity and changing velocity?
5. How do you indicate direction on a velocity vs. time graph?

Motion graph summary

Use this summary as a study tool and as a reference to help you remember the difference between position vs. time and velocity vs. time graphs.

Type of motion	Position vs. Time graph		Velocity vs. Time graph	
	Direction		Direction	
	(+) away from origin	(−) toward origin	(+) away from origin	(−) toward origin
No motion (standing still)				
Constant velocity				
Speeding up				
Slowing down				

High Tech Animal Trackers

April 22, 2007—A young harp seal was found stranded on a beach in Virginia's Chincoteague National Wildlife Refuge. He appeared slightly thin with some superficial injuries. Park rangers, optimistic that he would heal on his own, placed him under observation. Unfortunately, park visitors didn't heed requests to keep a respectful distance from the seal.

For the seal's and the public's safety, he was captured and sent to the Virginia Aquarium Stranding Center. Veterinarians treated him with antibiotics, and soon he was consuming 10 pounds of herring a day. In less than a month, the seal grew from 35 to 66 pounds.

During that time, a 13-year-old girl asked her birthday party guests to bring donations to the Aquarium's Stranding Response Program instead of gifts. With the money she collected, the aquarium purchased a satellite tag to track the seal's movements.

On May 19, 2007, the tag was attached and the healthy seal was released back to the ocean.

What is a satellite tag?

A satellite tag is a palm-sized, salt-water-resistant data collector with an antenna attached. It is glued to the fur of a seal's upper back, where it remains until the seal molts and the tag falls off.

With the satellite tag attached to his back, the seal moves toward the ocean.

The tag records information including the time, date, dive depth, dive duration, and amount of time at the surface over the last six hours. When the seal surfaces, the tag transmits this data to satellites orbiting Earth. Sometimes there are no satellites overhead when the animal surfaces, so data isn't received every day.

When data is received, instruments on the satellite record the location of the tag and relay the data to processing computers back on Earth. Organizations such as WhaleNet (Internet keyword search: whalenet) make this information available online, where it is used by marine scientists, government and conservation organizations, and students.

The seal's journey: position, time, and speed

WhaleNet's Satellite Tagging Observation Program (STOP) provided the following information about the seal's journey.

Date	Time (GMT)	Time Elapsed since previous point (h:min)	Latitude	Longitude from previous point	Distance Traveled
05/19/07	10:06	0	36.850 N	76.283 W	0 km (This is the release location–First Landing State Park, Virginia).
05/30/07	04:45	258:39	42.195 N	65.554 W	1096 km
06/03/07	07:27	98:42	44.317 N	63.137 W	307 km
06/05/07	19:20	59:53	45.294 N	60.812 W	214 km
06/11/07	03:11	127:51	45.749 N	59.440 W	119 km
06/16/07	20:16	137:05	47.669 N	58.009 W	240 km
06/19/07	08:11	59:55	46.594 N	56.125 W	186 km
06/25/07	13:17	149:06	48.523 N	51.069 W	437 km
06/28/07	06:25	65:08	50.412 N	51.192 W	210 km
07/03/07	08:46	122:21	54.127 N	54.070 W	458 km
07/05/07	00:40	39:54	54.889 N	55.558 W	128 km
07/09/07	19:08	114:28	56.665 N	59.970 W	340 km

This information can be used to determine the seal's average speed on each leg of his journey. To calculate his average speed on the first leg:

1. Convert elapsed time from h:min to hours.
   258 hours 39 minutes = 258 39/60 hours = 258.65 hours
2. Plug the values into the speed formula: speed = distance time.
   Speed = 1096 km / 258.65 h = 4.237 km/h

New insights, improved coexistence

Knowing the seal's average speed at various points on his journey can help us gain insight into his behavior. For example, between June 5 and June 11, his average speed slowed significantly. During that time, he remained in a small area just off the coast of Cape Breton Island. The satellite data suggests that this area may be a "critical habitat" for the harp seal. What was he doing there? Resting? Feeding? Finding answers to these questions can help us make better decisions about how and when we humans use this coastal region.

J. Michael Williamson, WhaleNet's founder and director, explains, "Similar data from tagging right whales has led to changes in shipping lanes around the whale's feeding areas and slowed shipping traffic through areas where whale calves are born. Satellite tagging research studies have led to many new laws and guidelines governing human activities around endangered species."

What's nice about sea ice?

Satellite tagging data can help us understand more about how animals adapt to changes in their environment. For example, marine scientists are paying careful attention to how far up the Davis Strait harp seals travel. Harp seals stop their northward journey when they run into sea ice, rather than swimming under it, since they need to breathe air like we do.

Harp seals rest, mate, molt, and grow new coats on the sea ice. They also give birth and nurse their pups on the ice. If the ice breaks up before the pups are weaned, the pups may drown or be crushed between large chunks of ice.

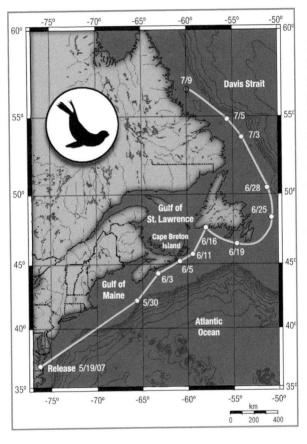

Sea ice formed late and broke up early for 7 of the 11 years between 1996 and 2007. Satellite tagging data helps us monitor how animals respond to these changing conditions. Some seals travel further north. Others have tried to adapt to new habitats—for example, seals have given birth on land instead of ice. There the pups face new predators like foxes, wolves, and domestic and wild dogs—animals that don't hunt on ice.

Marine scientists share information about seal population activity with government agencies that monitor seal hunting and fishing industries. If the seal population declines, new regulations could be enacted to restrict hunts and/or protect the seal's food sources and critical habitat areas, while areas with abundant resources can be opened to the fishing industry. The more we learn about how animals interact with their environments, the better decisions we can make about how we as humans use the oceans.

QUESTIONS

1. What was the seal's average speed between June 5 and June 11, 2007?

2. Name two ways satellite tagging can help humans make better decisions about how we use the oceans.

3. **Research:** Using an Internet keyword search for WhaleNet, find out what marine animal species are currently tagged. Use the website resources to create your own map of one animal's journey. Compare your animal's top speed to the harp seal's. What questions do you have about your animal's travels?

Chapter 2 Review

Understanding Vocabulary

Select the correct term to complete the sentences.

acceleration	frame of reference	position
average velocity	instantaneous velocity	relative velocity
constant velocity	origin	slope
displacement		

1. The rate at which speed changes is called _____.

2. _____ is a variable that gives location relative to an origin.

3. _____ describes the velocity of an object with respect to a frame of reference.

4. A moving object has _____ when both the speed and the direction of travel remain the same.

5. Dividing the total displacement by the total time taken determines the _____.

6. The _____ of a line is found by dividing the rise by the run.

Reviewing Concepts

Section 2.1

1. Compare and contrast the distance and displacement variables.

2. Olivia is doing a motion experiment with a car on a track. She records a negative displacement. Describe the motion of the car.

3. What is the difference between speed and velocity?

4. Can an object have a negative speed? Can it have a negative velocity?

5. What two values are needed to determine average velocity?

6. If an object has an acceleration of 20 cm/s², what do you know about how its velocity changes over time?

7. Give two ways the unit "meters per second per second" can be abbreviated.

8. An object accelerates if its velocity changes. What is the other way an object can accelerate (without changing speed)?

9. What is the acceleration of a car moving at a constant velocity of 50 mph?

Section 2.2

10. Explain how to calculate the slope of a line.

11. The slope of a position vs. time graph is equal to the object's _____.

12. Sam rolls down his driveway on a skateboard while Beth keeps track of his position every second for 15 seconds. When they make a graph of the data, the position vs. time graph is a curve that gets steeper as time increases. What does this tell you about Sam's velocity?

Section 2.3

13. The slope of a velocity vs. time graph is equal to the object's _____.

14. A graph is made of the velocity versus time of a plane as it flies from San Francisco to the Kahului Airport on Maui. How could the displacement of the plane be calculated from the graph?

Solving Problems

Section 2.1

1. Ryan's family drives from San Diego to Phoenix. They continue from Phoenix to Flagstaff, and finally back home to San Diego.

   a. What distance did his family travel?

   b. What is their displacement?

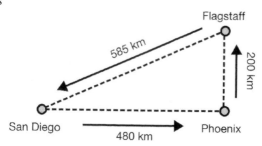

2. A car travels in one direction for 30 min at an average velocity of 20 km/h. What is the distance the car travels?

3. Emma is riding on a train. The train is moving at 50 m/s. Emma walks down the aisle at 1 m/s relative to the train in the same direction the train is moving. What is her relative velocity?

4. A car accelerates from 0 to 20 m/s in 10 seconds. Calculate its acceleration.

5. During a race, you speed up from 3 m/s to 5 m/s in 4 s.

 a. What is your change in velocity?

 b. What is your acceleration?

6. Marcus is driving his car at 15 km/h when he brakes suddenly. He comes to a complete stop in 2 s. What was his acceleration in km/h/s? Was his acceleration positive, negative, or zero?

7. You start from rest and ski down a hill with an acceleration of 2 m/s². Find your velocity at the following times:

 a. 1 s

 b. 2 s

 c. 3 s

 d. 10 s

Section 2.2

8. Rank the four points on the position vs. time graph in order from slowest to fastest.

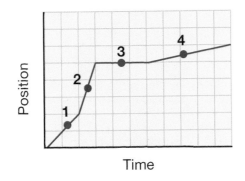

9. Draw the position vs. time graph for a person walking at a constant speed of 1 m/s for 10 s. On the same axes, draw the graph for a person running at a constant speed of 4 m/s.

10. Draw the position vs. time graph for an object that is not moving.

11. Why is the position vs. time graph for an object in free fall a curve?

Section 2.3

12. View the graph at right.

 a. Calculate velocity from the position vs. time graph. Show your work.

 b. Draw the velocity vs. time graph showing the same motion.

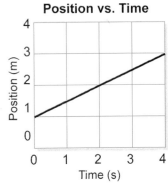

13. Draw a velocity vs. time graph for a car that starts at rest and steadily accelerates until it is moving at 40 m/s after 20 s. Then calculate the car's acceleration and displacement during the first 20 s.

14. Draw a velocity vs. time graph for an object accelerating from rest with a constant acceleration of 2 m/s².

Test Practice

Section 2.1

1. Jill drives from her house to school. After school, she drives to the library. What is her displacement?

 a. 0 km

 b. 5 km

 c. 10 km

 d. 15 km

2. An object in motion has a displacement of 50 m. The average velocity is 25 m/s. The time taken is —————— s.

    a. 0.5

    b. 1

    c. 2

    d. 5

3. The table shows the speed of a person riding a bike uphill. What is the person's acceleration?

    a. –2 m/s

    b. –1 m/s

    c. 1 m/s

    d. 2 m/s

Time (s)	Velocity (m/s)
1	8
2	6
3	4
4	2

4. A car starts at rest and accelerates at 2 m/s² for 10 s. What is the car's final velocity?

    a. 2 m/s

    b. 5 m/s

    c. 10 m/s

    d. 20 m/s

Section 2.2

5. What is the velocity of the moving object represented by the position vs. time graph?

    a. 0.5 m/s

    b. 1 m/s

    c. 2 m/s

    d. 5 m/s

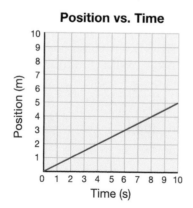

Position vs. Time

6. A car on a track moves away from the origin with a constant velocity. Which position vs. time graph could represent the car's motion?

    A. 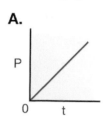   **B.**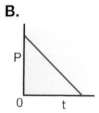

    C. 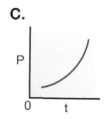   **D.**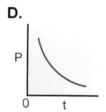

    a. A

    b. B

    c. C

    d. D

7. Which position vs. time graph represents the motion of an object with negative acceleration?

    a. A

    b. B

    c. C

    d. D

Section 2.3

8. The slope of a velocity vs. time graph represents the —————— of the moving object.

    a. velocity

    b. position

    c. acceleration

    d. displacement

9. Which velocity versus time graph represents a car moving at a constant velocity?

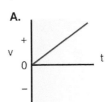 **A.**

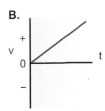 **B.**

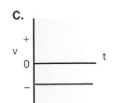 **C.**

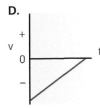 **D.**

a. A

b. B

c. C

d. D

10. The moving object represented by the velocity vs. time graph has an acceleration of _____ m/s/s.

a. 0

b. 0.5

c. 1

d. 2

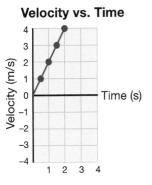

Velocity vs. Time

11. The velocity vs. time graph represents the motion of a person riding a bike. The person's displacement after 4 s is

a. 1 m.

b. 4 m.

c. 8 m.

d. 16 m.

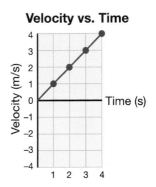

Velocity vs. Time

Applying Your Knowledge

Section 2.1

1. Research the accelerations from 0 to 60 mph for 10 different car models and make a table showing: the model of car, the mass of the car, the amount of time to go from 0 to 60 mph (in seconds), and the acceleration (in mph/s). Is there any relationship between the masses of the cars and their accelerations? Explain possible reasons.

2. Research the following: What is the fastest acceleration of a human in a sprint race? Which animal, using only its muscles, is capable of the fastest acceleration?

Section 2.2

3. This time vs. position graph shows the motion of two cars driving down the same road. Compare the starting positions and velocities. Is the acceleration of each car positive, negative, or zero? Describe what occurs when the lines on the graph intersect.

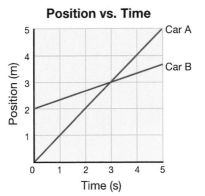

Position vs. Time

Section 2.3

4. As Joseph starts to ride his bike, he accelerates at a constant 1 m/s^2 from rest to final velocity of 10 m/s.

   a. Make a table of his velocity each second from 0 to 10 s. Make a velocity vs. time graph from your table.

   b. Make a table of his position each second from 0 to 10 s. Make a position vs. time graph from your table.

 *Your Turn* **Answers**

Using relative velocity (Section 2.1, page 34)

a. 150 s

Calculating acceleration (Section 2.1, page 36)

a. 5 m/s^2

b. −2 m/s^2

Finding acceleration from a velocity vs. time graph (Section 2.3, page 42)

a. 1.0 m/s^2

b. 0 m/s^2 because the rise is 0 m/s

Laws of Motion

The 53rd space shuttle mission crew brought some toys on board. During the flight, crew members played with the toys to see how they would work in "microgravity." Can you imagine trying to shoot a ball through a hoop while floating around in the space shuttle? Would a toy car be able to race around a loop track in space? You can learn how the toys behaved in space by doing an Internet search using the keywords "toys in space." But by reading this chapter first, you may be able to predict how the toys worked in space. This chapter presents the laws of motion as stated by Sir Isaac Newton (1642–1727). Newton discovered answers to many questions about motion. Many historians believe Newton's ideas about motion were the beginning of modern science.

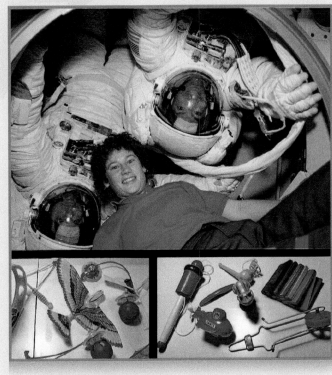

Crew members of the 53rd space shuttle mission with some of the toys they brought along for their "Toys in Space" experiments.

KEY QUESTIONS

✓ *Why do thrown objects fall to Earth instead of flying through the air forever?*

✓ *Is it possible for a feather and a hammer to hit the ground at the same time when dropped?*

✓ *What does a graph of motion look like?*

VOCABULARY

acceleration due to gravity	inertia	Newton's second law
air resistance	net force	terminal velocity
force	newton	weight
free fall	Newton's first law	

3.1 Newton's First Law of Motion

Sir Isaac Newton (1642–1727), an English physicist and mathematician, was one of the most brilliant scientists in history. Before age 30, he had made several important discoveries in physics and had invented a new kind of mathematics called *calculus*. Newton's three laws of motion are probably the most widely-used natural laws in all of science. The laws explain the relationships between the forces acting on an object, the object's mass, and its motion. This section describes Newton's first law of motion.

Changing an object's motion   Suppose you are playing miniature golf and it is your turn. What action must you take to make the golf ball move toward the hole? Would you yell at the ball to make it move? Of course not! You would have to hit the ball with the golf club to get it rolling. The club applies a force to the ball. This force is what changes the ball from being at rest to being in motion (Figure 3.1).

What is force?   A **force** is a push, pull, or any action that has the ability to change motion. The golf ball will stay at rest until you apply a force to set it in motion. Once the ball is moving, it will continue to move in a straight line at a constant speed, unless other forces change its motion. It takes force to start motion and to stop motion. Forces can also affect a moving object by increasing the speed, decreasing the speed, or changing the direction of motion.

How are forces created?   Forces are created in many different ways. For example, your muscles create force when you swing the golf club. Earth's gravity creates a force that pulls on everything around you. On a windy day, the movement of air can create forces. Each of these actions can create force because they all can change an object's motion.

Force is required to change motion   Forces create changes in motion, and *there can be no change in motion without the presence of a force.* Anytime there is a change in motion, a force must exist, even if you cannot immediately identify the force. For example, when a rolling ball hits a wall and bounces, its motion changes rapidly. That change in motion is caused by the wall exerting a force on the ball that changes the direction of the ball's motion.

force - a push, pull, or other action that has the ability to change motion

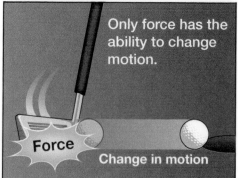

Figure 3.1: *Force is an action that has the ability to change motion. Without force, the motion of an object cannot be changed.*

Forces, mass, and inertia

Stopping a moving object Let's keep playing golf. Once the golf ball is moving, how can you stop it? To stop the ball, you must apply a force in a direction opposite its motion. In general, objects continue moving with the same motion once they start moving. This idea is known as Newton's first law of motion.

Newton's first law **Newton's first law** states that objects tend to continue the motion they already have unless they are acted on by outside forces. In the absence of such forces, an object at rest will stay at rest. An object that is moving will keep moving at the same speed and in the same direction. In other words, objects resist changes in their motion.

> *An object at rest will stay at rest and an object in motion will continue in motion with the same velocity* unless *acted on by an outside force.*

Inertia Some objects resist changes in motion more than others. **Inertia** is the property of an object that resists changes in its motion. To understand inertia, imagine trying to move a bowling ball and a golf ball. Which requires more force? Of course, the bowling ball needs more force to make it move at the same velocity as the golf ball (assuming the forces act for the same length of time). The bowling ball also requires more force to stop. A bowling ball has more inertia than a golf ball. The greater an object's inertia, the greater the force needed to change its motion. Because inertia is an important idea, Newton's first law is sometimes called the *law of inertia.*

Mass Inertia comes from mass. Objects with more mass have more inertia and are more resistant to changes in their motion. Mass is measured in kilograms (kg). A golf ball has a mass of about 0.05 kilograms, and a bowling ball can have a mass of 5 kilograms (Figure 3.2). A 5-kilogram bowling ball is 100 times as massive as the golf ball, so it has 100 times the inertia. For small amounts of mass, the kilogram is too large a unit to be convenient. One gram (g) is one-thousandth of a kilogram. A dollar bill has a mass of about a gram, so 1,000 dollar bills have a mass of approximately 1 kilogram.

> **Newton's first law** - an object at rest will stay at rest and an object in motion will continue in motion with the same velocity unless acted on by an outside force
>
> **inertia** - the property of an object that resists changes in motion

One dollar bill
1 gram
0.001 kilogram

A golf ball
50 grams
0.050 kilogram

One liter of soda
1,000 grams
1 kilogram

A bowling ball
5,000 grams
5 kilograms

Figure 3.2: *Mass can be measured in grams or kilograms.*

Units of force

Pounds   If you are mailing a package at the post office, how does the clerk know how much to charge you? The package is placed on a scale and you are charged based on the package's weight. For example, the scale shows that the package weighs 5 pounds. The pound is a unit of *force* commonly used in the United States. When you measure weight in pounds on a scale, you are measuring the *force of gravity* acting on the object (Figure 3.3, top).

The origin of the pound   The pound measurement of force is based on the Roman unit *libra,* which means "balance," and is the source for pound's abbreviation, lb. The word *pound* comes from the Latin word *pondus*, which means "weight." The definition of a pound has varied over time and from country to country.

The newton   Although the pound is commonly used to express force, scientists use the newton. The **newton** (N) is the SI unit of force. A force of 1 N is the exact amount of force needed to cause a mass of 1 kg to accelerate at 1 m/s per second (Figure 3.3, bottom). We use the name newton because the SI unit of force is defined by Newton's laws.

Converting newtons and pounds   The newton is a smaller unit of force than the pound. One pound of force equals about 4.448 newtons. How much would a 100-pound person weigh in newtons? Remember that 1 pound = 4.448 newtons. Therefore, a 100-pound person weighs 444.8 newtons.

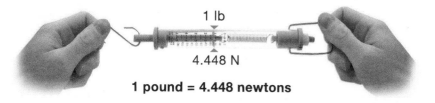

1 pound = 4.448 newtons

The force unit of newtons   When physics problems are presented in this book, forces will almost always be expressed in newtons. In the next section, on Newton's second law, you will see that the newton is closely related to the SI units for mass, distance, and time.

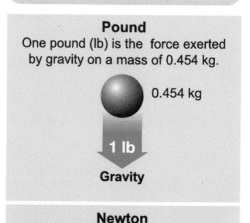

newton - the SI unit of force

Pound
One pound (lb) is the force exerted by gravity on a mass of 0.454 kg.

0.454 kg

1 lb

Gravity

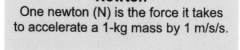

Newton
One newton (N) is the force it takes to accelerate a 1-kg mass by 1 m/s/s.

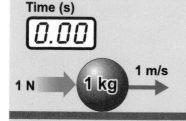

Time (s)

0.00

1 N   1 kg   1 m/s

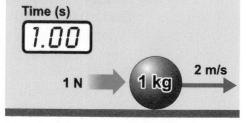

Time (s)

1.00

1 N   1 kg   2 m/s

Figure 3.3: *The definition of the pound and the newton.*

The net force

Multiple forces When you hit a golf ball, the force from the club is not the only force that acts on the ball. Gravity also exerts a force on the ball. Which force causes the change in the ball's motion—gravity or the force from the golf club? Does gravity stop while the golf club exerts its force?

Forces act together You are right if you are thinking "all forces act together." The motion of objects changes in response to the *total force* acting on the object, including gravity and any other forces that are present. In fact, it is rare that only one force acts at a time since gravity is always present.

Net force Adding up forces can be different from simply adding numbers because the *direction* of the forces matter. For this reason, the term **net force** is used to describe the total of all forces acting on an object. When used this way, the word *net* means "total." Net force means that the direction of the forces has been taken into account when calculating the total, too.

Forces in the same direction When two forces are in the same direction, the net force is the sum of the two. For example, think about two people pushing a box. If each person pushes with a force of 300 newtons in the same direction, the net force on the box is 600 N (Figure 3.4, top). The box speeds up in the direction of the net force.

Forces in opposite directions What about gravity acting on the box? Gravity exerts a force downward on the box. However, the floor holds the box up. In physics, the term *holds up* means "applies a force." In order to hold up the box, the floor exerts a force upward on the box. The net force on the box in the up-down (vertical) direction is *zero* because the force from the floor is opposed to the force of gravity. When equal forces applied to the same object are in opposite directions they cancel (Figure 3.4, bottom). The motion of the box in the up-down direction does not change because the net force in this direction is zero.

> **net force** - the total of all forces acting on an object

Forces in the horizontal direction

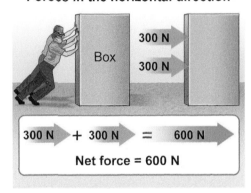

300 N + 300 N = 600 N
Net force = 600 N

Forces in the vertical direction

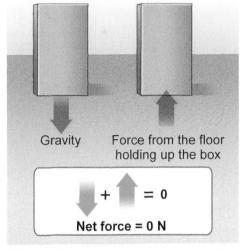

Gravity   Force from the floor holding up the box

+ = 0
Net force = 0 N

Figure 3.4: *The net force acting on a box being pushed by people and by gravity.*

Applications of Newton's first law

Seat belts and air bags
Two very important safety features of automobiles are designed with Newton's first law in mind: seat belts and air bags. Suppose you are driving down the highway in your car at 55 miles per hour when the driver in front of you slams on the brakes. You also slam on your brakes to avoid an accident. Your car slows down but the inertia of your body resists the change in motion. Your body tries to continue doing what it was doing—traveling at 55 miles per hour. Luckily, your seat belt or air bag or both supplies a restraining force. This force counteracts your inertia to slow your body down with the car (Figure 3.5).

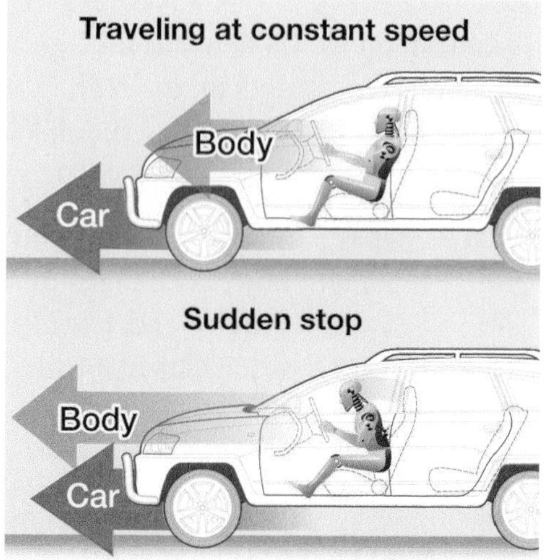

Cup holders
A cup holder does almost the same thing for a cup. Consider what happens if you have a can of soda on the dashboard. What happens to the soda can when you turn sharply to the left? Remember, the soda can was not at rest to begin with. It was moving at the same velocity as the car. When your car goes left, the soda can's inertia causes it to keep moving forward (Figure 3.6). The result can be quite a mess! Automobile cup holders are designed to keep the first law from making messes.

The tablecloth trick
Have you ever wondered how a magician is able to pull a tablecloth out from underneath dishes set on a table? It's not a trick of magic at all, but just physics. The dishes have inertia and therefore tend to resist changes in motion. Before the magician pulls on the cloth, the dishes are at rest. So when the tablecloth is whisked away, the inertia of the dishes keeps them at rest. This trick works best when the tablecloth is pulled very rapidly, the table is small, and there is very little friction between the objects involved.

Traveling at constant speed

Body

Car

Sudden stop

Body

Car

Figure 3.5: *Because of its inertia, your body tends to keep moving when your car stops suddenly. This can cause serious injury if you are not wearing a seat belt.*

Figure 3.6: *Because of its inertia, a soda can on the dashboard will tend to keep moving forward when the car turns left.*

3.1 Section Review

1. State Newton's first law in your own words.
2. How is mass related to inertia?
3. What do pounds and newtons measure? Why do scientists use newtons instead of pounds?
4. What is net force and how is it determined?
5. Why are vehicle seat belts and air bags designed with Newton's first law of motion in mind?

3.2 Newton's Second Law of Motion

Newton's first law says that a force is needed to change an object's motion. But what kind of change happens? The answer is *acceleration*. Acceleration is how motion changes. The amount of acceleration depends on both the force and the mass, according to Newton's second law. This section is about Newton's second law, which relates force, mass, and acceleration. The second law is probably the most well-used relationship in all of physics.

> Newton's second law - relates the net force acting on an object to its mass and acceleration

Force, mass, and acceleration

Newton's second law **Newton's second law** relates the net force acting on an object to its mass and acceleration. It states that the greater the net force on an object, the greater its acceleration. If twice the net force is applied, the acceleration will be twice as great. The law also says that the greater the mass, the smaller the acceleration for a given net force (Figure 3.7). An object with twice the mass will have half the acceleration if the same net force is applied.

Direct and inverse proportions In mathematical terms, the acceleration of an object is directly proportional to the net force and inversely proportional to the mass. These two relationships are combined in Newton's second law:

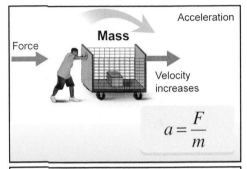

> *NEWTON'S SECOND LAW*
>
> Acceleration (m/s²) $a = \dfrac{F}{m}$ Force (N)
>
> Mass (kg)

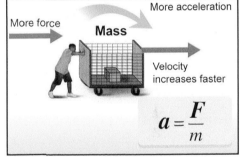

Changes in motion involve acceleration Net force is not necessary to keep an object in motion at constant velocity. A moving object will keep going at a constant velocity until a net force acts on it. Once a skater is moving, she will coast for a long time without any force to push her along. However, she does need force to speed up, slow down, turn, or stop. Changes in velocity always involve acceleration. *Force* causes *acceleration*, and *mass* resists *acceleration*.

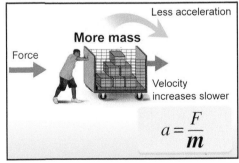

Figure 3.7: *Increasing the force increases the acceleration, and increasing the mass decreases the acceleration.*

Applying the second law

Some guidelines   To use Newton's second law properly, keep the following important ideas in mind. They can be used as guidelines for how to apply the second law to physics problems.

1. The *net* force is what causes acceleration.
2. If there is *no* acceleration, the net force *must* be zero.
3. If there *is* acceleration, there *must* also be a net force.
4. The force unit of newtons is based on kilograms, meters, and seconds.

Net force   When two forces are in the same direction, the net force is the sum of the two forces. When two forces are in opposite directions, the net force is the difference between them. To get the correct net force, we usually assign positive values to one direction and negative values to the other direction. Figure 3.8 shows how to calculate the net force for different forces.

Examples with and without acceleration   Objects at rest or moving with constant velocity have zero acceleration. This means the net force must also be zero. You can calculate unknown forces in these situations by using the knowledge that the net force is zero. The motion of a kicked ball or a car turning a corner are examples where the acceleration is not zero. Therefore, both situations have net forces that are not zero.

Using newtons in calculations   The newton is *defined* by the relationship of force, mass, and acceleration. A force of 1 newton is the exact amount of force needed to cause a mass of 1 kilogram to accelerate at 1 m/s² (Figure 3.9). The newton is a useful way to measure force because it connects force directly to its effect on matter and motion. A net force of 1 newton will always accelerate a 1-kilogram mass at 1 m/s² wherever you are in the known universe. In terms of solving physics problems, use the following units when using force in newtons:

- mass in kilograms (kg)
- distance or position in meters (m)
- time in seconds (s)
- velocity in meters per second (m/s)
- acceleration in meters per second per second (m/s²)

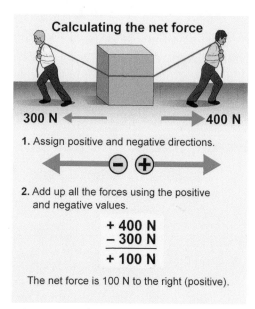

Figure 3.8: *Calculating the net force.*

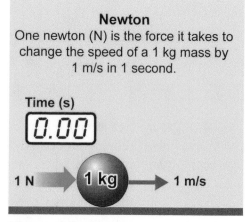

Figure 3.9: *The definition of a newton.*

Doing calculations with the second law

Writing the second law The formula for the second law of motion uses F, m, and a to represent force, mass, and acceleration. The way you write the formula depends on what you want to know. Three ways to write the formula are summarized in Table 3.1.

Table 3.1: Three forms of the second law

Use ...	... if you want to find ...	... and you know ...
$a = F/m$	acceleration (a)	force (F) and mass (m)
$F = ma$	force (F)	acceleration (a) and mass (m)
$m = F/a$	mass (m)	acceleration (a) and force (F)

Net force Remember, when using the second law, the force that appears is the net force. Consider all the forces that are acting and add them up to find the net force before calculating any accelerations. If you work in the other direction, calculating force from mass and acceleration, it is the net force that you get from the second law. You may have to do additional work if the problem asks for a specific force and there is more than one force acting.

Units and the second law

When using $F = ma$, the units of force (newtons) must equal the units of mass (kilograms) multiplied by the units of acceleration (m/s²). How is this possible? The answer is that 1 newton is 1 kg·m/s². The unit *newton* was created to be a shortcut way to write the unit of force. It is much simpler to say 5 N rather than 5 kg·m/s².

 Using Newton's second law

A car has a mass of 1,000 kg. If a net force of 2,000 N is exerted on the car, what is its acceleration?

1. *Looking for:*   You are asked for the car's acceleration.

2. *Given:*   You are given its mass in kilograms and the net force in newtons.

3. *Relationships:* $a = \dfrac{F}{m}$

4. *Solution:* $a = \dfrac{2,000\,\text{N}}{1,000\,\text{kg}} = \dfrac{2\,\text{kg}\cdot\text{m/s}^2}{\text{kg}} = 2\,\text{m/s}^2$

Your Turn:

a. What is the acceleration of a 1,500-kg car if a net force of 1,200 N is exerted on it?

b. As you coast down the hill on your bicycle, you accelerate at 0.5 m/s². If the total mass of your body and the bicycle is 80 kg, how much net force is pulling you down the hill?

c. You push a grocery cart with a force of 35 N and it accelerates at 2.5 m/s². What is its mass?

(Answers are listed at the end of the chapter.)

Force and energy

Energy moves through force   Force is the action through which energy moves. This important idea will help you understand why forces occur. Consider a rubber band that is stretched to launch a car. The rubber band has energy because it is stretched. When you let the car go, the rubber band's energy is transferred to the car. The transfer of energy from the stretched rubber band to the car occurs through the force that the rubber band exerts on the car (Figure 3.10, bottom).

Energy differences create force   Forces are created any time there is a difference in energy. A stretched rubber band has more energy than a relaxed rubber band (Figure 3.10, top). The difference in energy results in a force that the rubber band exerts on whatever is holding it in the stretched shape.

An example of energy differences   Energy differences can be created in many ways. A car at the top of a hill has more energy than when the car is at the bottom. This tells you there must be a force that pulls the car toward the bottom of the hill. You can predict that a downhill force must exist even though you may not know the cause of that force.

An important idea   Suppose there is an energy difference between one arrangement of a system (car at the top) and another arrangement (car at the bottom). Some force will *always* act to bring the system from the higher energy arrangement to the lower energy one *or to keep it in its high-energy state*. We will find many examples of this important principle throughout the course. The principle is true in all of science, not just physics.

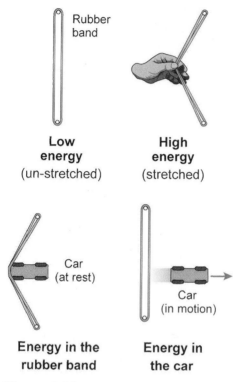

Figure 3.10: *Energy differences cause forces to be created. The forces can transfer energy from one object to another.*

3.2 Section Review

1. List three units in which acceleration can be measured.
2. According to Newton's second law, what causes acceleration? What resists acceleration?
3. An 8,000-kg helicopter's velocity increases from 0 m/s to 25 m/s in 5 s. Calculate its acceleration and the net force acting on it.
4. Define the term *net force*.
5. Describe the conceptual relationship between energy and force.

3.3 Gravity and Free Fall

Imagine dropping a baseball out of a second-floor window. What happens? Of course, the ball falls toward the ground. Is the velocity constant or does the ball accelerate? If it accelerates, at what rate? Do all objects fall at the same rate? You will find the answers in this section.

The acceleration due to gravity

The definition of free fall
An object is in **free fall** if it is accelerating due to the force of gravity. A dropped baseball is in free fall from the instant it leaves your hand until it reaches the ground. A ball thrown upward is also in free fall after it leaves your hand. Although you might not describe the ball as "falling," it is still in free fall. Birds, helicopters, and airplanes are *not* normally in free fall because forces other than gravity act on them.

The acceleration of gravity
Objects in free fall on Earth accelerate downward at 9.8 m/s², the **acceleration due to gravity**. Because this acceleration is used so frequently in physics, the letter g is used to represent its value. When you see the letter g in a physics problem, you can substitute the value 9.8 m/s².

Free-fall velocity
If you know the acceleration of an object in free fall, you can predict its velocity at any time after it is dropped. For example, the velocity of a dropped object will increase by 9.8 m/s every second (Figure 3.11). If it starts at rest, it will be moving at 9.8 m/s after 1 second, 19.6 m/s after 2 seconds, 29.4 m/s after 3 seconds, and so on. To calculate the object's velocity, you multiply the time it falls by the value of g. Because the units of g are m/s², the velocity must be in m/s and the time must be in seconds.

> **FREE FALL VELOCITY**
> (starting at rest)
>
> **Acceleration due to gravity** (m/s²)
>
> $$v = gt$$
>
> **Velocity** (m/s)   **Time** (s)

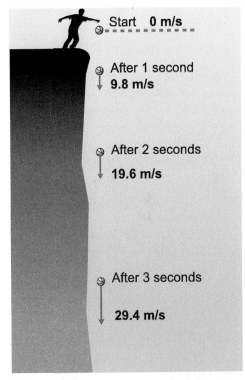

> **free fall** - the acceleration of a falling object due to Earth's gravity
>
> **acceleration due to gravity** - the acceleration of an object due to Earth's gravity that is equal to 9.8 m/s² and represented by g

Start   **0 m/s**

After 1 second
↓ **9.8 m/s**

After 2 seconds
↓ **19.6 m/s**

After 3 seconds

↓ **29.4 m/s**

Figure 3.11: *The velocity of a ball in free fall increases by 9.8 m/s every second.*

Upward launches

Throwing a ball upward When an object is in free fall, it accelerates *downward* at 9.8 m/s². Gravity causes the acceleration by exerting a downward force. So what happens if you throw a ball *upward*? The ball will slow down as it moves upward, come to a stop for an instant, and then fall back down. As it moves upward, the speed *decreases* by 9.8 m/s every second until it reaches zero. The ball then reverses direction and starts falling down. As it falls downward, the speed *increases* by 9.8 m/s every second.

Velocity When an object's direction is important, we use the term *velocity* instead of speed. Recall that velocity is speed with direction. In Figure 3.12, the ball's initial velocity is +19.6 m/s and its velocity four seconds later is –19.6 m/s. The positive sign means upward and the negative sign means downward.

Changes in velocity The acceleration of the ball is –9.8 m/s² (–g). That means you subtract 9.8 m/s from the velocity every second. Figure 3.12 shows what happens to a ball launched upward at 19.6 m/s. The velocity decreases for 2 seconds, reaches zero, and then increases for 2 seconds. *The acceleration is the same all the time* (–9.8 m/s²) even though the ball is slowing down as it goes up and speeding up as it comes back down. The acceleration is the same because the change in velocity is the same from one second to the next. The velocity always changes by –9.8 m/s every second.

Stopping for an instant Notice the ball's velocity is 0 m/s at the top of its path. If you watch this motion, the ball looks like it stops, because it is moving so slowly at the top of its path. To your eye, it may look like it stops for a second, but a slow-motion camera would show the ball's velocity immediately reverses at the top and does not stay zero for any measurable amount of time.

Acceleration You may want to say the acceleration is zero at the top, but only the *velocity* is zero at the top. The force of gravity causes the ball's acceleration. The force of gravity stays constant. Therefore, the acceleration is also constant and cannot be zero while the ball is in the air.

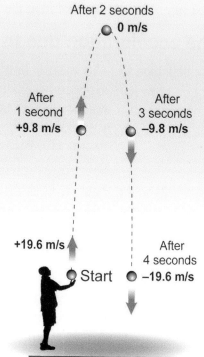

The velocity changes by –9.8 m/s every second.

Time (s)	Velocity (m/s)
0	19.6
1	9.8
2	0.0
3	–9.8
4	–19.6

Figure 3.12: *The motion of a ball launched upward at 19.6 m/s.*

Free fall and distance

Changing velocity   In Chapter 1, you used $d = vt$ to calculate distance. You cannot calculate distance in the same simple way when velocity is not constant, as happens in free fall. An object in free fall increases its velocity by 9.8 m/s each second, which means it moves a greater distance each second.

Average velocity   One way to calculate distance is to use the *average velocity*. In free fall and other situations of *constant* acceleration, the average velocity is the average of the starting or initial velocity (v_i) and the final velocity (v_f). Taking the average accounts for the fact that the velocity is not constant. Be careful when doing this calculation. The average velocity may *not* be $(v_f + v_i) \div 2$ if the acceleration is not constant.

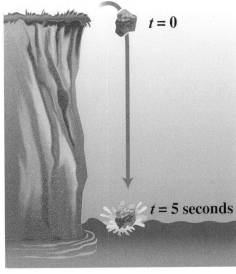

t = 0

t = 5 seconds

AVERAGE VELOCITY   *Final velocity* (m/s)   *Initial velocity* (m/s)

Average velocity (m/s)
$$v_{avg} = \frac{v_f + v_i}{2}$$

Figure 3.13: *What is the average velocity of a rock that falls for 5 seconds?*

➕ ➖ ✖ ➗ Using average velocity for an accelerating object

A rock falls off a cliff and splashes into a river 5 seconds later (Figure 3.13). What was the rock's average velocity?

1. Looking for: You are asked for the average velocity in m/s. You need to find the final velocity in m/s.

2. Given: You may assume zero initial velocity and are given the air time in seconds.

3. Relationships: $v_f = gt$ and $v_{avg} = \dfrac{v_i + v_f}{2}$ where $g = 9.8$ m/s^2

4. Solution: $v_f = (9.8\,\text{m/s}^2)(5\,\text{s}) = 49\,\text{m/s}$ $v_{avg} = \dfrac{0 + 49\,\text{m/s}}{2} = 24.5\,\text{m/s}$

Your Turn:

a. What is the average velocity of a baseball dropped from rest that falls for 2 s?

b. What is the average velocity of a ball with an initial velocity of 10 m/s that falls for 2 s?

(Answers are listed at the end of the chapter.)

Calculating distance Now that you know how to calculate the average velocity for an object in free fall, you can use the average velocity to find the distance it falls.

FREE FALL DISTANCE

Average velocity (m/s)

$$d = v_{avg} t$$

Distance (m) — Time (s)

Calculating free fall velocity and distance

A skydiver falls for 6 seconds before opening her parachute. Calculate her actual velocity at the 6-second mark and the distance she has fallen in this time.

1. *Looking for:* You are asked to find the final velocity and the distance.

2. *Given:* You may assume zero initial velocity, and are given the time in seconds.

3. *Relationships:* $v_f = gt \quad v_{avg} = \dfrac{v_i + v_f}{2} \quad d = v_{avg} t$

4. *Solution:* $v_f = (9.8 \text{ m/s}^2)(6.00 \text{ s}) = 58.8 \text{ m/s}$

   The speed after 6.00 seconds is 58.8 m/s.

   $v_{avg} = \dfrac{0 + 58.8 \text{ m/s}}{2} = 29.4 \text{ m/s}$

   $d = (29.4 \text{ m/s})(6.00 \text{ s}) = 176 \text{ m}$

   The skydiver falls 176 meters.

Your Turn:

a. Calculate the final velocity and distance for a skydiver who waits 4.00 seconds to open his parachute.

b. An apple falls from the top branch of a tree and lands 1.0 second later. How tall is the tree?

(Answers are listed at the end of the chapter.)

Another way to calculate free-fall distance

Using the average velocity to calculate the distance traveled by an object in free fall requires multiple steps. If you are only given the air time, you must first find the final velocity. Then, you must calculate the average velocity, and finally you can find the distance.

These three steps can all be combined into one formula. The general version of the formula is beyond the scope of this book, but can be simplified if the object starts at rest ($v_i = 0$).

1) If the initial velocity is zero and the object falls for t seconds, then the final velocity is gt.

2) The average velocity is half the final velocity or ½ gt.

3) The distance is the average velocity multiplied by the time or ½ gt^2.

The general formula is therefore:

$$d = \frac{1}{2} g t^2$$

Remember, this formula only works when the object starts at rest and is in free fall.

Gravity and weight

Gravity's force depends on mass
The force of gravity on an object is called **weight**. The symbol F_w is used to represent weight. At Earth's surface, gravity exerts a force of 9.8 N on every kilogram of mass. That means a 1-kilogram mass has a weight of 9.8 N, a 2-kilogram mass has a weight of 19.6 N, and so on. On Earth's surface, the weight of any object is its mass in kilograms multiplied by 9.8 N/kg. Because weight is a force, it is measured in units of force such as newtons and pounds.

Weight and mass
We all tend to use the terms *weight* and *mass* interchangeably. Heavy objects have lots of mass and light objects have little mass. People and things such as food are "weighed" in both kilograms and pounds. If you look on the label of a bag of flour, it lists the "weight" in two units: 5 pounds in English units and 2.3 kilograms in SI units. As long as we are on Earth, where $g = 9.8$ N/kg, a 2.3-kilogram object will weigh 5 pounds. But on the Moon, $g = 1.6$ N/kg, so a 2.3-kilogram object will weigh only 0.8 pounds (Figure 3.14).

Weight and the second law
You should recognize that the value of 9.8 N/kg is the same as g (9.8 m/s^2) but with different units. This is no coincidence. According to Newton's second law, a force of 9.8 newtons acting on 1 kilogram produces an acceleration of 9.8 m/s^2. For this reason, the value of g can also be used as 9.8 N/kg. Which units you choose depends on whether you want to calculate acceleration or the weight force. Both units are actually identical: 9.8 N/kg = 9.8 m/s^2.

> **WEIGHT**
>
> **Mass** (kg)
>
> **Weight or force of gravity** (N) —— $F_w = mg$ —— **Strength of gravity** (9.8 N/kg)

> **weight** - the force of gravity acting on an object

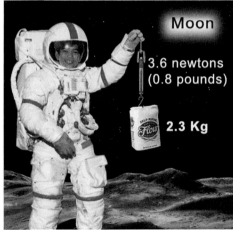

Figure 3.14: *An object that weighs 5 pounds on Earth weighs only 0.8 pounds on the Moon. It has the same mass but different weights because gravity is stronger on Earth.*

Mass is fundamental Although mass and weight are related, remember the difference in physics. Mass is a fundamental property of an object measured in kilograms. Weight is a *force* measured in *newtons* that depends on mass and gravity. A 10-kilogram object has a mass of 10 kilograms, no matter where it is in the universe. A 10-kilogram object's weight, however, can vary greatly depending on whether the object is on Earth, on the Moon, or in outer space.

Why accelerations are the same In the example, the weight of a 10-kilogram object is 10 times the weight of a 1-kilogram object. However, the heavier weight produces only one-tenth the acceleration. The increase in force is exactly matched by the increase in mass. As a result, the acceleration of all objects in free fall is the same.

 Weight and mass

Legend says that around 1587, Galileo dropped two balls from the Leaning Tower of Pisa to see which would fall faster. Suppose the balls had masses of 1 kilogram and 10 kilograms.

a. Use the equation for weight to calculate the force of gravity on each ball.
b. Use your answers from part a and Newton's second law to calculate each ball's acceleration.

1. **Looking for:** You are asked to find the force of gravity (weight) and the acceleration.

2. **Given:** You are given each ball's mass in kilograms.

3. **Relationships:** $F_w = mg$ $a = F/m$

4. **Solution:** For the 1.0-kg ball:
   a) $F_w = (1.0 \text{ kg})(9.8 \text{ m/s}^2)$ $F_w = 9.8 \text{ N}$
   b) $a = (9.8 \text{ N})/(1.0 \text{ kg})$ $a = 9.8 \text{ m/s}^2$

   For the 10.0-kg ball:
   a) $F_w = (10.0 \text{ kg})(9.8 \text{ m/s}^2)$ $F_w = 98 \text{ N}$
   b) $a = (98 \text{ N})/(10.0 \text{ kg})$ $a = 9.8 \text{ m/s}^2$ Both balls have the same acceleration.

Your Turn:
a. Calculate the weight of a 60.0-kilogram person (in newtons) on Earth and on Mars ($g = 3.70 \text{ m/s}^2$).

b. A 70.0-kg person travels to a planet where he weighs 1,750 N. What is the value of g on that planet?

(Answers are listed at the end of the chapter.)

Air resistance

Air resistance   We just found that the acceleration of objects in free fall is the same. So, why does a feather fall slower than a baseball? The answer is that objects on Earth are not truly in free fall because gravity is *not* the only force acting on them. When something falls through air, the air exerts an additional force. This force, called **air resistance**, acts opposite to the direction of the object's motion.

Factors affecting air resistance   The size and shape of an object affect the force of air resistance. A feather has its weight spread over a comparatively large area, so it must push a lot of air out of the way as it falls. The force of air resistance is large compared with the weight. According to the second law of motion, acceleration is caused by the net force. The net force is the weight minus the force of air resistance. The feather accelerates at much less than 9.8 m/s^2 because the net force is much smaller than the acceleration due to gravity alone.

Why the baseball falls faster   A baseball's shape allows it to move through the air more easily than a feather. The force of air resistance is much smaller than the baseball's weight. Since the net force is almost the same as its weight, the baseball accelerates at nearly 9.8 m/s^2 and falls much more rapidly than the feather.

Terminal velocity   If you observe a falling feather, it stops accelerating after a short distance and then falls at constant velocity. That is because air resistance increases with velocity. A feather only accelerates until the force of air resistance equals the force of gravity. The net force then becomes zero and the feather falls with a constant velocity called the **terminal velocity**. The terminal velocity depends on the ratio of an object's weight to its air resistance. A tightly-crumpled ball of paper has a higher terminal velocity than a flat piece of paper because the flat sheet has more air resistance even though the papers' masses are the same.

air resistance - a force that acts against the force of gravity on an object in free fall

terminal velocity - the maximum velocity reached by an object in free fall in which the forces of gravity and air resistance are equal

Terminal velocity

Parachutes use air resistance to reduce the terminal velocity of a skydiver. Without a parachute, the skydiver has a small area and can reach a velocity of over 100 mph. The parachute increases the area dramatically and creates greater air resistance. The skydiver's terminal velocity is then slow enough to allow for a safe landing.

3.3 *Section Review*

1. Describe the motion of a freely-falling object. Use the words *velocity*, *acceleration*, and *distance* in your answer.
2. What is the difference between mass and weight?
3. If you drop a feather and a baseball in a place where there is no air resistance, how will their motions compare? Why?

Parabolic Flights

Have you ever seen video footage of astronauts floating in a spacecraft? The term weightlessness *is used to describe this experience, but did you know that you can achieve this feeling even while Earth's gravity is pulling on you?*

Weightlessness

Every object with mass exerts gravitational force (also called weight) on every other object. As objects move farther apart, this force weakens. To be truly weightless, you would have to go to a location infinitely far away from every planet, star, moon, and other piece of mass in the universe. However, you *can* feel weightless if the force of gravity is the only force on you, and no other force is acting to balance your weight.

For example, suppose you weigh 500 newtons. You are standing on the ground. Gravity pulls you down with a force of 500 newtons, and the floor pushes you up with a force of 500 newtons. You are aware of your weight because you feel the ground pushing up on your feet.

Now, imagine you are in an elevator when the cable snaps. The elevator and your body experience free fall. You do not feel the force of the floor pushing up on your feet because the elevator is falling at the same rate as your body. Gravity is still pulling on you, but you feel weightless!

Astronauts in orbit around Earth feel weightless for the same reason. An orbiting spacecraft has a horizontal speed, but as it moves, gravity causes it to "fall" around the Earth. Astronauts float because the spacecraft is falling as fast as they are.

Parabolic Flights

Before going on missions, astronauts must practice working in an environment in which they feel weightless. This training is done on airplanes that fly in a path called a *parabola*. A parabola is the curved path an object follows when it is launched from the ground. If you kick a soccer ball up at an angle, its path is a parabola.

When flying in a parabola, the pilot maneuvers the plane so its path matches the path the passengers would follow if they were launched at an angle into the air at the speed of the plane. The passengers float around and feel weightless because the plane does not exert any forces on them. Each parabolic flight lasts about 30 seconds, when the plane is at the "top" of the parabola. The plane makes about 50 parabolas during a flight.

NASA has been conducting parabolic flights since the 1950s to train astronauts. Scientists and college students have also gone on parabolic flights to perform a wide variety of chemistry, biology, and physics experiments. They have studied how weightlessness affects muscles, bones, blood circulation, digestion, and respiration. This research helps NASA learn how long missions may affect astronauts.

NASA conducts parabolic flights to train astronauts.

ZERO-G

Before 2004, thrill seekers weren't able to take a ride on a parabolic flight simply for fun. Now, non-astronauts can have the experience of floating, spinning, and flying through the air with the Zero Gravity Corporation (ZERO-G). The company uses a specially-modified Boeing 727-200 plane called the G-FORCE-ONE to take people on parabolic flights.

Now, non-astronauts can have the experience of floating, spinning, and flying through the air.

Passengers attend a training session so they know what to expect in flight. The plane is obviously not a typical airplane. The rear third of the plane contains 35 seats. The front two-thirds is an open area called the Floating Zone. It is 90 feet long, with a padded floor and walls. During take-off, passengers remain in their seats.

Once the plane reaches an elevation of approximately 25,000 feet, passengers move to the Floating Zone and lie on the floor. ZERO-G flights contain three types of parabolas: Martian gravity (⅓ Earth gravity), Lunar gravity (⅙ Earth gravity), and zero gravity. The Martian and Lunar parabolas are not as steep as the zero gravity parabolas, so the floor of the plane provides some support force to the passengers. The effect is a feeling of being lighter than on Earth, making it possible to do one-handed push-ups and flips in the air. Martian and Lunar parabolas are done first to help passengers get used to the feeling of reduced gravity.

When the plane begins a parabola, it accelerates upward at a 45-degree angle. While lying on the floor, passengers feel like they are almost twice as heavy as on Earth. The engine thrust is then decreased so the plane begins to decelerate. Passengers feel the force of the floor on their bodies decrease. They can float, do flips, and try to catch floating water droplets squirted from the instructors' water bottles. Once the plane flies over the top of the parabola, it begins a descent toward Earth.

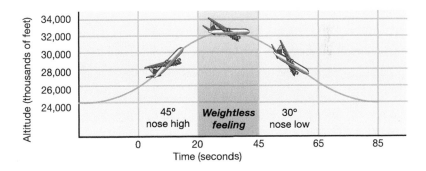

After approximately 25 seconds, passengers are alerted with the warning, "Feet down! Coming out!" Without the feeling of gravity pulling toward the bottom of the plane, it's impossible to tell up from down. As the plane begins to level off, the passengers slowly fall to the floor. Then the ride starts all over again, for a total of 15 fun-filled parabolas.

QUESTIONS

1. Why does a person in a freely-falling elevator feel weightless?
2. Are astronauts in orbit around Earth truly weightless? Explain.
3. List some ways parabolic flights are used.
4. Describe an experiment you could do on a parabolic flight to demonstrate one of Newton's laws. Explain which law the experiment demonstrates.

Astronaut and training photos courtesy of NASA. Zero-G photo courtesy of www.gozerog.com.

Chapter 3 Review

Understanding Vocabulary

Select the correct term to complete the sentences.

acceleration due to gravity	free fall	Newton's first law
air resistance	inertia	Newton's second law
force	net force	terminal velocity
	newton	weight

1. "Objects continue moving in the same way" is a way of stating _____.

2. An object with more mass also has more _____.

3. The total of all the forces acting on an object is called the _____.

4. _____ relates force, mass, and acceleration in the equation $F = ma$.

5. The force of gravity on an object is its _____.

6. When the force due to gravity equals the force due to air resistance, the speed of a falling object is called its _____.

Reviewing Concepts

Section 3.1

1. Define the term *force* and give three examples of forces.

2. Give an example of Newton's first law in everyday life.

3. Explain why Newton's first law is also known as the law of inertia.

4. List two units for measuring mass and two units for measuring force.

5. One newton is the _____ it takes to change the _____ of a _____ mass by _____ in 1 s.

Section 3.2

6. What is the net force on an object with zero acceleration?

7. Which of the following have zero acceleration?

   a. a car moving forward at a constant velocity

   b. a kicked ball

   c. a skater turning left

   d. a parked car

8. Write the equation for Newton's second law that you would use in each of the following scenarios. Let F = force, m = mass, and a = acceleration:

   a. You know mass and acceleration and want to find the force.

   b. You know mass and force and want to find the acceleration.

   c. You know force and acceleration and want to find the mass.

9. Give an example of Newton's second law in everyday life.

Section 3.3

10. By how much does the speed of an object in free fall change each second?

11. A ball is thrown straight up into the air. As it moves upward, its speed _____ by _____ each second. As it falls back down, its speed _____ by _____ each second.

12. An astronaut carries a rock from the Moon to Earth. Is the rock's mass the same on Earth as on the Moon? Is its weight the same? Explain.

13. What is the direction of air resistance on a falling object?

14. Which two forces are equal when an object is at its terminal speed?

Solving Problems

Section 3.1

1. Order the following mass measurements from smallest to largest: 0.5 kg, 1,000 g, 5 kg, 50 g.

2. Dani and Gina are pushing on a box. Dani pushes with 250 N of force and Gina pushes with 100 N of force.

   a. What is the net force if they both push in the same direction?

   b. What is the net force if they push in opposite directions?

Section 3.2

3. Use your knowledge of Newton's second law to answer the following:

   a. What is the net force required to accelerate a 1,000-kg car at 3 m/s²?

   b. You pull your little cousin in a wagon. You must pull with a net force of 50 N to accelerate her at 2 m/s². What's her mass?

   c. A 1,500-N force is applied to a 1,000-kg car. What is the car's acceleration?

Section 3.3

4. You drop a ball from the edge of a cliff. It lands 4 s later.

   a. Make a table showing the ball's speed each second for 4 s.

   b. What is the ball's average speed during the first second it is in free fall?

   c. What is the ball's average speed for the whole 4 s?

   d. What distance does the ball fall during the 4 s?

5. During a science experiment, your teacher drops a tennis ball out of a window. The ball hits the ground 3 s later.

   a. What was the ball's speed when it hit the ground? Ignore air resistance.

   b. What was the ball's average speed during the 3 s?

   c. How high is the window?

6. Answer the following questions about mass and weight:

   a. How many newtons does a 5-kg backpack weigh on Earth?

   b. How many newtons does a 5-kg backpack weigh on the Moon?

   c. Aya's mass is 45 kg. What is her weight in newtons on Earth?

   d. What is Aya's mass on the moon?

   e. What is Aya's weight in newtons on the Moon?

Test Practice

Section 3.1

1. According to Newton's first law, only _____ has the ability to change motion.

   a. inertia

   b. mass

   c. force

   d. gravity

2. A force of 1 N is applied to a 1-kg mass. What acceleration does the force produce?

   a. 4.454 m/s/s

   b. 4.448 m/s/s

   c. 9.8 m/s/s

   d. 1 m/s/s

3. The net force on the block is 200 N. How large is force A?

   a. 100 N

   b. 200 N

   c. 300 N

   d. 400 N

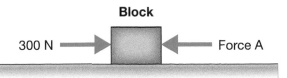

4. Because of their _____, a pair of sunglasses on the dashboard will continue moving forward when the car turns sharply.

   a. acceleration

   b. inertia

   c. velocity

   d. weight

Section 3.2

5. Which of the following does *not* represent Newton's second law?

   a. $a = F/m$

   b. $F = ma$

   c. $m = F/a$

   d. $F = m/a$

6. A 3,000-N force is applied to a car which causes an acceleration of 3 m/s/s. What is the mass of the car?

   a. 1,000 kg

   b. 3,000 kg

   c. 6,000 kg

   d. 9,000 kg

7. A skater is coasting at a constant velocity. A net force is necessary for all of the following *except*

   a. the skater accelerates.

   b. the skater continues in the same direction at the same speed.

   c. the skater stops.

   d. the skater turns to the right.

8. A 20-N force is applied to each block. How much greater is the acceleration of block A than the acceleration of block B?

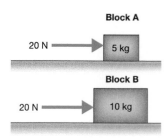

Block A

20 N ⟶ 5 kg

Block B

20 N ⟶ 10 kg

   a. two times greater

   b. four times greater

   c. five times greater

   d. They have the same acceleration.

Section 3.3

9. Anjali throws a soccer ball straight up in the air with an initial velocity of 19.6 m/s. What will the velocity of the ball be after 3 s?

   a. –9.8 m/s

   b. 0 m/s

   c. 9.8 m/s

   d. 48.8 m/s

10. A coconut falls from a tree. What is the average velocity after 2 s?

   a. 0 m/s

   b. 4.9 m/s

   c. 9.8 m/s

   d. 19.6 m/s

11. A 50-kg space explorer pilots a rocket to a newly discovered planet. The explorer's weight on the new planet is 250 N. What is the strength of gravity (g) on this planet?

   a. 0.2 N/kg

   b. 5 N/kg

   c. 9.8 N/kg

   d. 25 N/kg

12. The _____ velocity of an object in free fall is reached when the forces of gravity and air resistance are equal.

   a. average

   b. initial

   c. final

   d. terminal

Applying Your Knowledge

Section 3.1

1. Aristotle, Galileo Galilei, and Sir Isaac Newton all developed their own theories about motion. Research to find out how each scientist changed what people believed about motion. Were all of their theories correct?

Section 3.2

2. Write about Newton's first two laws of motion, giving examples from your own life. If you have ever ridden in an automobile, taken a bike ride, played a sport, or walked down the street, you have experienced Newton's laws. Be sure to describe the effects of both of Newton's laws on the activities you choose.

Section 3.3

3. A falling object reaches terminal velocity when the force of gravity is balanced by the air resistance of the object. Explain this in terms of Newton's first and second laws.

4. Imagine what it would be like if there suddenly were no air resistance. Explain three differences you might notice in the world around you.

 *Your Turn* **Answers**

Using Newton's second law (Section 3.2, page 61)
   a. 0.80 m/s²
   b. 40 kg·m/s² or 40 N
   c. 14 kg

Using average velocity for an accelerating object (Section 3.3, page 65)
   a. 9.8 m/s
   b. 14.8 m/s

Calculating free fall velocity and distance (Section 3.3, page 66)
   a. 39.2 m/s and 78.4 m
   b. 4.9 m

Weight and mass (Section 3.3, page 68)
   a. 588 N, 222 N
   b. 25 m/s²

Conservation Laws

Look around you. Do you see any changes taking place? Is a light bulb giving off heat and light? Is the Sun shining? Are your eyes moving across the page while you read this introduction? When an object falls toward Earth, when you play a sport or a musical instrument, when your alarm clock wakes you up in the morning, and when a bird flies through the air, there are changes taking place that could not occur without the effects of *energy*.

Energy is everywhere! Energy is responsible for explaining "how the world works." As you read this chapter, think about the examples and see if you can identify the forms of energy that are responsible for the changes that take place in each. Skateboarding, astronauts, cars moving, ball throwing, billiards, and tennis are just some of the physical systems you will encounter.

VOCABULARY

collision	Newton's third law	inelastic collision
joule	impulse	law of conservation of momentum
momentum	law of conservation of energy	
elastic collision		work
kinetic energy	potential energy	

KEY QUESTIONS

✓ *Do objects at rest ever have any forces acting on them?*

✓ *Why does a faster skateboarder take more force to stop than a slower one with the same mass?*

✓ *How can energy be so important when it cannot be smelled, touched, tasted, seen, or heard?*

4.1 Newton's Third Law and Momentum

In the last chapter, you learned that forces cause changes in motion. However, this does not mean that objects at rest experience no forces! What is it that keeps your book perfectly still on the table as you read it (Figure 4.1)? "Force" is a good answer to this question. **Newton's third law** of motion states that every action force creates a reaction force that is equal in strength and opposite in direction. In this section, you will learn more about this law and another important concept about motion, momentum.

> **Newton's third law** - whenever one object exerts a force on another, the second object exerts an equal and opposite force on the first

Newton on a skateboard

An imaginary skateboard contest Imagine a skateboard contest between Newton and an elephant. They can only push against each other, not against the ground. The fastest one wins. The elephant knows it is much stronger and pushes off Newton with a huge force thinking it will surely win. But who does win?

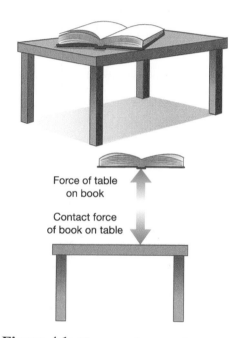

The winner Newton wins—and will always win. No matter how hard the elephant pushes, Newton always moves away at a greater speed. In fact, Newton doesn't have to push at all and he still wins. Why?

Forces always come in pairs It takes force to make both Newton and the elephant move. Newton wins because *forces always come in pairs*. The elephant pushes against Newton and that *action* force pushes Newton away. The elephant's force against Newton creates a *reaction* force against the elephant. Since the action and reaction forces are equal in strength and because of Newton's second law of motion ($a = F \div m$), Newton accelerates more because his mass is smaller.

Figure 4.1: *There are forces acting even when things are not moving. Here, the book exerts a force on the table due to gravity exerting a force on the book, and the table exerts a force on the book. The contact force the book exerts on the table is equal and opposite to the support force the table exerts on the book.*

The third law of motion

The first and second laws
The first and second laws of motion apply to single objects. The first law says an object will remain at rest or in motion at constant velocity unless acted upon by a net force. The second law says the acceleration of an object is directly proportional to force and inversely proportional to the mass ($a = F \div m$).

The third law operates with pairs of objects
In contrast to the first two laws, the Newton's third law of motion deals with pairs of objects. This is because *all forces come in pairs*. A simple way to state Newton's third law is to say for every action there is an equal and opposite reaction.

For every action force, there is a reaction force equal in strength and opposite in direction.

Forces *only* come in action-reaction pairs. There can never be a single force, alone, without its action-reaction partner. The force exerted by the elephant (action) moves Newton since it acts on Newton. The reaction force acting back on the elephant is what moves the elephant.

The labels "action" and "reaction"
The words *action* and *reaction* are just labels. It does not matter which force is called action and which is reaction. You choose one to call the action and then call the other one the reaction (Figure 4.2).

A skateboard example
Think carefully about moving the usual way on a skateboard. Your foot exerts a force backward against the ground. The force acts *on* the ground. However, *you* move, so a force must act on you. Why do you move? What force acts on you? You move because the action force of your foot against the ground creates a reaction force of the ground against your foot. You "feel" the ground because you sense the reaction force pressing on your foot. The reaction force is what makes you move because it acts on *you* (Figure 4.3).

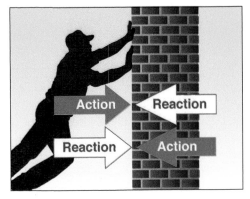

Figure 4.2: *It doesn't matter which force you call the action and which the reaction. The action and reaction forces are interchangeable.*

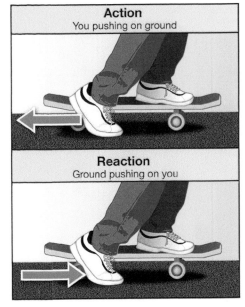

Figure 4.3: *All forces come in pairs. When you push on the ground (action), the reaction of the ground pushing back on your foot is what makes you move.*

Action and reaction forces

Action and reaction forces do not cancel   It is easy to get confused thinking about action and reaction forces. Why don't they cancel each other out? The reason is that action and reaction forces act on different objects. For example, think about throwing a ball. When you throw a ball, you apply the action force to the ball, creating the ball's acceleration. The reaction is the ball pushing back against your hand. The forces do not cancel because they act on different objects. You can only cancel forces if they act on the same object (Figure 4.4).

Draw diagrams   When sorting out action and reaction forces it is helpful to draw diagrams. Draw each object apart from the other. Represent each force as an arrow in the appropriate direction.

Identifying action and reaction   Here are some guidelines to help you sort out action and reaction forces:

- Both are always there, whenever any force appears.
- They always have the exact same strength.
- They always act in opposite directions.
- They always act on different objects.
- Both are real forces and either or both can cause acceleration.

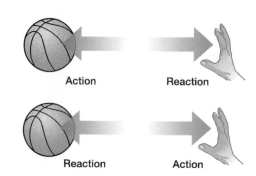

Figure 4.4: *An example diagram showing the action and reaction forces in throwing a ball.*

➕➖✖️➗ Action and reaction

A woman weighing 500 N is sitting on a chair. Describe an action-reaction pair of forces.

1. Looking for:	You are asked for a pair of action and reaction forces.
2. Given:	You are given one force in newtons.
3. Relationships:	Action-reaction forces are equal and opposite, and act on different objects.
4. Solution:	The downward contact force the woman exerts on the chair is an action. This action force happens to equal her weight, which is 500 N. The reaction force is the chair acting on the woman with an upward force of 500 N.

Your Turn:

a. A baseball player hits a ball with a bat. Describe an action-reaction pair of forces.

b. Describe the action-reaction pair for Earth and the Moon.

(Answers are listed at the end of the chapter.)

Momentum

Faster objects are harder to stop   Imagine two kids on skateboards are moving toward you (Figure 4.5). Each has a mass of 40 kilograms. One is moving at 1 meter per second and the other at 10 meters per second. Which one is harder to stop?

You already learned that inertia comes from mass. That explains why an 80-kilogram skateboarder is harder to stop than a 40-kilogram skateboarder. But how do you account for the fact that a faster skateboarder takes more force to stop than a slower one with the *same* mass?

Momentum   The answer is a new quantity called **momentum.** The momentum of a moving object is its mass multiplied by its velocity. Like inertia, momentum measures a moving object's resistance to changes in its motion. However, momentum includes the effects of speed and direction as well as mass. The symbol *p* is used to represent momentum.

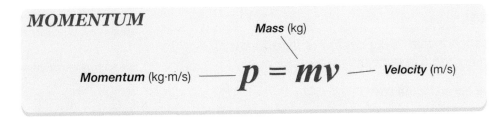

MOMENTUM

Momentum (kg·m/s) —— $p = mv$ —— Velocity (m/s)

Mass (kg)

momentum - the mass of an object multiplied by its velocity

Which one is harder to stop?

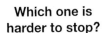

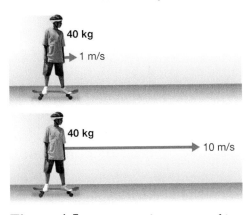

Figure 4.5: *Stopping a fast-moving object is harder than stopping a slow-moving one.*

Units of momentum   The units of momentum are the units of mass multiplied by the units of velocity. When mass is in kilograms and velocity is in meters per second, momentum is in kilogram-meters per second (kg·m/s).

Calculating momentum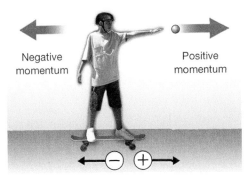

Negative momentum

Positive momentum

Momentum is calculated with velocity instead of speed because the direction of momentum is always important. A common choice is to make positive momentum to the right and negative momentum to the left.

Impulse

Force, momentum, and impulse
Momentum changes when velocity changes. Since force is what changes velocity, this gives us an important new way to look at force. A change in an object's momentum depends on the net force and also on the amount of time the force is applied. The change in momentum that is equal to the net force multiplied by the time the force acts is called **impulse**.

> **impulse** - the product of force and time that causes a change in momentum

$$IMPULSE \qquad Ft = mv_2 - mv_1$$

Force (N) Time (s) Initial velocity (m/s) Final velocity (m/s) Mass (kg) Impulse (N·s or kg·m/s)

Units of impulse
Notice that the force side of the equation has units of N·s, while the momentum side has units of momentum, kg·m/s. These are the same units, since 1 N is 1 kg·m/s². Impulse can be expressed either way (Figure 4.6).

Force and momentum

A net force of 100 N is applied for 5 seconds to a 10-kg car that is initially at rest. What is the speed of the car at the end of the 5 seconds?

1. **Looking for:**   You are asked for the speed.

2. **Given:**   You are given the net force in newtons, the time the force acts in seconds, and the mass of the car in kilograms.

3. **Relationships:** *impulse = force × time = change in momentum*
   momentum = mass × velocity

4. **Solution:** **The change in momentum = 100 N × 5 seconds = 500 kg·m/s**
   Speed is momentum divided by mass, or
   v = (500 kg·m/s) ÷ 10 kg = 50 m/s

Your Turn:

a. A 15-N force acts for 10 seconds on a 1-kg ball that is initially at rest. What is the ball's change in momentum?

b. How much time should a 100-N force take to increase the speed of a 10-kg car from 10 m/s to 100 m/s?

(Answers are listed at the end of the chapter.)

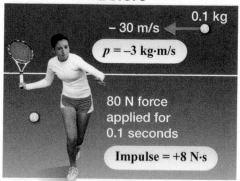

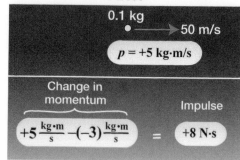

Figure 4.6: *Impulse can be expressed as a change in momentum (p). In the example above, the tennis ball's momentum changes after it is hit by the racquet with a force of 80 N for 0.1 seconds. Both the change of momentum and the impulse are +8 N·s.*

The law of momentum conservation

An important new law
We are now going to combine Newton's third law with the relationship between force and momentum. The result is a powerful new tool for understanding motion: the law of conservation of momentum. This law allows us to make accurate predictions about what happens before and after an interaction, even if we don't know the details about the interaction itself.

Momentum in an action-reaction pair
When two objects exert forces on each other in an action-reaction pair, their motions are affected as a pair. If you stand on a skateboard and throw a ball, you apply force to the ball. That force changes the momentum of the ball.

The third law says the ball exerts an equal and opposite force back on you. Therefore, *your* momentum also changes. Since the forces are exactly equal and opposite, the changes in momentum are also equal and opposite. If the ball gains +20 kg·m/s of forward momentum, you must gain −20 kg·m/s of backward momentum (Figure 4.7), assuming there is no friction.

The law of conservation of momentum
Because of the third law, the total momentum of two interacting objects stays constant. If one gains momentum, the other loses the same amount, leaving the total unchanged. This is the **law of conservation of momentum**. The law says the total momentum in a system of interacting objects cannot change as long as all forces act only between the objects in the system.

If interacting objects in a system are not acted on by outside forces, the total amount of momentum in the system cannot change.

Forces inside and outside the system
Forces outside the system, such as friction and gravity, can change the total momentum of the system. However, if *all* objects that exert forces are included in the system, the total momentum stays constant. When you jump up, the reaction force from the ground gives you upward momentum. The action force from your feet gives the *entire Earth* an equal amount of downward momentum! No one notices the planet move because it has so much more mass than you, so its increase in momentum creates negligible velocity (Figure 4.8).

> **law of conservation of momentum** - in the absence of external forces, the total momentum of a system remains constant

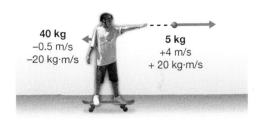

Figure 4.7: *The result of the skateboarder throwing a 5-kg ball at a speed of +4 m/s is that he and the board, with a total mass of 40 kg, move backward at a velocity of −0.5 m/s, if you ignore friction.*

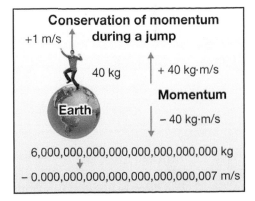

Figure 4.8: *When you jump, your body and Earth gain equal and opposite amounts of momentum.*

Using the momentum relationship

An astronaut floating in space throws a 2-kilogram hammer to the left at 15 m/s. If the astronaut's mass is 60 kilograms, how fast does the astronaut move to the right after throwing the hammer?

2 kg   60 kg

-15 m/s   ?

Photo courtesy NASA

1. **Looking for:**   You are asked for the speed of the astronaut after throwing the hammer.

2. **Given:**   You are given the mass of the hammer in kilograms and the speed of the hammer in meters per second and the mass of the astronaut in kilograms.

3. **Relationships:**   The total momentum before the hammer is thrown must be the same as the total momentum after it is thrown. Momentum = mass × velocity. A negative sign indicates the direction of motion is to the left.

4. **Solution:**   Both the astronaut and hammer were initially at rest, so the initial momentum was zero. Use subscripts a and h to distinguish between the astronaut and the hammer.

momentum after + momentum before = 0

$$m_a v_a + m_h v_h = 0$$

Substitute the known quantities:

$$(60 \text{ kg})(v_a) + (2 \text{ kg})(-15 \text{ m/s}) = 0$$

Solve:

$$(60 \text{ kg})(v_a) = +30 \text{ kg·m/s}$$

$$v_a = +0.5 \text{ m/s}$$

The astronaut moves to the right at a speed of 0.5 m/s.

Your Turn:

a. Two children on ice skates start at rest and push off from each other. One has a mass of 30 kg and moves away at 2 m/s. The other has a mass of 15 kg. What is the second child's speed?

b. Standing on an icy pond, you throw a 0.5 kg ball at 40 m/s. You move back at 0.4 m/s. What is your mass?

(Answers are listed at the end of the chapter.)

4.1 Section Review

1. List three action and reaction pairs in the picture at right.
2. Why don't action and reaction forces cancel?
3. Use impulse to explain how force is related to changes in momentum.
4. Explain the law of conservation of momentum and how it relates to Newton's third law.

4.2 Energy and the Conservation of Energy

Energy is one of the fundamental quantities in our universe. Without energy, nothing could ever change. Yet energy itself cannot be *directly* smelled, tasted, touched, seen, or heard. Energy appears in many forms, such as motion and heat. Energy can travel in different ways, such as in light and sound waves and in electricity. The workings of the universe (including all of our man-made technology) can be viewed from the perspective of energy flowing from one place to another and changing back and forth from one form to another.

What is energy?

Defining energy   Energy is a quantity that measures the ability to cause change. Energy can cause changes in temperature, speed, position, momentum, pressure, or other physical variables. Energy can also cause change in materials, such as burning wood changing into ashes and smoke.

Energy is a quantity that measures the ability to cause change in a physical system.

Examples
- A gust of wind has energy because it can move objects in its path.
- A piece of wood in a fireplace has energy because it can produce heat and light.
- You have energy because you can change the motion of your own body.
- Batteries have energy because they can be used in a radio to make sound.
- Gasoline has energy because it can be burned in an engine to move a car.
- A ball at the top of a hill has energy because it can roll down the hill and move objects in its path.

Units of energy   The unit of measurement for energy is the **joule**. One joule is the energy needed to push with a force of 1 newton over a distance of 1 meter (Figure 4.9). The joule can be abbreviated as J or as Newton-meter (N·m), which means 1 newton multiplied by 1 meter. If you push on a pen with a force of 1 newton for a distance of 1 meter across a table, 1 joule of your energy is converted into the energy of the pen's motion.

joule - a unit of energy and work that is equal to 1 newton of force times 1 meter of distance

The Calorie

The Calorie (C) is a unit of energy often used for food. One Calorie equals 4,187 joules. A small breath mint is about 5 Calories. How many joules is that?

1 joule is the amount of work done by a force of 1 newton acting over a distance of 1 meter.

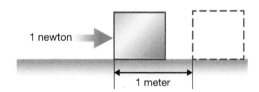

1 newton

1 meter

Figure 4.9: *Pushing with a force of 1 newton over a distance of 1 meter requires 1 joule of energy.*

What is work?

Work means different things

The word *work* is used in many different ways.

- You should always check over your *work* before handing in a test.
- You go to *work*.
- Your toaster doesn't *work*.
- You *work* with other students on a group project.

What work means in physics

In physics, **work** has a very specific meaning. Work is the transfer of energy that results from applying a force over a distance. To calculate work, you multiply the force by the distance the object moves in the direction of the force. If you lift a block with a weight of 1 newton for a distance of 1 meter, you do 1 joule of work. One joule of energy is transferred from your body to the block, changing the block's energy. Both work and energy are measured in the same units because work is a form of energy.

Work is done on objects

When thinking about work, you should always be clear about which force is doing the work on which object. Work is done *on* objects. If you lift a block 1 meter with a force of 1 newton, you have done 1 joule of work *on the block* (Figure 4.10).

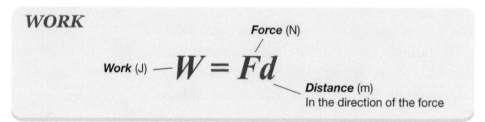

WORK

$$\text{Work (J)} \longrightarrow W = Fd$$

Force (N)

Distance (m)
In the direction of the force

Energy is needed to do work

An object that has energy is able to do work; without energy, it is impossible to do work. In fact, one way to think about energy is as *stored work*. A falling block has kinetic energy—the energy of motion—that can be used to do work. If the block hits a ball, it will do work on the ball and change its motion. In other words, some of the block's energy is *transferred to* the ball during the collision.

> **work** - a form of energy that is the product of force and distance when both force and distance are in the same direction

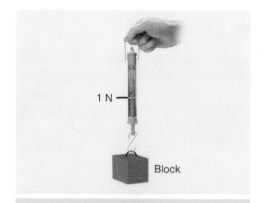

1 N

Block

Lifting the block 1 m requires 1 joule of work.

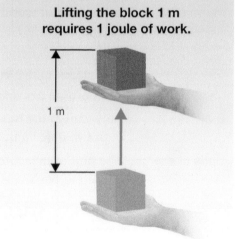

1 m

Figure 4.10: *When you lift a 1-newton block a height of 1 meter, you do 1 joule of work on the block.*

Potential energy

What is potential energy?

Potential energy is energy due to *position*. The word *potential* means that something is capable of becoming something else. Systems or objects with potential energy are able to exert forces by exchanging energy as they change. For example, a stretched spring has potential energy. If released, the spring will use this energy to move itself and anything attached to it back to its original length.

Gravitational potential energy

A block above a table has potential energy. If released, the force of gravity moves the block to a position of lower energy. The term *gravitational potential energy* describes the energy of an elevated object. The term is often shortened to just "potential energy" because a common type of potential energy in physics problems is gravitational. Unless otherwise stated, you can assume "potential energy" means gravitational potential energy.

How to calculate potential energy

How much potential energy does a raised block have? The block's potential energy is exactly the amount of work it can do as it goes down, which is equal to the amount of work done to lift it up to its height. Work is force multiplied by distance. The force is the weight (*mg*) of the block in newtons. The distance the block can move is its height (*h*) in meters. Multiplying the weight by the distance gives you the block's potential energy at any given height (Figure 4.11).

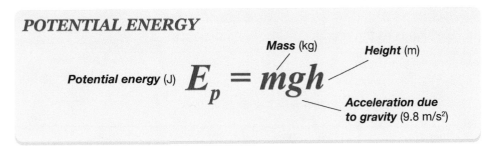

POTENTIAL ENERGY

Potential energy (J)   **Mass** (kg)   **Height** (m)

$$E_p = mgh$$

Acceleration due to gravity (9.8 m/s²)

> **potential energy** - stored energy that comes from position

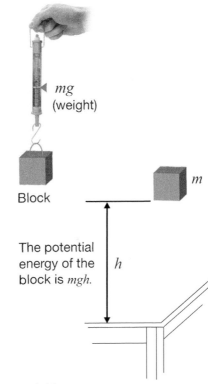

mg (weight)

Block

m

The potential energy of the block is *mgh*.

h

Figure 4.11: *The potential energy of the block is equal to the product of its mass, the strength of gravity, and the height from which the block falls.*

Kinetic energy

Kinetic energy is energy of motion
Objects that are moving also have the ability to cause change. Energy of motion is called **kinetic energy**. A moving billiard ball has kinetic energy because it can hit another billiard ball and change its motion. Kinetic energy can also be converted to potential energy. The kinetic energy of a basketball tossed upward converts into potential energy as its height increases.

Kinetic energy can do work
The amount of kinetic energy an object has equals the amount of work the object can do by exerting force as it stops. Consider a moving skateboard and rider (Figure 4.12). Suppose it takes a force of 500 N applied over a distance of 10 meters to slow the skateboard to a stop ($v = 0$). The kinetic energy of the skateboard and rider is 5,000 joules since that is the amount of work it takes to stop the skateboard: $500 \text{ N} \times 10 \text{ m} = 5,000$ joules.

Kinetic energy depends on mass and speed
If you had started with twice the mass—say, two skateboarders—you would have to do twice as much work to stop them both. Kinetic energy increases with mass. If the skateboard and rider are moving faster, it also takes more work to bring them to a stop. This means kinetic energy also increases with speed. Kinetic energy is related to *both* an object's speed and its mass.

The formula for kinetic energy
The kinetic energy of a moving object is equal to one half its mass multiplied by the square of its speed. This formula is derived by combining the relationships, including the distance equation for acceleration ($d = \frac{1}{2}at^2$), velocity ($v = at$), and Newton's second law ($F = ma$) with the definition of energy, which is as the product of force and distance: $E = F \times d = ma \times (\frac{1}{2})at^2 = (\frac{1}{2})ma^2t^2 = (\frac{1}{2})mv^2$.

KINETIC ENERGY

Kinetic energy (J) — $E_k = \dfrac{1}{2}mv^2$

Mass (kg)

Speed (m/s)

kinetic energy - energy that comes from motion and is related to mass and velocity

Moving skateboard and rider

A force of 500 N applied for 10 m . . .

500 N

. . . brings the skateboard and rider to a stop.

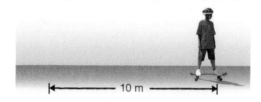

|← 10 m →|

Work done = 500 N × 10 m
= 5,000 J

Therefore . . .
The kinetic energy is 5,000 joules because that is the amount of work the skateboard can do as it stops.

Figure 4.12: *The amount of kinetic energy the skateboard has is equal to the amount of work the moving board and rider do as they come to a stop.*

Kinetic energy increases as the square of the speed Kinetic energy increases as the square of the speed. This means that if you go twice as fast, your energy increases by four times ($2^2 = 4$). If your speed is three times as fast, your energy is nine times bigger ($3^2 = 9$). A car moving at a speed of 100 km/h (62 mph) has *four times* the kinetic energy it had when going 50 km/h (31 mph). At a speed of 150 km/h (93 mph), it has *nine times* as much energy as it did at 50 km/h (Figure 4.13). The stopping distance of a car is proportional to its kinetic energy. A car going twice as fast has four times the kinetic energy and needs four times the stopping distance. This is why driving at high speeds can be so dangerous.

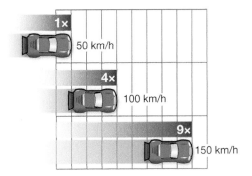

Figure 4.13: *Stopping distances.*

 Potential and kinetic energy

A 2-kg rock is at the edge of a cliff 20 meters above a lake. It becomes loose and falls toward the water below. Calculate its potential and kinetic energy when it is on the cliff edge and when it is halfway down. Its speed is 14 m/s at the halfway point.

1. *Looking for:*   You are asked for the potential and kinetic energy at two locations.

2. *Given:*   You are given the mass in kilograms, the height at each location in meters, and the speed halfway down in m/s. You can assume the initial speed is 0 m/s because the rock starts from rest.

3. *Relationships:* $E_p = mgh$ and $E_k = \frac{1}{2}mv^2$

4. *Solution:*   Potential energy at the top: $m = 2$ kg, $g = 9.8$ N/kg, and $h = 20$ m
    $E_p = (2$ kg$)(9.8$ N/kg$)(20$ m$) = 392$ J

    Potential energy halfway down: $m = 2$ kg, $g = 9.8$ N/kg, and $h = 10$ m
    $E_p = (2$ kg$)(9.8$ N/kg$)(10$ m$) = 196$ J

    Kinetic energy at the top: $m = 2$ kg and v $= 0$ m/s
    $E_k = (\frac{1}{2})(2$ kg$)(0^2) = 0$ J

    Kinetic energy halfway down: $m = 2$ kg and $v = 14$ m/s
    $E_k = (\frac{1}{2})(2$ kg$)(14$ m/s$)^2 = 196$ J

Your Turn:

a. Calculate the potential energy of a 4-kilogram cat crouched 3 meters off the ground.

b. Calculate the kinetic energy of a 4-kilogram cat running at 5 m/s.

(Answers are listed at the end of the chapter.)

Conservation of energy

Energy converts from potential to kinetic   What happens when you throw a ball straight up in the air (Figure 4.14)? The ball leaves your hand with kinetic energy it gains when your hand accelerates it from rest. As the ball goes higher, it gains potential energy. However, the ball slows down as it rises, so its kinetic energy *decreases*. The increase in potential energy is exactly equal to the decrease in kinetic energy. The kinetic energy converts into potential energy, and the ball's total energy stays the same.

Law of conservation of energy   The idea that energy converts from one form into another without a change in the total amount is called the **law of conservation of energy**. The law states that energy can never be created or destroyed, just converted from one form into another. The law of conservation of energy is one of the most important laws in physics. It applies to not only kinetic and potential energy, but to all forms of energy.

> *Energy can never be created or destroyed, just converted from one form into another*

Using energy conservation   The law of conservation of energy explains how a ball's launch speed affects its motion. As the ball in Figure 4.14 moves upward, it slows down and loses kinetic energy. Eventually it reaches a point where all the kinetic energy has been converted to potential energy. At that point, the ball is as high as it will go, and its upward speed has been reduced to zero. If the ball had been launched with a greater speed, it would have started with more kinetic energy. It would have gone higher before all of its kinetic energy was converted into potential energy. If the exact launch speed is known, the law of conservation of energy can be used to predict the height the ball reaches.

Energy converts from kinetic to potential   The ball's conversion of energy on the way down is opposite what it was on the way up. As the ball falls, its speed increases and its height decreases. The potential energy decreases as it changes into kinetic energy. If gravity is the only force acting on the ball, it returns to your hand with exactly the same speed and kinetic energy it started with, except that it returns to your hand from the opposite direction.

> **law of conservation of energy** - energy cannot be created or destroyed, although it can be changed from one form to another; also called the first law of thermodynamics

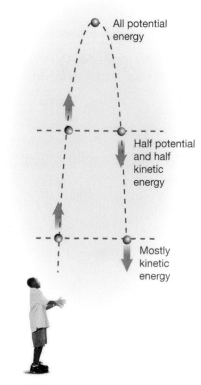

All potential energy

Half potential and half kinetic energy

Mostly kinetic energy

Figure 4.14: *When you throw a ball upward, the energy changes from kinetic, to potential, and then back to kinetic.*

Using energy conservation to solve problems

How to use energy conservation   Energy conservation is a direct way to find out what happens before and after a change (Figure 4.15) from one form of energy into another. The law of energy conservation says the total energy before the change equals the total energy after it. In many cases—with falling objects, for instance—you need not worry about force or acceleration. Applying energy conservation allows you to find speeds and heights very quickly.

Total energy = Total energy

Figure 4.15: *Applying energy conservation.*

 Energy conservation

A 2-kg car moving with a speed of 2 m/s starts up a hill. How high does the car roll before it stops?

1. *Looking for:*   You are asked for the height.

2. *Given:*   You are given the car's mass in kilograms, and its starting speed in meters per second.

3. *Relationships:*   The law of conservation of energy states that the sum of the kinetic and potential energy is constant. The ball keeps going uphill until all of its kinetic energy has been turned into potential energy.

4. *Solution:*   Find the kinetic energy at the start:

   $E_K = (½)(2 \text{ kg})(2 \text{ m/s})^2 = 4 \text{ J}$

   Use the potential energy to find the height:

   $mgh = 4 \text{ J}$

   Therefore:

   $h = (4 \text{ J}) \div (2 \text{ kg})(9.8 \text{ N/kg})$

   $= 0.2 \text{ m}$

   The car rolls to a height of 0.2 m above where it started.

Your Turn:

a. A 500-kg roller coaster car starts from rest at the top of a 60-meter-high roller-coaster tower. Find its potential energy when it is halfway to the bottom of the tower.

b. A 1-kg ball is tossed straight up with a kinetic energy of 196 J. How high does it go?

(Answers are listed at the end of the chapter.)

"Using" and "conserving" energy in the everyday sense

"Conserving" energy Almost everyone has heard that it is good to "conserve energy" and not waste it. This is good advice because energy costs money and uses resources. But what does it mean to "use energy" in the everyday sense? If energy can never be created or destroyed, how can it be "used up"?

"Using" energy When you "use" energy by turning on a light, you are really converting energy from one form (electricity) to other forms (light and heat). What gets "used up" is the amount of energy *in the form of electricity*. Electricity is a valuable form of energy because it is easy to move over long distances. In the "physics" sense, the energy is not "used up," but converted into other forms of energy. The total amount of energy stays constant.

Power plants Electric power plants don't make electrical energy. Energy cannot be created. What power plants do is convert other forms of energy (chemical, solar, or nuclear) into electrical energy. When someone advises you to turn off the lights to conserve energy, they are asking you to use less electrical energy. If people used less electrical energy, power plants would burn less oil, gas, or other fuels in "producing" the electrical energy they sell.

"Running out" of energy Many people are concerned about "running out" of energy. What they worry about is running out of certain *forms* of energy that are easy to use, such as oil and gas. When you use gas in a car, the chemical energy in the gasoline mostly becomes heat energy. It is impractical to put the energy back into the form of gasoline, so we say the energy has been "used up" even though the energy itself is still there, only in a different form.

Please turn out the lights when you leave!

There are about 308 million people living in the United States. If an average house has four light bulbs per person, it adds up to 1.23 billion light bulbs. The average bulb uses 100 joules of electrical energy each second. Multiplying gives an estimate of 123 billion joules every second, just for light bulbs!

A big electric power plant puts out 2 billion joules each second. That means 62 big power plants are burning up resources just to run light bulbs. If everyone were to switch their incandescent bulbs to fluorescent lights, it would save 75 percent of this amount of electricity. That means we could eliminate 50 big power plants and conserve the resources that 50 big power plants use up!

4.2 Section Review

1. What are the units of energy and what do they mean?
2. What is *work* in physics and what is the relationship between work and energy?
3. How can you increase an object's potential or kinetic energy?
4. What happens to the kinetic and potential energy of a ball as it falls toward the ground?
5. Explain what it means to say that energy is "conserved."

4.3 Collisions

A **collision** occurs when two or more objects hit each other. When we hear the word *collision*, we often picture a car crash. But a collision also takes place when a tennis ball hits a racket, your foot hits the ground, or your fingers press on a keyboard. During a collision, momentum and energy are transferred from one object to another. Different factors like mass, initial velocity, and the type of collision determine the velocity of objects after they collide. In this section, you will learn about two types of collisions—elastic and inelastic—and the momentum and energy changes that result.

Elastic and inelastic collisions

Elastic collisions   There are two main types of collisions, elastic and inelastic. When an **elastic collision** occurs, objects bounce off each other with no loss in the total kinetic energy of the system. The total kinetic energy before the collision is the same as the total kinetic energy after the collision. The collision between billiard balls is very close to a perfectly-elastic collision (Figure 4.16).

Inelastic collisions   In an **inelastic collision**, objects change shape or stick together, and the total kinetic energy of the system decreases. The energy is not destroyed, but it is transformed into forms other than kinetic energy, such as a permanent change in shape. An egg hitting the floor is one example of an inelastic collision; two vehicles colliding is another. In both cases, some of the kinetic energy is used to permanently change an object's shape.

Perfectly elastic collisions   Collisions you see in everyday life are a mix. When two billiard balls collide, it looks like they bounce without a loss of kinetic energy. But the sound of the collision tells you a small amount of kinetic energy is being changed into sound energy. However, we approximate the collision as elastic because it is very close to a perfectly-elastic collision. The balls bounce off each other and do not change shape. Perfectly-elastic collisions do occur on an atomic scale. The collision between two individual atoms in the air is an example of a perfectly-elastic collision. The kinetic energy may be transferred between atoms, but no kinetic energy is transformed into heat or sound. The movement of atoms and collisions between them are responsible for air pressure in balloons and tires.

collision - occurs when two or more objects hit each other

elastic collision - occurs when objects collide so that the total kinetic energy remains the same before and after the collision

inelastic collision - a type of collision in which the total kinetic energy after the collision is less than it was before the collision and which usually involves objects sticking together or changing shape

Figure 4.16: *The collision of two billiard balls is elastic. The collision of an egg with the floor is inelastic.*

Momentum conservation in collisions

Elastic and inelastic collisions   As long as there are no outside forces (such as friction), momentum is conserved in both elastic and inelastic collisions. This is true even when kinetic energy is not conserved. Conservation of momentum makes it possible to determine the motion of objects before or after colliding.

Problem-solving steps   Using momentum to analyze collision problems takes practice. Use the steps below to help you find solutions to such problems.

1. Draw a diagram.
2. Decide whether the collision is elastic or inelastic.
3. Let variables represent the masses and velocities of the objects before and after the collision.
4. Use momentum conservation to write an equation stating that the total momentum before the collision equals the total after. Then solve it.

Before collision

After collision

Figure 4.17: *An inelastic collision of two train cars*

 Momentum and collisions

An 8,000-kg train car moves to the right at 10 m/s. It collides with a 2,000-kg parked train car (Figure 4.17). The cars get stuck together and roll along the track. How fast do they move after the collision?

1. Looking for: You are asked for the velocity of the train cars after the collision.

2. Given: You are given both masses in kilograms and the initial velocity of the moving car in m/s. You know the collision is inelastic because the cars are stuck together.

3. Relationships: Apply the law of conservation of momentum. Because the two cars are stuck together, consider them to be a single larger train car after the collision. The final mass is the sum of the two individual masses:

initial momentum of car 1 + initial momentum of car 2 = final momentum of combined cars

$$m_1v_1 + m_2v_2 = (m_1 + m_2)v_3$$

4. Solution: $(8{,}000 \text{ kg})(10 \text{ m/s}) + (2{,}000 \text{ kg})(0 \text{ m/s}) = (8{,}000 \text{ kg} + 2{,}000 \text{ kg})v_3$

$v_3 = 8$ **m/s**. The train cars move together to the right at 8 m/s.

Your Turn:

a. Repeat the above problem, but with each car having a mass of 2,000 kg.

b. A 5-kg bowling ball with a velocity of +10 m/s collides with a stationary 2-kg bowling pin. If the ball's final velocity is +8 m/s, what is the pin's final velocity?

(Answers are listed at the end of the chapter.)

Forces in collisions

Collisions involve forces   Collisions create forces because the colliding objects' motion changes. Since most collisions take place quickly, the forces change rapidly and are hard to measure directly. However, momentum conservation can be used to estimate the forces in a collision. Engineers need to know the forces so they can design things that do not break when they are dropped.

Force and collisions   A rubber ball and a clay ball are dropped on a gymnasium floor (Figure 4.18). The rubber ball has a mostly-elastic collision and bounces back up with almost the same speed it had when it hit the floor. The clay ball has an inelastic collision, hitting the floor and staying there. Both balls have the same mass and are dropped from the same height. They hit the floor with the same speed. Which ball exerts a greater force on the floor?

Force changes momentum   The total change in momentum is equal to the force multiplied by the time during which the force acts. Remember from Section 4.1 that the product of force and time is called *impulse*.

Bounces have greater momentum change   Suppose each ball shown in Figure 4.18 has a mass of 1 kilogram and hits the floor at a velocity of –5 m/s; the negative is for downward motion. The momentum of the clay ball changes from –5 kg·m/s to 0. This is a change of 5 kg·m/s. The rubber ball also starts with a momentum of –5 kg·m/s. If the collision is perfectly elastic, it bounces up with the same momentum but in the opposite direction. Its momentum then goes from –5 kg·m/s to +5 kg·m/s, a change of +10 kg·m/s. The rubber ball has twice the change in momentum (Figure 4.19). The momentum change is always greater when objects bounce compared with when they do not bounce.

Bouncing versus stopping   Because we don't know the collision times, it is impossible to calculate the forces exactly. We can only say for certain that the impulse (force × time) is 10 N·s for the rubber ball (1 kg·m/s = 1 N·s). This could be a force of 10 N for 1 second, or 100 N for 0.1 seconds, or any product that results in 10 N·s. However, we can be pretty sure the force from the rubber ball is greater because the momentum of the rubber ball changed twice as much as the momentum of the clay ball. Bouncing nearly always results in a greater force than just stopping because bouncing creates a larger change in momentum.

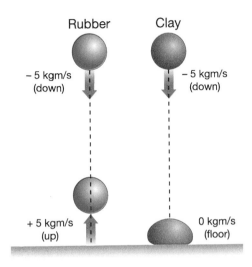

Figure 4.18: *Bouncing results in a greater change in momentum and therefore almost always creates a greater force.*

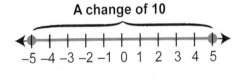

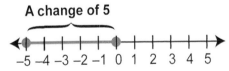

Figure 4.19: *A number line can help you see clearly that a change from –5 to +5 is twice as great as a change from –5 to 0.*

Solving impulse problems

Motion problems Impulse can be used to solve many practical problems. For example, how much force does it take to stop a 1,000-kilogram car in 10 seconds if the car is moving at 30 m/s (67 mph)? To solve this kind of problem, calculate the change in momentum and the impulse needed to stop the car. For the car, the change in momentum is 30,000 kg·m/s (1,000 kg × 30 m/s), so the impulse needed to stop the car must also be 30,000 kg·m/s (N·s). The time is 10 s, so the force is 3,000 N because the impulse is 3,000 N × 10 s = 30,000 N·s.

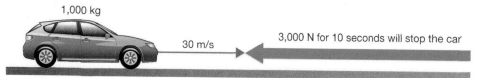

1,000 kg

30 m/s

3,000 N for 10 seconds will stop the car

Why does impulse equal the force multiplied by the time?

To find the relationship between momentum, force, and time, start with Newton's second law:

$$F = ma$$

Substituting for acceleration:

$$F = m\,\frac{\left(v_2 - v_1\right)}{t}$$

Rearranging:

$$Ft = m\left(v_2 - v_1\right)$$

$$Ft = mv_2 - mv_1$$

Therefore the change in momentum (impulse) equals the product of the force and time.

Collision-force problems If you know the time during which the colliding objects touch each other, you can calculate the average force of the collision. The maximum force is larger than the average because forces in collisions tend to rise as the colliding objects come together, reach a maximum, and then drop off as the objects move apart. However, knowing the average force can be useful.

Impulse

A 1-kg clay ball hits the floor with a velocity of –5 m/s and comes to a stop in 0.1 second. What force did the floor exert on it?

1. Looking for: You are asked for the force the floor exerts on the ball.

2. Given: You are given the ball's mass, initial speed, final speed, and stopping time.

3. Relationships: $Ft = mv_2 - mv_1$

4. Solution:

$$F\left(0.1\text{ s}\right) = \left(1\text{ kg}\right)\left(0\text{ m/s}\right) - \left(1\text{ kg}\right)\left(-5\text{ m/s}\right)$$

$$F\left(0.1\text{ s}\right) = 5\text{ kg}\cdot\text{m/s}$$

$$F = 50\text{ N}$$

Your Turn:

a. What braking force is needed to stop a 1,000-kg car moving at 30 m/s in a time of 2 seconds?

b. You pedal your bicycle with a force of 40 N. If you start from rest and have a mass of 50 kg, what is your final speed after 10 seconds?

(Answers are listed at the end of the chapter.)

Car crash safety

Stopping in an accident
The relationship between impulse, force, and time has been used by auto manufacturers to make vehicles safer in accidents. When a car comes to a stop, its momentum drops to zero. The shorter the amount of stopping time, the greater the force on the car. Car bodies are designed to crumple in a collision to extend the stopping time. The ideal car crumples enough to stop gradually, but not so much that the passenger compartment is affected.

Seat belts
The stopping time of a car in a collision is very short even when crumpling occurs. A passenger without a seat belt will have a momentum that drops from a large value to zero when hitting the windshield, steering wheel, or dashboard. Seat belts are made of a very strong fabric that stretches slightly when a force is applied. Stretching extends the time over which the passenger comes to a stop and results in less force being exerted on the person's body.

Air bags
Air bags work together with seat belts to make cars safer (Figure 4.20). An air bag inflates when the force applied to the front of a car reaches a specific level. The air bag deflates slowly as the person's body applies a force to the bag upon impact. The force of impact pushes the air out of small holes in the air bag, bringing the person to a gradual stop. Many cars now contain both front and side air bags.

Crash test dummies
Automakers use crash test dummies to study the effects of collisions on passengers (Figure 4.21). Crash test dummies contain electronic sensors to measure the forces exerted at various places on the body. Results of these tests have been used to make changes in automobile design, resulting in cars that are much safer than they were in the past.

Figure 4.20: *Seat belts and air bags work together to protect passengers in automobile collisions.*

Figure 4.21: *Crash test dummies are used in car safety tests.*

4.3 Section Review

1. List three examples of elastic collisions and three examples of inelastic collisions not mentioned in this chapter.
2. Are momentum and kinetic energy conserved in all collisions?
3. What is the definition of impulse?
4. Why will an egg break if it is dropped on the ground but not if it is dropped on a pillow?

Forensic Engineering: A Two-Part Science

We usually think of engineering as a science focused on designing and constructing things—like bridges, computers, automobiles, or sneakers. However, there is one branch of engineering that focuses on how things fail, collapse, or crash. It's called forensic engineering.

Forensic engineers are like time travelers, rewinding the clock to a point just before a bridge collapses or a car collision occurs. Their job is to gather and analyze information from the scene so they can reconstruct the event, step by step. A forensic engineer's work is often used in court as evidence in personal-injury or product-liability cases. Forensic engineers must play two roles in their work: that of a detective, gathering clues and evidence; and that of an engineer, using evidence to analyze an event.

Gathering information: the detective role

One task of a forensic engineer is to reconstruct automobile crashes. Working with law enforcement officials, forensic engineers act as detectives looking for clues about how a collision occurred. The vehicle or vehicles involved in the crash are the most important pieces of evidence. They can give the forensic engineer an idea of the angle of impact, the speeds involved, and seat-belt usage.

John Kwasnoski has been a forensic engineer and physics professor for more than 30 years. He is often asked to testify in court when collisions result in criminal charges. Many of his cases involve a driver (often alcohol-impaired) losing control of a vehicle and colliding with another vehicle or pedestrians. In other cases, a driver may have hit a telephone pole, concrete barrier, or some other stationary object, resulting in injury to passengers in the vehicle.

Professor Kwasnoski explains, "As an investigator at the scene of a crash, I'm most often looking for evidence of the transfer of energy. Before the crash, the vehicle has a certain amount of kinetic energy. The police find the car at rest. The law of conservation of energy tells us the vehicle's kinetic energy had to be transferred somewhere. Often it's found in damage to roadside obstacles or the roadway itself, and in change to the vehicle's shape."

"I investigated the crash of the car in the photo. This car hit a utility pole when the teenage driver lost control on a rural road. The front seat passenger was injured in the crash. The passenger was not wearing a seat belt that probably would have prevented her from striking the windshield."

This car hit a utility pole when the teenage driver lost control on a rural road.

After photographing the scene and making careful measurements of the damage to vehicles, the length of the skid marks, and other evidence of transfer of energy, forensic engineers like professor Kwasnoski head back to the lab.

Analyzing the information: the engineering role

The next step, explains Kwasnoski, is to figure out how much energy it took to cause the damage he observed. He looks at the results of crash tests where vehicles are crashed into concrete barriers at various speeds. The amount of damage depends on the specific properties (like stiffness) of the materials used to build the car, so it is important to analyze crash test records of the specific make and model of the vehicle involved in the crash. By comparing measurements of the vehicle's damage to the crash-test records, the speed of the vehicle at the time of the collision can be inferred. This information is often a crucial piece of evidence in a criminal trial.

The study of how vehicles moved before, during, and after a collision is called *vehicular kinematics*. Another important part of a forensic engineer's job is to analyze how the passengers moved before, during, and after the collision. This is called *occupant kinematics*. From crash test data, the forensic engineer can calculate peak accelerations of the occupants. These accelerations, especially those of the head and neck, can be greater than the vehicle's peak acceleration. Calculating an occupant's peak acceleration helps determine the cause of injuries.

Crash prevention through physics lessons

Investigating crashes has convinced professor Kwasnoski that if people understood the physics of force and motion, they would be better equipped to make good decisions about driving and seat-belt use. So, he often speaks to high school and community groups about crash prevention.

Sometimes audience members will comment that they don't think it's important to wear seat belts when they are driving in town, where the speed limit is 35 miles per hour.

"I point out to them that if you calculate acceleration due to gravity, 35 miles per hour is the speed you would be going when you hit the ground after falling off a four-story building. I ask, 'Would you rather be strapped into a padded steel cage or just hurtling through the air on your own in a fall like that?'"

"We also talk about Newton's first law of motion—objects in motion stay in motion, unless acted on by a force. So if a car is traveling at 35 miles per hour and crashes, an unbelted occupant will collide with the interior of the car at 35 miles per hour. There are also secondary crashes—your organs collide with your rib cage, and your brain collides with your skull at 35 miles per hour."

While seat belts can't prevent every internal injury, Kwasnoski points out that all of the significant automobile safety advances in the past 50 years—air bags, padded dashboards, stronger frames—are designed to protect people who stay in the car. After investigating over 650 collisions, Kwasnoski concludes, "You just do not want to be ejected from a vehicle in a crash." Human bodies are not designed to handle the impact of crashing into a stationary object after traveling through space at the speed of a car.

QUESTIONS

1. What two roles do forensic engineers play?

2. How does a forensic engineer use the law of conservation of energy in a crash investigation?

3. Explain the difference between *vehicular kinematics* and *occupant kinematics*.

4. Design a poster that uses physics principles to encourage seat belt usage.

   To learn more about professor Kwasnoski's work, try this Internet keyword search: Kwasnoski + "legal sciences"

Car photo courtesy of John Kwasnoski.

Chapter 4 Review

Understanding Vocabulary

Select the correct term to complete the sentences.

collision	joule	momentum
elastic collision	kinetic energy	Newton's third law
energy	law of conservation of energy	potential energy
impulse	law of conservation of momentum	work
inelastic collision		

1. _____ is calculated by multiplying a force and the time needed for the force to act.

2. According to _____, for every action force, there is a reaction force equal in strength and opposite in direction.

3. The mass of an object multiplied by its velocity equals its _____.

4. The _____ states that energy can never be created or destroyed, just changed from one form to another.

5. Energy due to position is known as _____.

6. When two objects collide and stick together or change shape, it is called a(n) _____.

Reviewing Concepts

Section 4.1

1. State Newton's third law in your own words.

2. Action and reaction forces always have the _____ strength and act in _____ directions.

3. You and a friend are sitting across from each other on chairs with wheels. You push off each other and move in opposite directions. Explain the following:

   a. How does the force you feel compare to the force your friend feels?

   b. If your mass is greater than your friend's mass, how do your accelerations compare?

4. A book rests on a table. The force of gravity pulls down on the book. What prevents the book from accelerating downward?

5. Give three examples of Newton's third law in everyday life. List the action and reaction forces in each example.

6. What two things does an object require to have momentum?

7. Consider an airplane at rest and a person walking through the airport.

   a. Which has greater mass?

   b. Which has greater velocity?

   c. Which has greater momentum? Explain.

8. Explain the two different ways to calculate impulse.

9. Is the unit used to represent impulse the same as the unit for momentum? Explain.

10. State the law of conservation of momentum in your own words.

11. You and your little cousin are standing on in-line skates. You push off of each other and both move backwards.

    a. Which of you moves back at a greater speed? Use the law of conservation of momentum to explain your answer.

    b. How does your impulse compare to your cousin's impulse?

12. When you jump, you move upward with a certain amount of momentum. Earth moves downward with an equal amount of momentum. Why don't you notice Earth's motion?

Section 4.2

13. What is anything with energy able to do?

14. The joule is an abbreviation for what combination of units?

15. When work is done, _____ is transferred.

16. How can you increase the gravitational potential energy of an object?

17. Explain why a bicycle at rest at the top of a hill has energy.

18. Which two quantities are needed to determine an object's kinetic energy?

19. What happens to a car's kinetic energy if its speed doubles? What if its speed triples?

20. A ball is thrown up into the air. Explain what happens to its potential and kinetic energies as it moves up and then back down.

21. Explain what it means to say energy is conserved as a ball falls toward the ground.

22. Will we ever run out of energy on Earth? Might we run out of certain forms of energy? Explain.

Section 4.3

23. Distinguish between elastic and inelastic collisions.

24. Classify each collision as elastic or inelastic.

    a. A dog catches a tennis ball in his mouth.

    b. A ping-pong ball bounces off a table.

    c. You jump on a trampoline.

    d. A light bulb is knocked onto the floor and breaks.

25. Is momentum conserved during elastic collisions? Is it conserved during inelastic collisions?

26. Why does bouncing nearly always cause a greater force than simply stopping during a collision?

27. Cars that crumple in a collision are safer than cars that bounce when they collide. Explain why this is so.

28. What is the secret to catching a water balloon without breaking it? Explain using physics.

Solving Problems

Section 4.1

1. You throw a basketball by exerting a force of 20 N. According to Newton's third law, there is another 20-N force created in the opposite direction. If there are two equal forces in opposite directions, how does the ball accelerate?

2. What is the momentum of a 2-kg ball traveling at 4 m/s?

3. How fast does a 1,000-kg car have to move to have a momentum of 50,000 kg·m/s?

4. Idil's momentum is 110 kg·m/s when she walks at 2 m/s. What's her mass?

5. Which has more momentum: a 5,000-kg truck moving at 10 m/s or a sports car with a mass of 1,200 kg moving at 50 m/s?

6. Two hockey players on ice skates push off of each other. One has a mass of 60 kg. The other has a mass of 80 kg.

    m = 60 kg   m = 80 kg

    a. If the 80-kg player moves back with a velocity of 3 m/s, what is his momentum?

    b. What is the 60-kg player's momentum?

    c. What is the 60-kg player's velocity?

7. A 75-kg astronaut floating in space throws a 5-kg rock at 5 m/s. How fast does the astronaut move backwards?

8. A 2-kg ball is accelerated from rest to a speed of 8 m/s.

    a. What is the ball's change in momentum?

    b. What is the impulse?

    c. A constant force of 32 N is used to change the momentum. For how much time does the force act?

9. A 1,000-kg car uses a braking force of 10,000 N to stop in 2 s.

    a. What impulse acts on the car?

    b. What is the change in momentum of the car?

    c. What was the initial speed of the car?

Section 4.2

10. A 5-kg can of paint is sitting on top of a 2-m-high step ladder. How much work did you do to move the can of paint to the top of the ladder? What is the potential energy of the can of paint?

11. How much work is done to move a 10,000-N car 20 m?

12. Which has more potential energy, a 5-kg rock lifted 2 m off the ground on Earth, or the same rock lifted 2 m on the Moon? Why?

13. At the end of a bike ride up a mountain, Chris was at an elevation of 500 m above where he started. If Chris's mass is 60 kg, by how much did his potential energy increase?

500 m

14. Alexis is riding her skateboard. If Alexis has a mass of 50 kg:

   a. What is her kinetic energy if she travels at 5 m/s?

   b. What is her kinetic energy if she travels at 10 m/s?

   c. Alexis's 50-kg dog Bruno gets on the skateboard with her. What is their total kinetic energy if they move at 5 m/s?

   d. Based on your calculations, does doubling the mass or doubling the speed have more of an effect on kinetic energy?

15. A 1-kilogram coconut falls out of a tree from a height of 12 m. Determine the coconut's potential and kinetic energy at each point shown in the picture. Its speed is zero at point A.

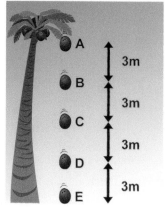

A

3m

B

3m

C

3m

D

3m

E

Section 4.3

16. A demolition derby is a car-crashing contest. Suppose an 800-kg car moving at 20 m/s crashes into the back of and sticks to a 1,200-kg car moving at 10 m/s in the same direction.

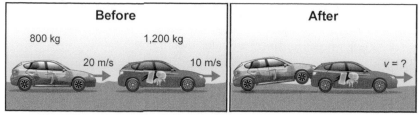

Before	After
800 kg 1,200 kg	
20 m/s 10 m/s	v = ?

   a. Is this collision elastic or inelastic? Why?

   b. Calculate the momentum of each car before the collision.

   c. What is the total momentum of the stuck-together cars after the collision? Why?

   d. What is the speed of the stuck-together cars after the collision?

17. A 5-kg ball moving at 6 m/s collides with a 1-kg ball at rest. The balls bounce off each other and the second ball moves in the same direction as the first ball at 10 m/s. What is the velocity of the first ball after the collision?

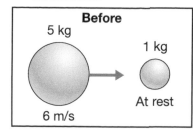

Before

5 kg

1 kg

At rest

6 m/s

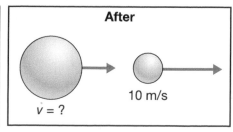

After

10 m/s

v = ?

18. Yanick and Nancy drive two identical 1,500-kg cars at 20 m/s. Yanick slams on the brakes and his car comes to a stop in 1 s. Nancy lightly applies the brakes and stops her car in 5 s.

    a. How does the momentum change of Yanick's car compare to the momentum change of Nancy's car?

    b. How does the impulse on Yanick's car compare to the impulse on Nancy's car?

    c. How does the force of Yanick's brakes compare to the force of Nancy's brakes?

    d. Calculate the stopping force for each car.

19. Your neighbor's car breaks down. You and a friend agree to push it two blocks to a repair shop while your neighbor steers. The two of you apply a net force of 800 N to the 1,000-kg car for 10 s.

    a. What impulse is applied to the car?

    b. At what speed is the car moving after 10 s? The car starts from rest.

Test Practice

Section 4.1

1. Newton's third law describes action and reaction forces which

    a. are equal in strength.

    b. are acting in the same direction.

    c. are always applied to the same object.

    d. always cancel each other out.

2. A person with a mass of 50 kg is in a canoe with a mass of 30 kg. The canoe is moving at 5 m/s. What is the momentum of the person and canoe?

    a. 16 kg·m/s

    b. 150 kg·m/s

    c. 250 kg·m/s

    d. 400 kg·m/s

3. Impulse is the product of

    a. force and mass.

    b. force and time.

    c. mass and acceleration.

    d. mass and velocity.

4. How much time should a 50-N force take to increase the speed of a 5-kg car from 10 m/s to 30 m/s?

    a. 0.5 s

    b. 1 s

    c. 2 s

    d. 3 s

Section 4.2

5. Joules are a unit of measurement for all of the following *except*

    a. kinetic energy.

    b. potential energy.

    c. momentum.

    d. work.

6. A 60-kg woman is on a ladder 2 m above the ground. What is her potential energy?

    a. 60 J

    b. 120 J

    c. 588 J

    d. 1,176 J

7. A 1-kg cat is perched in a tree 4 m off the ground. It jumps out of the tree. The cat's velocity halfway down is 10 m/s. What is the cat's kinetic energy halfway down?

    a. 5 J

    b. 8 J

    c. 50 J

    d. 100 J

8. At which point does the car on the ramp have the greatest potential energy?

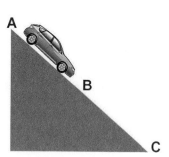

   a. A

   b. B

   c. C

   d. The potential energy is the same at all points.

Section 4.3

9. In a collision between objects, kinetic energy is *not* lost when

   a. the objects change shape.

   b. the objects stick together.

   c. the collision is inelastic.

   d. the collision is elastic.

10. A 6,000-kg train car moving at 10 m/s strikes a second 4,000-kg parked train car. The cars stick together and move along the track. What is their velocity after the collision?

   a. 4 m/s

   b. 6 m/s

   c. 10 m/s

   d. 15 m/s

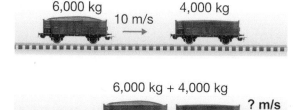

11. Which of the following is an example of a nearly-elastic collision?

   a. marbles collide and bounce off each other

   b. ice skaters collide and hold onto each other

   c. trucks crash and stick together

   d. a ceramic mug falls to the floor and breaks

12. A 15-kg child ice skating at 1 meter per second collides with a skater at rest. The skaters grab onto each other and continue moving at 0.5 m/s. What is the mass of the second skater?

   a. 7.5 kg

   b. 15 kg

   c. 30 kg

   d. 45 kg

Applying Your Knowledge

Section 4.1

1. Think up some strange scenarios that might happen if the universe changed so that Newton's third law was no longer true.

2. Identify at least *three* action-reaction force pairs in the picture of the firefighter seen here.

3. The greatest speed with which an athlete can jump vertically is around 5 m/s. Determine the speed at which Earth would move down if you jumped up at 5 m/s.

Section 4.2

4. A car going twice as fast requires four times as much stopping distance. What is it about the kinetic energy formula that accounts for this fact?

5. The energy in food is measured in Calories rather than joules. One Calorie is equal to 4,187 J. Look on the nutrition labels of three of your favorite foods. Determine the amount of energy in joules in one serving of each type of food.

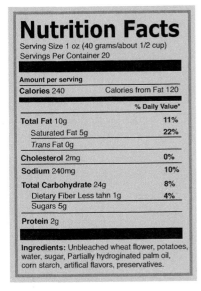

Nutrition Facts

Serving Size 1 oz (40 grams/about 1/2 cup)
Servings Per Container 20

Amount per serving

Calories 240   Calories from Fat 120

% Daily Value*

Total Fat 10g	**11%**
Saturated Fat 5g	**22%**
Trans Fat 0g	
Cholesterol 2mg	**0%**
Sodium 240mg	**10%**
Total Carbohydrate 24g	**8%**
Dietary Fiber Less tahn 1g	**4%**
Sugars 5g	
Protein 2g	

Ingredients: Unbleached wheat flower, potatoes, water, sugar, Partially hydroginated palm oil, corn starch, artifical flavors, preservatives.

Section 4.3

6. Major League Baseball requires players to use wooden bats, and does not allow the use of aluminum bats. Research to find out why this is. Relate what you find to what you learned in this chapter.

7. Research how cars are designed to be safer in collisions and how they are tested. Make a poster that summarizes what you learn.

 *Your Turn* **Answers**

Action and reaction (Section 4.1, page 78)

a. The force of the bat on the ball accelerates the ball. The force of the ball on the bat (reaction) slows down the swinging bat (action).

b. Earth attracts the moon (action) and the moon attracts Earth (reaction) in an action-reaction pair. Both action and reaction are due to gravity.

Force and momentum (Section 4.1, page 80)

a. 150 kg·m/s

b. 9 s

Using the momentum relationship (Section 4.1, page 82)

a. 4 m/s

b. 50 kg

Potential and kinetic energy (Section 4.2, page 87)

a. 118 J

b. 50 J

Energy conservation (Section 4.2, page 89)

a. 147,000 J

b. 20 m

Momentum and collisions (Section 4.3, page 92)

a. 5 m/s

b. +5 m/s

Impulse (Section 4.3, page 94)

a. 15,000 N

b. 8 m/s

Unit 2 FORCES

Forces in Equilibrium

Many people would not consider it extraordinary to get into an elevator and zoom to the top of a 50-story building. They might not be so nonchalant if they knew the balance of enormous forces that keeps a tall building standing up. Or, they might feel even more secure, knowing how well the building has been engineered to withstand the forces.

Tall buildings are impressive examples of equilibrium, or the balancing of forces. The average acceleration of a building should be zero! That means all forces acting on the building must add up to zero, including gravity, wind, and the movement of people and vehicles. A modern office tower is constructed of steel and concrete beams that are carefully designed to provide reaction forces to balance against wind, gravity, people, and vehicles.

In ancient times, people learned about equilibrium through trial-and-error. Then, as today, different builders and architects each wanted to make a building taller than the others. Without today's knowledge of equilibrium and forces, many builders experimented with designs that quickly collapsed. It is estimated that 10 cathedrals fell down for every 1 that is still standing today! Over time, humans learned the laws of forces and equilibrium that allow us to be much more confident about the structural strength of modern tall buildings.

VOCABULARY

axis of rotation	lever arm	scalar
components	line of action	sliding friction
contact force	lubricant	spring constant
equilibrium	magnitude	static friction
free-body diagram	normal force	torque
friction	resultant	vector
Hooke's law	rotational equilibrium	

KEY QUESTIONS

✓ *How do you precisely describe a force?*

✓ *How is the concept of equilibrium important to the design of buildings and bridges?*

✓ *What is friction?*

✓ *How is torque different from force?*

5.1 The Force Vector

Think about how to accurately describe a force. One important piece of information is the strength of the force. For example, 50 newtons would be a clear description of the strength of a force. But what about the direction? The direction of a force is important, too. How do you describe the direction of a force in a way that is precise enough to use in physics? In this section, you will learn that force is a *vector*. A vector is a quantity that includes information about size or strength and direction.

> **scalar** - a quantity that is completely described by its magnitude and measurement units
>
> **magnitude** - a quantity's size or amount without regard to its direction or other factors
>
> **vector** - a quantity that includes both magnitude and direction

Scalars and vectors

Scalars have magnitude
A **scalar** is a quantity that can be completely described by a single value called its **magnitude**. Magnitude means the size or amount, and always includes units of measurement. Temperature is a good example of a scalar quantity. If you are sick and use a thermometer to measure your temperature, it might show 101°F. The magnitude of your temperature is 101, and degrees Fahrenheit is the unit of measurement. The value of 101°F is a complete description of the temperature because you do not need any more information.

Examples of scalars
Many other measurements are expressed as scalar quantities. Distance, time, and speed are all scalars because all three can be completely described with a single number and a unit.

Vectors have direction
Sometimes a single number does not include enough information to describe a measurement. In giving someone directions to your house, you could not tell the person to simply start at the person's house and drive 4 kilometers. A single distance measurement is not enough to describe the path to follow. Giving complete directions would mean including instructions to go 2 kilometers to the north, turn right, then go 2 kilometers to the east (Figure 5.1). The information "2 kilometers to the north" is an example of a **vector**. A vector is a quantity that includes both magnitude and direction. Other examples of vectors are force, velocity, and acceleration. Direction is necessary to fully describe each of these quantities.

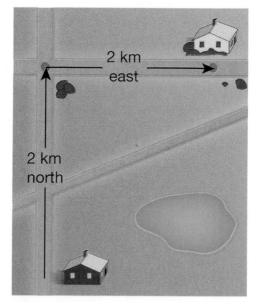

Figure 5.1: *Vectors are useful in giving directions.*

The force vector

What is a force vector? A force vector has units of newtons, just like all forces. In addition, the force vector also includes enough information to give the direction of the force. There are three ways to describe force vectors. You can represent a force vector with a graph, a magnitude-angle pair, or an *x-y* pair. You will read about all three in this chapter.

Three ways to describe the same force

Graph	Magnitude, angle	x-y pair
(graph showing 10 N at 30°)	(10 N, 30°)	(8.7, 5.0) N

Drawing a force vector The graph form of the force vector is a picture showing the strength and direction of a force. It is just like an ordinary graph except the *x*- and *y*-axes show the strength of the force in the *x* and *y* directions. The force vector is drawn as an arrow. The length of the arrow shows the magnitude of the vector, and the arrow points in the direction of the vector.

Scale When drawing a vector, you must choose a scale. A scale for a vector diagram is similar to a scale on any graph. For example, if you are drawing a vector showing a force magnitude of 10 N, you might use a scale of 1 cm = 1 N. You would draw the arrow 10 cm long (Figure 5.2). You should always state the scale you use when drawing vectors.

x and y forces When you draw a force vector on a graph, distance along the *x*- or *y*-axes represents the strength of the force in the *x*- and *y*-directions. A force at an angle has the same effect as two smaller forces aligned with the *x*- and *y*-directions. As shown in Figure 5.3, the 8.7-N and 5-N forces applied together have the same effect as a single 10-N force applied at an angle of 30° from the *x*-axis. This idea of breaking a force down into an equivalent pair of *x*- and *y*-forces is very important, as you will see.

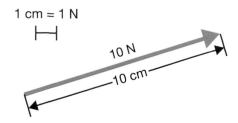

Figure 5.2: *A 10-N force vector, with a scale of 1 centimeter to 1 newton.*

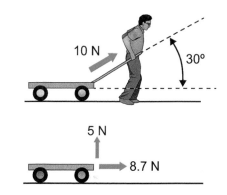

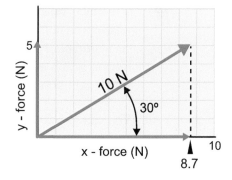

Figure 5.3: *A force at an angle has the same effect as two smaller forces applied at the same time along the* x- *and* y-*directions.*

Vector components

Components Every force vector can be replaced by perpendicular vectors called **components**. You can think of components as "adding up" to make the original force. When adding and subtracting forces, it is usually much easier to work with the components than it is with the original force.

> **components** - the two vectors, at right angles to each other, that add up to a given vector

Three ways to describe a force vector Recall that there are three ways to describe a force vector:

- by drawing a graph (Figure 5.4)
- by giving *polar coordinates* such as (10 N, 30°)
- by giving *cartesian coordinates* such as (8.7, 5) N

If you are given polar coordinates You can describe a force vector by giving its magnitude and direction. The force in Figure 5.4 is (10 N, 30°). The first number (10 N) is the magnitude, or strength of the force. The second number is the angle measured counterclockwise from the *x*-axis. This way of writing a vector is called *polar coordinates*. If you are given polar coordinates, you can find the vector components by using the graphing method shown in Figure 5.4.

If you are given cartesian coordinates If you know the *x*- and *y*-components, you can write a force vector with parentheses. The force in Figure 5.4 is written (8.7, 5) N. The first number is the *x*-component of the force, and the second number is the *y*-component. It is much easier to add or subtract forces when they are given as *x*- and *y*-components. Mathematically, when we write a vector as *(x, y)* we are using *cartesian coordinates*. Cartesian coordinates use perpendicular *x*- and *y*-axes like on graph paper. If you are given cartesian coordinates, you can find the vector components by using the graphing method shown in Figure 5.4.

Checking your components You can check your components by drawing a triangle (Figure 5.5). The *x*- and *y*-components are the lengths of the triangle's sides parallel to the *x*- and *y*-axes. The Pythagorean theorem can be used to find the lengths of the sides *a* and *b* of this right triangle. The original vector is the hypotenuse, or side *c*. The Pythagorean theorem states that $a^2 + b^2 = c^2$. In terms of the forces in the example, $(5\text{ N})^2 + (8.7\text{ N})^2 = (10\text{ N})^2$. If the left side of the equation equals the right side, you know that the components are correct.

1. Draw the force to scale.

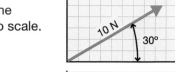

2. Extend lines to the *x* and *y* axes.

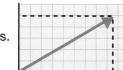

3. Read off the *x* and *y* components.

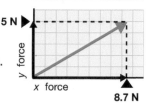

Figure 5.4: *Finding the components of a 10-N force vector at 30°.*

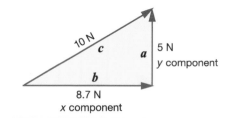

PYTHAGOREAN THEOREM

$$a^2 + b^2 = c^2$$

Figure 5.5: *Check your work by using the Pythagorean theorem.*

Free-body diagrams

Showing external forces acting on an object A **free-body diagram** is a valuable tool for studying forces. It is a diagram that uses vectors to show all of the external forces acting on an object. The forces acting on a book are shown. A free-body diagram shows only the forces acting *on* an object, and does not include the forces an object exerts on other things. When making a free-body diagram, draw only the object you are studying, not any other objects around it. Be sure to clearly label the strength of the force with a vector. Do this for *each* force.

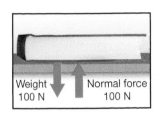

Drawing a free-body diagram You can draw forces where they are applied to the object, as in the illustration of the book and the table. Many times, however, it is useful to draw the vectors starting from a single point. Figure 5.6 shows a monkey hanging from two ropes. All forces acting on the monkey are shown. The tension forces of the ropes (T_1 and T_2) acts on the monkey, as well as gravity (F_w). Forces like tension, gravitational force, normal force, and frictional force will be described later in this section.

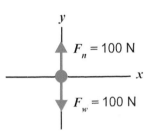

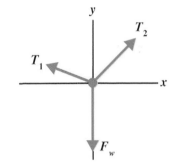

Figure 5.6: *Free-body diagram for a monkey hanging from two ropes.*

 Finding force components

A man pulls a wagon with a force of 80 N at an angle of 30 degrees. Find the x- (horizontal) and y- (vertical) components of the force.

1. *Looking for:* You are asked for the x- and y-components of the force.

2. *Given:* You are given the magnitude and direction of the force.

3. *Relationships:* The x- and y-components can found by graphing the force.

4. *Solution:* x component is 70 N, y component is 40 N (See the diagram.)

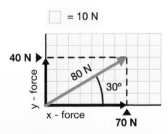

Your turn:

a. What is the vertical (y) component of a 100-newton force at an angle of 60 degrees to the x-axis?

b. Two people push on a heavy box. One pushes with a force of 100 newtons at an angle of 90°, and the other pushes with a force of 70 newtons at an angle of 180°. Use a scaled drawing (1 cm = 10 N) to find the net force.

(Answers are listed at the end of the chapter.)

Forces and free-body diagrams

Free-body diagrams are useful   When more than one force acts on an object, it is helpful to draw a free-body diagram. The free-body diagram will help you see all of the forces acting so you can find the net force, or perhaps an unknown force.

Types of forces   What types of forces can act on an object? Table 5.1 summarizes seven types of forces that you will study and investigate in this course. Use this table as a guideline to help you draw accurate free-body diagrams that include all of the forces acting on an object in a given situation (Figure 5.7).

(from previous page)
free-body diagram - a diagram showing all of the forces acting on an object

Table 5.1: Some forces to consider when drawing free-body diagrams

Type of force	Symbol	Description of force
Gravitational force	F_g or F_w	Force of attraction exerted by a massive object like Earth on other objects. The gravitational force is the weight of the object.
Normal force	F_n	Support force exerted on an object that is in contact with another object.
Applied force	F_{app}	A force applied to an object by a person or other object.
Tension force	F_t or T	A force felt through a string, rope, or cable when it is pulled tight by forces acting at its ends.
Frictional force	F_f	A force between two surfaces that usually acts opposite to an object's motion. See the next section for more details.
Air resistance force	F_f or F_{air}	A special type of friction that acts on objects as they travel through air.
Spring force	F_{spring}	A force exerted by a compressed or extended spring on any object attached to it.

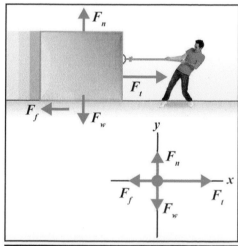

5.1 Section Review

1. Is each of these a scalar or a vector: speed, time, mass, weight, velocity, temperature?
2. Draw a scaled diagram of a vector that represents a force of 200 N at 120°.
3. Draw the force vector (6, 8) N. Is this the same as the force vector (100 N, 53°)? Explain.
4. A box is being pushed across a carpeted floor. Draw a free-body diagram for the box.

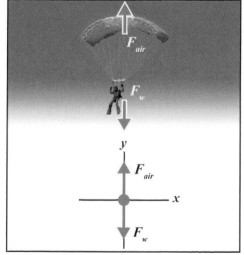

Figure 5.7: *Free-body diagrams showing common types of forces.*

5.2 **Forces and Equilibrium**

Sometimes you want things to accelerate and sometimes you don't. Cars should accelerate, bridges should not. In order for a bridge to stay in place, *all* the forces acting on the bridge must add up to produce zero net force. This section is about *equilibrium*, which is what physicists call any situation where the net force is zero. The concept of equilibrium is important in the design of buildings, bridges, and many other structures.

Equilibrium

Equilibrium and the first law   The net force on an object is the vector sum of all the forces acting on it. When the net force on an object is zero, we say the object is in **equilibrium**. Newton's first law says an object's motion does not change unless a net force acts on it. If the net force is zero, an object at rest will stay at rest and an object in motion will stay in motion with constant speed and direction.

Equilibrium and the second law   The second law says the acceleration of an object in equilibrium is zero because the net force acting on the object is zero. Zero acceleration means neither the speed nor the direction of motion can change.

Normal force   Imagine a book sitting on a table. The book exerts a **contact force** on the table. A contact force is a force between two objects that are in contact, or between an object and a surface. But what force balances the contact force from the book? The table exerts an upward force on the book called the **normal force**. The normal force is a support force exerted on an object by another object. The word *normal* here has a different meaning from what you might expect. In mathematics, normal means *perpendicular*. The force the table exerts is perpendicular to the table's surface.

Newton's third law   Newton's third law explains why normal forces exist (Figure 5.8). The book's contact force on the table is the action force, and the table's normal force on the book is the reaction force. The third law says that these forces are equal and opposite. If the book is at rest, these forces *must* be equal in magnitude but opposite in direction. If the book was heavier, it would exert a stronger downward contact force on the table. The table would then exert a stronger upward force on the book, or if the table could not support the extra weight, the table would break.

> **equilibrium** - occurs when the forces on an object are balanced so the net force on the object is zero
>
> **contact force** - a force between two objects that are in contact, or between an object and a surface
>
> **normal force** - a support force exerted on an object by another object that is perpendicular to the objects' contact surfaces

Action

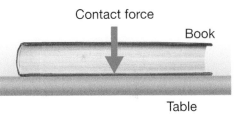

Reaction

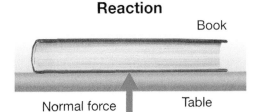

Figure 5.8: *The book pushes down on the table, and the table pushes up on the book. The force exerted by the table is called the normal force.*

Adding force vectors

An example Suppose three people are trying to keep an injured polar bear in one place. Each person has a long rope attached to the bear. Two people pull on the bear with forces of 100 N each (Figure 5.9). What force must the third person apply to balance the other two? The bear will not move if the net force is zero. To find the answer, we need to find the net force when the forces are not in the same direction. In other words, we need a way to *add vectors*.

Graphically adding vectors On a graph, you add vectors by drawing them end-to-end. The beginning of one vector starts at the end of the previous one. The total of all the vectors is called the **resultant**. The resultant starts at the origin and ends at the end of the last vector in the chain (Figure 5.10). The resultant in the example is a single force of approximately 141 newtons at 225 degrees. To cancel this force, the third person must pull with an equal 141-newton force in the opposite direction (45°). Adding force vectors this way is challenging because you must carefully draw each one to scale and at the proper angle.

Adding x-y components Adding vectors in *x-y* components is much easier. The *x*-component of the resultant is the sum of the *x*-components of each individual vector. The *y*-component of the resultant is the sum of the *y*-components of each individual vector. For the example, $(-100, 0)$ N + $(0, -100)$ N = $(-100, -100)$ N. The components are negative because the forces point in the negative-*x* and negative-*y* directions. The resultant vector is $(-100, -100)$ N.

Equilibrium To have zero net force, the forces in both the *x*- and *y*-directions must be zero. The third force must have *x*- and *y*-components that add up to zero when combined with the other forces. Here's the solution to the problem:

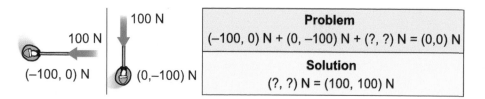

Problem
$(-100, 0)$ N + $(0, -100)$ N + $(?, ?)$ N = $(0,0)$ N
Solution
$(?, ?)$ N = $(100, 100)$ N

Following the rules we just gave, the third force must be $(100, 100)$ N. This is the same as a force of approximately 141 N at 45°.

> **resultant** - a vector that is the vector sum of two or more individual vectors

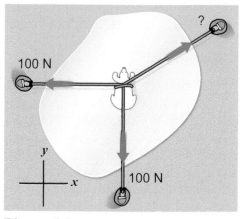

Figure 5.9: *Three people trying to keep a polar bear in the center of an ice floe.*

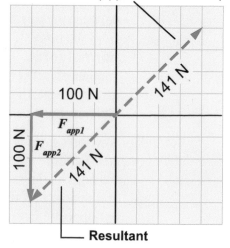

Figure 5.10: *Finding the resultant and solving the problem graphically.*

Solving equilibrium problems

Finding the net force For an object to be in equilibrium, the sum of all the forces acting *on the object* must equal zero. In many problems you will need Newton's third law to find reaction forces, like normal forces, that act on an object.

Using vectors In equilibrium, the net force *in each direction* must be zero. That means the total force in the *x*-direction must be zero and total force in the *y*-direction also must be zero. You cannot mix *x*- and *y*-components when adding forces. Getting the forces in each direction to cancel separately is easiest to do when all forces are expressed in *x-y* components.

Balancing forces If you are trying to find an unknown force on an object in equilibrium, the first step is to draw a free-body diagram. Then, use the fact that the net force is zero to find the unknown force. To be in equilibrium, forces must balance both horizontally and vertically. Forces to the right must balance forces to the left, and upward forces must balance downward forces.

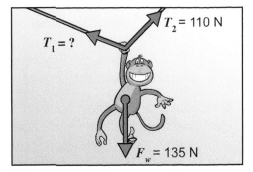

Figure 5.11: *What is the unknown tension force?*

 Solving equilibrium problems

A monkey hangs from two ropes (Figure 5.11). The weight of the monkey is 135 N. The tension force from one of the ropes is 110 N, exerted at an angle of 55°. What is the tension force exerted by the other rope on the monkey?

1. **Looking for:** You are asked for an unknown force (T_1) exerted by a rope.

2. **Given:** You are given the monkey's weight in newtons (F_w) and the force (T_2) and angle of the other rope in newtons and degrees.

3. **Relationships:** The net force on the monkey is zero.

4. **Solution:** Find the *x*- and *y*-components of T_2 by graphing the force. Using the graph, you find that the components are (63, 90).
Now that you know the components of two of the forces, find the third force:
$(63, 90) + (0, -135) + (x, y) = 0$
(x, y) for $T_1 = (-63, 45)$
Plot the *x*-and *y*-components for T_1. Draw the vector to find a force of 77 N.

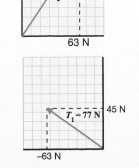

Your turn:

a. In the example, suppose $T_2 = 125$ N, but everything else is the same. What is T_1 in newtons?

(Answers are listed at the end of this chapter.)

The force from a spring

Uses for springs   Springs are used in many devices to keep objects in equilibrium or cause acceleration. Toasters use springs to pop up the toast, cars use springs in their suspension system, and retractable pens use springs to move the pen's tip. Springs can also be used to store energy. When you push the handle down on a toaster, potential energy is stored in the spring. Releasing the spring causes the potential energy to convert into kinetic energy as the toast pops up.

Stretching and compressing a spring   The most common type of spring is a coil of metal or plastic that creates a force when you stretch it or compress it. The force created by stretching or compressing a spring always acts to return the spring to its natural length. When you stretch a spring, it *pulls* back on your hand as the spring tries to return to its original length. When you compress a spring and make it shorter, it *pushes* on your hand as it tries to return to its original length.

Newton's third law   Newton's third law explains why a spring's force acts opposite to the direction it is stretched or compressed. The top spring in Figure 5.12 stretches when you apply a force to the right. The force of your hand on the spring is the action force. The spring applies a reaction force to the left on your hand. The force of "hand on spring" is equal and opposite to the force of "spring on hand." The bottom picture in Figure 5.12 shows what happens when the spring is compressed. You must exert an action force to the left to compress the spring. The spring exerts a reaction force to the right against your hand. As with compressing, the spring's force tries to return it to its original length.

Normal force and springs   How does a table "know" how much normal force to supply to keep a book at rest? A table cannot solve physics problems! The answer is that the normal force exerted by a surface is very similar to the force exerted by a spring in compression (Figure 5.13). When a book sits on a table, it exerts a downward contact force that compresses the table's top by a tiny amount. The tabletop exerts an upward force on the book and tries to return to its natural thickness. The matter in the table acts like a collection of very stiff compressed springs. The amount of compression is so small you cannot see it, but it can be measured with sensitive instruments.

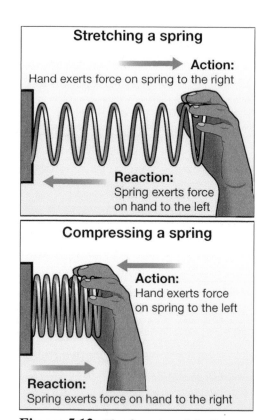

Figure 5.12: *The direction of the force exerted by the spring is opposite to the direction of the force exerted by the person.*

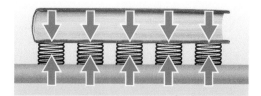

Figure 5.13: *The normal force exerted by a surface is similar to the force exerted by a compressed spring.*

Hooke's law

Hooke's law **Hooke's law** states that the force exerted by a spring is proportional to its change in length. For example, suppose a spring exerts a force of 5 newtons when it is stretched 2 centimeters. If you stretch that spring 4 centimeters, it will exert a force of 10 newtons. Doubling the extension doubles the force.

Spring constant Some springs exert small forces and are easy to stretch. Other springs exert strong forces and are hard to stretch. The relationship between the force exerted by a spring and its change in length is called the **spring constant**. A large spring constant means the spring is hard to stretch or compress and exerts strong forces when its length changes. A spring with a small spring constant is easy to stretch or compress and exerts weak forces. The springs in automobile shock absorbers are stiff because they have a large spring constant. A retractable pen's spring has a small spring constant.

Hooke's law equation Hooke's law equation is stated in Figure 5.14. The force exerted by a spring is directly related to the spring constant multiplied by the displacement of the spring. There is a negative sign on the right-hand side of the equation because the force of the spring always acts in a direction opposite to the displacement. For example, when you stretch a spring to the right, it exerts a force to the left.

> **Hooke's law** - states that the force exerted by a spring is proportional to its change in length
>
> **spring constant** - a constant that represents the relationship between the force exerted by a spring and its change in length

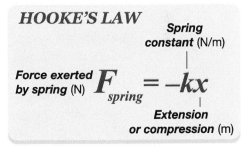

HOOKE'S LAW

Force exerted by spring (N) — $F_{spring} = -kx$ — Spring constant (N/m), Extension or compression (m)

Figure 5.14: *Hooke's law equation.*

 Using Hooke's law

A man weighing 600 N steps on a bathroom scale that uses a heavy spring to measure weight. The spring is compressed 1.0 cm by his weight. What is the spring constant for the scale's spring in N/m?

1. *Looking for:* You are asked for the spring constant in N/m.

2. *Given:* You are given the force exerted on the spring in newtons and its displacement in cm.

3. *Relationships:* $1 \, \text{cm} = 0.01 \, \text{m}$; $k = \dfrac{F}{x}$

4. *Solution:* $k = \dfrac{600 \, \text{N}}{0.01 \, \text{m}} = 60,000 \, \text{N/m}$ The negative sign can be ignored here since it just shows that the force exerted by the spring is opposite to the displacement

Your Turn:

a. What is the force exerted by a spring with a spring constant of 8.5 N/m that is stretched 0.45 m?

(Answers are listed at the end of the chapter.)

Spring scales

Spring scales The relationship between force and change in length is used in scales (Figure 5.15). When a hanging scale weighs an object, the distance the spring stretches is proportional to the object's weight. An object that is twice as heavy changes the spring's length twice as much. The scale is calibrated using an object of a known weight. The force amounts are then marked on the scale at intervals. A bathroom scale works like this, too, but uses a spring that is compressed. The greater the weight, the more the spring compresses.

Truck scales Have you ever seen a weigh station on the side of a highway? Most states collect taxes on the weight of transported goods. A weigh station serves as a checkpoint to keep everyone honest about the declared weight of shipments. Another purpose of a weigh station is to monitor trucks to make sure their weight doesn't exceed safety limits set by the federal and state governments. A truck scale does not use a spring like hanging scales or a bathroom scale. Trucks are much too heavy for scales that use springs to measure weight forces. Most truck scales have electrical wires embedded in steel or concrete. When the truck drives onto the scale, the electrical wire or *strain gauge* is compressed or changed. That change alters the resistance of the wire. The amount of change is converted to a weight. The heavier the truck, the more change in resistance the wire experiences.

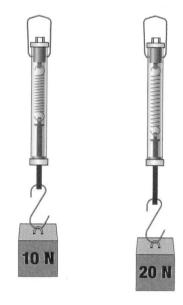

Figure 5.15: *A hanging scale uses a spring to measure weight.*

5.2 Section Review

1. What is true about the net force acting on an object in equilibrium? What is true about the acceleration of an object in equilibrium?
2. Study Figure 5.9. Suppose the person pulling to the left only exerts 50 N of force, while everything else stays the same. What would be the x- and y-components of the third force, if the forces on the polar bear are to keep it in equilibrium?
3. What is a *normal force*, and why is it called that?
4. How does Newton's third law explain the existence of normal forces?
5. The spring in a scale stretches 1 centimeter when a 5-newton object hangs from it. How much does an object weigh if it stretches the spring 2 centimeters?

5.3 Friction

Friction forces are constantly acting on you and the objects around you. When you are riding a bicycle and just coasting along, friction is what finally slows you down. But did you know that friction also helps you to speed up? Tires need friction to push against the road and create the reaction forces that move you forward. In this section, you will learn about different types of friction, the cause of friction, and how it affects the motion of objects.

What is friction?

friction - a force that results from relative motion between objects

sliding friction - resistance created when two surfaces slide across one another

static friction - a type of friction that keeps two surfaces from sliding across each other

What is friction?   **Friction** is a force that results from relative motion between objects. Friction *resists* the motion of objects or surfaces. For example, friction exists between the bottom of a cardboard box and the floor it slides across. Because friction exists in many different situations, it is classified into several types (Figure 5.16). This section will focus on sliding friction and static friction. **Sliding friction** is present when two objects or surfaces slide across each other. **Static friction** exists when forces are acting to cause an object to move but friction is keeping the object from moving.

The cause of friction   If you look at an object through a powerful microscope, you will see microscopic hills and valleys on its surface. As surfaces slide across each other, the hills and valleys grind against each other and cause friction. Contact between the surfaces can cause the tiny bumps to change shape or wear away. If you rub sandpaper on a piece of wood, friction affects the wood's surface by wearing away bumps or changing its shape.

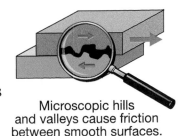

Microscopic hills and valleys cause friction between smooth surfaces.

Two surfaces are involved   Friction depends on *both* of the surfaces in contact. The force of friction on a rubber hockey puck is very small when it is sliding on ice. But the same hockey puck sliding on a piece of sandpaper is opposed by a large friction force. When the hockey puck slides on ice, a thin layer of water between the rubber and the ice allows the puck to slide easily. Water and other liquids, such as oil, can greatly reduce the friction between surfaces.

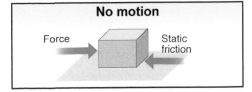

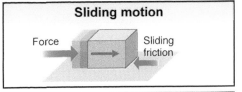

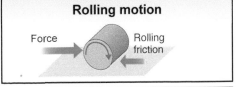

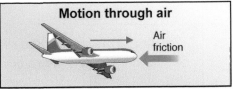

Figure 5.16: *There are many types of friction.*

Identifying friction forces

Direction of the friction force Friction is a force, measured in newtons just like any other force. You draw the force of friction as another arrow on a free-body diagram. To find the direction of the friction force, remember that friction is a *resistive* force. The force of friction acting *on* a surface always points *opposite* to the direction of motion *of that surface*. Imagine pushing a heavy box across the floor (Figure 5.17). If you push to the right, the sliding friction acts to the left on the surface of the box touching the floor. If you push the box to the left, the force of sliding friction acts to the right. This is what it means to say that friction resists motion.

Static friction Static friction acts to keep an object at rest from starting to move. Think about trying to push a heavy box with too small a force. The box stays at rest, so the net force is zero. That means the force of static friction is equal and opposite to the force you apply. As you increase the strength of your push, the static friction also increases, so the box stays at rest. Eventually your force becomes stronger than the maximum possible static friction force and the box starts to move (Figure 5.18). The force of static friction is equal and opposite to your applied force up to a limit. The limit depends on details such as the types of surface.

Sliding friction Sliding friction is a force that resists the motion of an object already moving. If you were to stop pushing a moving box, sliding friction would slow the box to a stop. To keep a box moving at constant speed you must push with a force equal to the force of sliding friction (Figure 5.17). This is because motion at constant speed means zero acceleration and therefore zero net force. Pushing a box across the floor at a constant speed is actually another example of *equilibrium*. In this case, the equilibrium is created because the force you apply cancels the force of sliding friction.

Comparing static and sliding friction How does sliding friction compare with the static friction? If you have ever tried to move a heavy sofa or refrigerator, you probably know the answer. It is harder to get something moving than it is to keep it moving. The reason is that static friction is greater than sliding friction for almost all combinations of surfaces.

Pushing a box

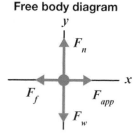

Free body diagram

Figure 5.17: *The direction of friction is opposite to the force applied to move the box.*

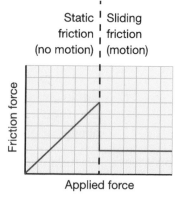

Figure 5.18: *How the friction forces on the box change with the applied force.*

A model for friction

Different amounts of friction The magnitude of the friction force that exists when a box is pushed across a smooth floor is very different from when it is pushed across a carpeted floor. Every combination of surfaces produces a unique amount of friction force. The force of friction depends on types of materials, degrees of roughness, presence of dirt or oil, and other factors. Even the friction between two identical surfaces changes as the surfaces are polished by sliding across each other. No one model or formula can accurately describe the many processes that create friction. Even so, some simple approximations are useful.

An example Suppose you pull a piece of paper across a table (Figure 5.19). To pull the paper at a constant speed, the force you apply must be equal in strength to the sliding friction. It is easy to pull the paper across the top of the table because the friction force is so small; the paper slides smoothly. Do you believe the friction force between the paper and the table is a value that cannot be changed? How could you test this?

Friction and the force between surfaces Suppose you place a brick on the piece of paper. The paper becomes much harder to slide. You must exert a greater force to keep the paper moving. The two surfaces in contact are still the paper and the tabletop, so why does the brick have an effect? The brick causes the paper to press harder into the table's surface. The tiny hills and valleys in the paper and in the tabletop are pressed together with a much greater force, so the friction increases.

The greater the force squeezing two surfaces together, the greater the friction force.

The friction force between two surfaces is proportional to the force the surfaces exert on each other. The greater the force squeezing the two surfaces together, the greater the friction force. This is why it is hard to slide a heavy box across a floor. The force between the bottom of the box and the floor is the weight of the box. Therefore, the force of friction is also proportional to the weight of the box. If the weight doubles, the force of friction also doubles. Friction is present between all sliding surfaces. Figure 5.20 shows the pairs of opposing forces for the brick-paper-table experiment.

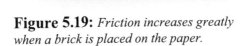

It takes very little force to slide paper across a table.

Adding a brick on top of the paper greatly increases the friction force.

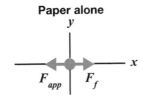

Figure 5.19: *Friction increases greatly when a brick is placed on the paper.*

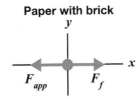

Figure 5.20: *Forces for the paper and paper-brick examples.*

Reducing the force of friction

All surfaces experience some friction
Any motion where surfaces move across each other or through air or water always creates some friction. Unless a force is applied continually, friction will slow all motion to a stop eventually. For example, bicycles have low friction, but even the best bicycle slows down if you coast on a level road. Friction cannot be eliminated, but it can be reduced.

Lubricants reduce friction in machines
Keeping a fluid such as oil between two sliding surfaces keeps them from touching each other. The tiny hills and valleys don't become locked together, nor do they wear each other away during motion. The force of friction is greatly reduced, and surfaces do not wear out as fast. A fluid used to reduce friction is called a **lubricant**. You add oil to a car engine so that the pistons will slide back and forth with less friction. Even water can be used as a lubricant under conditions where there is not too much heat. Powdered graphite is a common lubricant for locks. Spraying powdered graphite into a lock helps a key move more easily.

Ball bearings
In systems where there are rotating objects, ball bearings are used to reduce friction. Ball bearings change sliding motion into rolling motion, which has much less friction. For example, a metal shaft rotating in a socket generates a great amount of friction. Ball bearings that go between the shaft and the inside surface of the socket allow it to spin more easily. The shaft rolls on the bearings instead of rubbing against the walls of the socket. Well-oiled bearings rotate easily and greatly reduce friction (Figure 5.21).

Magnetic levitation
Another method of reducing friction is to separate the two surfaces with a cushion of air. A hovercraft floats on a cushion of air created by a large fan. Magnetic forces can also be used to separate surfaces. A magnetically levitated (or "maglev") train uses electromagnets to float on the track once the train is moving (Figure 5.22). Because there is no contact between the train and its track, there is far less friction than with standard train wheels on steel tracks. The ride is smoother, which allows faster speeds. Maglev trains are not widely used yet because they are much more expensive to build than regular trains. Maglev trains may become popular in the future, however.

lubricant - a fluid used to reduce friction

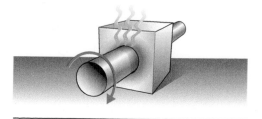

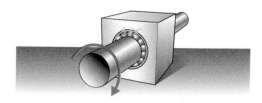

Figure 5.21: *The friction between a shaft and its housing produces a lot of heat. Friction can be reduced by adding ball bearings, which will reduce the heat.*

Figure 5.22: *With a maglev train, there is no contact between the moving train and the rail—and thus little friction.*

Using friction

Friction is useful for brakes and tires
There are many applications where friction is both useful and necessary. For example, the brakes on some bicycles create friction between two rubber brake pads and the rim of the wheel. Friction between the brake pads and the rim slows the bicycle. Friction is also necessary to make a bicycle go. Without friction, the bicycle's tires would not grip the road.

Weather condition tires
Rain and snow act like lubricants to separate tires from the road. As a tire rolls over a wet road, the rubber squeezes the water out of the way so that there can be good contact between rubber and road surface. Additionally, tire treads have grooves that allow space for water to be channeled away from where the tire touches the road (Figure 5.23). Special irregular groove patterns, along with tiny slits, have been used on snow tires to increase traction in snow. These tires keep snow from getting packed into the treads. The design also allows the tire to change shape slightly to grip the uneven surface of a snow-covered road.

Nails
Friction is the force that keeps nails in place (Figure 5.24). The material the nail is hammered into, such as wood, pushes against the nail from all sides. Each hit of the hammer drives the nail deeper into the wood, increasing the length of the nail being compressed. The strong compression force creates a large static friction force that holds the nail in place.

Cleated shoes
Shoes are designed to increase the friction between their soles and the ground. Many types of athletes, including football and soccer players, wear shoes with cleats that increase friction. Cleats are projections like teeth on the bottom of the shoe that dig into the ground for extra traction.

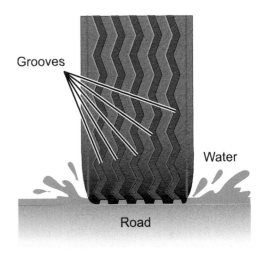

Figure 5.23: *Grooved tire treads allow water to be channeled away from the road-tire contact surface, allowing for more friction in wet conditions.*

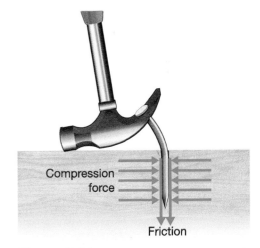

Figure 5.24: *Friction is what makes nails hard to pull out and gives them the strength to hold things together.*

5.3 *Section Review*

1. Explain the causes of sliding friction and static friction.
2. What do you know about the friction force on an object pulled at a constant speed?
3. What factors affect the friction force between two surfaces?
4. Give an example of friction that is useful and one that is not useful. Use examples not mentioned in the book.

5.4 Torque and Rotational Equilibrium

A canoe is gliding between two docks. On each dock is a person with a rope attached to either end of the canoe. Both people pull with equal and opposite forces of 100 newtons so that the net force on the canoe is zero. What happens to the canoe? It is *not* in equilibrium even though the net force is zero. The canoe rotates around its center! The canoe rotates because it is *not* in *rotational* equilibrium even though it *is* in *force* equilibrium. In this section, you will learn about torque and rotational equilibrium.

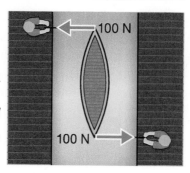

torque - a measure of how much a force acting on an object causes the object to rotate

axis of rotation - the point or line around which an object rotates

line of action - an imaginary line in the direction of the force and passing through the point where the force is applied

What is torque?

Torque and force   **Torque** is a measure of how much a force acting on an object causes the object to rotate. Torque causes objects to *rotate* or spin. Torque is the rotational equivalent of force. If force is a push or pull, you should think of torque as a twist.

The axis of rotation   The line about which an object turns is its **axis of rotation.** Some objects have a fixed axis: A door's axis is fixed at the hinges. A wheel on a bicycle is fixed at the axle in its center. Other objects do not have a fixed axis. The axis of rotation of a tumbling gymnast depends on her body position.

The line of action   Torque is created whenever the **line of action** of a force *does not* pass through the axis of rotation. The line of action is an imaginary line in the direction of the force and passing through the point where the force is applied. If the line of action passes through the axis, the torque is *zero*, no matter how strong the force is.

Creating torque   A force creates more torque when its line of action is far from an object's axis of rotation. Doorknobs are positioned far from the hinges to provide the greatest amount of torque (Figure 5.25). A force applied to the knob will easily open a door because the line of action of the force is the width of the door away from the hinges. The same force applied to the hinge side of the door does nothing because the line of action passes through the axis of rotation. The first force creates torque while the second does not.

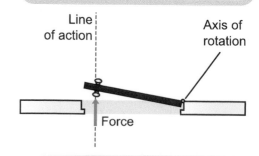

Figure 5.25: *A door rotates around its hinges and a force creates the greatest torque when the force is applied far from the hinges.*

The torque created by a force

Calculating torque   The torque created by a force depends on the strength of the force and also on the **lever arm**. The lever arm is the perpendicular distance between the line of action of the force and the axis of rotation (Figure 5.26). Torque is calculated by multiplying the force by the length of the lever arm. The Greek letter "tao" (τ) is used to represent torque; the lever arm is represented with a lower-case *r* from the word *radius*; and force, remember, is an uppercase *F*.

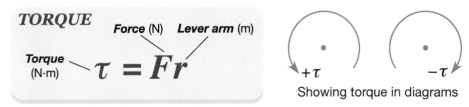

Showing torque in diagrams

Direction of torque   The direction of torque is often drawn with a circular arrow showing how the object would rotate. The words *clockwise* and *counterclockwise* are also used to specify the direction of a torque. Notice that *positive* torque is counterclockwise, and *negative* torque is clockwise.

Units of torque   When force is in newtons and distance is in meters, the torque is measured in newton·meters (N·m). To create 1 newton·meter of torque, you can apply a force of 1 newton to a point 1 meter away from the axis. A force of ½ newton applied 2 meters from the axis creates the *same* torque. Why?

How torque and force differ   Torque is created by force, but it is not the same thing as force. Torque depends on both force *and* distance. Torque (N·m) has different units from force (N). Finally, the same force can produce *any* amount of torque, depending on where and in what direction it is applied (Figure 5.27).

Torque is not work   The newton·meter used for torque is *not* the same as the newton·meter for work, and is *not* equal to a joule. Work is done when a force *moves* an object a distance in the direction of the force. The distance that appears in torque is the distance away from the axis of rotation. The object does *not* move in the direction of the rotation, so no work is done.

> **lever arm** - the perpendicular distance between the line of action of a force and the axis of rotation

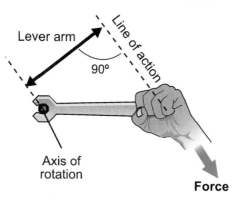

Figure 5.26: *The lever arm is the perpendicular distance between the line of action of the force and the axis of rotation.*

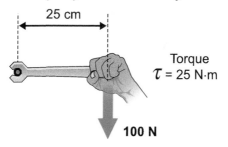

Figure 5.27: *The same force can create different amounts of torque depending on where it is applied and in what direction.*

Solving problems with torque

Reaction torque If you push *up* on a doorknob, you create a torque that tries to rotate the door upward instead of around its hinges. Your force *does* create a torque, but the hinges stop the door from rotating this way. The hinges exert reaction forces on the door that create torques in the direction opposite to the torque you apply. This reaction torque is similar to the normal force created when an object presses down on a surface.

Combining torques If more than one torque acts on an object, the torques are combined to determine the net torque. Calculating net torque is very similar to calculating net force. If the torques tend to make an object spin in the same direction, they are added. If the torques tend to make the object spin in opposite directions (Figure 5.28), the torques are subtracted.

Force **A** makes *negative* (clockwise) torque

Force **B** makes *positive* (counterclockwise) torque

Figure 5.28: *The torques created by force A and force B are opposite in direction.*

 Calculating torque

A force of 50 newtons is applied to a wrench that is 0.30 meters long. Calculate the torque if the force is applied perpendicular to the wrench.

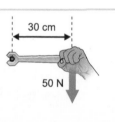

30 cm

50 N

1. **Looking for:** You are asked for the torque.

2. **Given:** You are given the force in newtons and the length of the lever arm in meters.

3. **Relationships:** Use the formula for torque, $\tau = Fr$.

4. **Solution:** $\tau = (0.30 \text{ m})(50 \text{ N}) = 15 \text{ N·m}$

Your Turn:

a. You apply a force of 10 newtons to a doorknob that is 0.8 meters from the edge of the door hinges. If the direction of your force is straight into (perpendicular to) the door, what torque do you create?

b. Calculate the net torque in diagram A.

c. Calculate the net force and the net torque in diagram B.

(Answers are listed at the end of the chapter.)

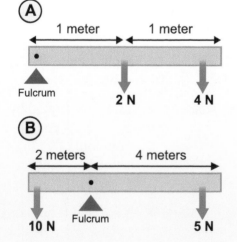

Rotational equilibrium

Rotational equilibrium An object is in **rotational equilibrium** when the net torque applied to it is zero. For example, if an object such as a seesaw is not rotating, you know the torque on each side is balanced (Figure 5.29). An object in rotational equilibrium can also be spinning at constant speed, like the blades on a fan.

Using rotational equilibrium Rotational equilibrium is often used to determine unknown forces. Any object that is not moving must have a net torque of zero *and* a net force of zero. Balances used in schools and scales used in doctors' offices use balanced torques to measure weight. When using such scales, you must slide small masses away from the axis of rotation until the scale balances. Moving the mass increases its lever arm and its torque. Engineers study balanced torques and forces when they design bridges, buildings, and other structures.

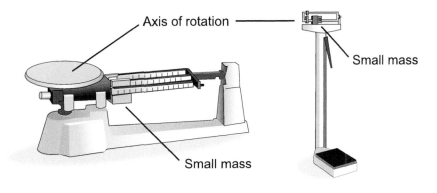

> **rotational equilibrium** - occurs when an object's net torque is zero

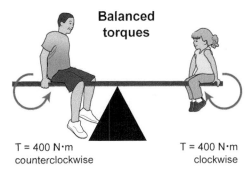

Figure 5.29: *A seesaw is in rotational equilibrium when the two torques are balanced.*

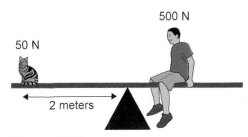

Figure 5.30: *How far must the boy sit from the center of the seesaw in order to balance with the cat?*

5.4 Section Review

1. List two ways in which torque is different from force.
2. In what units is torque measured?
3. Explain how the same force can create different amounts of torque on an object.
4. What is the net torque on an object in rotational equilibrium?
5. A boy and a cat sit on a seesaw as shown in Figure 5.30. Use the information in the picture to calculate the torque created by the cat. Then, calculate the boy's distance from the center of the seesaw.

Chapter 5 **Connection**

Architecture: Forces in Equilibrium

Four thousand years ago, the builders of the Pyramids of Egypt understood how a structure must be designed to remain standing. They used trial-and-error along with back-breaking effort to refine their design, keeping ideas that worked and discarding those that didn't. Some pyramids collapsed during construction, others lasted decades or centuries before failing, and some are still standing—over 80 pyramids remain in Egypt.

Over time, the process of designing buildings has evolved into a hybrid of science, engineering, and art called architecture. Modern buildings can be very complex and intricate. Whether a building is primitive or complex, its structural forces must be in equilibrium if it is to stand the test of time. The Pyramids of Giza have lasted about 5,200 years. How do modern buildings compare to the pyramids?

Most buildings today are not pyramids, but are rectangular with four walls and a roof. Also, few buildings are now constructed entirely of limestone and granite like the pyramids. Even though the shape and construction materials are different, the ultimate goal is the same—creation of a free-standing structure. A basic box-shaped building must have walls that support a roof. But what does "support" mean in terms of forces and equilibrium?

The physics of walls

Upright walls provide a platform for a roof. Walls that carry the weight of the roof are called *load-bearing walls*. This is where Newton's second law applies—force equals mass times acceleration ($F = ma$). Gravity pulls down on the mass of the roof, creating a force (weight). Why doesn't the roof accelerate toward the ground because of this force? This is where Newton's third law applies—for every action there is an equal and opposite reaction. If the roof isn't moving down, the load-bearing walls must be pushing back on the roof with a force equal to the weight of the roof. This action-reaction pair is in equilibrium, both forces balancing one another, illustrating Newton's first law: An object at rest remains at rest until acted on by an unbalanced force.

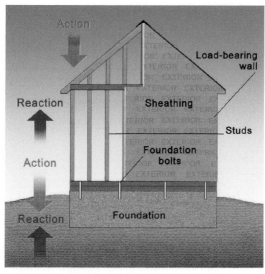

The Leaning Tower of Pisa

The foundation

The weight of the walls and roof combined pushes down on the foundation. Just like the action-reaction force pair of the roof and wall, the wall-roof structure and the foundation create another action-reaction pair. If the foundation can't provide an equal and opposite reaction, the building will not be in equilibrium. This is the case with the Leaning Tower of Pisa.

The tower began leaning even before construction was finished. The soft soil under the tower began to compress, indicating that the foundation was not large enough to provide a force equal to the tower's weight. The soil on one side compressed more than the other, causing the tower to lean to the northeast. Towers need to be built with very stable and solid foundations. New York City is an island with a thick layer of stable bedrock just below the topsoil, making it an ideal place for skyscrapers.

The roof

The roof is one of the most important design features of a building. While its major function is to protect the building's interior from outside elements, it also contributes to the beauty of the structure. Therefore, the design of the roof must be a balance of form and function. And, it must not be too heavy for the walls and foundation to support it. One of the most famous roofs in the world is the dome that tops the church of Santa Maria del Fiore in Florence, Italy. Called the Duomo, this roof seems to defy the laws of physics.

Fillippo Brunelleschi (1377-1446), an accomplished goldsmith and sculptor, travelled to Rome for a two-year study of ancient Roman architecture with fellow artist and friend Donatello. The Pantheon, an amazing dome finished in 126 CE was of particular interest to Brunelleschi.

Upon his return to Florence, he finished a design for his dome in 1402, but kept it secret. He claimed he would build a self-supporting dome without the use of scaffolding—an outlandish assertion many deemed impossible. Yet, even without explaining how he would accomplish the feat, construction began.

Brunelleschi knew that large domes tended to sag in the middle, lowering the roof and creating huge forces that pushed outward on the supporting base. He used an ingenious double-walled design, one to be seen from inside the church and another on the outside. He also used intricate herringbone patterns of brickwork and huge timbers linked together with metal fasteners around the dome to balance the forces like hoops on a barrel. This design was so innovative and beautiful it is said to have inspired many of the Renaissance's greatest artists including Leonardo da Vinci and fellow Florentine artist Michelangelo.

The Duomo - Florence, Italy

QUESTIONS

1. What are the action-reaction pairs in a typical building?
2. Why is New York City an ideal place for skyscrapers?
3. Explain the elements of Brunelleschi's dome design that keeps the Duomo standing in Florence, Italy.

Chapter 5 Review

Understanding Vocabulary

Select the correct term to complete the sentences.

axis of rotation	line of action	scalar
components	lubricant	sliding friction
equilibrium	magnitude	spring constant
free-body diagram	normal force	static friction
friction	resultant	torque
Hooke's law	rotational equilibrium	vector
lever arm		

1. The expression of a person's age as 15 years is an example of a(n) _____ quantity.

2. The sum of the squares of the two _____ of a force vector equals the square of the force vector.

Use the illustration below to answer questions 3–6:

3. The illustration of forces acting on an automobile is an example of a(n) _____ diagram.

4. Because the automobile in the illustration is not accelerating, the four forces acting on it are in _____.

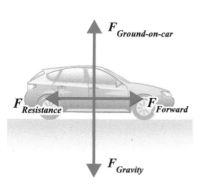

5. The force labeled $F_{Ground\text{-}on\text{-}car}$ could be labeled F_n and called the _____ force.

6. The _____ of the four forces in the illustration is zero.

7. If a carton is pushed at a constant speed along a level floor, the force directly opposing the motion is _____ friction.

8. The pin in a hinge on a door represents the _____ of the door.

9. A balanced see-saw and a bicycle wheel spinning at a constant speed are examples of _____.

Reviewing Concepts

Section 5.1

1. Give two examples of vector quantities and two examples of scalar quantities.

2. List the three different ways in which a force vector can be described.

3. Explain how to find the components of a vector.

4. Explain the Pythagorean theorem using an equation and a picture.

5. A 200-N television sits on a table. Draw a free-body diagram showing the two forces acting on the television.

Section 5.2

6. What is the net force on an object in equilibrium?

7. What is the mathematical meaning of the word *normal*?

8. As you sit on a chair, gravity exerts a downward force on you.
   a. What other force acts on you?
   b. What is the direction of this other force?
   c. What do you know about the magnitude or strength of this other force?

9. If an object is in equilibrium, the forces in the x direction must add to _____, and the forces in the y direction must add to _____.

10. You pull one end of a spring to the right.
    a. What is the action force?
    b. What is the reaction force?
    c. How do the *directions* of the two forces compare?
    d. How do the *strengths* of the two forces compare?

11. What happens to a spring's force as you stretch it?

12. What do you know about a spring if it has a large spring constant?

Section 5.3

13. List four types of friction.

14. In which direction does friction act?

15. What is the difference between static friction and sliding friction?

16. What causes friction?

17. Why is it easier to slide a cardboard box when it is empty compared to when it is full?

18. Explain two ways friction can be reduced.

19. Is friction something we always want to reduce? Explain.

Section 5.4

20. How are torque and force similar? How are they different?

21. Which two quantities determine the torque on an object?

22. In what units is torque measured? Do these units have the same meaning as they do when measuring work? Explain.

23. Why is it easier to loosen a bolt with a long-handled wrench than with a short-handled one?

24. In which of the following cases would a force cause the greatest torque on the shovel? Why?

    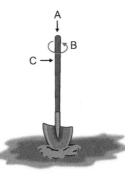

    a. You press straight down on the shovel so it stays straight up and down.

    b. You twist the shovel like a screwdriver.

    c. You push to the right on the shovel's handle so it tilts toward the ground.

25. What does it mean to say an object is in rotational equilibrium?

Solving Problems

Section 5.1

1. Use a ruler to draw each of the following vectors with a scale of 1 cm = 1 N.

   a. (5 N, 0°)

   b. (7 N, 45°)

   c. (3 N, 90°)

   d. (6 N, 30°)

2. Use a ruler to draw each of the following vectors. State the scale you use for each.

   a. (40 N, 0°)

   b. (20 N, 60°)

   c. (100 N, 75°)

   d. (500 N, 90°)

3. Use a scaled drawing to find the components of each of the following vectors. State the scale you use for each.

   a. (5 N, 45°)

   b. (8 N, 30°)

   c. (8 N, 60°)

   d. (100 N, 20°)

Section 5.2

4. Find the net force on each box.

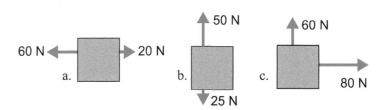

5. A 20-kg monkey hangs from a tree limb by both arms. Draw a free-body diagram showing the forces on the monkey. (*Hint*: Twenty kilograms is not a force!)

6. An 80-lb bag of cement is contained in a 5-lb bucket supported by a rope. Draw a free-body diagram to represent all the forces applied to the bucket. What is the tension in the rope?

7. A spring has a spring constant of 100 N/m. What force does the spring exert on you if you stretch it 0.5 m?

8. If you stretch a spring 3 cm, it exerts a force of 50 N on your hand. What force will it exert if you stretch it 6 cm?

Section 5.3

9. Your backpack weighs 50 N. You pull it across a table at a constant speed by exerting a force of 20 N to the right. Draw a free-body diagram showing all of the forces on it. State the strength of each.

10. You exert a 50-N force to the right on a 300-N box but it does not move. Draw a free-body diagram for the box. Label all the forces and state their strengths.

Section 5.4

11. You push down on a lever with a force of 30 newtons at a distance of 2 m from its fulcrum. What is the torque on the lever?

12. You use a wrench to loosen a bolt. It finally turns when you apply 300 N of force at a distance of 0.2 m from the center of the bolt. What torque did you apply?

13. A rusty bolt requires 200 N·m of torque to loosen it. If you can exert a maximum force of 400 N, how long a wrench do you need?

14. Calculate the net torque on the see-saw.

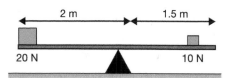

15. You and your cousin sit on a seesaw. You sit 0.5 m from the fulcrum, and your cousin sits 1.5 m from the fulcrum. You weigh 600 N. How much does she weigh?

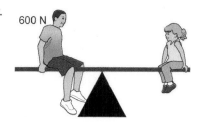

Test Practice

Section 5.1

1. An example of a vector quantity is
   a. speed.
   b. time.
   c. distance.
   d. force.

2. A force vector of 10 N is represented on a scale drawing by an arrow 5 cm in length. If the x-component is represented by an arrow 3 cm in length, the y-component of the force is
   a. 2 N.
   b. 4 N.
   c. 6 N.
   d. 8 N.

3. A worker slides a 50-N object to the right at constant speed across a horizontal surface using a force of 200 N. Which free-body diagram best represents the forces acting on the object?

a. 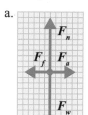   b. 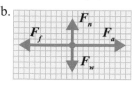   c.   d.

Section 5.2

4. The diagram represents two forces acting at point P.

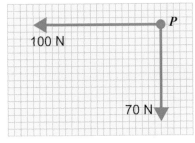

Which choice would create a condition of equilibrium with the forces shown?

a.  120 N

b.  120 N

c. 120 N

d. 120 N

5. Which pair of forces acting on the same point could produce a resultant of 10 N?

   a. 10 N, 10 N

   b. 10 N, 30 N

   c. 4.7 N, 4.7 N

   d. 4.7 N, 5 N

6. A force of 18 N is exerted to stretch a spring 0.3 m. The spring constant for this spring is

   a. 0.0167 N/m.

   b. 5.4 N/m.

   c. 6 N/m.

   d. 60 N/m.

Section 5.3

7. The force exerted on you by the floor as you stand in place is the

   a. gravitational force.

   b. mass.

   c. normal force.

   d. weight.

8. Block A is pulled at a constant velocity up an incline as shown. Toward which point will the force of friction be directed?

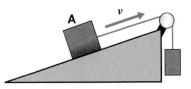

a.   b.   c.   d.

9. Which type of friction is most closely associated with a lack of motion?

   a. sliding friction

   b. air friction

   c. static friction

   d. rolling friction

10. To overcome sliding friction and keep an object sliding on a level surface, a 100-N force is used. The magnitude of the force needed to start the object sliding

    a. is less than 100 N.

    b. equals 100 N.

    c. is more than 100 N.

    d. cannot be calculated with the information given.

Section 5.4

11. The diagram on the right shows two forces applied to a lever. The net torque applied to the lever is

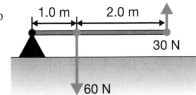

    a. +30 N·m.

    b. +60 N·m.

    c. −60 N·m.

    d. 0 N·m.

Applying Your Knowledge

Section 5.1

1. Is it possible to arrange three forces of 100 N, 200 N, and 300 N so they are in equilibrium? If so, draw a diagram.

2. Draw the forces acting on a ladder leaning against a building. Assume you are standing half-way up the ladder.

Section 5.2

3. Civil engineers analyze forces in equilibrium when they design bridges. Research a well-known bridge. Some of the questions you might want to answer are listed here.

   a. Who designed the bridge?

   b. How long did it take to build?

   c. Which type of bridge is it?

   d. How much weight was it designed to hold?

   e. What makes this bridge special?

Section 5.3

4. Many cars today have antilock brakes that help prevent them from skidding. Research how antilock brakes work.

Section 5.4

5. Can an object be in rotational equilibrium but not have a net force of zero? Can an object have a net force of zero but not be in rotational equilibrium? Explain your answers using diagrams.

   Your Turn **Answers**

Finding force components (Section 5.1, page 109)

a. 86.6 N

b. 122 N

Solving equilibrium problems (Section 5.2, page 113)

a. (x, y) for T_2 = (72, 102) N. That means T_1 = (−72, 33) N. Graphing T_1 gives a force of 79 N.

Using Hooke's law (Section 5.2, page 115)

a. −3.8 N (The negative sign means the spring exerts a force opposite to the displacement of the spring.)

Calculating torque (Section 5.4, page 124)

a. 8 N·m

b. 10 N·m

c. 5 N and 0 N·m

Systems in Motion

There is a recurring theme in cartoon film clips. One character is racing toward another, perhaps to cause some harm. The other character turns a road sign the wrong way, sending the chaser over a cliff. What happens next in the cartoon sequence? The chaser runs off the cliff, keeps running straight out over the canyon until it sees that there is no ground directly below, and at that moment, the chaser begins falling. Perhaps the character holds up a "help" sign before hitting the canyon floor and sending up a dust cloud.

The cartoon gag provides lots of laughs, but the physics is all wrong! Do you know what the correct path of the cartoon character would be when it runs off a cliff? Projectiles, bicycle wheels, planets in orbit, and satellites are just some of the interesting systems of motion you will study in this chapter. By the way, the true path of the unfortunate cartoon character is a curve, and the name given to this curved path is *trajectory*. The only thing more miraculous than defying physics during the fall is that the cartoon character survives every incredible disaster, only to return to the screen more determined than ever!

KEY QUESTIONS

✓ *How should you hit a golf ball so it goes as far as possible?*

✓ *Why does a skater spin faster when she pulls her arms in toward her body?*

✓ *Why do you move to the outside edge of the car seat when the car makes a sharp turn?*

✓ *How do satellites move around Earth without crashing into it?*

VOCABULARY

angular speed	center of mass	centripetal force
circumference	law of universal gravitation	orbit
projectile		trajectory
center of gravity	revolve	circular motion
gravitational constant	centrifugal force	parabola
range	linear speed	
	satellite	

6.1 Motion in Two Dimensions

Some systems have forces and motions that act in straight lines. Of course, real-life objects do not move in straight lines alone; their motion includes turns and curves. To describe a curve you need at least two dimensions (*x* and *y*). In this chapter, you will learn how to apply the laws of motion to curves. Curves *always* imply acceleration, and we will use *vectors* when we apply the motion laws.

Displacement vector

The displacement vector   Distance is scalar, but *displacement* is a vector. A *displacement vector* shows a change in position. The concept of displacement was introduced in Chapter 2. Displacement is the distance and direction between the starting and ending points of an object's motion. If you walk 5 meters east, your displacement can be represented by a 5-centimeter arrow pointing east (Figure 6.1).

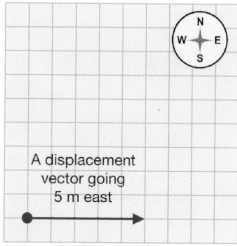

Scale: ⬚ ↕ = 1 meter

Figure 6.1: *A displacement of 5 m east.*

Writing the displacement vector   Displacement is always a vector. Like the force vectors you used in the last chapter, you can describe a displacement vector three ways:

* with a graph,
* as a magnitude-angle pair (also called polar coordinates), or
* as an *x-y* pair.

Telling direction   For example, this graph shows a displacement of 5 meters at 37 degrees. This vector can be abbreviated as a magnitude angle-pair: (5 m, 37°). Angles are measured from the positive *x*-axis in a counterclockwise direction (Figure 6.2).

A displacement vector's direction is often given using words. Directional words include left, right, up, down, and compass direction. Which coordinates you use depends on the problem you are trying to solve. Sometimes, you will make *x* horizontal and *y* vertical. Other times, you will choose *x* to be east and *y* to be north.

A displacement vector of (5 m, 37°)

5 m

37°

Scale: 1 cm = 1 meter

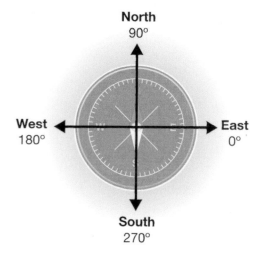

Figure 6.2: *Angles can be used to represent compass directions.*

Solving displacement problems

Displacement vectors for moving objects When an object moves in a straight line, you can tell its position with just one distance. If the motion is curved, it takes at least two distances to indicate where an object is. The motion of a basketball is described by both the x- and y-coordinates of each point along the basketball's path. The basketball's position at any time is represented by its displacement vector (Figure 6.3). To describe the motion of the basketball, we need to describe how the displacement vector changes over time.

Adding displacement vectors Displacement vectors can be added just like force vectors. To add displacements graphically, draw them to scale with each subsequent vector drawn at the end of the previous vector. The *resultant vector* represents the displacement for the entire trip. For most problems, however, it is much easier to find the x- and y-components of a displacement vector. The x-component is the distance in the x direction. The y-component is the distance in the y direction.

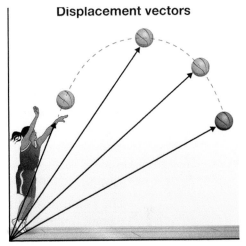

Displacement vectors

Figure 6.3: *When you throw a ball, it follows a curved path. The position of the ball is described by its displacement vector.*

 Adding vectors

A mouse walks 5 meters north and 12 meters west. Use a scaled drawing and a protractor to find the mouse's displacement. Use the Pythagorean theorem to check your work.

1. **Looking for:**	You are asked for the displacement.
2. **Given:**	You are given the distances and directions the mouse walks.
3. **Relationships:**	Pythagorean theorem: $a^2 + b^2 = c^2$
4. **Solution:**	Make a drawing with a scale of 1 cm = 1 meter.

Pythagorean theorem:
$$5^2 + 12^2 = c^2 \qquad 169 = c^2 \qquad 13 = c$$
The mouse's displacement is 13 meters at 157°.

Scale: 1 cm = 1 meter

12 cm

13 cm

5 cm

157°

Your Turn:

a. Your school is 5 kilometers south and 5 kilometers east of your house. Use a scaled drawing and a protractor to find your displacement as you ride from home to school. Then check your answer with the Pythagorean theorem.

b. A helicopter flies straight up for 100 meters and then horizontally for 100 meters. What is the displacement vector of the helicopter relative to where it started? Give your answer in *x-y* form assuming upward is *y*.

(Answers are listed at the end of the chapter.)

The velocity vector

Velocity and force vectors   Velocity is speed with direction, so velocity is a vector. As objects move in curved paths, their velocity vectors change because the direction of motion changes. The symbol $\vec{v}$ is used to represent velocity. The arrow tells you it is the velocity vector, not the speed.

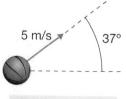

What the velocity vector means   Suppose a ball is launched at 5 m/s at an angle of 37° (Figure 6.4). At the moment after launch, the velocity vector for the ball written as a magnitude-angle pair is $\vec{v}$ = (5 m/s, 37°). In x-y components, the same velocity vector is written as $\vec{v}$ = (4, 3) m/s. Both representations tell you exactly how fast and in what direction the ball is moving at that moment. The x-component tells you how fast the ball is moving in the x-direction. The y-component tells you how fast it is moving in the y-direction.

Speed is the magnitude of the velocity vector   The *magnitude* of the velocity vector is the *speed* of the object. The ball in the example is moving with a speed of 5 m/s. Speed is represented by a lower case v *without* the arrow. When a velocity vector is represented graphically, the length is proportional to speed, not distance. For example, the graph in Figure 6.4 shows the velocity vector $\vec{v}$ = (4, 3) m/s as an arrow on a graph.

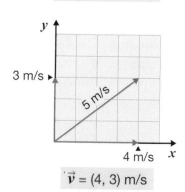

Figure 6.4: *Different ways to write a velocity vector. The length of a velocity vector is proportional to speed.*

 **Using velocity vectors**

A train moves at a speed of 100 km/h heading east. What is its velocity vector in x-y form?

1. *Looking for:*   You are asked for the velocity vector.

2. *Given:*   You are given speed in km/h and direction. The train is moving east.

3. *Relationships:*   x-velocity is east and y-velocity is north

4. *Solution:* $\vec{v}$ = (**100,0**) **km/h**   The y-component is 0 because the train has 0 velocity heading north.

Your Turn:

a. A race car is moving with a velocity vector of (50, 50) m/s. Sketch the velocity vector and calculate the car's velocity. You can use the Pythagorean theorem to check your sketch.

b. A hiker walks 1,000 meters north and 5,000 meters east in 2 hours. Calculate the hiker's velocity vector in x-y form.

(Answers are listed at the end of the chapter.)

Projectile motion

Definition of a projectile   Any object moving through air and affected only by the force of gravity is called a **projectile**. Examples include a ball in the air, a stunt car driven off a cliff, and a skier after going off a ski jump. Flying objects such as airplanes and birds are *not* projectiles, because they are affected by forces generated from their own power and not just the force of gravity.

Trajectories   The path a projectile follows is called its **trajectory**. The trajectory of a projectile is a special type of arch- or bowl-shaped curve called a **parabola**. The **range** of a projectile is the horizontal distance it travels in the air before touching the ground. A projectile's range depends on the speed and angle at which it is launched.

Two-dimensional motion   Projectile motion is two-dimensional because there is both horizontal and vertical motion. Both speed and direction change as a projectile moves through the air. The motion is easiest to understand by thinking about the vertical and horizontal components of motion separately.

Independence of horizontal and vertical motion   A projectile's velocity vector at any one instant has both a horizontal (v_x) and vertical (v_y) component. Separating the velocity into the two components allows us to look at them individually. The horizontal and vertical components of a projectile's velocity are *independent* of each other. The horizontal component does not affect the vertical component and vice versa. The complicated curved-motion problem becomes two separate straight-line problems like the ones you have already solved.

The horizontal and vertical components of a projectile's velocity are independent of each other.

Subscripts   Notice the *x and y* subscripts on the velocity components, v_x and v_y. Subscripts tell you the direction of the motion. Distance and velocity in the *x*-direction are identified by using *x* as a subscript. Distance and velocity in the *y*-direction are identified by using *y* as a subscript. It is important to carefully write the subscripts as you do projectile problems. Otherwise, you will quickly lose track of which velocity is which (Figure 6.5)!

> **projectile** - an object moving through the air and affected only by the force due to gravity
> **trajectory** - the path followed by a projectile
> **parabola** - the curved path a projectile follows
> **range** - the horizontal distance a projectile travels before touching the ground

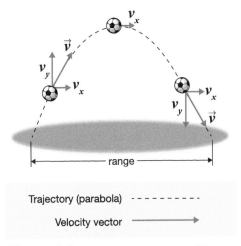

Trajectory (parabola) - - - - - - - -

Velocity vector ———————▶

Figure 6.5: *The velocity vector of the ball has both* x- *and* y-*components that are independent of each other.*

A ball rolling off a table

Constant horizontal velocity A ball rolling off a table is a projectile once it leaves the tabletop. Once the ball becomes a projectile, there is no horizontal force, so its horizontal velocity is *constant*. It moves the same distance horizontally each second. A ball rolling off a table at 5 meters per second moves 5 meters horizontally each second it is in the air (Figure 6.6). The ball's horizontal motion looks exactly like its motion if it were rolling along the ground at 5 m/s.

The horizontal velocity (v_x) is constant.

Figure 6.6: *The projectile's horizontal velocity does not change because no horizontal force acts on it.*

Horizontal and vertical velocities

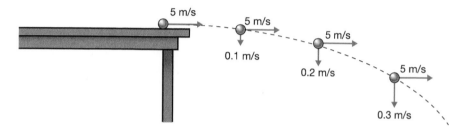

Vertical velocity changes The vertical motion of the ball is more complicated because of gravity. The ball is in *free fall* in the vertical direction. Just like other examples of free fall, the ball's vertical velocity increases by 9.8 m/s each second (Figure 6.7). The diagram shows the velocity vector as the ball falls. The horizontal (x) velocity stays constant. The vertical (y) velocity increases because of the acceleration of gravity. As a result, both the magnitude (velocity) and direction of the velocity vector change.

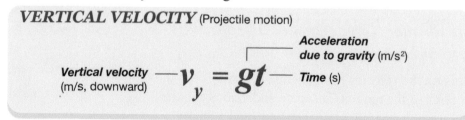

VERTICAL VELOCITY (Projectile motion)

$$v_y = gt$$

Vertical velocity (m/s, downward) — v_y

g = Acceleration due to gravity (m/s²)

t = Time (s)

The ball accelerates by 9.8 m/s each second.

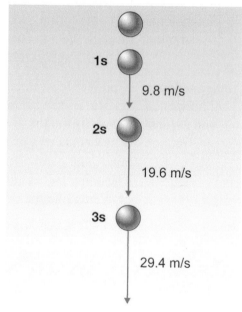

Figure 6.7: *A projectile's vertical velocity increases by 9.8 m/s each second.*

Horizontal and vertical distance

Horizontal distance   The horizontal distance a projectile travels is the horizontal velocity (v_x) multiplied by the time (t). Because the horizontal velocity is constant, the relationship between distance, velocity, and time is the same as you learned in Chapter 1. If you know any two of the variables, you can use the equation below to find the unknown third variable.

HORIZONTAL DISTANCE (Projectile motion)

$$\text{Distance (m)} — d_x = v_x t — \substack{\text{Horizontal velocity (m/s)} \\ \text{Time (s)}}$$

Vertical distance   The vertical distance the ball falls can be calculated using the equation $d = v_{avg}t$, as we did for free fall in Chapter 2. The *average* velocity must be used because the ball's vertical motion is accelerated. A more direct way to find the vertical distance is with the equation $d = \frac{1}{2}at^2$. The vertical acceleration in free fall is 9.8 m/s², so the equation then becomes $d = 4.9\,t^2$. Keep in mind that this equation is only correct on Earth, when the object starts with a vertical velocity of zero (Figure 6.8).

VERTICAL DISTANCE (Projectile motion)

$$\text{Vertical distance (m)}\ d_y = 4.9t^2\ \text{Time (s)}$$

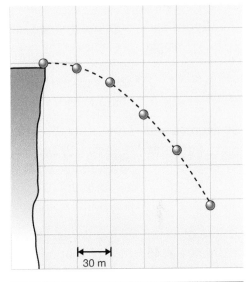

Time (s)	Horizontal position (m)	Vertical drop (m)
0	0	0
1	30	4.9
2	60	19.6
3	90	44.1
4	120	78.4
5	150	122.5

Figure 6.8: *The horizontal and vertical positions of a ball rolling off a cliff at 30 meters per second.*

Caution!   The equations above are suitable *only* for situations where the projectile starts with zero vertical velocity, such as a ball rolling off a table, and taking place here on Earth. If the projectile is launched up or down at an angle, the equations are more complicated. If the projectile is launched anywhere other than on Earth the equations will be different, too.

The range of a projectile

Speed and angle
Suppose you are hitting golf balls and you want the ball to go as far as possible on the course. How should you hit the ball? The two factors you control are the force with which you hit it and the angle at which you hit it. You want the ball to go as fast as possible so it will have as much velocity as possible. But what is the best angle at which to hit the ball?

90 degrees and 0 degrees
Launching the ball straight upward (90°) gives it the greatest air time (Figure 6.9) and height. However, a ball flying straight up does not move horizontally at all and has a range of zero. Launching the ball completely horizontally (0°) makes it roll on the ground. The ball has the greatest horizontal velocity, but it hits the ground immediately, so its range is zero.

The greatest range at 45 degrees
To get the greatest range, you must find a balance between horizontal and vertical motion. The vertical velocity gives the ball its air time, and the horizontal velocity causes it to move down the fairway. The angle that gives the greatest range is 45 degrees, halfway between horizontal and vertical.

Other angles
The more the launch angle differs from 45 degrees, the smaller the range. A ball launched at 30 degrees has the same range as one launched at 60 degrees because both angles are 15 degrees away from 45. The same is true for any pair of angles adding up to 90 degrees—the range will be the same.

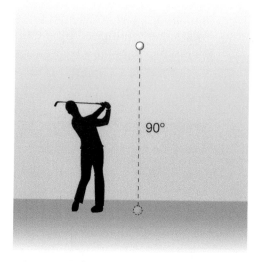

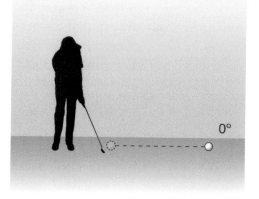

Figure 6.9: *The air time and height are greatest when a ball is hit at an angle of 90 degrees. The air time and height are zero when a ball is hit at an angle of 0 degrees.*

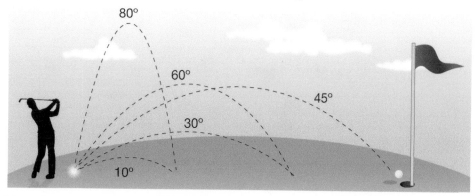

Air resistance
Air resistance can also affect a projectile's range. The trajectory of a projectile is usually not a perfect parabola. The range is less than would be expected, because of air resistance.

Projectile-motion problems

Distinguishing between horizontal and vertical Projectile-motion problems can be tricky because you have to keep track of so many variables. When solving such problems, you should first determine what the problem is asking you to find and whether it is a horizontal or a vertical quantity. Then you can use the right relationship to answer the question. Remember the horizontal velocity is constant and uses the distance equation for constant velocity motion. The vertical velocity changes by 9.8 m/s each second and the vertical motion is the same as in free fall.

   Projectile motion

A stunt driver steers a car off a cliff at a speed of 20.0 m/s. The car lands in a lake below 2.00 s later. Find the horizontal distance the car travels and the height of the cliff (the vertical distance it travels).

1. *Looking for:*   You are asked for the vertical and horizontal distances.

2. *Given:*   You are given the time in seconds and initial horizontal speed in m/s.

3. *Relationships:*   **Horizontal:** $d_x = v_x t$ **Vertical:** $d_y = 4.9t^2$

4. *Solution:*   **Horizontal:** $d_x = (20 \text{ m/s})(2 \text{ s}) = 40 \text{ meters}$

   Vertical: $d_y = (4.9 \text{ m/s}^2)(2 \text{ s})^2 = (4.9 \text{ m/s}^2)(4 \text{ s}^2) = 19.6 \text{ meters}$

Your Turn:

a. Repeat the problem with a time of 3.00 s instead of 2.00 s.

b. You kick a soccer ball, and it travels a horizontal distance of 12 m during the 1.5 s it is in the air. What was the ball's initial horizontal speed?

(Answers are listed at the end of the chapter.)

6.1 Section Review

1. What is the word for the horizontal distance a projectile travels?
2. What does it mean to say a projectile's horizontal and vertical velocity are independent of each other?
3. A football is kicked down a field. Describe what happens to its horizontal and vertical velocities as it moves through the air.
4. What launch angle gives a projectile its greatest range?

6.2 Circular Motion

Circular motion occurs when a force causes an object to move in a circle about a fixed point. The planets orbiting the Sun, a child on a merry-go-round, and a basketball spinning on a fingertip are examples of circular motion.

Describing circular motion

Rotating and revolving A basketball spinning on your fingertip and a child on a merry-go-round both have circular motion. Each moves around its axis of rotation. The basketball's axis runs from your finger up through the center of the ball (Figure 6.10). The axis about which a child is moving is a vertical line in the center of the merry-go-round. While their motions are similar, there is a difference. The ball's axis is *internal* or inside the object. We say an object *rotates* about its axis when the axis is internal. A child on a merry-go-round moves around an axis that is *external* or outside of the child. An object **revolves** when it moves around an external axis.

Angular speed When an object moves in a line, we can measure its linear speed. Recall that linear speed is the distance traveled per unit of time. **Angular speed** is the amount an object in circular motion spins per unit of time. Angular speed can describe either the rate of revolving or the rate of rotating.

> **circular motion** - motion that results when a force causes an object to curve in a full circle
> **revolve** - to move around, or orbit, an external axis
> **angular speed** - the amount an object spins per unit of time in circular motion

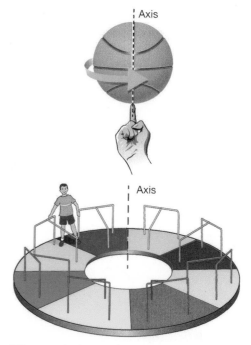

Figure 6.10: *The basketball rotates and the child revolves.*

Linear speed

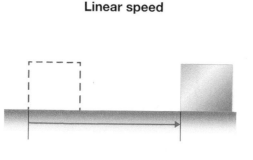

Distance traveled per time

Angular speed

Amount of spin per time

Angular speed

Units of angular speed   The angular speed is the rate at which something in circular motion turns. The rpm, or rotations per minute, is commonly used for angular speed. Another common unit is the angle covered per unit of time. There are 360 degrees in a full rotation, so one rotation per minute is the same angular speed as 360 degrees per minute (Figure 6.11).

Calculating angular speed   To calculate angular speed you divide the number of rotations or the number of degrees an object has rotated by the time taken. For example, if a basketball turns 15 times in three seconds, its angular speed is five rotations per second (15 rotations × 3 s).

Figure 6.11: *One rotation is the same as 360 degrees.*

ANGULAR SPEED

$$Angular\ speed = \frac{rotations\ or\ degrees}{time}$$

 **Calculating angular speed**

A merry-go-round makes 10 rotations in 2 minutes. What is its angular speed in rpm?

1. *Looking for:*   You are asked for the angular speed in rotations per minute.

2. *Given:*   You are given the number of rotations and the time in minutes.

3. *Relationships:* $angular\ speed = \dfrac{rotation\ or\ degrees}{time}$

4. *Solution:* $angular\ speed = \dfrac{10\ rotations}{2\ minutes} = 5\ rpm$

Your Turn:

a. Calculate the angular speed of a bicycle wheel that spins 1,000 times in 5 minutes.

b. A bowling ball rolls at two rotations per second. What is its angular speed in degrees per second?

(Answers are listed at the end of the chapter.)

Relating angular speed, linear speed, and distance

Angular speed is the same

Each point on a rotating object has the same angular speed. Suppose three children sit on a merry-go-round (Figure 6.12). When the merry-go-round rotates once, each child makes one revolution. The time for one revolution is the same for all three children, so their angular speeds are the same.

Distance during a revolution

The **linear speed** of each child is *not* the same because they travel different distances. The distance depends on how far each child is sitting from the center. Dwayne sits near the edge. He moves in the biggest circle and travels the greatest distance during a revolution. Ryan moves in a medium circle and travels a smaller distance. Huong sits exactly in the center of the merry-go-round, so she does not revolve at all. She rotates about the axis in the center.

Linear speed depends on radius

The linear speed of a person on a merry-go-round is the distance traveled around the circle divided by the time. The distance depends on the radius of the circle in which the person moves. Therefore, the linear speed also depends on the radius. Dwayne moves in a circle with the largest radius, so his linear speed is the fastest. Two people sitting at different places on the same merry-go-round always have the same *angular* speed. But a person sitting farther from the center has a faster linear speed.

Circumference

The distance traveled during one revolution equals the **circumference** of the circle. The radius of the circle equals the person's distance from the axis of rotation at the center. A person sitting 2 meters from the center of a merry-go-round travels in a circle with twice the circumference of that of a person sitting 1 meter from the center. The person sitting 2 meters away therefore has twice the linear speed.

> **linear speed** - distance traveled per unit of time
> **circumference** - the distance traveled during one revolution

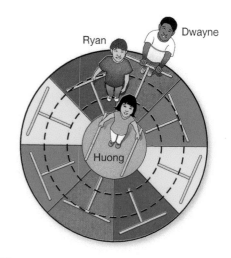

Figure 6.12: *Each child has the same angular speed, but Dwayne has the fastest linear speed, because he travels the greatest distance in the same time as the others.*

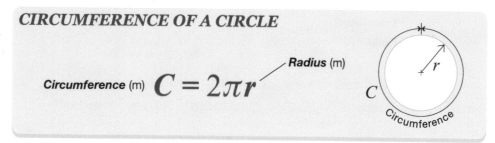

CIRCUMFERENCE OF A CIRCLE

Circumference (m) $C = 2\pi r$ Radius (m)

Solving linear speed problems

Calculating linear speed The linear speed of any point on a rotating object is directly proportional to the distance between the point and the axis of rotation. You can calculate the linear speed of any point if you know the time it takes to make one revolution and its distance from the axis of rotation. If you are given the angular speed, you can determine how much time it takes to make one revolution.

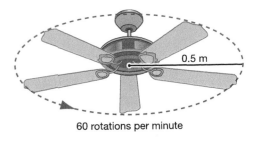

60 rotations per minute

Figure 6.13: *What is the linear speed of the tip of the fan blade?*

LINEAR SPEED (from angular speed)

$$v = \frac{2\pi r}{t}$$

Linear speed (m/s) v

$2\pi r$ Radius (m)

t Time for one revolution (s)

 Calculating linear speed

The blades on a ceiling fan spin at 60 rotations per minute (Figure 6.13). The fan has a radius of 0.5 meters. Calculate the linear speed of a point at the outer edge of a blade in meters per second.

1. *Looking for:*   You are asked for the linear speed in meters per second.

2. *Given:*   You are given the angular speed in rpm and the radius in meters.

3. *Relationships:* $v = \dfrac{2\pi r}{t}$

4. *Solution:*   The blades spin at 60 rotations per minute, so they make 60 rotations in 60 seconds. Therefore it takes 1 second to make one rotation.

$$v = \frac{(2\pi)(0.5 \text{ m})}{1 \text{ s}} \approx 3.14 \text{ m/s}$$

Your Turn:

a. Calculate the linear speed of a point 0.25 meters from the center of the fan in the example.

b. The fan slows to 30 rpm. Calculate the linear speed of a point at the outer edge of a blade and 0.25 meters from the center.

(Answers are listed at the end of the chapter.)

Rolling

Linear and rotational motion

Rolling is a combination of linear motion and rotational motion (Figure 6.14). Linear motion occurs when an entire object moves from one place to another. Holding a bicycle wheel up in the air and moving it to the right is an example of linear motion. Rotational motion occurs when an object spins around an axis that stays in place. If you lift a bicycle's front wheel off the ground and make it spin, the spinning wheel is in rotational motion.

Rolling motion

Rolling is a combination of linear and rotational motion. As a wheel rolls, its axis moves in a line. Look at the motion of the axis in the picture below. As the wheel rolls, its axis moves in a straight line. The linear speed of a bicycle riding on the wheel is equal to the linear speed of the wheel's axis.

Linear distance equals circumference

The distance the bicycle moves depends on the wheel's size and angular speed. When the wheel makes one full rotation, the bicycle goes forward one circumference of the wheel. The point that contacts the ground at the beginning of the rotation travels once around the circle. The linear speed of the bicycle is therefore equal to the distance the point moves around the circle divided by the time taken for the wheel to rotate once.

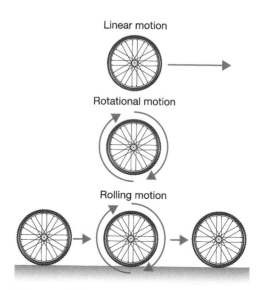

Figure 6.14: *Rolling is a combination of linear and rotational motion.*

A wheel moves forward one circumference in one rotation.

Contact point — Circumference of wheel —

Speedometers

A bicycle speedometer uses a small magnet on the front wheel to measure speed. Before using it, you must enter your wheel's circumference. The speedometer divides the circumference by the time it takes for the magnet to revolve and calculates the speed. It can also measure distance by counting rotations. A car's speedometer works in a similar way. It is programmed for tires of a certain size. If tires of the wrong radius are used, the speed and distance measurements will be inaccurate.

6.2 Section Review

1. Give your own examples of rotating and revolving objects and an object that does both.
2. List two units in which angular speed can be measured.
3. Several US cities have rotating restaurants high atop buildings. Does every person in such a rotating restaurant have the same angular speed and linear speed? Explain.

6.3 Centripetal Force

Force is needed to accelerate an object. We usually think of acceleration as a change in speed, but it can also be a change in direction. An object moving in a circle is constantly changing direction, so a force must act on it. In this section, you will learn how force can create circular motion. You will also learn about the force that keeps planets, moons, and satellites in orbit.

> **centripetal force** - any force that causes an object to move in a circle

Centripetal force

Centripetal force causes circular motion Any force that causes an object to move in a circle is called a **centripetal force**. Even though it is given its own name, centripetal force is not a new type of physical force. Any force can be a centripetal force if its action causes an object to move in a circle. For example, a car can move in a circle because friction provides the centripetal force. The lack of friction on an icy road is what makes it difficult for a car to turn.

The effect of a force depends on direction Whether a force makes an object accelerate by changing its speed or by changing its direction or both depends on the direction of the force (Figure 6.15). A force in the same direction as the motion causes the object to speed up. A force exactly opposite the direction of motion makes the object slow down. A force *perpendicular* to the direction of motion causes the object to change its path from a line to a circle, without changing its speed.

Centripetal force acts toward the center Centripetal force is always directed toward the center of the circle in which an object moves. Imagine tying a ball to the end of a string and twirling it in a circle over your head. The string exerts the centripetal force on the ball to move it in a circle. The direction of the pull is toward your hand at the center of the circle. Notice that the direction of the centripetal force changes as the object moves around you. If the ball is on your right, you pull to the left and vice versa. Centripetal forces change direction so they will always remain pointed toward the center of the circle.

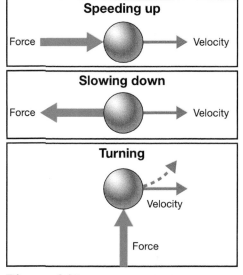

Figure 6.15: *The effect of a force depends on its direction.*

F

Centripetal force, inertia, and velocity

Inertia Why doesn't centripetal force pull a revolving object toward the center of its circle? Inertia is the key to answering this question. Suppose you want to move a ball tied to a string in a circle on the top of a smooth table. You place the ball on the table, straighten out the string, and give it a hard pull along its length. Will the ball move in a circle? No! The ball will simply move straight toward your hand. The ball has a tendency to remain at rest, but the force of the string accelerates it toward your hand in the direction of the roll.

Getting circular motion started Now, suppose you hold the string with your right hand and use your left hand to toss the ball in a direction perpendicular to the string. As soon as the ball starts moving, you pull on the string. This time you can get the ball to move in a circle around your hand.

Centripetal force changes direction Let's examine exactly what is happening (Figure 6.16). If you give the ball an initial velocity to the left at point A, it will try to keep moving straight to the left. But the centripetal force pulls the ball to the side. A short time later, the ball is at point B and its velocity is 90 degrees from what it was. But now the centripetal force pulls to the right. The ball's inertia makes it move straight, but the centripetal force always pulls it towards the center. This process continues, moving the ball in a circle as long as you keep supplying the centripetal force.

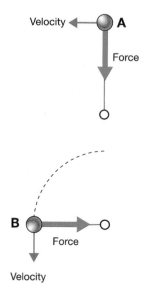

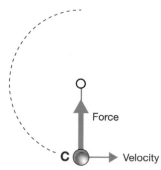

Velocity and force are perpendicular Notice that the velocity is always perpendicular to the string and therefore to the centripetal force. The centripetal force and velocity are perpendicular for any object moving in a circle. What happens if you release the string? Because there is nothing to provide the centripetal force, the ball stops moving in a circle. It moves in a straight line in the direction of the velocity the instant you let go. It moves at a 90-degree angle from the string.

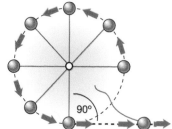

Figure 6.16: *The ball keeps moving in a circle as long as you supply centripetal force.*

Newton's second law and circular motion

Acceleration   An object moving in a circle at a constant speed accelerates because its direction changes. The faster its change in direction, the greater its acceleration. How quickly an object changes direction depends on its speed and the radius of the circle. If an object moves faster, and stays moving in the same circle, its direction changes more quickly and its acceleration is greater. If an object stays at the same speed but the radius of the circle of its motion expands, the change in direction becomes more gradual and the acceleration is reduced. *Centripetal acceleration* increases with speed and decreases as the radius gets larger.

Force, mass, and acceleration   Newton's second law relates force, mass, and acceleration. According to the law, more force is needed to cause a greater acceleration. More force is also needed when changing the motion of an object with a larger mass. Therefore, the strength of the centripetal force needed to move an object in a circle depends on its mass, speed, and the radius of the circle (Figure 6.17).

1. Centripetal force is directly proportional to the mass. A 2-kilogram object needs twice the force to have the same circular motion as a 1-kilogram object.
2. Centripetal force is inversely proportional to the radius of its circle. The smaller the circle's radius, the greater the force. An object moving in a 0.5-meter circle needs twice the force it does when it moves in a 1-meter circle at the same speed.
3. Centripetal force is directly proportional to the *square* of the object's speed. *Doubling* the speed requires *four* times the centripetal force. *Tripling* the speed requires *nine* times the centripetal force.

Driving around bends   The relationship between centripetal force and speed is especially important for automobile drivers to recognize. A car moves in a circle as it turns a corner. The friction between the tires and the road provides the centripetal force that keeps the car following the radius of the turn. This is why high-speed turns on freeways have a larger radius than low-speed turns on city streets. You may have seen signs at highway ramps with sharp curves that warn drivers to reduce their speeds. Friction decreases when a road is wet or icy, and there may not be enough force to keep the car following the turn.

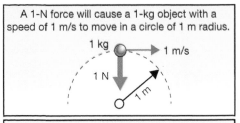

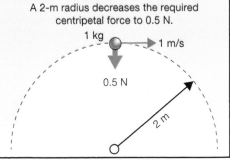

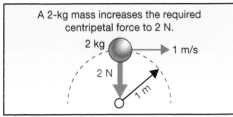

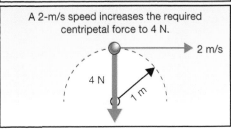

Figure 6.17: *The centripetal force needed to move an object in a circle depends on its mass, speed, and the radius of the circle.*

Inertia and circular motion

A turning car   Have you ever noticed that when a car makes a sharp turn, you are pushed toward the outside edge of the car? If the car turns to the right, you slide to the left. If the car turns to the left, you slide to the right. Although the centripetal force pushes the car toward the center of the circle, it seems as if there is a force pushing *you* to the *outside*. This apparent outward force is called **centrifugal force**. While it feels like there is a force acting on you, *centrifugal force is not a true force*.

Newton's first law   According to Newton's first law, an object in motion tends to keep moving with the same speed and direction. Objects—including you—have inertia and inertia resists changes in motion. When you are in a turning car, what seems like centrifugal force is actually your own inertia. Your body tries to keep moving in a straight line and is pushed toward the outside of the car. The car pushes back on you to force you into the turn, and that is the true *centripetal* force. This is one good reason why you should wear a seat belt!

An example   Figure 6.18 shows a view from above of what happens when a truck turns. Suppose a box is in the center of the bed as the truck travels along a straight road. The box and the truck are both moving in a straight line. If the truck suddenly turns to the left, the box tries to keep moving in that same straight line. While it seems like the box is being thrown to the right side of the truck, the truck is actually turning under the box.

The role of friction   The truck is able to turn because of the friction between the road and the tires. However, the box is not touching the road, so this force does not act on it. There is friction acting on the box from the truck bed, but this force may be small in comparison to the centripetal force if the truck bed is smooth. The box slides to the right until it is stopped by the side of the truck.

A useful example   *Centrifugal* force is an effect of inertia that you feel whenever your body is forced to move in a circle. Although not a force, the centrifugal effect is quite useful and is the basis of the centrifuge. Centrifuges are used to separate mixtures by density. A centrifuge spins a liquid mixture at high speed. The rapid spinning causes all the heavier particles in the mixture to move to the farthest point away from the center of rotation.

> **centrifugal force** - the effect of inertia on an object moving in a curve

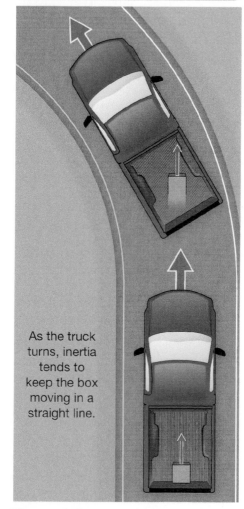

As the truck turns, inertia tends to keep the box moving in a straight line.

Figure 6.18: *As the truck turns, the box keeps going straight ahead because of inertia.*

Gravitational force

Planets and moons A centripetal force is needed to move any object in a circle. What is the force that makes Earth orbit the Sun, and the Moon orbit Earth? Newton first realized that this force is the same force that causes objects to fall toward the ground. The force of gravity between Earth and the Sun provides the centripetal force to keep Earth in its orbit. The force of gravity between Earth and the Moon keeps the Moon in orbit (Figure 6.19).

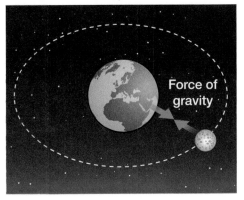

Figure 6.19: *Gravitational force keeps the Moon in orbit around Earth.*

The force of gravity between Earth and the Sun keeps Earth in orbit.

Weight Gravitational force exists between *all* objects that have mass. The strength of the force depends on the mass of the objects and the distance between them. Your *weight* is the force of gravity between you and Earth. It depends on your mass, the planet's mass, and your distance from the center of the planet. Until now, you have used the equation $F_w = mg$ to calculate weight. Your mass is represented by m. The value of g depends on Earth's mass and the distance between its center and surface. If you travel to a planet with a different mass and/or radius, the value of g and your weight would change.

Gravitational force exists between all objects You do not notice the attractive force between ordinary objects because gravity is a relatively weak force. It takes a great deal of mass to create gravitational forces that can be felt. For example, a gravitational force exists between you and your textbook, but you cannot feel it because both masses are small. You notice the force of gravity between you and Earth because the planet's mass is huge. Gravitational forces tend to be important only when one of the objects has an extremely large mass, such as a moon, star, or planet.

Direction of the gravitational force The force of gravity between two objects always lies along a line connecting their centers. As objects move, the direction of this force changes to stay pointed along the line between their centers. For example, the force between Earth and your body points from your center to the center of Earth. The direction of the planet's gravitational force is what we use to define "down." If you tell a person on the north pole and another on the south pole to point down, they will be pointing in opposite directions (Figure 6.20).

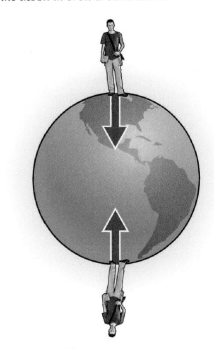

Figure 6.20: *The direction "down" is opposite on the north and south poles.*

The gravitational force between objects

Mass and gravity
The force of gravity between two objects is proportional to the mass of each object. If one object doubles in mass, then the gravitational force doubles. If both objects double in mass, then the force doubles twice, becoming four times as strong (Figure 6.21).

Distance and gravity
The distance between objects, measured from center to center, is also important when calculating gravitational force. The closer objects are to each other, the greater the force between them. The farther apart, the weaker the force. The decrease in gravitational force is related to the square of the distance. Doubling the distance divides the force by four ($2^2 = 4$). If you are twice as far from an object, you feel one-fourth the gravitational force. Tripling the distance divides the force by nine ($3^2 = 9$). If you are three times as far away, the force is one-ninth as strong.

Changing elevation
If you climb a hill or fly in an airplane, your distance from the center of Earth increases. The gravitational force on you—your weight—decreases. However, this change in distance is so small when compared with Earth's radius that the difference in your weight is not noticeable.

Measuring distance
When calculating the force of Earth's gravity, distance is measured from the center of the object to the center of Earth. This is *not* because gravity "comes from" the center of the planet. Every part of Earth's mass contributes to the gravitational force. You measure the distance to the center because your distance from all the particles making up the planet varies. You are close to the mass under your feet but far from the mass on the other side of Earth. The distance used to calculate the force of gravity is the average distance between you and all the particles making up Earth's mass. This average distance is the distance to the planet's center.

The law of universal gravitation
Newton's **law of universal gravitation** gives the relationship between gravitational force, mass, and distance (Figure 6.22). The **gravitational constant** (*G*) is the same everywhere in the universe (6.67×10^{-11} N·m²/kg²). Its small value shows why gravity is weak unless at least one mass is huge.

Mass and the force of gravity

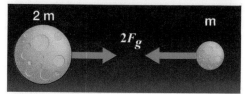

Figure 6.21: *Doubling one mass doubles the force of gravity. Doubling both quadruples the force of gravity.*

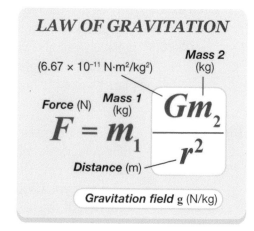

Figure 6.22: *The law of universal gravitation.*

Using the law of universal gravitation

The force on each object
The force calculated using the law of universal gravitation is the force felt by *each* object as seen here. The gravitational force of Earth on the Moon has the same strength as the gravitational force of the Moon on Earth.

(from previous page)
law of universal gravitation - the relationship between gravitational force, mass, and distance
gravitational constant - the constant in the law of universal gravitation that is equal to 6.67×10^{-11} N·m²/kg²

 Using the law of universal gravitation

Use the following information to calculate the force of gravity between Earth and the Moon: mass of Earth: 5.97×10^{24} m; mass of the Moon: 7.34×10^{22} kg; distance between Earth's and the Moon's centers: 3.84×10^{8} m.

1. *Looking for:*   You are asked for the force of gravity between Earth and the Moon.

2. *Given:*   You are given Earth's and the Moon's masses (kg) and the distance between their centers (m).

3. *Relationships:* $F_g = G\dfrac{m_1 m_2}{r^2}$

4. *Solution:*

$$F_g = \left(6.67 \times 10^{-11}\,\frac{\text{N·m}^2}{\text{kg}^2}\right)\frac{\left(5.97 \times 10^{24}\ \text{kg}\right)\left(7.34 \times 10^{22}\ \text{kg}\right)}{\left(3.84 \times 10^{8}\ \text{m}\right)^2}$$

$$F_g = \left(6.67 \times 10^{-11}\,\frac{\text{N·m}^2}{\text{kg}^2}\right)\frac{\left(4.38 \times 10^{47}\ \text{kg}^2\right)}{\left(1.47 \times 10^{17}\ \text{m}^2\right)} = 1.99 \times 10^{20}\ \text{N}$$

Your Turn:

a. Calculate the force of gravity on a 50-kg person on Earth who is 6.38×10^6 m from its center.

b. Calculate the force of gravity on a 50-kg person on the Moon who is 1.74×10^6 m from its center.

(Answers are listed at the end of the chapter.)

Orbital motion

Satellites
A **satellite** is an object that circles around another object with gravity providing the centripetal force. Earth, its moon, and the other planets are examples of natural satellites. Artificial satellites that **orbit**, or revolve around, Earth include the Hubble Space Telescope, the International Space Station, and satellites used for communications.

Launching a satellite
The motion of a satellite is closely related to projectile motion. If an object is launched above Earth's surface at a slow speed, it follows a parabolic path and falls back to the planet (Figure 6.23). The faster it is launched, the farther it travels before reaching the ground. At a launch speed of about 8 kilometers per second, the curve of a projectile's path matches the curvature of Earth. The object goes into orbit instead of falling back to Earth. A satellite in orbit *falls around Earth*. But, as it falls, Earth curves away beneath it.

Elliptical orbits
An orbit can be a circle or an oval shape called an *ellipse*. Any satellite launched above Earth at more than 8 kilometers per second will have an elliptical orbit. An object in an elliptical orbit does not move at a constant speed. It moves fastest when it is closest to the object it is orbiting because the force of gravity is strongest there.

Planets and comets
The planets' orbits are elliptical, too, but almost circular in shape. Comets, however, orbit the Sun in very long elliptical paths (Figure 6.24). Their paths bring them close to the Sun and far out into space, often beyond the dwarf planet Pluto. Some comets take only a few years to orbit the Sun once, while others travel so far out that an orbit takes thousands of years.

> **satellite** - an object that circles around another object with gravity providing the centripetal force
>
> **orbit** - a regular, repeating path that an object in space follows around another object

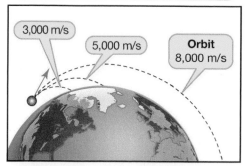

Figure 6.23: *A projectile launched fast enough from Earth becomes a satellite.*

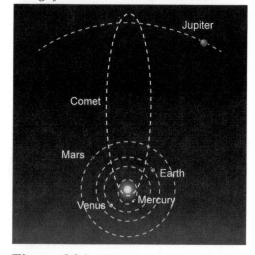

Figure 6.24: *The planets move in nearly circular orbits. Comets travel in elliptical orbits around the Sun.*

6.3 Section Review

1. Draw a diagram of a ball at the end of a string moving in a clockwise circle. Draw vectors to show the direction of the centripetal force and velocity at three different locations on the circle.
2. Explain the difference between centrifugal force and centripetal force.
3. What factors affect the force of gravity between two objects?
4. What is the force that keeps Earth in orbit around the Sun?

6.4 Center of Mass

The shape of an object and the way its mass is distributed affects the way it moves and balances. For example, a tall stool tips over more easily than a low, wide chair. Wheels and other objects that spin are designed to rotate with as little effort as possible. In this section, you will learn about the factors that affect an object's rotation.

> **center of mass** - the point about which an object naturally spins

What is center of mass?

The motion of a tossed object   What if you hold the top of an empty soda bottle and toss it across a field? You will notice that the bottle rotates as it moves through the air. The rotation comes from the torque you exerted in throwing it. If you filmed the bottle and carefully looked at the video, you would see that one point on the bottle moves in a perfect parabola. The bottle spins around this point as it moves.

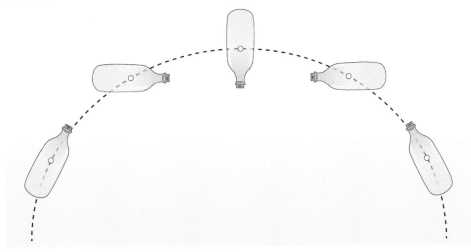

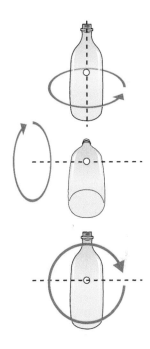

Figure 6.25: *An object naturally spins about three different axes.*

Defining center of mass   The point about which an object naturally spins is its **center of mass**. Since a solid object has length, width, and height, there are three different axes about which an object can spin. These three axes intersect at the center of mass (Figure 6.25). The center of mass is important because it is the average position of all the particles that make up the object's mass.

Finding the center of mass

The center of mass may not be "in" an object
It is easy to find the center of mass for a symmetric object made of a single material such as a solid rubber ball or a wooden cube—the center of mass is located at the geometric center of the object. If an object is irregularly shaped, it can be found by spinning the object, as with the soda bottle on the previous page. The center of mass of some objects may not be inside the object. The center of mass of a doughnut is at its center—where there is only space!

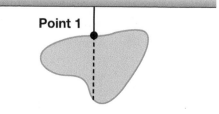

center of gravity - the average position of an object's weight

Finding the center of mass

Solid ball   Donut   Football   Brick   Cup   Person   Center of mass

The center of gravity
Closely related to the center of mass is the **center of gravity**, or the average position of an object's weight. If the acceleration due to gravity is the same at every point in an object, its centers of gravity and of mass are at the same point. This is the case for most objects, so the two terms are often used interchangeably. However, gravity toward the bottom of a skyscraper is slightly stronger than it is toward its top. The top half therefore weighs less than the bottom half, even when both halves have the same mass. The center of mass is halfway up the building, but the center of gravity is slightly lower.

Finding the center of mass
An object's center of mass can easily be found experimentally. When an object hangs from a point on its edge, the center of mass falls on the line drawn directly below the point of suspension. If the object is hung from two or more points, the center of mass can be found by tracing the line below each point and finding the intersection of the lines (Figure 6.26).

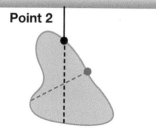

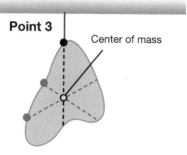

Point 1   Point 2   Point 3   Center of mass

Figure 6.26: *The center of mass of an irregularly-shaped object can be found by suspending it from two or more points.*

Center of mass and stability

Balancing an object
To balance an object such as a book or a pencil on your finger, you must place your finger directly under the object's center of mass. The object balances because the torque caused by the force of the object's weight is equal on each side.

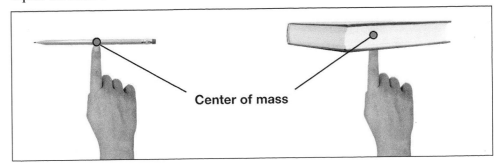

Center of mass

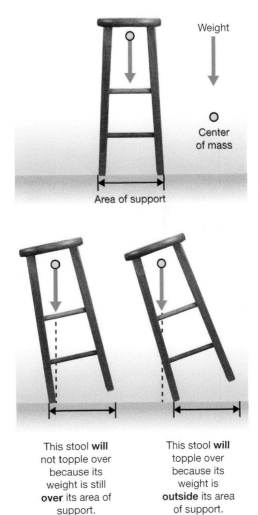

The area of support
For an object to stay upright, its center of mass must be above its area of support. The area of support includes the entire region surrounded by the actual supports. For example, a stool's area of support is the entire rectangular area surrounded by its four legs. Your body's support area is not only where your feet touch the ground, but also the region between your feet. The larger the area of support, the less likely an object is to topple over.

When will an object topple over?
An object will topple over if its center of mass is not above its area of support. A stool's center of mass is slightly below the center of the seat. A vector showing the force of gravity or the stool's weight points from the center of mass toward the center of Earth (Figure 6.27). If this vector passes through the area of support, the object will not topple. If the weight vector passes outside that area, the object will topple. Tall stools topple over more easily than low ones for this reason.

This stool **will** not topple over because its weight is still **over** its area of support.

This stool **will** topple over because its weight is **outside** its area of support.

Figure 6.27: *A stool will topple if its weight vector is outside its area of support.*

6.4 Section Review

1. Compare and contrast center of mass and center of gravity.
2. Explain how you can find an object's center of mass.
3. Is a pencil easier to balance on its sharp tip or on its eraser? Why?

Sailboat Racing: Vectors to Victory

Racing the 1,022 kilometers from Newport, Rhode Island, to Bermuda in a sailboat is one of the great adventures in sailing. With the Gulf Stream current, giant waves, and unpredictable weather, staying on course is difficult. Most of the race is out of sight of land, without the visual navigation aids of lighthouses, buoys, or landmarks.

A Challenging Course

What are some of the challenges along the course of the Newport-Bermuda race? At the beginning of the race, the ocean water is very cold, and the battle is against low visibility and fog. You have to use radio navigation to avoid hitting anything. As you sail into the Gulf Stream current, the water temperature may warm up by 10°C in just a few miles. This temperature difference powers the thunderstorms and high winds along the edge of the Gulf Stream. Just inside the Gulf Stream current, smaller swirls of current, called "eddies," can add to or subtract from your speed through the water. In the center of the Gulf Stream current, the water and the weather are calmer. The end of the race becomes a navigational challenge to both find the island of Bermuda and pick your way through the barrier reefs to avoid running aground.

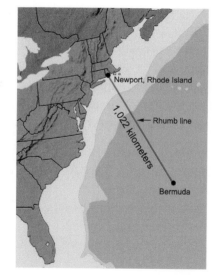

Current strategy

Before the boat ever starts the race, the planning begins. From enhanced color satellite pictures of the sea surface temperatures, you can distinguish where the Gulf Stream is moving and where any eddies are located. Eddies are smaller swirling currents moving within the Gulf Stream. If you can see where an eddy is today on the satellite picture, you need to calculate its velocity vector in the Gulf Stream current to figure out where it will be when your boat gets close. If you know that an eddy is moving through the current at 3 kph, then in 36 hours it will have traveled 108 kilometers.

The strategy is to predict where the eddies are, and use them to increase your speed. You want to steer your boat along the side of the eddy that is moving in the same direction as the boat. It's a straightforward addition of two velocity vectors. If the current within the eddy is swirling counterclockwise at 5 kph, and your boat travels at 12 kph through the eddy, you can either pass on the side where the current works against the boat and have a velocity of 7 kph, or you can sail the side of the eddy going in the direction of your boat and have a velocity of 17 kph. Predicting the currents and eddies correctly has helped boats win this race.

Eddies form along the Gulf Stream

Into the wind

So, how do you figure out where you're going and when you'll get there while 950 kilometers of the race is out in the open ocean? The *rhumb line* is the course you'd take if you followed one compass reading between where you are and where you want to go. The rhumb line from Newport to Bermuda is 1,022 kilometers at a 164° compass reading. That means that when you start the race in Newport, if you point your boat in a direction of 164° and travel in that direction for 1,022 kilometers, you would reach Bermuda. But what if the wind is blowing in the opposite direction? A sailboat can't move directly into the wind. Sailboats need to take a zigzagging course called "tacking" to move the boat in the direction opposite the wind's force. Each tack has a velocity vector, and by adding the vectors for each leg of the journey together, you get the resultant velocity for the entire course. The optimal course of tacking will depend on the wind direction and speed, how the sails are set, and the sailboat design.

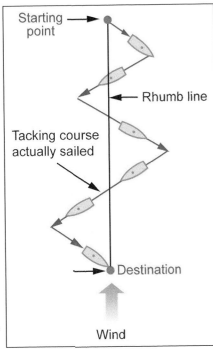

Tacking moves the boat in the direction opposite the wind's force.

The weather factor

Weather is another consideration that can help in this race. Stormy conditions have higher winds, which will help your boat go faster. In a race, you want to plan a course toward a storm if it will give you a speed advantage. High winds are both exhilarating and dangerous. The race organizers require safety-at-sea training with good reason.

To get to Bermuda fast and in one piece takes both advance planning and the ability to make quick decisions under pressure. The fastest resultant velocity vector of the tacking has to be calculated while assessing the changing winds and currents through the Gulf Stream. Heading through thunderstorms can be risky, but will increase your speed. Your crew needs to keep a close watch on all the boat systems around the clock, even if they're tired or seasick after three days at sea. At the end of it all, as the finish line gets closer, you have to avoid adding your boat to the more than 500 shipwrecks off Bermuda. Once you arrive, you can look back and appreciate the competition, the camaraderie, and the challenge.

QUESTIONS

1. How does a sailboat sail against the wind?

2. In the 2010 Newport-Bermuda race, *Speedboat* was first to cross the finish line in 59 hours, 17 minutes, 56 seconds. What was *Speedboat*'s average velocity for the race?

3. **Challenge:** The rhumb line is drawn as a straight line on a marine chart. What would the rhumb line from Newport to Bermuda look like if you plotted it on a globe? Is it the shortest distance between the two locations?

Newport to Bermuda Race photo by Daniel Forster/PPL
Satellite photo courtesy NOAA.

Chapter 6 Review

Understanding Vocabulary

Select the correct term to complete the sentences.

angular speed	law of universal gravitation	revolution
center of gravity	parabola	rotation
center of mass	projectile	satellite
centripetal force	range	trajectory
displacement		

1. A bullet fired into the air follows a curved trajectory called a(n) _____.

2. The Moon makes one monthly _____ around Earth, while Earth makes one daily _____ around its axis.

3. A(n) _____ is an object that orbits around another object.

4. A string attached to a ball you whirl overhead exerts _____ force on the ball.

5. An object's _____ is the average position of its weight.

Reviewing Concepts

Section 6.1

1. List the three ways to describe a displacement vector.

2. The directions north, south, east, and west can be described using angles. List the angle for each of the four directions.

3. Explain how a vector diagram can be used to find an object's displacement.

4. A velocity vector tells you the object's _____ and _____ of motion.

5. State whether each of the following is a projectile.

    a. a diver who has jumped off a diving board

    b. a soccer ball flying toward the net

    c. a bird flying up toward its nest

6. What does it mean to say that the horizontal and vertical components of a projectile's velocity are independent of each other?

7. Is the horizontal velocity of a projectile constant? Is the vertical velocity of a projectile constant? Explain your answers.

8. Why does a projectile move in a curved path?

9. You kick a ball off the ground with a horizontal speed of 15 m/s and a vertical speed of 19.6 m/s. As it moves upward, its vertical speed _____ by _____ each second. It gets to its highest point _____ seconds after it is kicked. At the highest point, its vertical speed is _____ and its horizontal speed is _____. As it falls, its vertical speed _____ by _____ each second. It reaches the ground _____ seconds after it is kicked. Its horizontal speed is always _____.

10. At which angle should you kick a soccer ball if you want it to have the greatest range?

11. A ball kicked off the ground at an angle of 20 degrees and a ball kicked at an angle of _____ degrees have the same range.

Section 6.2

12. State whether each object is rotating or revolving.

    a. a satellite orbiting Earth

    b. a toy train moving on a circular track

    c. a fan blade

13. Which of the following units is appropriate for angular speed: rotations per second, meters per second, revolutions per minute?

14. How many degrees are in one revolution or rotation?

15. Two ants are sitting on a spinning record. One sits near the center and the other near the edge.

    a. How do their angular speeds compare?

    b. How do their linear speeds compare?

16. Rolling is a combination of _____ motion and _____ motion.

17. How far does the center of a wheel move in a line as the wheel rolls through one rotation?

Section 6.3

18. A force acts on a moving object. The force makes the object _____ if it acts in the same direction as the velocity. The force makes it _____ if it acts opposite the velocity. The force makes it _____ if it is perpendicular to the velocity.

19. A sports car moves around a sharp curve (small radius) at a speed of 50 mph. A four-door family car moves around a wider curve (large radius) at the same speed. The cars have equal masses.

    a. Which car changes its direction more quickly?

    b. Which car has the greater acceleration?

    c. Which car has the greater centripetal force acting on it?

    d. What provides the centripetal force on each car?

20. Explain the relationship between velocity and centripetal force in creating circular motion.

21. Explain how the centripetal force needed to move an object in a circle is related to its mass, speed, and the radius of the circle.

22. A force is needed to change an object's linear motion. What is needed to change its rotational motion?

23. What is centrifugal force? Is it a real force?

24. What keeps the Moon in orbit around Earth?

25. Is there a gravitational force between you and your pencil? Do you notice this force? Explain.

26. You experience a gravitational force that attracts you to Earth. Does Earth also experience a force? Explain.

27. What is a satellite?

28. Do all satellites move in perfect circles?

Section 6.4

29. Explain how you can find the location of an object's center of mass.

30. What is the difference between the center of mass and the center of gravity?

31. Explain how you can find the location of an object's center of gravity.

32. Why is a tall SUV more likely than a car to roll over in an accident?

33. Tightrope walkers often use long poles to help them balance. Explain why this makes sense.

Solving Problems

Section 6.1

1. Use a scaled drawing to find the displacement for each of the following. Then check your work with the Pythagorean theorem.

    a. an ant that walks 3 m north and 3 m east

    b. a cat who runs 6 m west and 2 m north

    c. a car that drives 8 km south and 6 km west

    d. a plane that flies 200 mi north, turns, and flies 200 mi south

2. Draw a vector to scale to represent each velocity. Specify your scale.

    a. (20 m/s, 60°)

    b. (40 mph, 150°)

    c. (500 km/h, 180°)

3. Calculate the speed of each velocity given in component form. Then draw the velocity vector to scale. State the scale you use.

    a. (5, 8) m/s

    b. (60, 20) m/s

4. You run straight off a high diving board at a speed of 6 m/s. You hit the water 2 s later.

    a. How far did you travel horizontally during the 2 s?

    b. How far did you travel vertically during the 2 s?

    c. How fast were you moving horizontally when you hit the water?

    d. How fast were you moving vertically when you hit the water?

5. A monkey throws a banana horizontally from the top of a tree. The banana hits the ground 3 s later and lands 30 m from the base of the tree.

   a. How fast did the monkey throw the banana?

   b. How high is the tree?

   c. How fast was the banana moving horizontally as it hit the ground?

   d. How fast was the banana moving vertically as it hit the ground?

   e. What was the resultant velocity of the banana as it hit the ground?

6. A bowling ball rolls off a high cliff at 5 m/s. Complete the chart that describes its motion during each second it is in the air.

Time (s)	Horizontal velocity (m/s)	Vertical velocity (m/s)	Horizontal distance (m)	Vertical distance (m)
0				
1				
2				
3				
4				

7. You kick a football off the ground with a horizontal velocity of 12 m/s to the right and a vertical velocity of 29.4 m/s upward. Draw a diagram showing the football's trajectory. Draw vectors showing its horizontal and vertical velocity at each second until it returns to the ground.

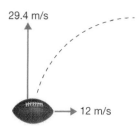

29.4 m/s

12 m/s

Section 6.2

8. Find the angular speed of a Ferris wheel that makes 12 rotations during a 3-min ride. Express your answer in rotations per minute.

9. A wheel makes 10 rotations in 5 s.

   a. Find its angular speed in rotations per second.

   b. How many degrees does it turn during the 5 s?

   c. Find its angular speed in degrees per second.

10. You are sitting on a merry-go-round at a distance of 2 m from its center. It spins 15 times in 3 min.

   a. What distance do you move as you make one revolution?

   b. What is your angular speed in RPM?

   c. What is your angular speed in degrees per minute?

   d. What is your linear speed in meters per minute?

   e. What is your linear speed in meters per second?

2 m

Section 6.3

11. A car requires a centripetal force of 5,000 N to drive around a bend at 20 mph. What centripetal force is needed for it to drive around the bend at 40 mph? At 60 mph?

12. A 1,000-kg car drives around a bend at 30 mph. A 2,000-kg truck drives around the same bend at the same speed. How does the centripetal force on the car compare to the force on the truck?

13. What would happen to the force of gravity on you if you doubled your distance from the center of Earth?

14. What would happen to the force of gravity on you if Earth's mass suddenly doubled but the radius stayed the same?

15. Use Newton's law of universal gravitation to find the force of gravity between Earth and a 60-kg person.

16. Use Newton's law of universal gravitation to find the force of gravity between Earth and the Sun.

Section 6.4

17. Choose the point that is at the center of mass of each object.

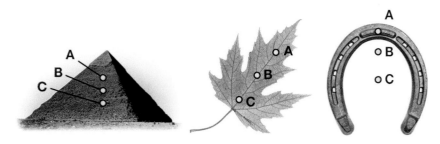

18. Which object(s) will topple? The center of gravity of each is marked.

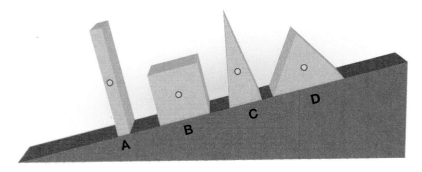

Test Practice

Section 6.1

A ball rolling at 4.00 m/s falls from a table 0.750 m high. Answer the following questions based upon this information.

1. The time required for the ball to hit the floor is
   a. 0.153 s.
   b. 0.391 s.
   c. 1.91 s.
   d. 3.68 s.

2. What is the range of the ball before hitting the floor?
   a. 0.111 m
   b. 0.600 m
   c. 1.56 m
   d. 3.00 m

3. What is the vertical speed of the ball the instant it hits the floor?
   a. 3.8 m/s
   b. 1.9 m/s
   c. 0.080 m/s
   d. 0.039 m/s

Section 6.2

The wheel of a bicycle is 0.700 m in diameter and makes 2.00 rotations in 3.00 s as the bicycle rolls along a bike path. Answer the following questions using the information above.

4. The angular speed of the wheel is
   a. 1.4 m/s.
   b. 2,40 degrees/s.
   c. 2.2 m/s.
   d. 0.67 rpm.

5. What is the linear speed of the wheel at a distance of 0.200 m from the center of the wheel?
   a. 1.88 m/s
   b. 2.09 m/s
   c. 2.46 m/s
   d. 6.28 m/s

6. What is the linear speed of the axle of the bicycle wheel as it rolls along the path?
   a. 0.233 m/s
   b. 0.350 m/s
   c. 1.05 m/s
   d. 3.30 m/s

Section 6.3

Base your answers to the following questions on the diagram at right which represents a ball attached to a string. The ball moves at a constant speed around a flat horizontal circle of radius R.

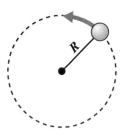

7. If the speed of the ball is doubled, the centripetal force exerted by the string on the ball

   a. is halved.

   b. is doubled.

   c. remains the same.

   d. is quadrupled.

8. If the length of string is cut in half while the speed of the ball remains the same, the centripetal force exerted by the string on the ball

   a. is halved.

   b. is doubled.

   c. remains the same.

   d. is quadrupled.

9. A 60-kg adult and 30-kg child are passengers on a rotating amusement park ride. How does the centripetal acceleration experienced by the adult compare to the centripetal acceleration experienced by the child?

   a. The child's is ½ as much as the adult's.

   b. The child's is twice as much as the adult's.

   c. The child's is the same as the adult's.

   d. The child's is ¼ as much as the adult's.

10. If the distance between two masses is increased by three times, the gravitational force between them is increased by

    a. 3 times as much.

    b. 2 times as much.

    c. 9 times as much.

    d. 8 times as much.

11. Which graph best represents the gravitational force between two bodies as a function of the distance between their centers of mass?

    a. A

    b. B

    c. C

    d. D

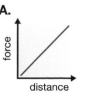   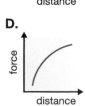

Section 6.4

12. Where is the center of mass of a gold ring?

    a. in the gold of the ring

    b. in the air at the center of the ring

    c. in the air outside the ring

    d. it depends on the density of the gold

Applying Your Knowledge

Section 6.1

1. What is the mathematical equation for a parabola shaped like a projectile's trajectory? How is the equation for a parabola similar to the equations for projectile motion?

2. You want to throw a banana up to a monkey sitting in a tree. The banana is directed straight toward the monkey as you release it. While throwing it you make a sound that scares the monkey. He jumps down from the tree at the instant you let go of the banana. Will the monkey catch it as he falls through the air?

Section 6.2

3. Research to find out how the angular speeds of music CDs and DVDs compare.

4. How are projectile motion and circular motion similar? How are they different?

Section 6.3

5. There are many satellites orbiting earth for communications, weather monitoring, navigation, and other purposes. Research one of the uses of satellites and prepare a poster summarizing your results.

6. A geosynchronous satellite makes one revolution around the Earth each day. If positioned above the equator, it is always over the same point on Earth. Geosynchronous satellites must be a distance of approximately 42,000 km from the center of the Earth (36,000 km above Earth's surface). Calculate the linear speed of a geosynchronous satellite in km/h.

7. The International Space Station is an Earth satellite. Research the history and purpose of this space station.

Section 6.4

8. The toy bird shown can be easily balanced on a fingertip, and it sways side-to-side without falling if it is tapped. How do you think the bird balances this way?

➕ ➖ ✖ ➗ Your Turn Answers

Adding vectors (Section 6.1, page 135)

a. 7.1 km southeast (or 315°)

b. (100, 100) m

Using velocity vectors (Section 6.1, page 136)

a. (71 m/s, 45°)

b. (2,500, 500) m/h or (2.5, 0.5) km/h; in polar coordinates, (2.5 km/h, 11°)

Projectile motion (Section 6.1, page 141)

a. 60 m, 44.1 m

b. 8 m/s

Calculating angular speed (Section 6.2, page 143)

a. 200 rpm

b. 720 degrees/s or 720° per second

Calculating linear speed (Section 6.2, page 145)

a. 1.57 m/s

b. 0.79 m/s

Law of universal gravitation (Section 6.3, page 153)

a. 489 N

b. 81 N

Unit 3 ENERGY AND SYSTEMS

Machines, Work, and Energy

The Egyptian pyramids were built about 4,000 years ago. It took workers approximately 80 years to build the Pyramids of Giza. The largest, called the Great Pyramid, contains about 1 million stone blocks, each weighing about 2.5 tons. How were the ancient Egyptians able to build such an incredible monument?

What did the ancient Egyptians use to help them build the pyramids? Egyptologists, men and women who study ancient Egypt, disagree about the details of how the gigantic structures were built. However, most agree that a system of ramps and levers (simple machines) was necessary for moving and placing the blocks. The fact that they could move such massive blocks of stone to build the Great Pyramid to a height of 481 feet—roughly equivalent to a 48-story building—is fascinating, don't you think? Perhaps the most amazing part of this story is that the Great Pyramid at Giza still stands, and is visited by tens of thousands of people each year.

VOCABULARY

efficiency	machine	reversible
fulcrum	mechanical advantage	simple machine
horsepower	output	tension
input	output arm	watt
input arm	power	work-energy theorem
irreversible		

KEY QUESTIONS

✓ *Why does stretching a rubber band increase its potential energy?*

✓ *How much power can a highly-trained athlete produce?*

✓ *What is one of the most perfect machines ever invented?*

✓ *Why does time always move forward and never backward?*

7.1 Work, Energy, and Power

Doing work always means transferring energy. The energy may be transferred to the object to which you apply the force, or it may go elsewhere. For example, the work you do in stretching a rubber band is stored as potential energy by the rubber band (Figure 7.1, top). The rubber band can then use the energy to do work on a paper airplane by giving it kinetic energy (Figure 7.1, bottom). In this section, you will learn about the relationship between work and energy.

Work and energy

Work can be positive or negative You can do work on a block by pushing it across a level table. You are doing *positive* work on the block because your force is in the direction of the block's motion. Friction does *negative* work on the block because it acts *against* the direction of motion. If you are pushing the block at a constant speed, your force equals the force of friction. This means that the total work done on the block is zero, and its speed does not change.

Not all force does work Sometimes force is applied to an object, but no work is done. If you push down on a block sitting on a table and it doesn't move, you have not done any work on the block (force A, seen below). If you use $W = Fd$ to calculate the work, you will get zero no matter how strong the force because the distance is zero.

Force at an angle to a direction There are times when only *some* of a force does work. Force B is applied at an angle to the direction of motion of a block. Only a portion of the force is in the direction the block moves, so only that portion of the force does work.

Doing the most work To do the greatest amount of work, you must apply force *in the same direction* the object will move (force C). If forces A, B, and C have equal strengths, force C will do the most work because it is entirely in the direction of the motion.

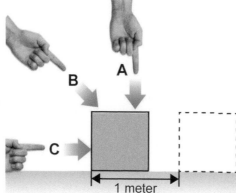

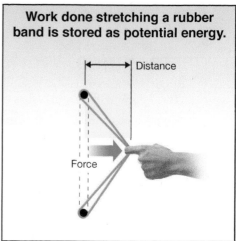

Work done stretching a rubber band is stored as potential energy.

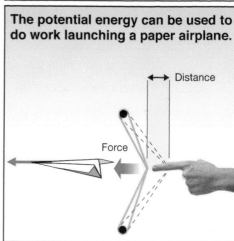

The potential energy can be used to do work launching a paper airplane.

Figure 7.1: *You do work to increase an object's potential energy. That potential energy can be converted to kinetic energy.*

Work done against gravity

Lifting force equals the weight Many situations involve work done by or against the force of gravity. To lift something off the floor, you must apply an upward force with a strength equal to the object's weight. The work done while lifting an object is equal to its change in potential energy. It does not matter whether you lift the object straight up or you carry it up the stairs. The work is the same in either case. Work done against gravity is calculated by multiplying the object's weight (mg) by its change in height (h).

Why the path does not matter The reason the path does not matter is found in the definition of work: Work is force times the distance moved *in the direction of the force*. If you move an object at an angle to the force, only the vertical distance moved matters because the force of gravity is vertical (Figure 7.2). It is easier to climb stairs or go up a ramp even though the work done *against gravity* is the same as if you jumped straight up. In the end, the total work done against gravity is the same no matter what path you take.

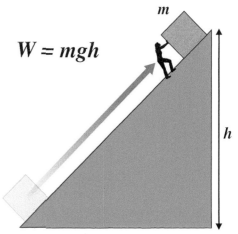

$$W = mgh$$

Figure 7.2: *The work done here equals the product of its mass, acceleration of gravity, and change in its height.*

    Calculating work

Alexander has a mass of 70 kilograms. His apartment is on the second floor, 5 meters up from ground level. How much work does he do against gravity each time he climbs the stairs to his apartment?

1. Looking for:	You are asked for the work.	
2. Given:	You are given the mass in kilograms and the height in meters. You know that $g = 9.8$ m/s².	
3. Relationships:	$Fg = mg$ $W = Fd$	
4. Solution:	The force is equal to Alexander's weight.	
	$Fg = (70$ kg$)(9.8$ m/s²$)$ $Fg = 686$ N	
	Use the force to calculate the work.	
	$W = (686$ N$)(5$ m$)$ $W = 3,430$ J He does 3,430 joules of work.	

Your turn...

a. How much additional work does Alexander have to do if he is carrying 5 kilograms of groceries?

b. A car engine does 50,000 J of work to accelerate at 10 m/s² for 5 meters. What is the mass of the car?

(Answers are listed at the end of the chapter.)

The work-energy theorem

Work equals change in kinetic energy The **work-energy theorem** says that the work done by a system equals the change in kinetic energy of that system. Another way to say this is that the kinetic energy of a moving object is exactly equal to the amount of work required to get the object from being at rest to its final speed. To understand how work and kinetic energy are related, let's suppose a ball of mass (m) is at rest. A force (F) is applied and creates an acceleration (a). After moving a distance (d), the ball has reached a speed (v).

Step 1 Work is force times distance, and force is mass times acceleration. Therefore, the work done on the ball is its mass times acceleration times distance.

$$W = Fd = (ma) \times d = mad$$

Step 2 The kinetic energy formula involves only mass and speed. Is there a way to get speed from acceleration and distance? Yes! When an object starts from rest, you can relate distance traveled, acceleration, and time using the formula that includes all three.

$$d = \frac{1}{2}at^2$$

Step 3 Using this relationship, you can replace distance in the equation for work and combine similar terms:

$$W = ma\left(\tfrac{1}{2}at^2\right) = \tfrac{1}{2}ma^2t^2$$

Step 4 When an object starts from rest with constant acceleration, its speed is equal to its acceleration multiplied by the time it has been accelerating. Mathematically, $v = at$, therefore $v^2 = a^2t^2$. This is the result that is needed. Replace the a^2t^2 with v^2, and the resulting work (W) is exactly the formula for kinetic energy.

$$v = at \rightarrow \boxed{v^2} = a^2t^2 \qquad W = \tfrac{1}{2}m\boxed{a^2t^2} \longrightarrow W = \tfrac{1}{2}mv^2$$

Why it works Remember, this calculation is the work done on the ball to bring it from rest up to a final speed (v). As with potential energy, the kinetic energy of a moving object is equal to the work done to create the energy. The problem in the sidebar gives you an opportunity to practice your understanding of how work and kinetic energy are related. When you have completed the problem, try the extension. How does doubling speed or mass affect stopping distance?

---

work-energy theorem - the work done by a system equals the change in kinetic energy of that system

Calculating the kinetic energy of a moving car

A car with a mass of 1,000 kg is going straight ahead at a speed of 10 m/s. The brakes can supply a force of 10,000 N. Calculate

a) the kinetic energy of the car.

b) the distance it takes to stop.

1. You are asked for the kinetic energy and stopping distance.
2. You are given mass, speed, and the force from the brakes.
3. Kinetic energy: $Ek = \frac{1}{2}mv^2$
   Work: $W = Fd$
4. Solve: $Ek = \frac{1}{2}$ (1,000 kg)(10 m/s)^2
   = 50,000 J

To stop the car, the kinetic energy must be reduced to zero by work done by the brakes.

50,000 J = (10,000 N) × d
d = 5 meters

Extension: Repeat this calculation for these situations: The car has the same braking force but (1) moves at twice the speed and (2) has twice the mass.

Power

What is power? Suppose Michael and Jim each lift a barbell weighing 100 newtons from the ground to a height of 2 meters (Figure 7.3). Michael lifts quickly and Jim lifts slowly. Because the barbell is raised the same distance, it gains the same amount of potential energy in each case. Michael and Jim do the same amount of work. However, Michael's *power* is greater because he gets the work done in less time. **Power** is the rate at which work is done.

Units of power The unit for power is equal to the unit of work (joules) divided by the unit of time (seconds). One **watt**, symbolized with a *W*, is equal to 1 joule per second. The watt was named after James Watt (1736–1819), the Scottish engineer who invented the steam engine. Another unit of power that is often used for engine power is the **horsepower**. Watt expressed the power of his engines as the number of horses an engine could replace. One horsepower is equal to 746 watts.

A note about W The symbol *W* is used for work and also for watts. When you are working with a physics problem, the context of the problem tells you whether the *W* stands for work or watts. So, its important to know your definitions for these terms: *Work* is force times distance, and a *watt* is a unit of power, which is work divided by time.

POWER

$$\text{Power (W)} \quad P = \frac{W}{t} \quad \begin{array}{l} \text{Work (J)} \\[4pt] \text{Time (s)} \end{array}$$

Calculating work So, how much power do Michael and Jim produce? You must first calculate the work they do, using $W = Fd$. The force needed to lift the barbell is equal to its weight (100 N). The work is therefore 100 newtons times 2 meters, or 200 joules. Each of them does 200 joules of work.

Calculating power To find Michael's power, divide his work (200 joules) by his time (1 second). Michael has a power of 200 watts. To find Jim's power, divide his work (200 joules) by his time (10 seconds). Jim's power is 20 watts. Jim takes 10 times as long to lift the barbell, so his power is one-tenth as great.

power - the rate at which work is done and which is measured in watts or joules per second

watt - the metric unit of power that is equal to 1 joule per second

horsepower - a unit of power equal to 746 watts

Figure 7.3: *Michael and Jim do the same amount of work, but do not produce the same power.*

Calculating power

Human power   The maximum power output of a person is typically around a few hundred watts. However, it is only possible to keep up this power for a short time. Highly-trained athletes can keep up a power of 350 watts for about an hour. An average person can keep up a power of about 200 watts for an hour.

    **Calculating power**

A roller coaster is pulled up a hill by a chain attached to a motor. The roller coaster has a total mass of 10,000 kg. If it takes 20 seconds to pull the roller coaster up a 50-meter hill, what is the power produced by the motor?

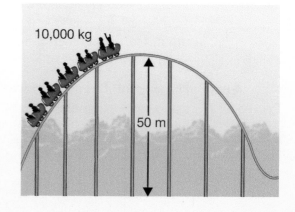

1. Looking for: You are asked for the power of the motor.

2. Given: You are given the mass in kilograms, the time in seconds, and the height in meters.

3. Relationships: $Fg = mg$ $W = Fd$ $P = W/t$

4. Solutions: Calculate the weight of the roller coaster:
$Fg = (10,000 \text{ kg})(9.8 \text{ m/s}^2) = 98,000 \text{ N}$
Calculate the work:
$W = (98,000 \text{ N})(50 \text{ m}) = 4,900,000 \text{ J or } 4.9 \times 10^6 \text{ J}$
Calculate the power:
$P = (4.9 \times 10^6 \text{ J}) (20 \text{ s}) = 245,000 \text{ W or } 2.45 \times 10^5 \text{ W}$

Your turn...

a. What would the motor's power be if it took 40 seconds to pull the same roller coaster up the hill?

b. What is the power of a 70-kilogram person who climbs a 10-meter hill in 45 seconds?

(Answers are listed at the end of the chapter.)

7.1 Section Review

1. Explain how work is related to energy.
2. Who does more work, a person who lifts a 2-kilogram object 0.5 m or a person who lifts a 3-kilogram object 0.4 m?
3. While sitting in class, your body exerts a force of 600 N on your chair. How much work do you do?
4. Is your power greater when you run or walk up a flight of stairs? Explain your answer.

7.2 Simple Machines

How do you move something that is too heavy to carry? How did the ancient Egyptians build the pyramids long before the invention of powered machines? The answer to these questions has to do with the use of simple machines. In this section, you will learn how simple machines multiply forces to accomplish many tasks.

Using machines

What technology allows us to do
Today's technology allows us to do incredible things. Moving huge steel beams, digging tunnels that connect two islands, and building 1,000-foot skyscrapers are examples. What makes these accomplishments possible? Have we developed super powers since the days of our ancestors?

What is a machine?
In a way we *have* developed super powers. Our powers come from the clever human invention of machines. A **machine** is a device with moving parts that work together to accomplish a task. A bicycle is made of a combination of machines that work together (Figure 7.4). All the parts of a bicycle work as a system to transform forces from your muscles into motion. A bicycle allows you to travel at faster speeds and for greater distances than is possible on foot.

> **machine** - a mechanical system capable of performing work
>
> **input** - the force, work, energy, or power applied to a machine
>
> **output** - the force, work, energy, or power produced by a machine

Parts of a Bicycle

Wheels   Gears   Pedals

Figure 7.4: *A bicycle contains machines working together.*

Work output
Forward motion of bicycle

Work input
Forces applied to bicycle pedals

The concepts of input and output
Machines are designed to do work. To understand how machines work, it is useful to define an **input** and **output**. The *input* includes everything you do to make the machine work, like pushing on the bicycle pedals, for instance. The *output* is what the machine does for you, like climbing a steep hill. For the machines that are the subject of this chapter, the input and output may be force, power, or energy.

Simple machines

The beginning of technology   The development of the technology that created cars, airplanes, and other modern conveniences began with the invention of **simple machines**. A simple machine is a mechanical device that accomplishes a task with only one movement. For example, a simple lever allows you to move a rock that weighs 10 or more times what you weigh. Some important types of simple machines are shown below.

> **simple machine** - an unpowered mechanical device, such as a lever, that works by a single movement

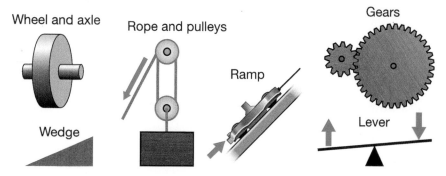

Rope and pulleys

Input force and output force   Simple machines work with forces. The *input force* is the force you apply to the machine. The *output force* is the force the machine applies to what you are trying to do. The graphic at right shows how a lever can be arranged to create a large output force from a small input force.

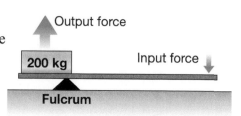

Ropes and pulleys   A rope-and-pulley system is a simple machine made by connecting a rope to one or more pulleys. You apply the input force to the rope and the output force is exerted on the load you are lifting. One person could easily lift an elephant with a properly-designed system of pulleys (Figure 7.5).

Figure 7.5: *A simple machine made with a rope and pulley allows one person to lift tremendous loads.*

Machines within machines   Most of the machines we use today are made up of combinations of different types of simple machines. For example, the bicycle uses wheels and axles, levers (the pedals and kickstand), and gears. Combinations of simple machines are also found in clocks, car engines, and many household appliances, such as vacuum cleaners, sewing machines, and blenders.

Mechanical advantage

Ratio of output to input force   Simple machines are best understood through the concepts of input and output forces. The **mechanical advantage** of a machine is the ratio of the output force to the input force. If the mechanical advantage of a machine is larger than one, the output force is larger than the input force. A mechanical advantage smaller than one means the output force is smaller than the input force. Mechanical advantage is a ratio of forces, so it is a number without any units.

> **mechanical advantage** - the ratio of output force to input force

MECHANICAL ADVANTAGE OF A SIMPLE MACHINE

Mechanical advantage $MA = \dfrac{F_o \quad \text{— Output force (N)}}{F_i \quad \text{— Input force (N)}}$

➕ ➖ ✖ ➗ **Calculating mechanical advantage**

What is the mechanical advantage of a lever that allows Jorge to lift a 24-newton box with a force of 4 newtons?

1. Looking for:	You are asked for the mechanical advantage.
2. Given:	You are given the input force and the output force in newtons:
3. Relationships:	$MA = F_o/F_i$
4. Solution:	$MA = (24\ N)/(4\ N)$
	$MA = 6$

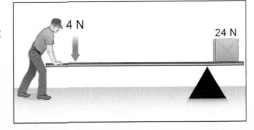

Your turn:

a. Calculate the mechanical advantage of a rope-and-pulley system that requires 10 newtons of force to lift a 200-newton load.

b. A block and tackle (a type of rope-and-pulley system) has a mechanical advantage of 30. How heavy a load can you lift with an input force of 100 N?

(Answers are listed at the end of the chapter.)

Work and machines

Input and output work
A simple machine does work because it exerts forces over a distance. If you are using the machine, you also do work, because you apply forces to the machine that moves its parts. By definition, a simple machine has no source of energy except the forces you apply. That means the only way to get output work from a simple machine is to do input work on the machine. In fact, the output work done by a simple machine can never exceed the input work done on the machine. This is an important result.

> *The output work done by a simple machine can never exceed the input work done on the machine.*

Perfect machines
In a *perfect* machine, the output work equals the input work. Of course, there are no perfect machines. Friction always converts some of the input work to heat, so the output work is always *less* than the input work. However, for a well-designed machine, friction can be small so we can assume that input and output work are approximately equal.

An example
Figure 7.6 shows a simple machine that has a mechanical advantage of two. The machine lifts a 10-newton weight a distance of one-half meter. The output work is 5 joules (10 N × 0.5 m). If you assume the machine is perfect, then you must do exactly 5 J of input work to get 5 J of output work. The input force is only 5 newtons since the machine has a mechanical advantage of two. That means the input distance must be 1 meter because 5 N × 1 m = 5 J. You have to pull 1 meter of rope to raise the weight one-half meter.

The cost of multiplying force
The rule that the output work of a machine can never be greater than the input work is *true for all machines*. You cannot get something for nothing. When you design a machine that has a greater output force than input force, you pay by having to apply the input force over a greater distance. For example, if the machine has a mechanical advantage greater than one, the input force is less than the output force. However, the input force must be applied over a longer distance to satisfy the rule about input and output work being equal.

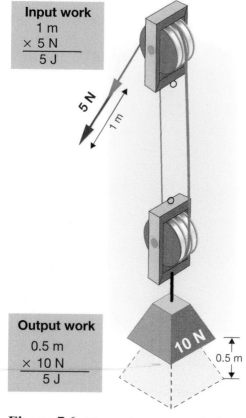

Input work
1 m
× 5 N
―――
5 J

5 N

1 m

Output work
0.5 m
× 10 N
――――
5 J

10 N

0.5 m

Figure 7.6: *The work output equals the work input, even though the forces differ.*

Using work to solve problems

Mechanical advantage   To solve mechanical advantage problems, start by assuming a perfect machine, with nothing lost to friction. Set the input and output work equal and use this relationship to find the mechanical advantage.

Force or distance   Many problems give three of the four quantities: input force, input distance, output force, and output distance. If the input and output work are equal, then the input force times distance equals the output force times distance at the output. Solve this equation for the unknown force or distance.

To solve mechanical advantage problems, assume a perfect machine, with nothing lost to friction.

  **Calculating work by machines**

A jack is used to lift one side of a car in order to replace a tire. To lift the car, the jack handle moves 30 centimeters for every one centimeter that the car is lifted. If a force of 150 newtons is applied to the jack handle, what force is applied to the car by the jack? You can assume all of the input work goes into producing output work.

1. Looking for: You are asked for the output force in newtons.

2. Given: You are given the input force in newtons, and the input distance and output distance in centimeters. (Convert these distances to meters.)

3. Relationships: *Work = Fd*   and   **Input work = Output work**

4. Solution:
Input work: $W = (150 \text{ N})(0.30 \text{ m}) = 45 \text{ J}$
Output work: 45 J of input work = $F \times 0.01$ m
$F = 45 \text{ J}/0.01 \text{ m} = 4{,}500 \text{ N}$

The jack exerts an upward force of 4,500 newtons on the car every time the jack handle moves 30 centimeters (0.30 m).

Your turn:

a. A mover uses a pulley to lift a 2,400-newton piano up to the second floor. Each time he pulls the rope down 2 meters (input distance), the piano moves up 0.25 meters (output distance). With what force does the mover pull on the rope?

b. A nutcracker is a very useful lever. The center of the nutcracker, where the nut is placed, moves 1 centimeter for each 2 centimeters your hand squeezes down. If a force of 40 newtons is needed to crack a walnut shell, what force must you apply?

(Answers are listed at the end of the chapter.)

How a lever works

An example of a lever
A lever can be made by balancing a board on a log (Figure 7.7). Pushing down on one end of the board lifts a load on the other end of the board. The downward force you apply is the input force. The upward force the board exerts on the load is the output force.

Parts of the lever
As you can see in Figure 7.7, levers include a stiff structure that rotates around a fixed point called the **fulcrum**. The side of the lever where the input force is applied is called the **input arm**. The **output arm** is the side of the lever that applies the output force. The fulcrum, input arm, and output arm can be arranged on a lever to make almost any mechanical advantage.

When the fulcrum is not in the center
When the fulcrum is in the middle of the lever, the input and output forces are the same. An input force of 100 newtons makes an output force of 100 newtons and there is no mechanical advantage. The input and output forces are different if the fulcrum is not in the center of the lever. The side of the lever with the longer arm exerts the smaller force. If the input arm is 10 times longer than the output arm, the output force is 10 times greater than the input force.

Mechanical advantage of a lever
One way to calculate a lever's mechanical advantage is to use the lengths of the input and output arms. The mechanical advantage of a lever is also found using distance and force (Figure 7.8). The output work is the output force multiplied by the output distance. The input work is the input distance multiplied by the input force. By setting the input and output work equal, you can show that the ratio of forces is the inverse of the ratio of distances. For example, a larger input distance goes with a smaller force. (*Note*: The ratio of distances equals to the ratio of the lengths of the arms of the lever.)

> **MECHANICAL ADVANTAGE OF A LEVER**
>
> Mechanical advantage $MA_{lever} = \dfrac{L_i}{L_o}$ — Length of input arm (m)
> — Length of output arm (m)

fulcrum - a fixed point on a lever about which the lever rotates

input arm - the side of a lever between the fulcrum and the input force

output arm - the side of a lever between the fulcrum and the output force

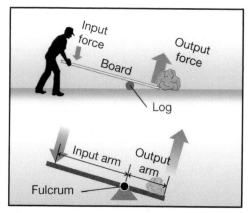

Figure 7.7: *A board and log can be used to make a lever used to lift a rock.*

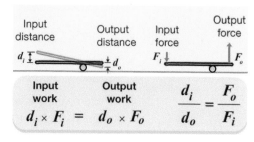

Input work	Output work	
$d_i \times F_i$ =	$d_o \times F_o$	$\dfrac{d_i}{d_o} = \dfrac{F_o}{F_i}$

Figure 7.8: *How to determine the mechanical advantage of a lever.*

Classes of levers

The output force can be *less* than the input force   You can make a lever that has an output force less than the input force. The input arm is shorter than the output arm on this kind of lever. You might design a lever this way if you need the motion on the output side to be larger than the motion on the input side. A very small downward motion on the input side can cause the load to lift a large distance on the output side. Your arms and legs are actually levers that perform in this way!

Three classes of levers   Levers are used in common machines, such as pliers or a wheelbarrow. And, as mentioned above, human arms and legs. The human body is often described as a machine. In fact, it is a machine. Bones and muscles in your limbs and your jaw work as levers. Levers are classified as one of three types or classes, which are defined by the location of the input and output forces relative to the fulcrum (Figure 7.9).

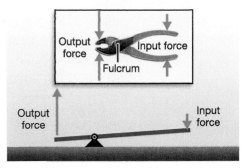

First-class lever

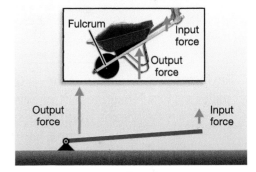

Second-class lever

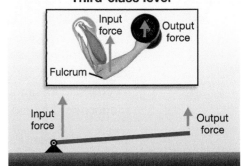

Third-class lever

 Mechanical advantage of levers

A lever has a mechanical advantage of 4. Its input arm is 60 centimeters long. How long is its output arm?

1. Looking for: You are asked for the output arm in centimeters.

2. Given: You are given the mechanical advantage and the length of the input arm in centimeters.

3. Relationships: $MA = L_i \div L_o$

4. Solution: $4 = 60 \text{ cm} \div L_o = 60 \text{ cm} \quad L_o = 60 \text{ cm} \div 4 = 15 \text{ cm}$

Your turn:

a. What is the mechanical advantage of a lever with an input arm of 25 cm length and an output arm of 100 cm length?

b. A lever has an input arm 100 cm long and an output arm 10 cm long. What is the mechanical advantage of this lever? How much input force is needed to lift a 100-N load with the lever?

(Answers are listed at the end of the chapter.)

Figure 7.9: *There are three classes of levers.*

How a rope and pulley system works

Tension in ropes and strings
Ropes and strings carry forces along their length. The force in a rope is called **tension** and is a pulling force that acts along the direction of the rope. The tension is the same at every point in a rope. If the rope is not moving, its tension is equal to the force pulling on each end. Ropes or strings do *not* carry pushing forces. This is obvious if you ever tried pushing a rope.

tension - a force that causes a stretching or pulling of a material or object

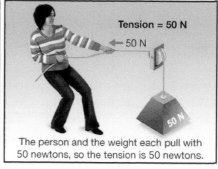

Tension = 100 N
← 100 N   100 N →
Each person pulls with a force of 100 newtons, so the tension is 100 newtons.

Tension = 50 N
← 50 N
The person and the weight each pull with 50 newtons, so the tension is 50 newtons.

The forces in a pulley system
Figure 7.10 shows three different configurations of ropes and pulleys. Imagine pulling with an input force of 5 newtons. In case A, the 5-newton load is lifted by the matching 5-newton input force. In case B, there are two strands of rope supporting the load, so the load feels twice the input force. A 10-newton load can be lifted in case B. In case C, there are three strands so the output force is three times the input force.

Mechanical advantage
The mechanical advantage of a pulley system depends on the number of strands of rope directly supporting the load. In case C, three strands directly support the load, so the output force is three times the input force. The mechanical advantage is 3. To make a rope and pulley system with a greater mechanical advantage, you can increase the number of strands directly supporting the load by using more turns around the pulleys.

Work
To raise the load 1 meter in case C, the input end of the rope must be pulled for 3 meters because *each* of the three supporting strands must shorten by 1 meter. The mechanical advantage is 3 but the input force must be applied for three times the distance as the output force. This is another example of the rule stating that output and input work are equal for a perfect machine.

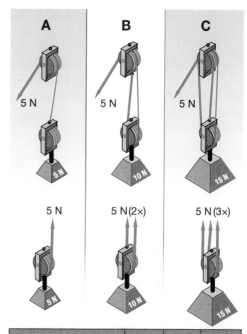

	A	B	C
Input force	5 N	5 N	5 N
Output force	5 N	10 N	15 N
Mechanical advantage	**1**	**2**	**3**

Figure 7.10: *A rope-and-pulley system can be arranged to have different mechanical advantages.*

Gears and ramps

Rotating motion Many machines require that rotating motion be transmitted from one place to another. The transmission of rotating motion is often done with gears (Figure 7.11). Some machines that use gears, such as small drills, require small forces at high speeds. Other machines, such as the paddle wheel on the back of a steamboat, require large forces at low speed.

How gears work The rule for how two gears turn depends on the number of teeth on each gear. The teeth don't slip, so moving 36 teeth on one gear means that 36 teeth have to move on any connected gear. Suppose a large gear with 36 teeth is connected to a small gear with 12 teeth. As the large gear turns once, it moves 36 teeth on the smaller gear. The smaller gear must turn three times ($3 \times 12 = 36$) for every single turn of the large gear (Figure 7.11).

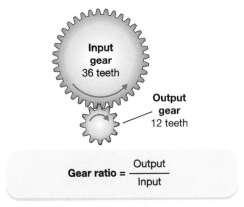

$$\text{Gear ratio} = \frac{\text{Output}}{\text{Input}}$$

Figure 7.11: *The smaller gear makes three turns for each turn of the larger gear.*

Ramps A ramp is another type of simple machine. Using a ramp allows you to push a heavy cart higher with less force than is needed to lift it straight up. Ramps reduce the input force needed by increasing the distance over which the input force acts. For example, suppose a 10-meter ramp is used to lift a cart 1 meter. If the weight of the car is 500 newtons, then the output work is 500 joules (output work = mgh = 500 N × 1 m = 500 J).

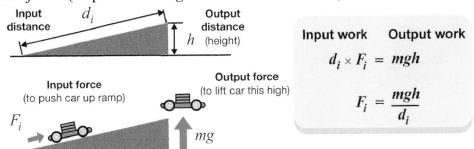

Input work   Output work

$$d_i \times F_i = mgh$$

$$F_i = \frac{mgh}{d_i}$$

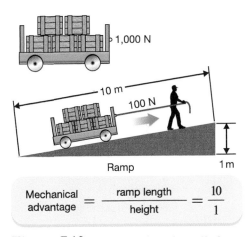

$$\text{Mechanical advantage} = \frac{\text{ramp length}}{\text{height}} = \frac{10}{1}$$

Figure 7.12: *The load must be pulled 10 meters to lift it 1 meter, but only one-tenth the force is needed.*

Mechanical advantage of a ramp The input work is the input force multiplied by the length of the ramp (10 meters). If you set the input work equal to the output work, you quickly find that the input force is 50 newtons (input work = Fd = $F \times$ 10 m = 500 J; F = 50 N). The input force is one-tenth of the output force. For a frictionless ramp, the mechanical advantage is the length of the ramp divided by the height. In this case, the mechanical advantage is 10 (Figure 7.12).

Screws

Screws A screw is a simple machine that turns rotating motion into linear motion (Figure 7.13). A screw works like a ramp that curves as it gets higher. The "ramp" on a screw is called a *thread*. Imagine unwrapping one turn of a thread to make a straight ramp. Each turn of the screw advances the nut the same distance it would have gone sliding up the ramp. The *lead* of a screw is the distance it advances in one turn. A screw with a lead of 1 millimeter advances 1 millimeter for each turn.

A screw and screwdriver The combination of a screw and a screwdriver has a very large mechanical advantage. The mechanical advantage of a screw is found by thinking about it as a ramp. The vertical distance is the lead of the screw. The length of the ramp is the same as the circumference of the thread. A quarter-inch screw in a hardware store has a lead of 1.2 millimeters and a circumference of 17 millimeters along the thread. The mechanical advantage is 14. If you use a typical screwdriver with a mechanical advantage of 4, the total mechanical advantage is 14×4 or 56, ideally. Friction between the screw and the surface with which it is joined causes the actual mechanical advantage to be somewhat less than the theoretical value, but still very large.

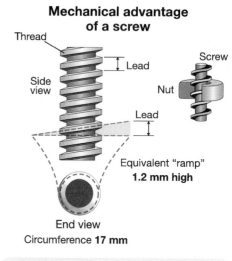

Mechanical advantage of a screw

Thread

Lead

Side view

Screw

Nut

Lead

Equivalent "ramp" **1.2 mm high**

End view
Circumference **17 mm**

Mechanical advantage = 17 mm/1.2 mm = **14**

Figure 7.13: *A screw is a rotating ramp.*

7.2 Section Review

1. Name two simple machines that are found on a bicycle.
2. Find the mechanical advantage of the crowbar shown at right.
3. Classify each of these as a first-, second-, or third-class levers: see-saw, baseball bat, door on hinges, and scissors (Figure 7.14).
4. A large gear with 48 teeth is connected to a small gear with 12 teeth. If the large gear turns twice, how many times will the small gear turn?
5. What is the mechanical advantage of a 15 meter ramp that rises 3 meters?

40 cm

2 cm

Figure 7.14: *Which type of lever is shown in each picture?*

7.3 **Efficiency**

In a perfect machine, there is no friction and the output work equals the input work. Of course, there are no perfect machines. This section is about efficiency, which is how we measure how close to perfect a machine is. The bicycle comes as close to perfect as any machine ever invented. Nearly all of the work done by the rider on the pedals becomes kinetic energy of the bicycle (Figure 7.15). Most machines are much less perfect. An automobile engine converts less than 15 percent of the chemical energy in gasoline into output work to move a car.

Friction

Friction   Friction is a force that opposes motion. Friction can be caused by rubbing or sliding surfaces. Friction can also be caused by moving through liquid, such as oil or water. Friction can even be caused by moving though air, as you can easily feel by sticking your hand out the window of a moving car.

Friction and energy   Friction converts energy of motion to heat. The brakes on a car use friction to slow the car down and they get hot. Heat causes the bonds between atoms in the brake materials to break down, eventually causing them to wear away. One way to describe this is to say that energy is "lost" to friction. However, it is important to remember that the energy does not disappear. "Lost" simply implies that the energy is converted to other forms of energy that are not useful.

Machines   In an actual machine, the output work is less than the input work because of the heat energy due to friction forces. When analyzing a machine it helps to think like the diagram below. The input work is divided between output work and "losses" due to friction.

100 J
Input work from forces applied to pedals

96 J ➡
Output work is kinetic energy of bicycle and rider

4 J ➡
Work done against friction

Figure 7.15: *A bicycle is highly efficient. In this example, the bicycle is 96 percent efficient!*

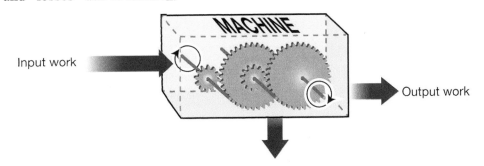

Efficiency

One hundred percent efficient   A machine has an **efficiency** of 100 percent if the work output of the machine is equal to the work input. If a machine is 100 percent efficient, no energy is diverted by friction or other factors. Although it is impossible to create a machine with 100 percent efficiency, machine designers try to achieve as high an efficiency as possible.

> **efficiency** - the ratio of a machine's output work to its input work

The definition of efficiency   The efficiency of a machine is the ratio of work output to work input. Efficiency is usually expressed in percent. A machine that is 75 percent efficient can produce 3 joules of output work for every 4 joules of input work (Figure 7.16). One joule out of every 4 (25 percent) is lost to friction. You calculate efficiency by dividing the work output by the work input. You can convert the ratio into a percent by multiplying by 100.

A machine with 75% efficiency

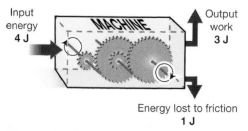

Figure 7.16: *If the input work is 4 joules, and the output work is 3 joules, then the efficiency is 75 percent.*

Improving efficiency   An important way to increase the efficiency of a machine is to reduce friction. Ball bearings and oil reduce rolling friction. Slippery materials such as Teflon™ reduce sliding friction. Designing a car with a streamlined shape reduces air friction. All of these techniques increase efficiency.

    Calculating efficiency

A person uses a 75-newton force to push a 51-kilogram car up a ramp. The ramp is 10 meters long and rises 1 meter. Calculate the efficiency.

1. Looking for:	You are asked for the efficiency.
2. Given:	You are given the input force and distance, and the mass and height for the output.
3. Relationships:	**Efficiency = Output work ÷ Input work. Input: $W = Fd$. Output: work done against gravity ($W = mgh$)**
4. Solution:	**Output work = (51 kg)(9.8 N/kg)(1 m) = 500 J** **Input work = (75 N)(10 m) = 750 J** **Efficiency = 500 J ÷ 750 J = ⅔, or ≈ 67%**

Your turn:

a. If a machine is 80 percent efficient, how much input work is required to do 100 J of output work?

b. A solar cell needs 750 J of input energy to produce 100 J of output energy. What is its efficiency?

(Answers are listed at the end of the chapter.)

Efficiency and time

Why time moves forward The efficiency is less than 100 percent for virtually all processes that convert energy to any other form except heat. Scientists believe this is connected to why time flows forward and not backward. Think of time as an arrow pointing from the past into the future. All processes move in the direction of the arrow, never backward.

The arrow of time

Things that have already happened | Things that have not happened yet

Past   *Future*

Present

reversible - an ideal process that can run forward or backward

irreversible - a process that can only run in one direction and which is less than 100 percent efficient

Reversible processes Suppose a process is 100 percent efficient. As an example, think about connecting two marbles of equal mass by a string passing over an ideal pulley with no friction (Figure 7.17). One marble can go down, transferring its potential energy to the other marble, which goes up. The motion of the marble is **reversible** because it can go forward and backward as many times as you want. In fact, if you watched a movie of the marbles moving, you could not tell if the movie was being played forward or backward.

Friction and the arrow of time Now, suppose friction makes the process 99 percent efficient. Because some potential energy is lost to friction, every time the marbles exchange energy, some is lost. The marbles don't rise quite as high as they did the last time. If you made a movie of the motion, you could tell whether the movie was running forward or backward. Any process with an efficiency less than 100 percent runs only one way: *forward, with the arrow of time.*

Irreversible processes Friction turns energy of motion into heat. Once energy is transformed into heat, the energy cannot ever completely get back into its original form. Because 100 percent of the heat energy cannot get back to potential or kinetic energy, any process with less than 100 percent efficiency is **irreversible**. Irreversible processes can only go forward in time. Since processes in our universe almost always lose a little energy to friction, time cannot run backward.

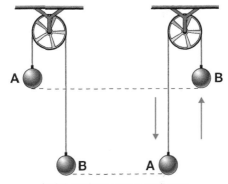

A   B

B   A

100% efficient energy exchange

Figure 7.17: *Exchanging energy with a perfect, frictionless pulley.*

7.3 Section Review

1. Why can the output work of a simple machine never be greater than the input work?
2. Use the concept of work to explain the relationship between input and output forces and lengths.
3. How does the efficiency of a car compare to the efficiency of a bicycle? Why do you think there is such a big difference?

Electric Wind

Malawi

Fourteen-year-old William Kamkwamba pushed aside the tall grass that grew among the decaying tractor parts and broken machinery of the junkyard near his hometown of Wimbe, Malawi. He smiled as he spotted a few nuts and bolts that weren't too rusty. To most of his neighbors, this stuff was just trash. But to William, the junkyard contained hidden treasure: a tractor fan, a shock absorber, some ball bearings. He had big plans for this stuff: He would build a windmill.

Students from the Kachokolo Secondary School across the street teased him from the schoolyard, calling out "Hey, look, it's William, digging in the garbage again." Despite the taunts, William wished he, too, was in school. But a severe drought had struck Malawi the previous year (2002), and corn crops failed. His family could no longer afford the $80 per year tuition. He was forced to drop out.

William didn't want to fall behind in his studies. When he learned that a small public library had opened in his old primary school, he decided to see if he could find any books to help him keep up.

Library book sparks idea

In a textbook called *Explaining Physics*, William read that if you spin a coil of wire inside a magnetic field, an electric current is created. This is called *electromagnetic induction*. William learned that electromagnetic induction enables pedal-powered bicycle lamps to light up. He had always wondered how those worked.

Back at the library, William stumbled across another textbook called *Using Energy*. It had a row of windmills on its cover. He'd never seen a windmill before, but he had made pinwheels from plastic lids as a little boy. What were these giant pinwheels good for? The book said that windmills could be used to generate electricity.

An idea began to take shape in William's mind. If he could build a windmill, he could have light in the evenings. Electric lights were a luxury enjoyed by only two percent of Malawians. And even better, maybe he could build a windmill to operate a water pump. Then, his family could irrigate their crops. They could have a good harvest, even in a dry year. Perhaps there would be extra food to sell, and then he could go back to school!

Slowly William gathered the things he needed to build his windmill. He salvaged parts of his father's broken bicycle to serve as the body of the windmill. He cut and flattened strips of plastic pipe to make blades. His best friend purchased a beat-up second hand bicycle lamp with its pedal-powered generator.

William had to pay a welder to attach the shaft from the junkyard shock absorber to the bicycle sprocket so it could spin, and to melt holes in the tractor fan so he could attach the long blades. To earn the money, he worked long hours loading wood into a truck for a driver at the local market. Finally, he was ready to assemble his windmill.

William made a drill using a corncob handle and a sharp nail. He heated the point in a fire and then melted holes in the plastic blades. He gathered bottle tops and hammered them flat to use as washers.

He bolted the pieces together. Finally, he attached the bicycle lamp generator to the bike tire. Now it could be turned by the spinning motion of the windmill blades instead of pedals.

Next, William and two friends built a five-meter-tall tower out of tree trunks and branches they cut by hand. The next day, they hoisted the windmill with a rope and pulley system created from William's mother's clothesline wire. They bolted the windmill to the tower.

Soon, a dozen or so people from the village wandered down to see what this tall contraption could be. Some of them laughed at the sight of all this useless junk lashed together. A man who worked in the market asked William what he called his machine. Since there is no word in his native language for windmill, William answered, "Electric wind."

William had jammed a bent bicycle spoke into the wheel to prevent it from spinning before he was ready. He ran to get the bicycle lamp bulb, then attached it to the generator wires hanging from the windmill. Meanwhile, the crowd grew to about 60. William took a deep breath and pulled the spoke away. The windmill began to turn, faster and faster. The bicycle lamp flickered, and then glowed with a steady bright light. All the people began to clap and cheer.

Windmill power transforms lives

Afterward, William installed some lights in his family home. He began making a little money using his generator to charge cell phones. Then, in 2006, some people from the organization that built the library came to inspect it. They noticed the windmill and asked the librarian who made it. A few days later they sent a colleague to see it. He asked

William installs lights in his family's home.

William to tell him all about how he built the windmill.

A few days later, the man returned with some reporters. Several radio stations and newspapers ran stories about William's windmill. A man in Lilongwe, Malawi's capital, read about the windmill and shared William's story on his blog. As a result, William was invited to speak at a conference called TEDglobal 2007, in Tanzania. Many global investors there chose to support William's work, enabling him to build a second windmill to power a water pump, and to return to school.

William graduated from the African Leadership Academy in 2010 and went on to engineering school in the United States. His goal is to start his own windmill company in Malawi, bringing a reliable, affordable source of electricity to his fellow citizens.

William at the TEDglobal conference in 2007

QUESTIONS

1. Name three ways the windmill benefited William and his family.

2. What challenges might have prevented William from building the windmill? How did he overcome them?

3. What simple machine can you see in the windmill photo? Name the input and output forces.

To learn more about William Kamkwamba, visit www.movingwindmills.org and read his book: Kamkwamba, William, and Bryan Mealer. (2009). *The Boy Who Harnessed the Wind.* New York: HarperCollins Publishers.

Photos by Tom Rielly

Chapter 7 Review

Understanding Vocabulary

Select the correct term to complete the sentences.

efficiency	irreversible	simple machines
fulcrum	machine	tension
horsepower	mechanical advantage	watt
input	output	work
input arm	power	work-energy theorem

1. The _____ states that the work done by a system equals the change in kinetic energy for that system.

2. _____ is the rate of doing work.

3. The ramp, the lever, and the wheel and axle are examples of _____.

4. To calculate a machine's _____, you divide the output force by the input force.

5. _____ is the ratio of work output to work input and is usually expressed as a percent.

6. A process with less than 100% efficiency is _____.

Reviewing Concepts

Section 7.1

1. Why are work and energy both measured in joules?

2. If you lift a box of books 1 m off the ground, you are doing work. Compared with the example above, how much work are you doing if you lift the box of books off the ground 2 m?

3. Decide whether work is being done (using your physics definition of work) in the following situations.

   a. picking up a bowling ball off the floor

   b. two people pulling with the same amount of force on each end of a rope

   c. hitting a tennis ball with a tennis racket

   d. pushing hard against a wall for an hour

   e. pushing against a book so it slides across the floor

   f. standing very still with a book balanced on your head

4. In which direction should you apply a force if you want to do the greatest amount of work?

5. What is the difference between work and power?

6. What is the meaning of the unit of power called a watt?

Section 7.2

7. List five types of simple machines.

8. Which two types of simple machines are in a wheelbarrow?

9. A certain lever has a mechanical advantage of 2. How does the lever's output force compare to the input force?

10. Can simple machines multiply input forces to get increased output forces? Can they multiply work input to increase the work output?

11. Draw a diagram of each of the three types of levers. Label the input force, output force, and fulcrum on each.

12. You and a friend pull on opposite ends of a rope. You each pull with a force of 10 N. What is the tension in the rope?

13. A pulley system has four strands of rope supporting the load. What is its mechanical advantage?

14. A screw is very similar to which other type of simple machine?

Section 7.3

15. Why can't the output work for a machine be greater than the input work? Explain your answer.

16. Can a simple machine's efficiency ever be greater than 100%? Explain your answer.

17. List two examples of ways to increase efficiency in a machine.

Solving Problems

Section 7.1

1. Calculate the amount of work you do in each situation.

   a. You push a refrigerator with a force of 50 N and it moves 3 m across the floor.

   b. You lift a box weighing 25 N to a height of 2 m.

   c. You apply a 500-N force downward on a chair as you sit on it while eating dinner.

   d. You lift a baby with a mass of 4 kg up 1 m out of her crib.

   e. You climb a mountain that is 1,000 m tall. Your mass is 60 kg.

2. Sal has a weight of 500 N. How many joules of work has Sal done against gravity when he reaches 4 m high on a rock-climbing wall?

3. You do 200 J of work against gravity when lifting your backpack up a flight of stairs that is 4 m tall. What is the weight of your backpack in newtons?

4. A moving object has a mass of 2,000 kg and a speed of 10 m/s. A force of 5,000 N is applied.

   a. What is the object's kinetic energy?

   b. What is the distance it takes to stop?

5. You lift a 200-N package to a height of 2 m in 10 s.

   a. How much work did you do?

   b. What was your power?

6. One machine can perform 500 J of work in 20 s. Another machine can produce 200 J of work in 5 s. Which machine is more powerful?

7. Two cranes use rope and pulley systems to lift a load from a truck to the top of a building. Crane A has twice as much power as crane B.

   a. If it takes Crane A 10 s to lift a certain load, how much time does Crane B take to lift the same load?

   b. If Crane B can do 10,000 J of work in a minute, how many joules of work can Crane A do in a minute?

8. An elevator lifts a 500-kg load up a distance of 10 m in 8 s.

   a. Calculate the work done by the elevator.

   b. Calculate the elevator's power.

Section 7.2

9. A lever has an input force of 5 N and an output force of 15 N. What is the mechanical advantage of the lever?

10. A simple machine has a mechanical advantage of 5. If the output force is 10 N, what is the input force?

11. You use a rope and pulley system with a mechanical advantage of 5. How big an output load can you lift with an input force of 200 N?

12. A lever has an input arm 50 cm long and an output arm 20 cm long.

    a. What is the mechanical advantage of the lever?

    b. If the input force is 100 N, what is the output force?

13. You want to use a lever to lift a 2,000-N rock. The maximum force you can exert is 500 N. Draw a lever that will allow you to lift the rock. Label the input force, output force, fulcrum, input arm, and output arm. Specify measurements for the input and output arms. State the mechanical advantage of your lever.

14. A rope and pulley system is used so that a 20-N force can lift a 60-N weight. What is the minimum number of ropes in the system that must support the weight?

15. A rope and pulley system has two ropes supporting the load.

    a. Draw a diagram of the pulley system.

    b. What is its mechanical advantage?

    c. What is the relationship between the input force and the output force?

    d. How much can you lift with an input force of 20 N?

16. You push a heavy car weighing 500 N up a ramp. At the top of the ramp, it is 2 m higher than it was initially.

    a. How much work did you do on the car?

    b. If your input force on the car was 200 N, how long is the ramp?

17. A lever is used to lift a heavy rock that weighs 1,000 N. When a 50-N force pushes one end of the lever down 1 m, how far does the load rise?

18. A system of pulleys is used to lift an elevator that weighs 3,000 N. The pulley system uses three ropes to support the load. How far would 12,000 J of input work lift the elevator? Assume the pulley system is frictionless.

Section 7.3

19. A 60-W light bulb uses 60 J of electrical energy every second. However, only 6 J of electrical energy is converted into light energy each second.

    a. What is the efficiency of the light bulb? Give your answer as a percentage.

    b. What do you think happens to the "lost" energy?

20. The work output is 300 J for a machine that is 50% efficient. What is the work input?

21. A machine is 75% efficient. If 200 J of work are put into the machine, how much work output does it produce?

Test Practice

Section 7.1

1. Work is done in all of the following situations *except*

    a. a crane lifts a heavy crate.

    b. a person carries groceries up a set of stairs.

    c. a person pushes on a car which does not budge.

    d. two people push on a car which moves 1 m.

2. You push on a piano with a force of 50 N and move it 2 m. How much work have you done?

    a. 2 J

    b. 25 J

    c. 50 J

    d. 100 J

3. Sonya performs 98 J of work against gravity while lifting a 10-kg barbell. How high does she lift the barbell?

    a. 1 m

    b. 10 m

    c. 20 m

    d. 50 m

4. Alex weighs twice as much as Bob. Bob weighs twice as much as Carlos. They each climb a flight of stairs in the same amount of time. Who has more power?

    a. Alex

    b. Bob

    c. Carlos

    d. they all have the same power

Section 7.2

5. Which of the following is *not* a simple machine?

    a. screw

    b. clock

    c. ramp

    d. gears

6. What is the mechanical advantage of this lever?

    a. ⅓

    b. 2

    c. 3

    d. 6

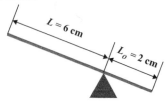

7. The input force on the rope and pulley is 2 N. What is the output force?

   a. 2 N

   b. 4 N

   c. 6 N

   d. 8 N

8. The mechanical advantage of the ramp is 10. What is the height?

   a. 2 m

   b. 5 m

   c. 10 m

   d. 20 m

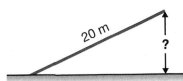

Section 7.3

9. You can increase a machine's efficiency by decreasing the

   a. power.

   b. friction.

   c. gravity.

   d. energy.

10. You build a machine which is 80% efficient. How many joules of work are put into the machine to produce 400 J of output work?

    a. 50 J

    b. 320 J

    c. 400 J

    d. 500 J

11. An elevator carries a 50 kg person up 10 m. The elevator does 7,000 J of input work. What is the efficiency of the elevator?

    a. 50%

    b. 70%

    c. 90%

    d. 100%

Applying Your Knowledge

Section 7.1

1. Imagine we had to go back to using horses for power. The power of one horse is 746 W (1 hp). How many horses would it take to light up all the light bulbs in your school?

   a. First, estimate how many light bulbs are in your school.

   b. Estimate the power of each light bulb, or get it from the bulb itself where it is written on the top.

   c. Calculate the total power used by all the bulbs.

   d. Calculate how many horses it would take to make this much power.

Section 7.2

2. Look for simple machines in your home. List as many as you can find.

3. A car is made of a large number of simple machines all working together. Identify at least five simple machines found in a car.

4. Exactly how the ancient pyramids of Egypt were built is still a mystery. Research to find out how simple machines may have been used to lift the huge rocks of which the pyramids are constructed.

Section 7.3

5. A perpetual motion machine is a machine that, once given energy, transforms the energy from one form to another and back again without ever stopping. You have probably seen a Newton's cradle like the one shown below.

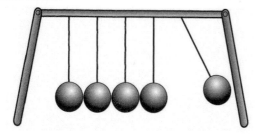

   a. Is a Newton's cradle a perpetual motion machine?

   b. According to the laws of physics, is it possible to build a perpetual motion machine?

   c. Many people have claimed to have built perpetual motion machines in the past. Use the Internet to find one such machine. Explain how it is supposed to work and why it is not truly a perpetual motion machine.

6. A food Calorie is equal to 4,184 J. Determine the number of joules of energy you take in on a typical day.

 *Your Turn* **Answers**

Calculating work (Section 7.1, page 169)

   a. 245 J

   b. 1,000 kg

Calculating power (Section 7.1, page 172)

   a. 122,500 W

   b. 152 W

Calculating mechanical advantage (Section 7.2, page 175)

   a. 20

   b. 3,000 N

Calculating work by machines (Section 7.2, page 177)

   a. 300 N

   b. 20 N

Calculating mechanical advantage of levers
(Section 7.2, page 179)

   a. 0.25

   b. MA_{lever} = 10; 10 N of force would be needed

Calculating efficiency (Section 7.3, page 184)

   a. 125 J

   b. 13%

Energy Flow and Systems

There is a country, about the same size as the state of Virginia, that can be reached from London by airplane in about 3 hours. It is a country of contrasts, and is often referred to as the land of fire and ice. Eleven percent of the country is covered by glaciers, yet there are many places where Earth's molten rock, or magma, is very close to the surface. This magma heats underground reservoirs of water. Wells have been drilled to tap into the hot water that is available. This water is used in homes and in the generation of electricity.

Do you know the name of this country? As you study this chapter, you will become familiar with the many ways that energy is used in a variety of different systems. Energy-flow diagrams, power in flowing energy, efficiency, and thermodynamics are topics that will be discussed in this chapter. These topics will help you recognize the role of energy and power in technology, nature, and living things. The country described above is Iceland. Did you guess correctly?

Think of all the different things you do each day that require energy. Where does all this energy come from? Which energy-converting systems are the most efficient? How does the efficiency of the energy flow in a natural system compare to the energy-flow efficiency in human-technology systems?

VOCABULARY

chemical energy	entropy	radiant energy
electrical energy	first law of thermodynamics	second law of thermodynamics
energy conversion	food chain	steady state
energy flow diagram	mechanical energy	thermodynamics
energy of pressure	nuclear energy	

KEY QUESTIONS

✓ *Can a person lift a 1,000-kilogram car 1 meter off the ground? How about in a time period of 10 seconds?*

✓ *Why can average automobiles use only about 13 percent of the energy available from the gasoline they burn?*

✓ *Why do natural systems have a much greater range of power than human technology?*

8.1 Energy Flow

Looking at the big picture, our universe is matter and energy organized into *systems*. There are large systems, like our solar system that is composed of the Sun, planets, asteroids, comets, smaller bits of matter, and lots of energy. There are smaller systems within the solar system, such as Earth (Figure 8.1). There are systems within systems ranging in scale from the solar system, to Earth, to a single animal, to a single cell in the animal, right down to the scale of a single atom. In every such system, energy flows and creates change.

Energy and systems

Energy as nature's "money"   Energy exists in many forms and can be changed from one form to another. You can think of energy as nature's money. It is spent and saved in a number of different ways. You can use energy to "buy" speed, height, temperature, mass, and other things. But, you have to have some energy to start with, and what you spend decreases what you have left.

An example   The energy available to a system determines how much the system can change. We often use this line of thinking to tell whether something is possible or not. Consider the Rube Goldberg machine in Figure 8.2. The blue ball is dropped and makes things happen that are eventually supposed to swing the hammer and launch the green ball. How fast will the green ball be launched? Will it be launched at all? Can things be adjusted to launch the green ball at 1 m/s? These are the questions that we can answer by looking at how the energy moves in the machine. This example is fun to think about, but thinking about it is very similar to how we analyze much more important systems, such as machines, planets, and even living bodies.

Possible or impossible?   You can only have as much "change" as you have energy to use as "pay." By looking at how much energy there is in a system, and how much energy is used by the system, you can tell a lot about what kinds of changes are possible. You can also tell what changes are impossible. The ideas in this chapter apply to much more than just physics. Plants and animals need energy to survive and grow. The number of plants and animals that can be supported in a particular place depends partly on the amount of energy available and being in the right forms to be used.

Photo courtesy of NASA Goddard Space Flight Center

Figure 8.1: *Earth is a system.*

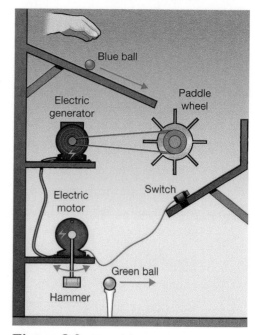

Figure 8.2: *How fast will the green ball be launched if the only source of energy is the falling blue ball?*

Energy exists in many different forms

Forms of energy   There are many forms of energy. Any form of energy can be converted into any other form. Most human technology involves converting one form of energy into another (Figure 8.3).

Mechanical energy   **Mechanical energy** is the energy an object has due to its *motion* or *position*. Kinetic and potential energy are both forms of mechanical energy. Work is a form of mechanical energy and so is the energy in a stretched rubber band or a spring.

Radiant energy   **Radiant energy** is also known as *electromagnetic* energy. Light is made up of waves called electromagnetic waves. There are many different types of electromagnetic waves, including visible light, ultraviolet light, x-rays, infrared radiation, radio waves, and microwaves.

Electrical energy   **Electrical energy** is carried by the flow of electric current. Batteries and electricity from power plants are common sources of electrical energy. You will learn about electricity and electric circuits in Unit 5.

Chemical energy   **Chemical energy** is energy stored in the bonds that join atoms. Chemical energy can be released when atoms in a molecule are rearranged into different molecules. Gasoline and food are common sources of chemical energy. Batteries change chemical energy into electrical energy.

Nuclear energy   **Nuclear energy** results from splitting large atoms like uranium or fusing the nuclei of small atoms like hydrogen. The nuclear energy resulting from the fusing of hydrogen atoms is the basic source for all other energy forms. It is how the Sun and stars create energy.

Thermal energy   Heat is a form of thermal energy. Thermal energy can be used to do work whenever there is a temperature difference. The combustion of gasoline and the splitting of uranium atoms release thermal energy. This thermal energy does work in a car or can generate electricity in a power plant.

Pressure   The pressure in a fluid is a form of energy. If you blow up a balloon and then let the air escape from it, you will see the **energy of pressure** converted to kinetic energy.

mechanical energy - the energy an object or system has due to motion or position

radiant energy - another term for electromagnetic energy

electrical energy - energy resulting from electric currents

chemical energy - energy that is stored in the chemical bonds that join atoms

nuclear energy - energy that is stored in the nucleus of an atom which can be absorbed or released by nuclear reactions

energy of pressure - energy stored in and resulting from the pressure of a fluid

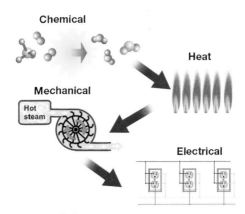

Figure 8.3: *Some of the forms energy takes on its way to your house or apartment.*

Solving a mystery in the laboratory

An experiment   Here is a mystery. Several groups of students are doing an experiment with a small car that rolls along a track. The track starts with a down-hill section then becomes flat. The car bounces off a rubber band at the end of the flat section, and the students measure the speed after the car bounces. One group measures a speed of 5 m/s while all the other groups get an average speed of 2.5 m/s (Figure 8.4). The group with the higher speed claims they did not push the car at the start, but the other groups are suspicious. Did the faster car get pushed or not? How can you tell?

The energy at the start   Some detective work with energy can solve this case. At the start, the only energy in the system should be the potential energy of the car. Remember, potential energy is given by: $E_p = mgh$, where m is the mass of the car (kg), g is the strength of gravity (9.8 N/kg), and h is the height (m). Using these values for the experiment, the potential energy is 0.49 J (Figure 8.5).

The kinetic energy   Let's calculate the kinetic energy if the car moves at 5 m/s. The kinetic energy depends on mass and speed: $E_k = \frac{1}{2}mv^2$ where v is the speed of the car (m/s). Using a mass of 0.1 kg, gives a kinetic energy of 1.25 J (Figure 8.5)! This is not possible. A system that starts with 0.49 J of energy cannot just "make" 0.76 J *more* energy. The energy had to come from somewhere else. The scientific evidence supports the conclusion that a student pushed the car at the start. That would explain the extra energy.

Analyzing energy   Using energy to investigate is a powerful tool because it does not matter what goes on between start and finish. Notice our detective analysis didn't mention the rubber band. As long as nothing adds energy to the system, there can never be more energy at the end than there was at the beginning. It does not matter what happens in between.

Friction   There *can* be less kinetic energy at the finish however. Friction steadily converts kinetic energy into heat. The kinetic energy is 0.31 J when the speed of the car is 2.5 m/s. Since the car started with 0.49 J, the difference (0.18 J) is "lost" to friction. Recall that this energy isn't really "lost." It is just changed to a form of energy (heat) that is not easily recovered and reused.

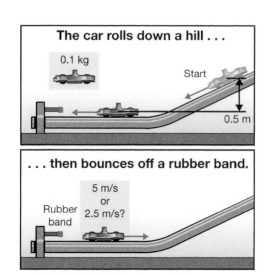

The car rolls down a hill . . .

0.1 kg

Start

0.5 m

. . . then bounces off a rubber band.

5 m/s
or
Rubber   2.5 m/s?
band

Figure 8.4: *An experiment in energy conservation.*

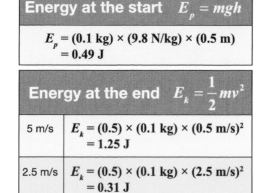

Energy at the start $E_p = mgh$
$E_p = (0.1 \text{ kg}) \times (9.8 \text{ N/kg}) \times (0.5 \text{ m})$ $= 0.49 \text{ J}$

Energy at the end $E_k = \dfrac{1}{2}mv^2$	
5 m/s	$E_k = (0.5) \times (0.1 \text{ kg}) \times (0.5 \text{ m/s})^2$ $= 1.25 \text{ J}$
2.5 m/s	$E_k = (0.5) \times (0.1 \text{ kg}) \times (2.5 \text{ m/s})^2$ $= 0.31 \text{ J}$

Figure 8.5: *Looking at the energy of the system solves the mystery.*

What happens to the energy "lost" from a system?

Where "lost" energy goes   Most often, "lost" energy is work done against friction. This work changes other forms of energy into heat and wear. If you could measure every form of energy, you would find that the tires of the car and the track became a little warmer. The air that the car pushed out of the way also became warmer. Some rubber was worn off the tires and some wood was worn off the track. Wear means grinding away molecules from surfaces. This means breaking bonds between molecules, which takes energy. If you could add it all up, you would find that *all* the energy at the start is still there at the end, just in different forms.

Open and closed systems   It would be easiest to study energy conservation in a *closed system*. A system is closed if *all* forms of energy and matter are counted and neither is allowed in or out of the system. In a closed system, the total matter and energy stays the same forever. However, it is difficult to make a truly closed system. An *open system* is one that counts only *some* forms of matter or energy or allows either or both to go in or out of the system. Many physics problems are about open systems because you count only potential and kinetic energy and ignore energy that is converted to heat.

Energy flow diagrams   An **energy flow diagram** is a good way to show what happens to the energy in a system that is changing. To make an energy flow diagram, first write down the different forms that energy takes in the system. In the car experiment, energy changes from potential to kinetic, to elastic (rubber band), and back to kinetic again. An energy flow diagram can look like Figure 8.6. Each place where energy changes form is called a *conversion*. Like the car and track, systems change by converting energy from one form to another.

> **energy flow diagram -** a diagram showing the transformations and conversions of energy in a system

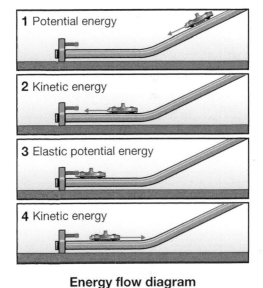

Energy flow diagram

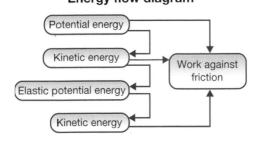

Figure 8.6: *An energy flow diagram for the experiment with the car.*

8.1 Section Review

1. In an experiment, you learn that the total energy at the end is a little less than it was at the beginning. Explain how is this possible. Use the law of conservation of energy in your answer and explain how energy can be "lost."

2. Draw an energy flow diagram that shows at least four energy conversions that occur as energy becomes light from the electric lights in your classroom.

8.2 Power, Efficiency, and Thermodynamics

Can a single person lift a 1,000-kilogram car 1 meter in 10 seconds using just their own muscles? In Chapter 7, you learned about simple machines that would easily allow a person to lift the car. In order to raise a 1,000-kilogram car 1 meter, you need 9,800 joules of energy (Figure 8.7). Doing the lift in 10 seconds requires a power output of 980 watts. This is more than a human can do. When doing detective work with energy you also need to think about how *fast* the energy flows. What power is involved? Lifting the car in five minutes would be no problem for one person. If you can spread 9,800 joules of energy over five minutes, the power required is only 32 watts. Even a child could do this with the right system of ropes and pulleys!

Power doing work

How fast work is done Power is the rate of converting energy, or doing work. Suppose you drag a box with a force of 100 newtons for 10 meters in 10 seconds. Your power is 100 joules per second, or 100 *watts*. Your friend drags a similar box and takes 60 seconds. Your friend's power is only 16.7 watts even though the actual work done (force × distance) is the same as yours. However, your friend used one-sixth the power for six times longer.

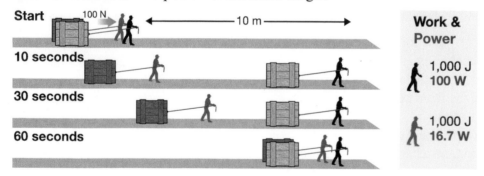

Power is the rate of doing work or using energy Power is the amount of energy changed or work done divided by the time it takes. Power is measured in watts (W). One watt is 1 joule per second. When you see the word *power*, you should think "energy used divided by time taken." This is similar to thinking about speed as "distance traveled divided by time taken." Doing 1,000 joules of work in 10 seconds equals a power of 100 watts (1,000 J ÷ 10 s = 100 W).

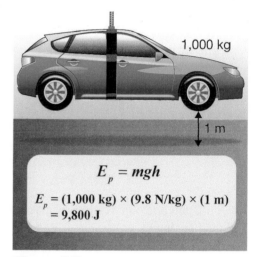

$$E_p = mgh$$

E_p = (1,000 kg) × (9.8 N/kg) × (1 m)
= 9,800 J

Figure 8.7: *Lifting a 1,000-kg car a height of 1 meter takes at least 9,800 joules of energy.*

Power in flowing energy

Horsepower The horsepower is a commonly used unit of power. One horsepower is 746 watts. The power output of car engines or electric motors is usually given in horsepower because it is a larger unit than a watt.

Three ways to look at power Power is used to describe these three similar situations. In each, you calculate the power by dividing the energy or work by the time it takes for the energy to change or the work to be done.

1. Work is done by a force. Power is the rate at which the work is done.
2. Energy flows from one place to another; power is the rate of energy flow.
3. Energy is converted from one form to another. Power is the rate at which energy is converted.

Calculating power Hoover Dam converts the potential energy of the Colorado River into electricity. Each second, 700,000 kilograms of water drops 200 meters through tunnels in the dam. The change in potential energy is 1.4 billion joules each second (Figure 8.8). The power produced is 1.4 billion watts. However, because the process is not 100 percent efficient, Hoover Dam produces less electrical power that this amount.

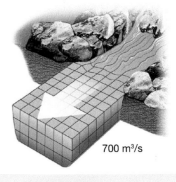

700 m³/s

$$Energy = mgh$$
$$= (700,000 \text{ kg})$$
$$\times (9.8 \text{ N/kg})$$
$$\times (200 \text{ m})$$
$$= 1,400,000,000 \text{ J}$$

Figure 8.8: *The Colorado River flows at 700 m³/s. Water's density is 10³ kg/m³, so the river moves water at a rate of 700,000 kg/s.*

    Calculating the power in a system

A 2-kg owl gains 30 m of height in 10 s. How much power does the owl use?

1. *Looking for:* You are asked for power.

2. *Given:* You are given the owl's mass, height, and time.

3. *Relationships:* **Power = energy ÷ time.** Potential energy: $E_p = mgh$

4. *Solution:* $E_p = (2 \text{ kg})(9.8 \text{ N/kg})(30 \text{ m}) = 588 \text{ joules}$

   $P = 588 \text{ J} \div 10 \text{ s} = 58.8 \text{ watts, or about half the power of a 100-W lightbulb}$

Your Turn:

a. A 50-gram frog leaps 1 meter in 0.5 seconds. Calculate the frog's power output.

b. To go from 0 to 60 mph in 5 seconds (0 to 27 m/s), a sports car engine produces a force of 9,180 N. The car moves a distance of 67.5 m in the 5 s it is accelerating. Calculate the power.

(Answers are listed at the end of the chapter.)

Efficiency

Efficiency   The efficiency of a process describes how well energy or power is converted from one form into another. Efficiency is the ratio of useful output energy or power divided by input energy or power. Because of friction, the efficiency of any process that uses power or energy is always less than 100 percent. Some machines, like a car, have efficiencies a lot lower than 100 percent (Figure 8.9).

Efficiencies always add up to 100 percent   In any system, it is important to remember that all of the energy goes somewhere. For example, rivers flow downhill. Most of the potential energy lost by water moving downhill becomes kinetic energy as the motion of the water. Also, some of the energy is used to slowly change the land by wearing away rocks and soil. Friction takes some of the energy and heats up the water. If you could add up the efficiencies for *every single process* in a system, that total would be 100 percent.

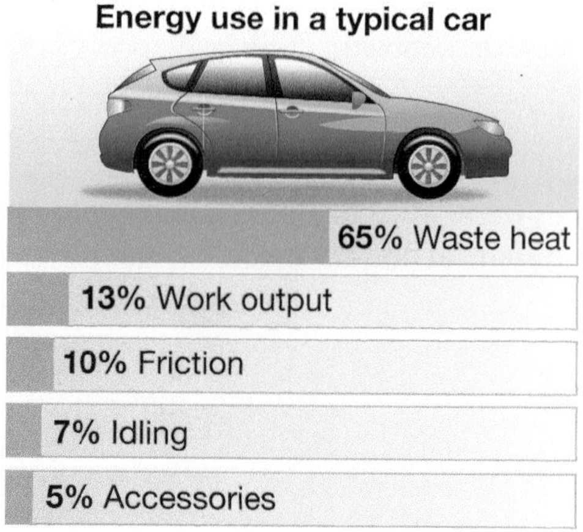

Energy use in a typical car

65% Waste heat

13% Work output

10% Friction

7% Idling

5% Accessories

Figure 8.9: *The average car converts 13 percent of gasoline energy to output work.*

Calculating the efficiency of a process

A 12-gram paper airplane is launched at a speed of 6.5 m/s with a rubber band. The rubber band is stretched with a force of 10 N for a distance of 15 cm. Calculate the efficiency of the process of launching the plane.

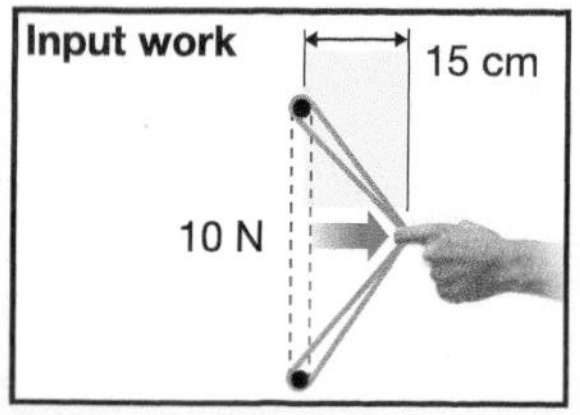

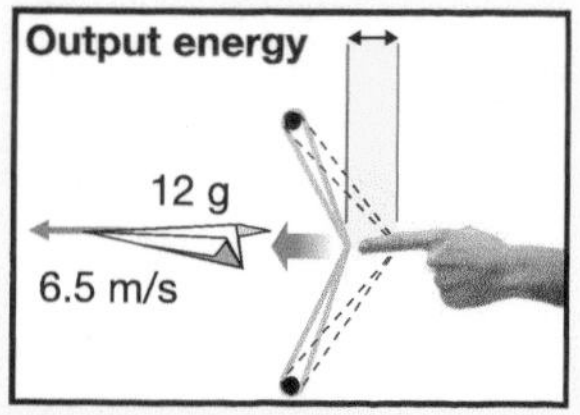

1. **Looking for:**   You are asked for the efficiency.

2. **Given:**   You are given the input force (N), distance (cm), output mass (g), and speed (m/s).

3. **Relationships:**   Efficiency = output energy ÷ input energy; $e = E_o \div E_i$
   Input energy is **work** = $F \times d$;
   Output energy: $E_o = (\frac{1}{2})\, mv^2$

4. **Solution:** $e = [(0.5)(0.012 \text{ kg})(6.5 \text{ m/s})^2] \div [(10 \text{ N})(0.15 \text{ m})]$
   $= 0.17 \text{ or } 17\%$

Input work   15 cm

10 N

Output energy

12 g

6.5 m/s

Your Turn:

a. A sled drops 50 m in height on a hill. The mass of the sled and rider is 70 kg. The sled is going 10 m/s at the bottom of the hill. What is the efficiency of energy conversion from potential to kinetic?

b. A car engine has an efficiency of 15 percent. How much power must go into the engine to produce 75,000 W of output power (100 hp)?

(Answers are listed at the end of the chapter.)

Thermodynamics

Technology and thermodynamics   In the United States, about 89 percent of the energy sources used to generate electricity power are fossil fuels—coal, gas, oil—or nuclear energy (Figure 8.10). About 11 percent of the energy sources are from hydroelectric, solar, wind, and other renewable resources. Both fossil fuels and nuclear power first convert chemical energy to heat, and then use that heat to operate machines such as cars or generators in power plants. **Thermodynamics** is the physics and study of heat.

The first law   The law of conservation of energy is also called the **first law of thermodynamics**. It states that energy cannot be created or destroyed, only converted from one form into another.

The second law   The **second law of thermodynamics** states that when work is done by heat flowing, the output work is always *less* than the amount of heat that flows. A car engine is a good example. From the physics point of view, an engine produces output work from the flow of heat. In Chapter 9, you will read that the rate of heat flow depends on the difference between high and low temperatures. Gasoline burns very hot in comparison to the outside air. Heat from the gasoline does work as it moves from hot to cold.

The efficiency of a heat engine   The *best* efficiency you can *ever* have in any heat engine is $1 - (T_c/T_h)$ where T_h and T_c are the hot and cold temperatures in degrees Kelvin of the engine operates. A typical engine has a combustion temperature of 400°C (673 K). When the outside air is 21°C (294 K) the efficiency is $1 - (294 \text{ K} \div 673 \text{ K})$ or 0.56 or 56 percent. Because the heat does not flow all the way to absolute zero, not all of its energy is available to do work. This lowers the efficiency, even *without any friction*! Friction takes another 20 percent, which gives an overall efficiency of only 36 percent. That means 64 percent of the energy in gasoline flows out the car's tailpipe, radiator, and other parts as waste heat!

Entropy is a measure of the energy in a system that is "lost" as waste heat and that cannot be used to do work. For this reason, entropy is a component of the second law of thermodynamics. In Chapter 7, you learned about the arrow of time. Entropy helps explain why processes that are not 100 percent efficient are irreversible and why time only moves forward.

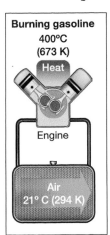

Burning gasoline
400°C
(673 K)
Heat
Engine
Air
21° C (294 K)

thermodynamics - the branch of physics that deals with heat, energy, and work

first law of thermodynamics - the law of conservation of energy: Energy cannot be created or destroyed, only converted from one form into another

second law of thermodynamics - when work is done by heat flowing, the output work must be less than the amount of heat flowing

entropy - a measure of the energy in a system that is not available to do work

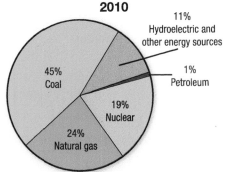

Energy sources for generating electricity in the U.S.
2010

11% Hydroelectric and other energy sources
1% Petroleum
45% Coal
19% Nuclear
24% Natural gas

Approximate values based on information at www.eia.doe.gov.

Figure 8.10: *Energy sources for generating electricity in the United States.*

How energy efficient are living things?

Calories in food   Living things convert chemical energy in food to work done by muscles, heat, reproduction, and other processes. The energy in foods is measured in *kilocalories*, also called *food* Calories. One Calorie is equal to 4,187 joules. Next time you eat a pint of ice cream, consider that it represents 4 million joules of energy (Figure 8.11). By comparison, you do 1 joule of work by lifting that pint of ice cream 21 centimeters.

$$1 \text{ kilocalorie} = 1 \text{ Calorie} = 4,187 \text{ joules}$$

Efficiency is low for living things   In terms of output work, the energy efficiency of living things is quite low. Most of the energy in the food you eat becomes heat; very little becomes physical work. Of course, you do much more than just physical work. For example, you are reading this page. Reading and thinking take energy, too!

Estimating the efficiency of a human   To estimate the efficiency of a person doing physical work, consider climbing a mountain 1,000 meters high. For the average person with a mass of 70 kilograms, the increase in potential energy is 686,000 joules. A human body doing strenuous exercise uses about 660 kilocalories per hour. If it takes three hours to climb the mountain, the body uses 1,980 kilocalories (8,300,000 J). The energy efficiency is about 8 percent (Figure 8.12).

Efficiency of plants   The efficiency of plants is similar. Photosynthesis in plants takes input energy from sunlight and creates sugar, a form of chemical energy. To an animal, the output of a plant is the energy stored in sugar, which can be eaten. The efficiency of pure photosynthesis is 26 percent, meaning 26 percent of the sunlight absorbed by a leaf is stored as chemical energy. As a system however, plants are 1–3 percent efficient at *making sugar* because some energy goes into reproduction, growth, and other plant functions.

Figure 8.11: *A pint of ice cream is the equivalent of 4 million joules of work!*

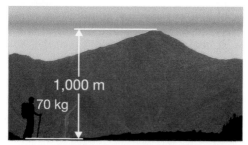

$$E_p = mgh$$
$$= (70 \text{ kg})(9.8 \text{ N/kg})(1,000 \text{ m})$$
$$= 686,000 \text{ J}$$

Figure 8.12: *The output work done against gravity when climbing a mountain equals the gain in potential energy.*

8.2 Section Review

1. Which is greater, the power output of a human or that of an electric light bulb (100 W)?
2. What is thermodynamics and how does it relate to energy?
3. What is your efficiency if you eat 1 million joules of food energy to do 1,000 joules of work?

8.3 Systems in Technology and Nature

You use energy conversion every day and you live in a universe where energy conversions are constantly occurring in all systems. Energy and power are important from the size of atoms to the scale of the entire universe, and everything in between.

> **energy conversion** - the transformation of or changing from one kind of energy to one or more other kinds of energy

Energy flow

The energy flow in a pendulum   A pendulum is a mechanical system in which a mass swings back and forth on a string. At its highest point, a pendulum has only potential energy, because it is not moving. At its lowest point, a pendulum has kinetic energy. As the pendulum swings back and forth, the energy flows back and forth between potential and kinetic, with a little lost as heat from friction (Figure 8.13).

Energy conversion   The flow of energy almost always involves **energy conversion**. In a pendulum, the main conversion is between potential and kinetic energy. A smaller conversion is between kinetic energy and other forms of energy created by friction, such as heat and the wearing away of the string.

Another example   Look at the energy flow diagram for an electric drill (below). Chemical energy, stored in the battery, is converted to electrical energy flowing through wires. The motor converts electrical energy to mechanical energy. The rotation of the motor is transferred to the drill bit by gears. The output work of the drill is the force turning the drill bit and cutting metal or wood. After all these energy conversions are done, the drill is able to produce 28 joules of output work with 72 joules of energy "lost" as heat due to friction. Therefore, the drill is 28 percent efficient.

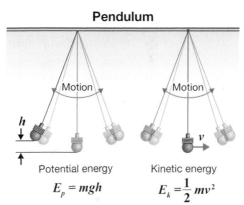

Pendulum

Potential energy
$$E_p = mgh$$

Kinetic energy
$$E_k = \frac{1}{2}mv^2$$

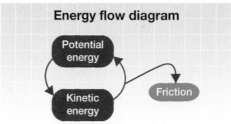

Energy flow diagram

Figure 8.13: *In a pendulum, the energy mostly flows back and forth between potential energy and kinetic energy. Some energy is lost to friction on every swing.*

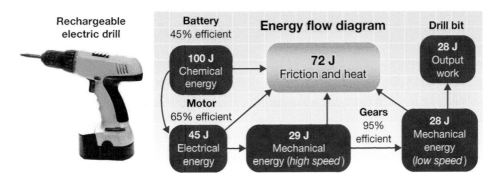

Power in machines

Ranges of power

An average person generates about 150 watts of work and generates about the same amount of heat. You probably use machines with both more and less power every day. On the high end of the power scale are cars and trucks. A typical small car engine has an output power of 150 horsepower (hp), which is 112,000 watts (W). This power is delivered in the form of work done by the wheels to move the car. Moderate power devices include appliances such as washing machines, fans, and blenders. Many household machines have electric motors that do the work, and all use power.

Motors

Most electric motors found around the house range from 1 horsepower (746 watts) down to 1⁄20th of a horsepower (37 watts). Many appliances have “power ratings” that indicate their power. For example, an electric blender might say it uses ⅓ hp, which is a power of about 250 watts. Gasoline engines produce much more power for their weight than electric motors. That is why gasoline engines are used for lawn mowers, tractors, cars, and other machines that need more power. Figure 8.14 lists the power used by some everyday machines.

Estimating power requirements

You can calculate the power required if you know the force you need and the rate at which things have to move. For example, suppose your job is to choose a motor for an elevator. The elevator must lift 10 people, each with a mass of 70 kilograms. The elevator car itself has a mass of 800 kilograms. The plans for the elevator say it must move 3 meters between floors in 3 seconds.

The elevator needs a 60-hp motor

This is work done against gravity so the energy required is $E_p = mgh$. Substituting the numbers gives a value of 44,100 J (Figure 8.15). This amount of energy is used in 3 seconds, so the power required is given by this calculation: 44,100 J ÷ 3 seconds = 14,700 W. Motors are rated by horsepower, so divide again by 746 W/hp to get about 19.7 hp. The smallest motor that would do the job is 19.6 hp. The actual motor required would be about three times larger (60 hp) because our calculation did not include any friction and assumed an efficiency of 100 percent. Engineers do calculations like this when they design buildings, cars, and other systems that use power.

Machine	Power used (W)
Small car	112,000
Lawn mower	2,500
Refrigerator	700
Washing machine	400
Computer	200
Electric drill	200
Television	100
Desk lamp	100
Small fan	50

Figure 8.14: *Power used by some common machines.*

$$m = 10 \times 70\text{ kg} + 800\text{ kg} = 1{,}500\text{ kg}$$

$$\begin{aligned} E_p &= mgh \\ &= (1{,}500\text{ kg}) \times (9.8\text{ N/kg}) \times (3\text{ m}) \\ &= 44{,}100\text{ J} \end{aligned}$$

$$\begin{aligned} P &= E/t \\ &= 44{,}100\text{ J}/3\text{ s} \\ &= 14{,}700\text{ W} \end{aligned}$$

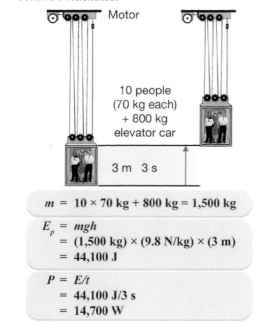

Figure 8.15: *Calculating the power of an elevator.*

Energy flow in natural systems

Steady-state energy balance
Unlike mechanical systems, energy flow in natural systems tends to be in a steady state. **Steady state** means there is a balance between energy in and energy out so that the total energy remains the same. For example, on Earth, radiant energy from the Sun is *energy input*. That energy is converted into many different forms through different processes. However, the average energy of the Earth stays about the same because energy input is balanced by its *energy output,* energy that is radiated back into space (Figure 8.16).

The Sun and the water cycle
An example of a natural system on Earth is the *water cycle*. The main source of energy for the water cycle is the Sun. As shown in the diagram below, the Sun's energy heats the water on Earth's surface. Then, some of this water evaporates, carrying energy from the warm water into the atmosphere. The water vapor goes into the atmosphere and cools, releasing its energy to the air. The cooled water condenses into droplets as precipitation, which falls back to the ground. Eventually, the water makes its way back to the ocean through rivers and groundwater, and the cycle begins again. You may not be surprised to learn that the water cycle and the Sun's energy are responsible for Earth's weather—wind, precipitation, and storms.

> **steady state** - a condition in which the variables describing a system remain constant over time and relative to each other

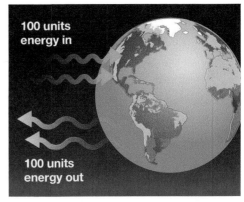

Figure 8.16: *The total energy of Earth stays relatively steady because the energy input from the Sun equals the energy radiated back into space.*

The water cycle

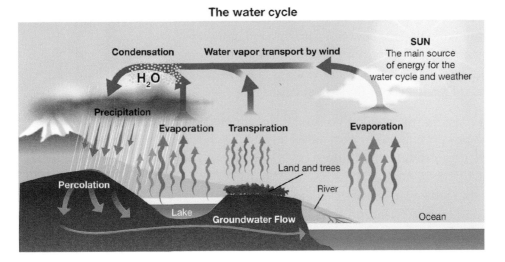

Power in natural systems

Stars and supernovae   Natural systems exhibit a wide range of power, much greater than man-made systems. At the top of the power scale are stars. The Sun has a power output of 3.8×10^{26} watts. This is tremendous power, especially considering the Sun has been shining continuously for more than 4 billion years. A supernova is the explosion of an old star at the end of its normal life. These explosions are among the most powerful events in the known universe, releasing 10 billion times the power of the Sun. Fortunately, supernovae are rare, occurring about once every 75 years in the Milky Way galaxy.

Energy from the Sun   Almost all of the Sun's power comes to Earth as radiant energy, including light. The top of Earth's atmosphere receives an average of 1,373 watts per square meter. In the summer at northern latitudes in the United States, about half that power (660 W/m²) makes it to Earth's surface. The rest is absorbed by the atmosphere or reflected back into space. In the winter, the solar power reaching the surface drops to 350 W/m². About half of the power reaching Earth's surface is in the form of visible light. The remaining power is mostly infrared and ultraviolet light.

Estimating the mass of a gust of wind   The power received from the Sun drives the weather on Earth. To get an idea of the power involved in weather, suppose we estimate the power in a gust of wind. A moderate wind pattern covers 1 square kilometer and involves air up to 200 meters high (Figure 8.17). This represents a volume of 200 million cubic meters (2×10^8 m³). The density of air is close to 1 kg/m³, so the mass of this volume of air is 200 million kilograms.

Estimating the power   Assume that it takes 3 minutes for the wind to go from 0 to 10 meters per second (22 mph). The power required to start the wind blowing is the kinetic energy of the moving air divided by 180 seconds (3 minutes). The result is 56 million watts. Fifty-six million watts is a lot of power! But, 1 square kilometer of Earth's surface receives 1.3 *billion* watts of solar power. A 10-meter-per-second wind gust represents only 4 percent of the available solar power on the 1-square-kilometer area. A storm like a cyclone or hurricane delivers much more power than 56 million watts because much more air is moving (Figure 8.18).

Estimating the power of a gust of wind

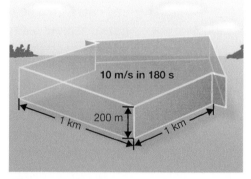

Figure 8.17: *Estimating the power in a gust of wind.*

Image courtesy of NOAA

Figure 8.18: *A powerful storm system like this hurricane has a power of billions of watts. Photo courtesy NASA.*

Energy flow in living systems

Food chains and food pyramids   A **food chain** is a way of describing the flow of energy between living things (Figure 8.19). As shown here, the food chain is often drawn as a pyramid to show that producers are the basis for all other life and also the most abundant.

Producers   Organisms at the bottom of the food chain are *producers*. A producer is a plant or one-celled organism that converts energy from the Sun into chemical energy, such as molecules like sugar. Different types of phytoplankton are producers. Grass and trees are producers, as are corn, wheat, and all the crops we grow for food.

Herbivores   Next up on the food chain are the *herbivores*. A herbivore gets energy by eating plants. Herbivores include rabbits, most insects, and many land and sea animals that eat phytoplankton. Herbivores concentrate energy from plants into complex molecules but they also use energy for living. It takes many producers to support one herbivore. Think of how many blades of grass a single rabbit can eat!

Carnivores   *Carnivores* get their energy by eating herbivores or other carnivores. A hawk is an example of a carnivore. Hawks eat mice and other small herbivores. The shark is also an example of a carnivore that lives in the ocean.

Decomposers   Another important group in a food chain are *decomposers*. Decomposers break down waste and the bodies of other animals into simple molecules that can be used by plants. Earthworms, fungi, crabs in the sea, and many bacteria are examples of decomposers. You can think of decomposers as *recycling* raw materials such as carbon and nitrogen so they can be used by producers.

> **food chain** - a series of steps through which energy and nutrients are transferred from organism to organism in an ecosystem

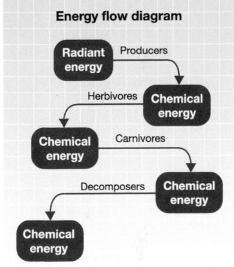

Figure 8.19: *Energy flow in an ecosystem.*

8.3 *Section Review*

1. Draw an energy flow diagram for a person who eats and then runs a race.
2. Describe at least three examples of energy and power in a natural system.

Energy from Ocean Tides

Did you ever build a sand castle along the ocean shore, only to see it swept away by the rising tide? Did you wonder what causes the water level to rise and fall each day? Did you imagine that we could invent machines to transform the kinetic energy of this moving water into electricity to power signal lights, radio beacons, and even entire towns?

Tides are enormous flows of water created by gravity in the Earth-Moon system. Here's how the system works: The Moon causes the water in Earth's oceans to form two bulges. One bulge forms on the side of Earth facing the Moon, while the other bulge forms on the opposite side, the side facing away from the Moon. These bulges turn slowly with the Moon as it orbits Earth, but Earth turns much faster in its daily motion. This spells doom for sand castles built too close to the water's edge! Why? Because the combination of these motions causes most places on Earth to turn through two high-tide bulges about every 25 hours.

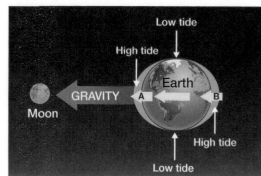

The gravity of the moon causes the tides on Earth.

Power in tides

The energy and power in tides is enormous. A simple estimate can be made using what you know about energy. The surface area of Earth is 511 billion square kilometers, 71 percent of which is covered by water. Suppose half the water in the oceans is lifted ½ meter higher than average. That means lifting 180,000 trillion (1.8×10^{17}) kilograms of water, and creating a potential energy difference of 1.8 million trillion joules (1.8×10^{18} J). Since tides go up and down in most places twice per day, this flow of energy occurs over approximately 12 hours, representing a power of 41 trillion watts (4.1×10^{13} W). This simple estimate is five times the total power used by the 6 billion people living on the planet today.

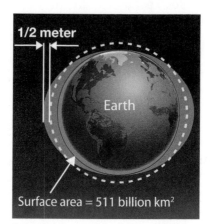

Estimating the energy and power available in the tides.

Extracting tidal power

Many experimental projects have been built to harness the power of tides. Like hydroelectric power, energy from tides creates no pollution, nor does it use up fossil fuels such as petroleum or coal. Three promising techniques are being evaluated and several power plants that use each design have been built.

The simplest approach is to create a basin that fills up at high tide, when the ocean is at its highest level. At low tide, the basin empties through a turbine. The potential energy of the water is converted to mechanical energy that spins the turbine. The spinning turbine causes a coil of wire to rotate inside a magnetic field, transforming the mechanical energy into electrical energy. You will learn more about this process in Unit 6. The tidal power stations in the Bay of Fundy in eastern

Canada produce 20 million watts of electric power when the tide goes out, twice a day. The St. Malo tidal power station in France generates a peak power of 240 million watts.

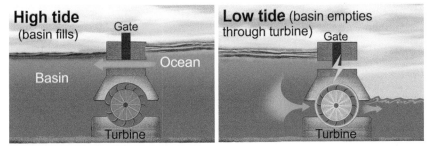

High tide (basin fills)
Gate
Ocean
Basin
Turbine

Low tide (basin empties through turbine)
Gate
Turbine

How a tidal-basin power plant works. The turbine only makes power when the tide is low. The basin fills when the tide is high.

The second approach uses underwater propellers that act like windmills. The propeller blades can swivel so that they generate power when the tide is going out and when it is coming in. This is an advantage over the basin approach, which can only generate power when the tide goes out.

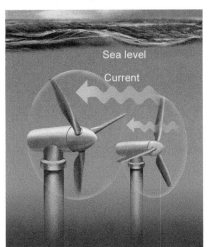

Sea level
Current

A third approach makes small amounts of power for signal lights, radio beacons, and other instruments that need to operate continuously and are relatively close to shore. A tether anchors a cable to the ocean floor. A sliding weight on the cable is attached to a float and the weight goes up and down with the tides. The falling weight operates a tiny generator that provides electric power for the instruments.

Developing tidal power is an active area of engineering research around the world. The idea is simple, but a practical tidal power plant is not simple at all. Because equipment is out in the ocean, a real-world tidal power plant must be extremely rugged to withstand hurricanes, ice storms, and other violent weather. Salt water is very corrosive and moving parts must be well protected from rust. Repair work underwater or in the open ocean is difficult and expensive, so tidal power machines must be very reliable.

The power that moves the oceans and creates tides comes from the total potential and kinetic energy of the Earth-Moon system. Tides are also a frictional force on the motion of Earth and the Moon. Every day, the tides take a bit of energy from the system. Friction from tides slows the rotation of Earth, making the day longer by 0.0016 seconds every 100 years. The Moon also takes longer to make one revolution in its orbit by a tiny fraction of a second. Fifty billion years from now, the slow energy transfer of tides will cause the rotation of Earth to become synchronized with the orbit of the Moon, making a day and a month for both equal to 47 hours. Fortunately, 50 billion years is so far into the future that we need not worry much about days and months getting longer.

QUESTIONS

1. Draw an energy flow diagram for the tidal-basin power plant.

2. You have read that no machine is 100 percent efficient. Think about the float-and-weight device. Where might energy be "lost" in this system? Where would this energy actually go?

3. Name three challenges engineers must overcome to build a reliable tidal power machine.

Chapter 8 Review

Understanding Vocabulary

Select the correct term to complete the sentences.

chemical energy	entropy	radiant energy
electrical energy	first law of	second law of
energy conversion	thermodynamics	thermodynamics
energy flow diagram	food chain	steady state
energy of pressure	mechanical energy	thermodynamics
	nuclear energy	

1. Light is a form of _____.

2. Energy stored in a candy bar is an example of _____.

3. Kinetic and potential energy are both forms of _____.

4. When work is done by heat transfer, the output work is always less than the amount of heat transferred. This is a statement of the _____.

5. _____ means there is a balance between energy "in" and energy "out," so the total energy of a system remains the same.

6. A(n) _____ is a way of describing the flow of energy between living things.

Reviewing Concepts

Section 8.1

1. Why can energy be thought of as "nature's money"?

2. Chemical energy is sometimes thought of as a form of potential energy. Explain this statement.

3. Explain what is meant by the "energy of pressure."

4. Is a stretched rubber band a form of potential or kinetic energy? Explain.

5. Why is work done against friction "lost" to a system?

Section 8.2

6. Describe the meaning of power and how it is calculated.

7. Name two units of power and an application for each.

8. List two different ways to describe power.

9. What is efficiency and how is it calculated?

10. Use the example of a car engine to explain the second law of thermodynamics.

11. Explain, in terms of work output, why the efficiency of living things is quite low.

12. Would the efficiency of a motorcycle be higher or lower than the efficiency of a bicycle? Explain your answer.

Section 8.3

13. Describe the energy conversions that occur with a swinging pendulum.

14. List two devices you use each day that have a high power rating, and two devices that have a relatively low power rating. Explain why these devices have high and low power ratings.

15. What is the primary energy input on Earth? What happens to that energy once it gets to Earth?

16. Why are herbivores more abundant than carnivores?

17. What are decomposers and what is their role in energy transfer?

Solving Problems

Section 8.1

1. A 1-kg ball rolls down a 1-m-high hill and reaches a speed of 20 m/s at the bottom. Was the ball pushed? Explain your answer using calculations of potential and kinetic energy.

2. A ball at the top of a hill has 12.5 J of energy. After it rolls down the hill, it converts 11.6 J to kinetic energy. How much energy is "lost" to the system? Where did that energy go?

3. Use the diagram below to answer questions a–d.

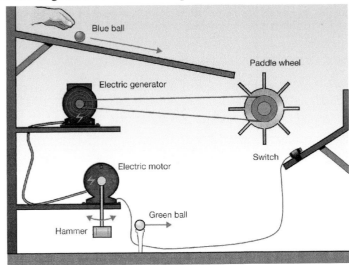

a. Where does the initial energy come from in the apparatus?

b. What forms of energy are involved in the operation of the apparatus?

c. Draw an energy flow diagram for this system.

d. Do you think the apparatus will work? Why or why not?

Section 8.2

4. Michelle weighs 75 kg. She climbs up a 3-m staircase in 3 s.

a. How many joules of work does she do?

b. What is her power in watts?

c. What is her power in horsepower?

d. If Michelle uses 10 Calories to do the work, what is her efficiency?

5. A motor pushes a car with a force of 35 N for a distance of 350 m in 6 s.

a. How much work has the motor accomplished?

b. How powerful is the motor in watts?

c. How powerful is the motor in horsepower?

6. How much power is required to do 55 J of work in 55 s?

7. The manufacturer of a machine says that it is 86% efficient. If you use 70 J of energy to run the machine, how much output work will it produce?

8. Carmen uses 800 J of energy on a jack that is 85% efficient to raise her car to change a flat tire.

a. How much energy is available to raise the car?

b. If the car weighs 13,600 N, how high off the ground can she raise the car?

9. Suppose you exert 200 N of force to push a heavy box across the floor at a constant speed of 2 m/s.

a. What is your power in watts?

b. What would happen to your power if you used the same force to push the box at a constant speed of 1 m/s?

Section 8.3

10. Suppose your job is to choose a motor for an escalator. The escalator must be able to lift 20 people at a time, each with a mass of 70 kg. The escalator must move between two floors, 5 m apart, in 5 s.

a. What energy is required to do this work?

b. What is the power rating of the required motor, in horsepower?

11. Fill in the joules of energy for each box below. Compute the output work and total wasted energy. What is the overall efficiency of the model solar car?

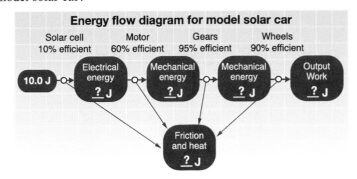

Energy flow diagram for model solar car

Test Practice

Section 8.1

1. The potential energy in a stretched spring is
   a. radiant energy.
   b. mechanical energy.
   c. chemical energy.
   d. energy of pressure.

2. Microwaves are a form of _____ energy.
   a. radiant
   b. mechanical
   c. chemical
   d. nuclear

3. The combustion of gasoline in a car and the splitting of uranium atoms both release _____ as output work.
   a. mechanical energy
   b. radiant energy
   c. thermal energy
   d. energy of pressure

4. A child on a sled is at rest at the top of a hill 10 m high. The child and sled combined have a mass of 20 kg. They sled down the hill and attain a speed of 12 m/s. How much energy was lost to friction when they slid down the hill and converted their potential energy to kinetic energy?
   a. 520 J
   b. 1,240 J
   c. 1,440 J
   d. 1,960 J

Section 8.2

5. Joshua weighs 50 kg. He takes 4 s to carry a 10-kg suitcase up a flight of stairs 3 m high. What is his power?
   a. 45 W
   b. 74 W
   c. 368 W
   d. 441 W

6. An arrow drawn back in a bow has a potential energy of 100 J. If the efficiency of the bow-and-arrow system is 75%, how much kinetic energy will the arrow have when it is launched?
   a. 0 J
   b. 75 J
   c. 100 J
   d. 133 J

7. The second law of thermodynamics states that
   a. energy cannot be created or destroyed, only converted from one form to another.
   b. for every action, there is a reaction force, equal to the action force and opposite in direction.
   c. when work is done by heat flowing, the output work must be less than the amount of heat flow.
   d. the total momentum in a system of interacting objects cannot change as long as all forces act only between objects in the system.

8. Maria uses 30 Calories of energy to climb a hill. Her increase in potential energy is 9,800 J. What is her energy efficiency?
   a. 6%
   b. 7%
   c. 8%
   d. 9%

Section 8.3

9. This energy diagram could represent

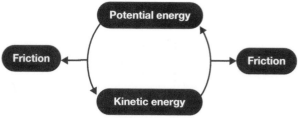

   a. a car rolling down a ramp.
   b. a child on a swing.
   c. a ball rolling across the floor.
   d. all of the above

10. You are hired to design a crane to lift a 500-kg weight to a height of 20 m in 40 s. Assuming the crane is 100% efficient, what is the minimum power rating you should choose for the motor?

    a. 0.3 hp

    b. 1.3 hp

    c. 3.3 hp

    d. 13.1 hp

11. Which of the following systems can reach a steady state of energy flow?

    a. radiant energy on Earth

    b. the water cycle

    c. a food chain

    d. all of the above

12. Producers use photosynthesis to convert radiant energy from the Sun into

    a. chemical energy.

    b. electrical energy.

    c. solar energy.

    d. mechanical energy.

Applying Your Knowledge

Section 8.1

1. Solar or photovoltaic cells are used to power satellites in outer space, yet they are not as commonly used to power households on Earth. Use the Internet to research the use of solar cells to generate electricity for homes. Prepare a short report that answers the following questions:

    a. Why is it more difficult to use solar cells on Earth's surface as opposed to outer space?

    b. What are the advantages and disadvantages of using solar cells to power homes?

    c. What percentage of homes in the United States currently use solar cells to generate some of their power? Is this number on the rise or decline?

    d. Which state currently leads the nation in using solar cells to power homes? What are the reasons?

Section 8.2

2. A typical car is about 13% efficient at converting energy from gasoline to energy of motion. The average car today gets about 25 mi for each gallon of gasoline.

    a. Name at least four energy transformations that occur in a car.

    b. Name three things that contribute to lost energy and prevent a car from ever being 100% efficient.

    c. If a car that currently gets 25 mpg was 100% efficient, what would be its miles-per-gallon rating?

3. Two mountain lions run up a steep hillside. One animal is twice as massive as the other, yet the smaller animal gets to the top of the hill in half the time. Which animal does the most work? Which delivers the most power?

4. Steve lifts a toolbox 0.5 m off the ground in 1 s. If he does the same thing on the Moon, does he have to use more power, less power, or the same amount of power? Explain your answer.

Section 8.3

5. At each level of the food pyramid, about 90% of the usable energy is lost in the form of heat.

    a. Which level requires the most overall input of energy to meet its energy needs?

    b. Use the diagram to explain why a pound of steak costs more than a pound of corn.

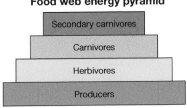

Food web energy pyramid

Secondary carnivores

Carnivores

Herbivores

Producers

 Your Turn **Answers**

Calculating the power in a system (Section 8.2, page 199)

a. 0.98 W

b. 123,930 W or 166 hp

Calculating the efficiency of a process (Section 8.2, page 200)

a. 10%

b. 500,000 W or 670 hp

Unit 4 MATTER AND ENERGY

$$T_{Fahrenheit} = \frac{9}{5} T_{Celsius} + 32$$

Matter and Energy

Have you ever imagined what it would be like to live in an atom-sized world? You may have seen movies where the characters are shrunk to the size of a flea or an even tinier animal. If you were that small, what would the matter around you look like? What if you were even smaller, say the size of an atom? In this world, even the air around you can be dangerous. Everywhere you looked, you would see atoms and molecules whizzing around at amazingly fast speeds and occasionally colliding with one another. Watch out! You might be hit by those particles!

If you were the size of an atom, you would notice that the particles that make up everything are in constant motion. In liquids, the particles slide over and around each other. In solids, the particles vibrate in place. In gases, the particles are moving around freely. Ordinary air would look like a crazy three-dimensional bumper-car ride where you are bombarded from all sides by giant beach balls. It will be helpful to imagine life as an atom as you study this chapter.

VOCABULARY

absolute zero	gas	plasma
atom	heat	pressure
boiling point	heat conduction	solid
calorie	intermolecular forces	specific heat
Celsius scale	Kelvin	temperature
compound	liquid	thermal conductor
convection	melting point	thermal energy
element	mixture	thermal insulator
evaporation	molecule	thermal radiation
Fahrenheit scale		

KEY QUESTIONS

✓ *How is the motion of molecules in an object related to its temperature?*

✓ *Why does it take more energy to heat water than it does to heat steel or aluminum?*

✓ *How does heat get from the Sun to Earth?*

9.1 Matter, Temperature, and Pressure

Lying next to a hot cup of tea, a sugar cube looks like a single piece of matter. But up close, you can tell it is made up of tiny, individual crystals of sugar fused together (Figure 9.1). Can those sugar crystals be broken into even smaller particles? What is the smallest particle of sugar that is still sugar? And what happens to the solid sugar when its placed in hot the tea?

Matter is made of tiny particles in constant motion

The idea of atoms The idea that matter is made of tiny particles goes back to 430 BCE. The Greek philosophers Democritus and Leucippus proposed that matter is made of tiny particles called *atoms*. For 2,300 years, there was little belief in atoms. In 1803, John Dalton revived the idea of atoms, but lacked proof.

Brownian motion In 1827, Robert Brown, a Scottish botanist, was looking through a microscope at tiny grains of pollen in water. He saw that the grains moved in an irregular, jerky way. After observing the same motion in tiny dust particles, he concluded that all tiny particles move in the same way. The irregular, jerky motion was named *Brownian motion* in Brown's honor.

Evidence for atoms In 1905, Albert Einstein proposed that Brownian motion is caused by collisions between visible particles, like pollen grains, and smaller, invisible particles. Einstein's work provided evidence that matter was made of atoms.

An example of smooth motion As a comparison, imagine throwing marbles at an inflatable rubber tube floating in the water. The impact of any single marble is much too small to make the tube move. However, if you throw enough marbles, the tube will start moving slowly. The motion of the tube will appear smooth because the mass of a single marble is tiny compared to the mass of the tube (Figure 9.2).

An example of jerky motion Now, imagine throwing marbles at a foam cup floating in the water. The cup's motion is not smooth at all. The motion is jerky, and the impact of the marbles can be seen. The mass of the cup is not much greater than the mass of a marble. A pollen grain suspended in water moves around in a jerky manner like the foam cup. The irregular motion is caused by the impact of individual water molecules on the pollen grain. Like the cup, the mass of a pollen grain is not so large that impacts with water molecules are smoothed out.

Figure 9.1: *Up close, you can see that a sugar cube is made of crystals.*

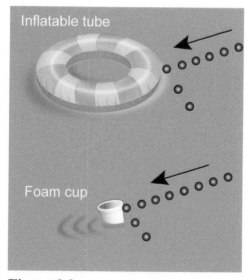

Figure 9.2: *Throwing marbles at an inflatable rubber tube in water moves it smoothly. Throwing the same marbles at a foam cup moves the cup in a jerky way, like Brownian motion.*

Atoms are the smallest particles that make up elements

Elements and atoms An **element** is a substance made up of one kind of atom. A single **atom** is the smallest particle of an element that has the chemical identity of the element. For example, you can keep cutting a piece of the element gold into smaller and smaller pieces until you cannot cut it any more. That smallest particle you can divide it into is one atom. A single atom of gold is the smallest piece of gold. If you split the gold atom, it will no longer be gold.

> **element** - a pure substance that contains only atoms with the same number of protons in each atom's nucleus
>
> **atom** - the smallest particle of an element that exists alone or in combination with other atoms

Gold atom

Atomic magnification

How small are atoms? A single atom is like a sphere with a diameter of about 10^{-10} meters. This means that you can fit 10,000,000,000 (10^{10}) atoms side-by-side in a 1-meter length. You may think a sheet of aluminum foil is thin, but it is actually more than 200,000 atoms thick (Figure 9.3).

Atoms of an element are similar Each element has a unique type of atom. The diagram below illustrates the relative sizes of some atoms you may be familiar with. All atoms of a given element are defined by their *atomic number*, which is the number of *protons* in the nucleus of each atom. If you could examine a million atoms of carbon you would find them all to have the same number of protons, or atomic number. You will find more details about atoms and elements in Chapter 10.

Sodium atom   Carbon atom   Aluminum atom   Oxygen atom   Hydrogen atom

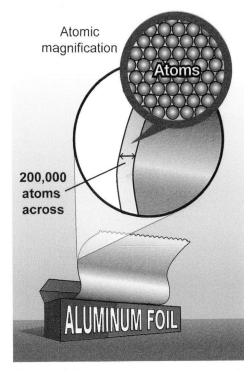

Atomic magnification

Atoms

200,000 atoms across

ALUMINUM FOIL

Figure 9.3: *A thin sheet of aluminum foil is 200,000 atoms thick.*

Compounds contain two or more elements

Compounds Sometimes elements are found in their pure form, but more often they are combined with other elements. Most substances contain several elements combined together. A **compound** is a substance that contains two or more different elements chemically joined and that has the same composition throughout. For example, water is a compound that is made from the elements hydrogen and oxygen. Figure 9.4 shows some familiar compounds.

Molecules If you could magnify a sample of pure water so you could see its atoms, you would notice that the hydrogen and oxygen atoms are joined together in groups of two hydrogen atoms and one oxygen atom. These groups are called *molecules*. A **molecule** is a group of two or more atoms joined together by *chemical bonds*. A compound is made up of only one type of molecule. Some compounds, like table salt (sodium chloride), are made of equal numbers of different atoms, bound together in multi-atom groups. This is different from individual molecules consisting of the least number of each type of atom in the compound (Figure 9.4, bottom).

Mixtures Most of the things you see and use in everyday life are mixtures. A **mixture** contains more than one kind of atom, molecule, or compound. Cola is a mixture that contains water, carbon dioxide, corn syrup, caramel color, phosphoric acid, natural flavors, caffeine, and other substances.

compound - a substance made of two or more elements that cannot be separated by physical means

molecule - the smallest particle of a compound that has the identity of the compound

mixture - a substance that contains more than one kind of atom, molecule, or compound

Compounds contain more than one type of atom joined together.

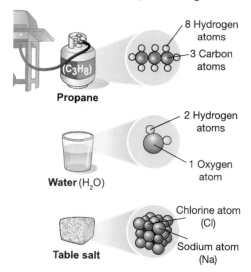

8 Hydrogen atoms

3 Carbon atoms

Propane

2 Hydrogen atoms

1 Oxygen atom

Water (H_2O)

Chlorine atom (Cl)

Sodium atom (Na)

Table salt

Table salt is a compound made of equal numbers of sodium and chlorine atoms.

Element
One single kind of atom

Compound
One type of molecule.

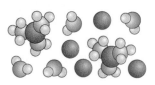

Mixture
Combination of different compounds and/or elements

Figure 9.4: *Examples of compounds.*

Particles of matter and temperature

Particles in motion The atoms and molecules of an object are in constant motion, even if the object is a solid. Particles in a solid act like they are connected by springs (Figure 9.5). Each particle is free to move a certain amount.

Temperature and energy The **temperature** of a solid, for example, is a measure of the average kinetic energy of the particles in the solid. Therefore, at higher temperatures, kinetic energy increases and this energy of motion is greater, so the particles move more vigorously.

Random motion and temperature At any given temperature, the motion of the particles in a solid is random motion. This means that at any instant, there are as many particles moving in one direction as in the opposite direction. When you look at the object as a whole, it stays at rest even though its particles are individually moving. As the object's temperature increases, the particles shake more quickly. Suppose you place a rock in a hot oven. The particles in the rock move around more quickly, but the rock as a whole stays at rest.

If you throw a rock does it get hotter? Now, suppose you throw the rock at a velocity of 5 m/s to the right. Although the individual particles are still shaking randomly, they are now moving an additional 5 m/s due to the kinetic energy you gave the rock. The motion of the thrown rock is average motion in one direction. Temperature and the random motion of particles are not affected by kinetic energy of average motion. So, throwing a rock at 5 m/s does not make it hotter (Figure 9.6).

Average motion versus random motion Each particle in the rock has kinetic energy from its random motion, as well as from the average motion of the whole rock. Temperature measures the kinetic energy in the random motion only. Therefore, temperature is not affected by any kinetic energy associated with average motion. When you heat a rock, each particle moves with more energy but the whole rock stays in the same place.

Melting and boiling At high enough temperatures, the particles in a rock get so much energy that they start to break away from each other. The rock *melts*. If you keep heating rock, it will turn to a liquid and start to boil. In *boiling*, some particles have enough energy to leave the liquid altogether.

temperature - a measure of the average kinetic energy of the particles in a sample of matter

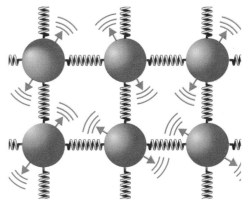

Figure 9.5: *Particles in a solid are connected by bonds that act like springs.*

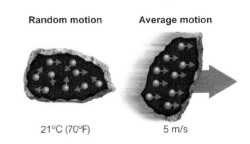

Figure 9.6: *Temperature is related to the random motion of particles in a rock. The velocity of a rock is related to its average motion in one direction.*

The phases of matter

Solid, liquid, and gas
Most of the matter you find around you is in one of three phases: solid, liquid, or gas. A **solid** holds its shape and does not flow. The molecules in a solid vibrate in place, but on average, don't move far from their places. A **liquid** has a definite volume, but does not hold its shape—it flows. The molecules in a liquid are about as close together as they are in a solid, but have enough energy to exchange positions with their neighbors and move around. A **gas** flows like a liquid, but can also change shape to fill its container. In other words, the volume of a gas can change. The molecules in a gas have enough energy to break away from each other, since they are much farther apart than molecules in a liquid or solid.

Intermolecular forces
Neighboring atoms and molecules are attracted through *intermolecular forces*. These **intermolecular forces** have different strengths for different molecules. The strength of the intermolecular forces determines whether matter exists as a solid, liquid, or gas at any given temperature.

Temperature verusus intermolecular forces
Within all matter, there is a competition between temperature and intermolecular forces (Figure 9.7). The kinetic energy from temperature tends to push molecules apart. When the temperature is higher, it wins the competition: The molecules separate, and you have a gas. The intermolecular forces tend to bring molecules together. When intermolecular forces are higher, they win the competition: Molecules clump tightly together and you have a solid. A liquid is somewhere in between. Molecules in a liquid are not stuck firmly together, but they cannot escape and fly away, either.

Strength of intermolecular forces
Iron is a solid at room temperature. Water is a liquid at room temperature. This tells you that the intermolecular forces between iron atoms are stronger at room temperature than those between water molecules. In fact, iron is used for building things because it so strong. Its strength is an effect of the strong intermolecular forces between iron atoms.

Temperature
As the temperature changes, the balance between temperature and intermolecular forces changes. At temperatures below 0°C, the intermolecular forces in water are strong enough to overcome temperature and water becomes a solid—ice!

solid - a phase of matter that holds its volume and shape and does not flow

liquid - a phase of matter that has definite volume but can change its shape and flow

gas - a phase of matter that flows and can expand or contract to fill its container

intermolecular forces - the forces between atoms or molecules that determine their phase—solid, liquid, or gas—at any given temperature

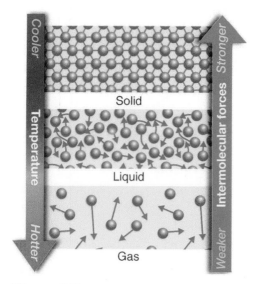

Figure 9.7: *Atoms and molecules in the solid, liquid, and gas phases.*

Changing phases

Melting and freezing
The **melting point** is the temperature at which a substance changes from solid to liquid (melting) or from liquid to solid (freezing). For this reason, the melting point can be called the freezing point, too. Melting points vary among substances because different substances have different intermolecular forces. When these forces are strong, it takes more energy to separate the molecules from each other. Water melts at 0°C. Iron melts at a much higher temperature, about 1,500°C. The difference in melting points indicates the intermolecular forces between iron atoms are stronger than those between water molecules.

Boiling and condensing
When enough energy is added, the intermolecular forces are overcome and a liquid becomes a gas. The **boiling point** is the temperature at which a substance changes from liquid to gas (boiling) or from gas to liquid (condensing). When water boils, you can see the change in the liquid as bubbles of water vapor (gas) form and rise to the surface. The bubbles in boiling water are not air, but water vapor.

Changes in phase require energy
As you add energy to an ice cube, its temperature increases. Once it reaches 0°C, the temperature stops increasing as ice starts to melt and form liquid water (Figure 9.8). With more energy, more ice melts but the temperature stays the same. This is because the energy is being used to break the intermolecular forces and change the solid into a liquid. Once all the ice is melted, the temperature starts to rise again as energy is added. Figure 9.8 shows the temperature change in an experiment. When energy is added or subtracted, either the temperature changes or the phase changes, but usually not both at the same time.

Evaporation
Evaporation occurs when molecules go from liquid to gas at temperatures below the boiling point. Temperature is a measure of the average random kinetic energy of molecules. Some molecules have energy above the average and some below. Some of the highest-energy molecules have enough energy to evaporate if they are near the surface. As the molecules become a gas, they carry energy away. The average energy of the liquid molecules left behind is lowered. Evaporation cools the surface of a liquid. This is how your body cools off on a hot day. The evaporation of sweat cools your skin.

melting point - the temperature at which a substance changes from solid to liquid (melting) or liquid to solid (freezing)

boiling point - the temperature at which a substance changes from liquid to gas (boiling) or from gas to liquid (condensing)

evaporation - the process by which atoms or molecules leave a liquid and become a gas at a temperature below the boiling point

Start with ice at –20°C.   Then, add heat energy at a constant rate.

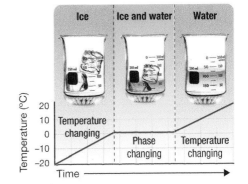

Figure 9.8: *Phase changes.*

Measuring temperature

Fahrenheit There are two commonly-used temperature scales. On the **Fahrenheit scale**, water freezes at 32 degrees and boils at 212 degrees (Figure 9.9). There are 180 Fahrenheit degrees between the freezing point and the boiling point of water. Temperature in the United States is commonly measured in Fahrenheit. For example, 68°F is a comfortable room temperature.

Celsius The **Celsius scale** divides the difference between the freezing and boiling points of water into 100 degrees. Water freezes at 0°C and boils at 100°C. Most science and engineering temperature measurements are in Celsius because 0 and 100 are easier to remember and work with than 32 and 212. Most other countries use the Celsius scale for all descriptions of temperature, including daily weather reports.

Converting between the scales Because the United States still uses the Fahrenheit scale, it is useful to know how to convert between the two scales.

> **CONVERTING BETWEEN FAHRENHEIT AND CELSIUS**
>
> $$T_{Fahrenheit} = \frac{9}{5}T_{Celsius} + 32 \quad \bigg| \quad T_{Celsius} = \frac{5}{9}(T_{Fahrenheit} - 32)$$

> **Fahrenheit scale** - a temperature scale on which water freezes at 32 degrees Fahrenheit (or 32°F) and water boils at 212°F
>
> **Celsius scale** - a temperature scale on which 0 equals the temperature at which water freezes (0°C) and 100 is the temperature at which water boils (100°C)

 Converting between temperature scales

A French recipe says to bake a cake at a temperature of 200°C for 45 minutes. At what temperature should you set your oven, which uses the Fahrenheit scale?

1. ***Looking for:***   You are asked for the temperature in degrees Fahrenheit.

2. ***Given:***   You are given the temperature in degrees Celsius.

3. ***Relationships:***   Use the conversion formula: $T_F = \frac{9}{5}T_C + 32$

4. ***Solution:*** $T_F = \left(\frac{9}{5}\right)(200) + 32 = 392°F$

Your Turn:

a. The average July temperature in Iceland is 11.2°C. What is the average July temperature in degrees Fahrenheit?

(Answers are listed at the end of the chapter.)

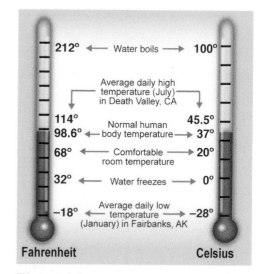

Figure 9.9: *The Celsius and Fahrenheit temperature scales.*

Absolute zero

Absolute zero There is a limit to how cold matter can get. As the temperature is reduced, molecules move more and more slowly. When the temperature gets down to **absolute zero**, molecules have the lowest energy they can have. The temperature cannot get any lower. You can think of absolute zero as the temperature where molecules are completely frozen, like ice, with no motion. Technically, molecules never become absolutely motionless, but the kinetic energy is so small it might as well be zero. Absolute zero occurs at −273°C (−459°F). You cannot have a temperature lower than absolute zero.

The Kelvin scale The **Kelvin** temperature scale is useful for many scientific calculations because it starts at absolute zero. For example, the pressure in a gas depends on how fast the atoms are moving. The Kelvin scale is used because it measures the actual energy of atoms. A temperature in Celsius measures only the relative energy, which is relative to zero Celsius.

Converting to Kelvin The Kelvin (K) unit of temperature is the same size as the Celsius unit with one difference: You add 273 to the temperature in Celsius to get the temperature in Kelvins. For example, a temperature of 21°C is equal to 294 K (21 + 273 = 294).

A fourth state of matter at high temperatures Temperature can be raised almost indefinitely. As the temperature increases, an exotic form of matter appears called **plasma**. For example, at 10,000°C atoms become ionized; electrons break loose from the rest of the atom. The resulting matter is composed of positive ions and negative electrons. Because the electrons are free to move independently, a plasma can conduct electricity. Lightning and the Sun are examples of plasmas. In fact, astronomers have found that many parts of the universe are made of plasma, including the Eagle nebula in Figure 9.10.

absolute zero - the lowest possible temperature—0 K on the Kelvin temperature scale—where molecules have the lowest energy they can have

Kelvin - the temperature scale that starts at absolute zero and measures the actual energy of atoms

plasma - an ionized gas phase of matter such as found in stars, lightning, and some kinds of electric lights

Figure 9.10: *Many parts of the universe are made of plasma, including the Eagle nebula, shown here.*

Summarizing the phases of matter

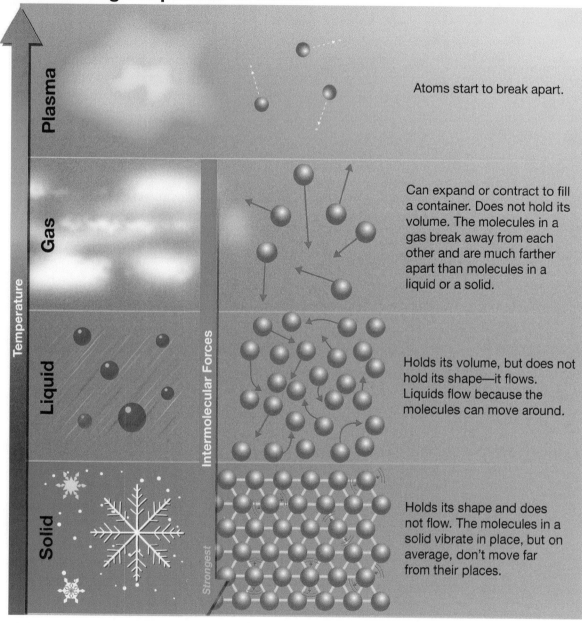

Plasma

Atoms start to break apart.

Gas

Can expand or contract to fill a container. Does not hold its volume. The molecules in a gas break away from each other and are much farther apart than molecules in a liquid or a solid.

Liquid

Holds its volume, but does not hold its shape—it flows. Liquids flow because the molecules can move around.

Solid

Holds its shape and does not flow. The molecules in a solid vibrate in place, but on average, don't move far from their places.

Temperature

Intermolecular Forces

Strongest

Engineering and Technology: Internal Combustion Engines

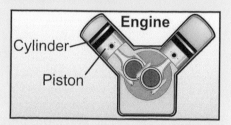

One of the ways to make car engines more efficient is to let them reach higher temperatures. Unfortunately, steel melts at about 1,500°C. Steel gets soft before it melts, so engines typically can't operate at temperatures even close to the melting point. Some new engine technologies use cylinders and pistons made of ceramics. A ceramic stays hard and strong at a much higher temperature than steel.

Particles of matter and pressure

Pressure and particles   Like temperature, pressure is related to the motion of particles. **Pressure** is associated with fluids—gases and liquids. The intermolecular forces among particles in gases and liquids are weak compared to those between particles in solids. Therefore, particles in fluids move around. They collide with each other and with the solid walls of a container creating pressure.

> **pressure** - the force exerted per unit area by particles of matter in a fluid and which acts in all directions in a container

Pressure and the third law   Think about water in a glass pitcher. On a molecular level, water molecules are moving around; they bounce off of the inner surface of the pitcher. It takes force to make a molecule reverse its direction and bounce the other way. That force is applied to the molecule by the surface. According to Newton's third law, an equal and opposite reaction force is exerted by the molecule on the surface. The reaction force is what creates the pressure acting on the inner surface of the pitcher. Trillions of molecules per second are constantly bouncing against every square millimeter of that inner surface. Pressure comes from the collisions of those molecules.

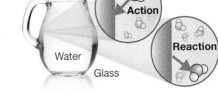

PRESSURE AND FORCE

Force (N)   Pressure (Pa or N/m²)

$$F = P \times A$$

Area (m²)

Figure 9.11: *Pressure creates a force on any surface immersed in a liquid. The force is equal to the pressure times the area of the surface on which the force acts.*

Pressure creates forces on surfaces   Pressure creates a force on any surface immersed in fluid. That force is equal to the pressure times the area on which the force acts (Figure 9.11). Units of pressure include the pascal (Pa) and newtons per meter squared (N/m^2). Dams and submarines are built to withstand the tremendous pressures found deep underwater. Figure 9.12 illustrates how air pressure in a car tire influences the shape of the tire.

9.1 Section Review

1. Which system has a higher random, average kinetic energy of its atoms, a glass of iced tea or a cup of hot tea?
2. Explain why particles in a gas are free to move far away from each other.
3. Why might you experience lower air pressure at the top of a mountain than at sea level?

Figure 9.12: *The pressure inside the tires holds the car up. When the tire pressure is too low, the shape of the tire changes because more area is needed to exert enough force to hold up the car.*

9.2 What is Heat?

To change the temperature of a system you must add or subtract energy. For example, when it's cold outside, you turn up the *heat* in your home and the temperature goes up. You know that adding heat increases the temperature, but have you ever thought about exactly what "heat" is? What does "heat" have to do with the temperature?

Heat, temperature, and thermal energy

Thermal energy   When you heat a pot of soup on an electric stove, *electrical energy* is converted into *thermal energy*. Thermal energy is related to temperature. Temperature measures the average, random kinetic energy of particles—molecules or atoms—in a sample. **Thermal energy** is the *sum* of all the kinetic energies of *all* of the particles in a sample.

Thermal energy depends on mass and temperature   The amount of thermal energy depends on the temperature and also on the *amount* of matter you have. Think about heating two pots of water. One pot contains 1,000 grams of water and the other contains 2,000 grams of water. Both pots are heated to the same final temperature (Figure 9.13). Which takes more energy? The pot holding 2,000 grams of water takes twice as much energy as the pot with 1,000 grams, even though both start and finish at the same temperature. The two pots illustrate the difference between temperature and thermal energy. Thermal energy is the energy of *all* the particles in a sample of matter, and therefore depends on mass and temperature.

Moving thermal energy   When you hold an ice cube in your hand, thermal energy moves from your hand to the ice cube and the ice begins to melt. The movement of thermal energy is called **heat**. Thermal energy moves when there is a temperature difference. Thermal energy moves in a predictable way from a warmer object (higher energy) to a cooler one (lower energy). In the ice cube example, the thermal energy lost by your hand equals the thermal energy gained by the ice. Movement of thermal energy stops when the objects involved reach the same temperature.

> **thermal energy** - the sum of the kinetic energies of *all* of the atoms and molecules in a mass
>
> **heat** - the movement of thermal energy from one object to another object due to a temperature difference

Both pots of water boil at 100°C

2,000 grams

1,000 grams

Figure 9.13: *It takes twice as much energy to heat a 2,000-gram mass of water compared to a 1,000-gram mass.*

Units of heat and thermal energy

The joule There are three units that are commonly used for heat and thermal energy. Conversion factors for these units are given in Figure 9.14. The metric unit for measuring heat is the *joule*. This is the same joule used to measure all forms of energy, not just heat. A joule is a small amount of heat. The average hair dryer puts out 1,200 joules of heat every second!

The calorie The **calorie** is defined as the quantity of heat needed to increase the temperature of 1 gram of water by 1 degree Celsius. One calorie is a little more than 4 joules. You may have noticed that most food packages list "Calories per serving." The unit used for measuring energy content of food is the kilocalorie, which equals 1,000 calories. The kilocalorie is often written as Calorie (with a capital *C*). If a candy bar contains 210 Calories, it contains 210,000 calories, or 879,060 joules!

The British thermal unit Still another unit of heat energy you may encounter is the *British thermal unit*, or Btu. The Btu is often used to measure the heat produced by heating systems or heat removed by air-conditioning systems. A Btu is the quantity of heat it takes to increase the temperature of 1 pound of water by 1 degree Fahrenheit. One Btu is a little more than 1,000 joules.

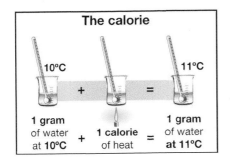
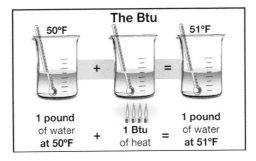

Why so many units? The calorie and Btu were being used to measure heat well before scientists knew what heat really was. They are still used because people give up familiar ways very slowly, even 100 years after heat was shown to be a form of energy!

> **calorie** - a unit of energy equal to 4.184 joules, which is the amount of heat energy required to raise the temperature of 1 gram of water by 1°C

Units	Is equal to
1 calorie	4.184 joules
1 kilocalorie	1,000 calories
1 Btu	1,055 joules
1 Btu	252 calories

Figure 9.14: *Conversion table for units.*

Heat and Work

Many human inventions use heat to do work, since work can be done when heat flows from a higher temperature to a lower temperature. This happens in a car engine, which uses the heat released by the burning of gasoline. However, only a small fraction of the heat is converted into work that makes the car move. This is why a running car gives off so much heat through the radiator and exhaust.

Specific heat

Temperature and mass

If you add heat to an object, how much will its temperature increase? It depends in part on the mass of the object. If you double the mass of the object you are going to heat, you need twice as much energy to increase the temperature.

Temperature and type of material

The amount of temperature increase also depends on the kind of material you are heating. It takes different amounts of energy to raise the temperature of different materials. For example, you need to add 4,184 joules of heat to 1 kilogram of water to raise the temperature by 1°C. (Figure 9.15). You only need to add 470 joules to raise the temperature of a kilogram of steel by 1°C. It takes nine times more energy to raise the temperature of water by 1°C than it does to raise the temperature of the same mass of steel by 1°C. Knowing how materials resist temperature change is important. For example, if you know that an apple pie's filling is much more resistant to temperature change than its crust, you might test the filling temperature before taking a bite!

Specific heat

The **specific heat** of a substance is a property that indicates how much heat is needed to raise the temperature of 1 kilogram of a material by 1 degree Celsius. A large specific heat means you have to put in a lot of energy for each degree increase in temperature. Specific heat is measured in joules per kilogram per degree Celsius (joule/kg·°C).

The specific heat is the amount of energy that will raise the temperature of 1 kilogram by 1 degree Celsius.

Uses for specific heat

Knowing the specific heat tells you how quickly the temperature of a material will change as it gains or loses energy. If the specific heat is *low* (like steel), then temperature will change relatively quickly because each degree of change takes less energy. If the specific heat is *high* (like water), then the temperature will change relatively slowly because each degree of change takes more energy. Hot apple pie filling stays hot for a long time because it is mostly water, and therefore has a large specific heat. Pie crust has a much lower specific heat and cools much more rapidly (Figure 9.16).

> **specific heat** - a property of a substance that tells us how much heat is needed to raise the temperature of 1 kg by 1°C

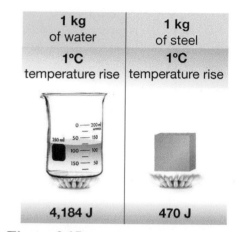

Figure 9.15: *It takes 4,184 joules to raise the temperature of 1 kilogram of water by 1°C. The same temperature rise takes only 470 joules for a kilogram of steel.*

Figure 9.16: *The filling of apple pie has a higher specific heat than the crust.*

Calculating energy changes from heat

How can you find how much energy it would take to heat a swimming pool or boil a liter of water? The heat equation below tells you how much energy (E) it takes to change the temperature (T) of a mass (m) of a substance with a specific heat value (Cp). Figure 9.17 shows the specific heat values for some common materials.

Material	Specific heat (J/kg·°C)
water	4,184
oil	1,900
wood	1,800
aluminum	900
concrete	880
glass	800
steel	470
silver	235
gold	129

HEAT EQUATION

Heat energy (J) — $E = mC_p (T_2 - T_1)$ — Specific heat (J/kg·°C)

Mass (kg)   Change in temperature (°C)

Figure 9.17: *Specific heat values of some common materials. Note: Specific heat values vary with temperature and air pressure.*

Calculating the heat required to reach a temperature

How much heat is needed to raise the temperature of a 250-liter hot tub from 20°C to 40°C? The specific heat of water is 4,184 J/kg·°C. (Hint: One liter of water has a mass of 1 kilogram.)

1. *Looking for:*   You are looking for the amount of heat energy needed in joules.

2. *Given:*   You are given the volume in liters, the temperature change in °C, and the specific heat in J/kg·°C. You are also given a conversion factor for volume to mass of water.

3. *Relationships:* $E = mC_p(T_2 - T_1)$

4. *Solution:* $E = (250\ \text{L} \times 1\ \text{kg/L}) \times 4{,}184\ \text{J/kg}°\text{C}\ (40°\text{C} - 20°\text{C}) = 20{,}920{,}000\ \text{J}$

Your Turn:

a. How much heat energy is needed to raise the temperature of 2 kilograms of concrete from 10°C to 30°C? The specific heat of concrete is 880 J/kg·°C.

b. How much heat energy is needed to raise the temperature of 5 grams of gold from 20°C to 200°C? The specific heat of gold is 129 J/kg·°C.

(Answers are listed at the end of the chapter.)

Why is specific heat different for different materials?

Why specific heat varies   In general, a material made up of heavy atoms or molecules has a low specific heat compared with a material made up of lighter ones. This is because temperature measures the average kinetic energy *per particle*. Heavy particles mean fewer per kilogram. Energy that is divided among fewer particles means more energy per particle, and therefore more temperature change.

An example: silver and aluminum   Silver's specific heat is 235 J/kg·°C and 4,000 joules is enough heat to raise the temperature of one kilogram of silver by 17°C. Aluminum's specific heat is 900 J/kg·°C, and 4,000 joules only raises the temperature of 1 kilogram of aluminum by 4.4°C. The silver has fewer atoms than the aluminum because silver atoms are heavier than aluminum atoms. When energy is added, each atom of silver gets more energy than each atom of aluminum because there are fewer silver atoms in a kilogram. Because the energy per atom is greater, the temperature increase in the silver is also greater.

Silver
Specific heat: 235 J/kg·°C
Heavier atoms mean fewer atoms per kilogram

1 kilogram

- Energy is spread over *fewer* atoms
- *More* energy per atom
- *Higher* temperature gain per joule (lower specific heat)

Aluminum
Specific heat: 900 J/kg·°C
Lighter atoms mean more atoms per kilogram

1 kilogram

- Energy is spread over *more* atoms
- *Less* energy per atom
- *Lower* temperature gain per joule (higher specific heat)

The specific heat of water

Water has a higher specific heat than many other common materials. Its specific heat is more than four times greater than the specific heat of rocks and soil. The high specific heat of water is very important to our planet. Water covers about 75 percent of Earth's surface. One of the fundamental reasons our planet is habitable is that the huge amount of water on it helps regulate the temperature. Land, because it has a low specific heat, experiences large changes in temperature when it absorbs heat from the Sun. Water tends to have smaller changes in temperature when it absorbs the same amount of heat. During the day, oceans help keep Earth cool, while at night, they keep Earth warm by slowing the rate at which heat is emitted back into space.

Image courtesy NASA

9.2 Section Review

1. What is the difference between temperature and thermal energy? Discuss particles of matter in your answer.

2. Calculate the heat energy needed to raise the temperature of 20 kg of water from 0°C to 35°C?

9.3 Heat Transfer

Thermal energy flows from a material at a higher temperature to a material at a lower temperature. This process is called *heat transfer*. How is heat transferred from material to material, or from place to place? It turns out there are three ways that heat flows. In this section, you will learn about *heat conduction*, *convection*, and *thermal radiation*.

Heat conduction

What is conduction? **Heat conduction** is the transfer of heat by the direct contact of particles of matter. If you have ever held a mug of hot cocoa, you have experienced conduction. Heat is transferred from the mug to your hand. Conduction only occurs between two materials at different temperatures when they are touching each other. In conduction, heat can also be transferred *through* materials. If you stir hot cocoa with a metal spoon, heat is transferred from the cocoa, *through* the spoon, and *to* your hand.

> *Conduction is the transfer of heat by the direct contact of particles of matter.*

How does conduction work? Imagine placing a cold spoon in the mug of hot cocoa (Figure 9.18). The molecules in the cocoa have a higher average kinetic energy than those of the spoon. The molecules in the spoon exchange energy with the molecules in the cocoa through collisions. The molecules in the spoon spread the energy up the spoon through the intermolecular forces between them. Conduction works through both collisions and also through the intermolecular forces between molecules.

Thermal equilibrium As collisions continue, the molecules of the hotter material (the cocoa) lose energy and the molecules of the cooler material (the spoon) gain energy. The kinetic energy of the hotter material is transferred to the cooler material, as the molecular collisions occur. Eventually, both materials are at the same temperature. When this happens, they are in *thermal equilibrium*. Thermal equilibrium occurs when two bodies have the same temperature. No heat flows in thermal equilibrium because the temperatures are the same.

> **heat conduction** - the transfer of thermal energy by the direct contact of particles of matter

Figure 9.18: *Heat flows by conduction from the hot cocoa into and up the spoon.*

Thermal conductors and insulators

Which state of matter conducts heat best? Conduction can happen in solids, liquids, and gases. Solids make the best conductors because their particles are packed closely together. Because the particles in a gas are so far apart, relatively few collisions occur; air, for instance, is a poor conductor of heat. This explains why many materials used to keep things warm, such as fiberglass insulation and down jackets, contain air pockets (Figure 9.19).

Thermal conductors and insulators Materials that conduct heat easily are called **thermal conductors** and those that conduct heat poorly are called **thermal insulators**. For example, metal is a thermal conductor, and a foam cup is a thermal insulator. The words *conductor* and *insulator* are also used to describe a material's ability to conduct electrical current. In general, good electrical conductors—like silver, copper, gold, and aluminum—are also good thermal conductors.

> **thermal conductor** - a material that conducts heat easily
> **thermal insulator** - a material that conducts heat poorly

Figure 9.19: *Because air is a poor conductor of heat, a down jacket keeps you warm in the cold of winter.*

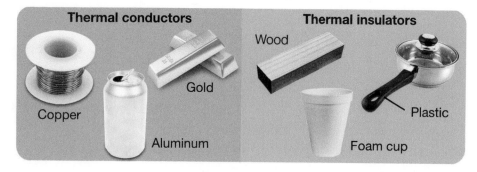

Heat conduction cannot occur through a vacuum Conduction happens only if there are particles available to collide with one another. For this reason, heat transfer by conduction cannot occur in the vacuum of space. One way to create an excellent thermal insulator on Earth is to make a vacuum. A thermos bottle keeps liquids hot for hours using a vacuum. It is a container consisting of a bottle surrounded by a slightly larger bottle. Air molecules have been removed from the space between the bottles to create a vacuum. This prevents heat transfer by conduction. A small amount of heat is conducted through the cap and the glass where the two walls meet, so eventually the contents will cool, only much slower than they would otherwise (Figure 9.20).

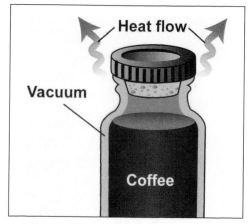

Figure 9.20: *A thermos bottle uses a vacuum to prevent heat transfer by conduction and convection.*

Convection

What is convection? Have you ever watched water boil in a pot? Bubbles form on the bottom and rise to the top. Hot water near the bottom of the pan circulates up, forcing cooler water near the surface to sink. This circulation carries heat through the water (Figure 9.21). This heat transfer process is called **convection**. Convection is the transfer of heat through the motion of fluids, such as air and water.

Natural convection Fluids expand when they heat up. Since expansion increases the volume, but not the mass, a warm fluid has a lower mass-to-volume ratio (called *density*) than the surrounding cooler fluid. In a container, warmer fluid floats to the top and cooler fluid sinks to the bottom. This is called *natural convection*.

Forced convection In many houses, a boiler heats water and then pumps circulate the water to the rooms. Since the heat is being carried by a moving fluid, this is another example of convection. However, since the fluid is *forced* to flow by the pumps, this is called forced convection.

Natural and forced convection Both natural and forced convection often occur at the same time. Forced convection transfers heat to a hot radiator. The heat from the hot radiator then warms the room air by natural convection The warmer air rises and cooler air from the far side of the room replaces it. Then the cooler air is warmed and rises. The circulation distributes heat throughout the room.

> **convection** - the transfer of thermal energy by the motion of a fluid

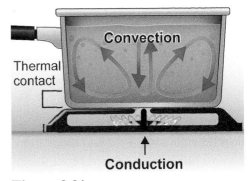

Figure 9.21: *Convection currents in water. The hot water at the bottom of the pot rises to the top and replaces the cold water.*

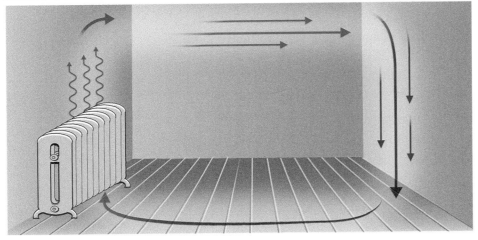

Thermal radiation

Definition of thermal radiation

If you stand in the Sun on a cold, calm day, you will feel warmth from the Sun. Heat from the Sun is transferred to Earth by thermal radiation. **Thermal radiation** is electromagnetic waves produced by objects because of their temperature. All objects with temperatures above absolute zero (–273 °C or–459°F) emit thermal radiation. To *emit* means to give off.

What is an electromagnetic wave?

An electromagnetic wave is the result of oscillating electric and magnetic fields. For example, visible light is an electromagnetic wave. You will learn more about electromagnetic waves in Chapter 23.

Thermal radiation comes from atoms

Thermal radiation comes from the thermal energy of atoms. The energy in thermal radiation increases with higher temperatures because the thermal energy of atoms increases with temperature (Figure 9.22). Because the Sun is extremely hot, its atoms emit lots of thermal radiation.

Objects emit and absorb radiation

Thermal radiation is also *absorbed* by objects. An object constantly receives thermal radiation from everything else in its environment. Otherwise, all objects would eventually cool down to absolute zero by radiating their energy away. The temperature of an object rises if more radiation is absorbed. The temperature falls if more radiation is given off. The temperature adjusts until there is a balance between radiation absorbed and radiation emitted.

Some surfaces absorb more energy than others

The amount of thermal radiation absorbed depends on the surface of a material. Black surfaces absorb almost all the thermal radiation that falls on them. For example, black asphalt pavement gets very hot in the summer sunlight because it effectively absorbs thermal radiation. A silver mirror surface reflects most thermal radiation; it absorbs very little (Figure 9.23). A mirrored screen reflects the Sun's heat back out of your parked car, helping it stay cooler on a hot day.

Radiation can travel through space

Thermal radiation can travel through the vacuum of space. Conduction and convection cannot carry heat through space because both processes require matter to transfer heat. Thermal radiation is different because it is carried by electromagnetic waves that do not require matter to provide a path for heat flow. Thermal radiation also travels fast—at the speed of light in a vacuum.

> **thermal radiation** - heat transfer in the form of electromagnetic waves, including light

Thermal radiation power
(emitted per cm² at different temperatures)

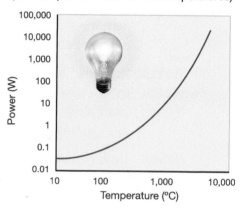

Figure 9.22: *The higher the temperature of an object, the more thermal radiation it emits.*

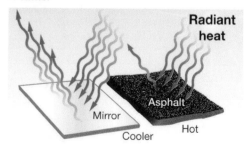

Figure 9.23: *Dark surfaces absorb most of the thermal radiation they receive. Silvered or mirrored surfaces reflect most of the thermal radiation they receive.*

The rate of heat transfer

The cause of heat transfer In nature, heat transfer *always* occurs from hot to cold until thermal equilibrium is reached. The rate of heat transfer is proportional to the difference in temperature. If the temperature difference is large, heat flows faster than when the temperature difference is small.

Heat transfer in living things Heat flow is necessary for life. Biological processes release energy. Your body regulates its temperature through the constant flow of heat. The inside of your body averages 98.6°F. Humans are most comfortable when the air temperature is about 75°F because the rate of heat flow out of the body matches the rate at which the body generates heat internally. If the air is 50°F, you get cold because heat flows too rapidly from your skin to the air. If the air is 100°F, you feel hot, partly because heat flows from the air to your body and partly because your body cannot get rid of its internal heat fast enough (Figure 9.24).

Heat transfer is everywhere All three forms of heat transfer are usually working at the same time to transfer energy from warmer objects to cooler objects. Heat flow continues as long as there is a temperature difference. If you look around you, you can see heat transfer virtually everywhere—between air and objects, between objects, and even between you and the environment!

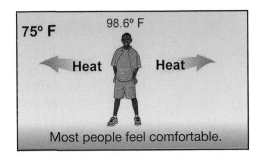

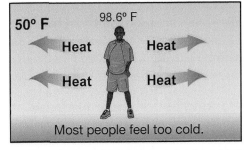

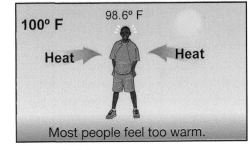

Figure 9.24: *Heat flow depends on temperature differences.*

9.3 Section Review

1. Name one example of heat transfer through conduction.
2. What is the primary type of heat transfer that occurs between a hot and a cold fluid when they are mixed together?
3. Which object would you expect to emit more thermal radiation: a lamp that is turned on, or a rock at room temperature? Explain your answer.
4. In which direction will heat flow between an ice cube and the air in the room where it is located? Explain your answer.

Gear Up for a Space Walk!

Have you ever wondered why astronauts need those big, bulky protective suits to venture outside of their spacecraft? Obviously, they need oxygen. But why can't they just wear a tank and mask, like a scuba diver?

It turns out that Earth's atmosphere does a lot more to help humans maintain homeostasis (internal balance) than just providing oxygen. It keeps global temperatures within a narrow range, shields us from harmful radiation, breaks up most meteoroids, and provides the pressure our bodies need to function properly.

Working better under pressure

If you're standing on Earth's surface at sea level, the weight of the column of air above you is about 9,800 newtons. That's roughly equal to the weight of a small car. Why aren't we crushed by this pressure? First, there is air inside our bodies that is pushing out with the same amount of pressure, so the forces are balanced. Second, our skeletons are designed to withstand the pressure of our environment.

Weight of a column of air **9,800 N (2,200 lbs)** = Weight of a small car

Those of us who have lived our entire lives blanketed by this atmospheric pressure rarely even notice it. But if you stepped outside of it—into the vacuum of space—you would immediately notice its absence. First, all the air in your lungs would rush out. The dissolved gases in your body fluids would expand. This would make your skin swell like an inflating balloon, and delicate tissues like eardrums would burst.

When external pressure decreases, gas bubbles form easier in liquids, including blood. Gas bubbles in blood can actually block small vessels so that the bloodstream can no longer transport oxygen and nutrients to body cells. NASA scientists estimate that without protective gear, an astronaut stepping outside the space shuttle would lose consciousness within 15 seconds and would not survive more than a few minutes.

Extraterrestrial hazards

Although we think of outer space as almost entirely empty, there are some additional hazards to consider before stepping outside of a spacecraft. You have to watch out for meteoroids—tiny bits of solid matter that are traveling at high velocities. There's also debris from previous space missions. NASA scientists explain that even a little paint chip traveling at thousands of kilometers per hour can do significant damage to human tissue.

A bit of orbital debris from a test firing of a Shuttle solid rocket booster

Meteoroids and space junk aren't the only hazards out there. Temperature extremes are another threat to living organisms in space. Objects outside of Earth's atmosphere, but still about the same distance from the Sun, face temperatures up to 120°Celcius on their sunlit side and lows of –100° Celcius on their shaded side. There's also harmful radiation of electrically-charged particles from the Sun and ultraviolet radiation that human skin can't block.

A little piece of home: NASA's Extravehicular Mobility Unit (EMU)

The only way for astronauts to navigate safely through these hazards is to surround themselves with a mini-environment that provides the conditions they need to maintain homeostasis. This mini-environment, or space suit, is officially known as the Shuttle extravehicular mobility unit, or EMU.

Astronauts go outside the space shuttle for various reasons. They may collect samples, take pictures, repair satellites, or inspect or install equipment. To prepare for extravehicular activity, the astronaut enters a special chamber called an air lock and puts on the EMU.

The EMU's innermost layer is basically an adult-sized diaper. Even on a spacewalk, a living organism must be able to get rid of waste products. Next comes what looks like a one-piece, zippered, long-underwear garment. It is made of stretchy fabric and contains 91.5 meters of plastic tubing. Chilled water is circulated through the tubes to help the astronaut maintain a constant temperature. There is a venting system in this suit that keeps carbon dioxide and perspiration from building up.

The astronaut attaches an in-suit drink bag and a food bar to a fiberglass shell called the Hard Upper Torso. He or she puts on a communication system with a microphone and headphones, and attaches a biomedical instrument system that allows mission control on Earth to monitor the astronaut's vital signs.

The next step is to put on the two-piece outer garment. This garment has a pressure bladder and restraint layer, covered by a nylon liner. Together, these layers keep the astronaut's body from swelling. Surrounding the pressure restraint layers is an insulating seven-layer "thermal micrometeoroid garment"

Astronaut Bruce McCandless II wearing the liquid cooling and ventilation garment (LCVG).

Astronaut Soichi Noguchi dons the communication cap in preparation for a seven-hour spacewalk.

covered with a woven anti-abrasion outer layer. The astronaut steps into the suit pants and then wiggles into the upper portion, which is hanging on the wall. The Primary Life Support Subsystem (PLSS) is attached to the hard shell of the garment's upper torso. It is a backpack unit containing an oxygen supply, CO_2-removal equipment, a water cooling system, ventilating fan, electrical supply, and radio.

Finally, it is time to put on the gloves and helmet. The helmet is coated with a gold material that shields the wearer from harmful radiation. When the entire EMU is assembled, it functions like a person-sized capsule of Earth, that provides the conditions necessary to support life. The EMU takes care of the astronaut's needs for oxygen, food, water, temperature control, waste management, pressure, radiation shielding, and micrometeoroid-impact protection.

Wrapped in the safety of their EMUs, astronauts can open the air lock hatch, climb out of the space shuttle, and begin their extravehicular mission with all the comforts of home.

Extravehicular Mobility Unit (EMU)

Helmet and Visor · Primary Life Support Subsystem · Displays and Control Module · Gloves · Hard Upper Torso · Lower Torso Assembly

Astronaut Kathryn Thornton works on a satellite.

QUESTIONS

1. Name three ways that Earth's atmosphere helps humans maintain homeostasis.

2. How does the EMU protect astronauts from the lack of atmospheric pressure in the vacuum of space?

3. Name two additional hazards that astronauts encounter when they leave the space shuttle. How does the EMU shield them from each?

Photos courtesy of NASA

Chapter 9 Review

Understanding Vocabulary

Select the correct term to complete the sentences.

absolute zero	gas	plasma
atom	heat	pressure
boiling point	heat conduction	solid
calorie	intermolecular forces	specific heat
Celsius scale	Kelvin	temperature
compound	liquid	thermal conductors
convection	melting point	thermal energy
element	mixture	thermal insulators
evaporation	molecule	thermal radiation
Fahrenheit scale		

1. Because the atoms of carbon, hydrogen, and oxygen are combined in a specific ratio and cannot be separated by physical means, a sugar molecule is a(n) _____.

2. Water melts at 0°C and iron at 1,500°C because _____ forces are higher between iron atoms.

3. A change of 1° in the _____ represents the same change in temperature as 1 Kelvin.

4. The most common form of matter found throughout the universe but *not* on Earth is _____.

5. Knowledge of an object's temperature and mass are required to determine the quantity of _____ it contains.

6. Of the three forms of heat transfer, those that *cannot* occur in a vacuum are _____ and _____.

Reviewing Concepts

Section 9.1

1. What is Brownian movement and what is its importance in the explanation of matter?

2. Describe the appearance of table salt at the macroscopic and atomic levels.

3. Explain the difference between an element and a compound, and give one example of each.

4. Explain how a mixture is different than a compound.

5. Explain the difference between the kinetic energy association with temperature and then kinetic energy of an object moving in a certain direction.

6. Name two factors that determine the phase of matter for a substance.

7. Describe the four phases of matter.

8. Give an example for each of the following: a solid-solid mixture, a liquid-solid mixture, a liquid-liquid mixture, liquid-gas mixture, and a gas-gas mixture.

9. Describe the processes of melting and freezing on the molecular level.

10. Describe the process of water boiling on the macroscopic and molecular level.

11. What is evaporation and how does it differ from boiling?

12. Compare the difference between the freezing points and boiling points of water on the Fahrenheit scale and the Celsius scale. Which degree represents a larger temperature change?

13. If any exist, what are the upper and lower limits of temperature?

14. What is the source of pressure in fluids?

15. What makes the Kelvin scale of temperature more useful to scientists than the Fahrenheit or Celsius scales?

16. A student in Italy flies to visit a family in New York. He hears the pilot report the weather on arrival as "clear and sunny with temperatures in the low 20s." He changes on the plane into shorts and a T-shirt. Explain his behavior.

Section 9.2

17. Explain the difference between temperature and thermal energy.

18. What is heat? How is heat related to temperature?

19. Which has higher thermal energy, a swimming pool of water at 70°F or a teacup of water at 80°F? Does higher thermal energy mean higher temperature?

20. Name three units of energy used to measure heat and describe what type of situations each is usually used for.

21. What is the meaning of the term *specific heat*? What causes it to vary from substance to substance?

22. Referring to the specific heat of water, explain how oceans help to regulate the temperature on Earth.

Section 9.3

23. Define the three main types of heat transfer.

24. Describe the flow of thermal energy when you hold a cold can of soda in your hand. What types of heat transfer are occurring?

25. Why do you think pots and pans for cooking are made out of metal?

26. What properties make a material a good thermal insulator? Give three examples of good thermal insulators.

27. Compare the ability of solids, liquids, and gases to conduct heat.

28. Why does hot air rise? What type of heat transfer is occurring?

29. Why does convection *not* occur in solid materials?

30. Name a property of matter that increases its ability to absorb thermal radiation.

31. Explain, using your knowledge of heat transfer, why it is difficult to keep cool when it is 100°F outside.

Solving Problems

Section 9.1

1. Identify the following substances as an element, a compound, or a mixture.

   a. vanilla pudding

   b. oxygen gas

   c. table salt (sodium chloride)

   d. fruit salad

2. Convert the average human body temperature (98.6°F) to the temperature on the Celsius scale?

3. Convert the Celsius temperature of the surface of the Sun (5,000°C) to degrees Fahrenheit.

4. If a recipe says to bake a pizza in a 250°C oven, at what temperature should you set your oven that uses the Fahrenheit scale?

5. Convert the Fahrenheit temperature at which paper burns (451°F) to degrees Celsius.

6. Earth is a watery planet. About 70% of Earth's surface is covered by water. There is water underground and in the atmosphere. State the temperature range for each of the following phases of water and give the common name for that phase.

   a. solid

   b. liquid

   c. gas

7. You place 1 L of a substance into a 2-L bottle and tightly cover the bottle. The substance completely fills the bottle. What state is the substance in?

8. A sealed can 6.50 cm in diameter and 12.0 cm in height contains a gas at a pressure of 1,030 N/m². What is the total force applied by the gas on the inner surface of the can?

Section 9.2

9. How much heat is needed to raise the temperature of 10.0 kg of wood from 20.0°C to 25.0°C? The specific heat of wood is 2,500 J/kg°C.

10. A teapot contains 0.5 kg of water. Five thousand joules of heat are added to the teapot. What is the increase in the temperature of the water? The specific heat of water is 4,184 J/kg°C.

11. You add 47,000 J of heat to 1.00 kg of steel. What is the temperature change in the steel? The specific heat of steel is 470 J/kg°C.

12. How much heat is needed to raise the temperature of 10.0 kg of aluminum from 10.0°C to 40.0°C? The specific heat of aluminum is 900 J/kg°C.

13. How many calories does it take to increase 1.00 g of water by 20.0°C?

Section 9.3

14. Why does a chickadee fluff its feathers when it gets cold outside?

15. You pour some hot water into a metal cup. After a minute, you notice that the handle of the cup has become hot. Explain, using your knowledge of heat transfer, why the handle of the cup heats up. How would you design the cup so the handle does not heat up?

16. What primary type of heat transfer occurs in the following situations?

    a. A cool breeze blows off the water when you are at the beach.

    b. You burn your hand on a hot pan.

    c. The Sun warms your skin.

    d. Your feet feel cool on a tile floor.

    e. Smoke rises up a chimney.

    f. You feel warmer in a black T-shirt than a white T-shirt.

Test Practice

Section 9.1

1. The illustrations below represent elements. The diagram which best represents a mixture of two compounds is:

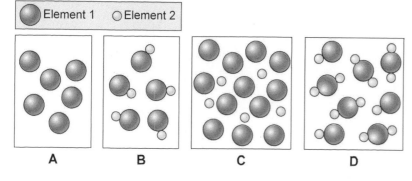

2. Which diagram best represents a gas in a closed container?

The graph below represents the uniform cooling of a substance starting with the substance as a gas above its boiling point. Use it to answer the following two questions.

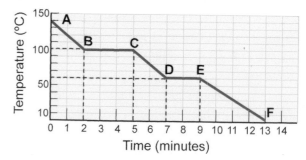

3. The interval which represents a phase change is

    a. A–B.

    b. C–D.

    c. D–E.

    d. E–F.

4. The melting point of this substance is about

    a. 10°C.

    b. 50°C.

    c. 100°C.

    d. 140°C.

5. A temperature of 50°F is equal to

    a. 323K.

    b. 50°C.

    c. –223K.

    d. 10°C.

6. A round balloon, 50 cm in diameter, is filled with a gas to a pressure of 1.01×105 N/m2. What force does the gas exert on the inside wall of the balloon? (**surface area of a sphere** $= \frac{4}{3}\pi r^3$)

    a. 6,600 N

    b. 420,000 N

    c. 6.60 N

    d. 420 N

Section 9.2

7. The heat energy that must be added to raise the temperature of 3 kg of steel from 20°C to 30°C is about (Cp for steel = 470 J/kg°C)

    a. 470 J.

    b. 1,410 J.

    c. 4,700 J.

    d. 14,100 J.

8. Compared to a gold atom, the mass of an aluminum atom is smaller. The specific heat of aluminum is

    a. lower because there are more atoms per kilogram.

    b. higher because there are more atoms per kilogram.

    c. lower because energy is spread over fewer atoms.

    d. higher because energy is spread over fewer atoms.

Section 9.3

9. The transfer of heat through the motion of fluids is called

    a. conduction.

    b. reflection.

    c. radiation.

    d. convection.

10. Heat will always flow from object A to object B if object B has a lower

    a. mass.

    b. total energy.

    c. specific heat.

    d. temperature.

Applying Your Knowledge

Section 9.1

1. Design a poster to illustrate the classification of matter. Be sure to use the terms *matter*, *element*, *compound*, and *mixture*. Provide examples of everyday objects that belong in each category.

2. Design a demonstration of Brownian motion for your class.

3. Research how a scanning tunneling electron microscope (STM) works. Prepare a short report of your findings.

4. Research why plasmas, or ionized gases as they are sometimes called, are of great interest to scientists and manufacturers. Describe at least two current uses of plasmas, and describe one way scientists and engineers hope to use plasmas in the future.

5. Prepare a short report that describes how different types of thermometers work. Be sure to apply what you know about the behavior of atomic particles.

6. Imagine you are the size of an atom. Write a short story that describes what your life would be like as a solid, liquid, and a gas. Be creative in your descriptions.

Section 9.2

7. Research one or both of the following and write a short paper or give a presentation based on your findings.

   a. Scottish chemist Joseph Black (1728–1799) developed the theory of specific heat. Research his life and how he made this discovery.

   b. Lord Kelvin (1824–1907), a British Physicist, developed the idea of absolute zero, the coldest possible temperature. Research absolute zero, the Kelvin scale, and Lord Kelvin's life.

8. Explain, using your knowledge of specific heat, why coastal areas are often warmer at night and cooler in the day compared to inland areas.

Section 9.3

9. Describe the heating system in your home. What type or types of heat transfer does it use?

10. Find out how much insulation is recommended for homes in your community. Where is the most insulation recommended: in the ceiling, walls, or floors? Using what you know about heat transfer, explain why.

11. The diagram shows an automobile engine cooling system. Describe, using your knowledge of heat transfer, how this system works.

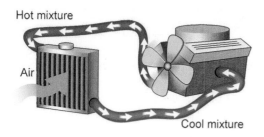

Hot mixture

Air

Cool mixture

Your Turn Answers

Converting between temperature scales (Section 9.1, page 222)

a. 52.2°F

Calculating the heat required to reach a temperature (Section 9.2, page 229)

a. 35,200 J

b. 116 J

The Atom

Based on its size and the laws of probability, the odds are excellent that there are other planets in the universe. But finding one is another story. Astronomers estimate that there are over 200 billion stars in our galaxy, and that there are at least 50 billion galaxies in the universe! This photograph, taken by the Hubble Space Telescope, shows countless galaxies in a tiny speck of space.

Since 1995, some planets outside our solar system have been found. Astronomers discovered them *indirectly*, by observing the effects of the planet on its companion star. Even though a planet has a much smaller mass than the star it orbits, its gravitational force "tugs" on the star, causing it to wobble slightly. That wobble can be detected by analyzing the light given off by the star.

Finding out about atoms is much like searching for planets in the universe. Both endeavors rely on indirect evidence. In fact, atoms are so small that there are far more atoms in a drop of water than there are stars in our galaxy!

Image courtesy of NASA/ESA/STScI/HUDF Team

VOCABULARY

alpha decay	half-life	quantum state
atomic number	isotopes	quantum theory
atomic theory	mass number	radioactive
beta decay	neutron	radioactive decay
chain reaction	nuclear reaction	spectral line
charge	nucleus	spectrometer
electromagnetic force	photon	spectrum
electron	probability	strong nuclear force
gamma decay	proton	uncertainty principle

KEY QUESTIONS

✓ *What is the strongest force in the universe? (Hint: It exists inside atoms!)*

✓ *How do atoms emit light?*

✓ *What is the difference between fission and fusion?*

10.1 Atomic Structure

You have read that atoms, by themselves or combined with other atoms in molecules, are the building blocks of every type of matter. Even though scientists have only recently been able to see atoms directly, they have been able to *infer* a model for atomic structure that is based on an enormous amount of evidence. Like good detective work, to infer is to draw a conclusion that is supported by all the available evidence, including direct and indirect observations.

> **atomic theory** - a theory which states that all matter is composed of tiny particles called atoms

The atomic theory

What is the atomic theory? English scientist John Dalton (1766–1844) started experimenting with gases in the atmosphere in 1787. He found that water existed as a gas in the air. Since air and water could not occupy the same space at the same time, he concluded that they must be made of tiny particles that mixed together. His careful measurements gave him repeatable evidence that matter is made up of *atoms*. In 1808, Dalton published a detailed **atomic theory** that contained the following statements:

1. Matter is composed of tiny, indivisible, and indestructible particles called *atoms*.

2. An *element* is composed entirely of one type of atom (Figure 10.1, top). The properties of all atoms of one element are identical and are different from those of any other element.

3. A *compound* (Figure 10.1, bottom) contains atoms of two or more different elements. The relative number of atoms of each element in a particular compound is always the same.

4. Atoms do not change their identities in chemical reactions. They are just rearranged into different substances.

Exceptions to the atomic theory Dalton's theory has been amended as we learned more about the atom. Today, we know that atoms are not indivisible, but are made of smaller particles. Atoms are not indestructible, but can be split. Not all of the atoms of a given element are *exactly* identical. In this section, you will read about some changes to the first two statements of Dalton's atomic theory.

Element

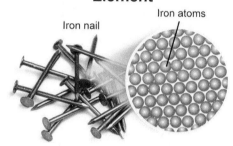

Iron nail

Iron atoms

Compound

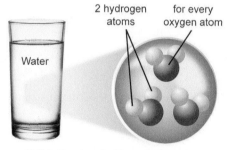

2 hydrogen atoms

for every oxygen atom

Water

H_2O is the chemical formula for water. This formula indicates that there are two hydrogen atoms and one oxygen atom in every water molecule.

Figure 10.1: *An element is composed of one type of atom. A compound contains atoms of more than one element in specific ratios.*

The puzzle of the inside of the atom

The electron identified English physicist J. J. Thomson (1856–1940) observed that streams of particles could be made to come from different gases placed in tubes carrying electricity. Thomson identified a negatively-charged particle he called the *electron*. These electrons must have come out of the atoms of the gas. Thomson proposed a "plum pudding model" of the atom, in which the atom was a positive sphere—the pudding—with negative electrons—the plums—embedded in it (Figure 10.2).

The proton and the nucleus discovered In 1911, Ernest Rutherford (1871–1937), Hans Geiger (1882–1945), and Ernest Marsden (1889–1970) did a clever experiment to test Thomson's theory. They launched fast, positively-charged helium ions at extremely thin pieces of gold foil. They expected the helium ions would deflect a small amount as a result of hitting gold atoms. Instead, most of the helium ions passed straight through the foil (Figure 10.3). Even more surprising, a few bounced back in the direction from which they came! This unexpected result prompted Rutherford to describe it as if someone had fired an artillery shell at a piece of tissue paper and it came back and hit him in the head!

The nuclear model of the atom The best way to explain the "pass-through" result was if the gold atoms were mostly empty space, allowing most of the helium ions to go through undeflected. The best way to explain the bounce-back result was if nearly all the mass of a gold atom was concentrated in a tiny, hard core at its center. Further experiments confirmed Rutherford's ideas. We now know that every atom has a tiny *nucleus*, that contains more than 99 percent of the atom's mass. Electrons occupy a large volume of space outside the nucleus.

The neutron The positively-charged *proton* was soon discovered and located in the nucleus. But, there was still a serious problem with the atomic model. Protons could only account for about half of the atom's observed mass. This problem was solved in 1932 by James Chadwick (1891–1974). Chadwick bombarded a thin sheet of beryllium with positively-charged particles. His experiment showed a third type of subatomic particle, about the same mass as the proton, called the *neutron*. The missing mass was now explained. The nucleus contains protons *and* neutrons.

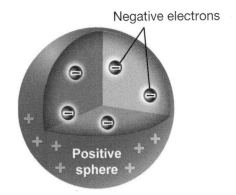

Figure 10.2: *Thomson's model of the atom.*

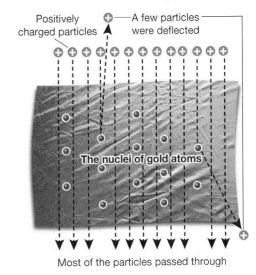

Figure 10.3: *The famous gold foil experiment led to the discovery of the nucleus.*

Three subatomic particles make up an atom

Protons, neutrons, and electrons
Today we know that atoms are made up of three *subatomic particles*: protons, neutrons, and electrons. A **proton** is a particle with a positive charge. An **electron** is a particle with a negative charge. A **neutron** is a neutral particle and has a zero charge. The charges on one proton and one electron are exactly equal and opposite. **Charge** is an electrical property of particles that causes them to attract and repel each other. If you put a proton and an electron together—a hydrogen atom—the total charge is zero. Atoms with the same number of protons and electrons have a net charge of zero.

The nucleus
The protons and neutrons are grouped together in the **nucleus**, which is at the center of the atom. The mass of the nucleus determines the mass of an atom. This is because protons and neutrons are much larger and more massive than electrons. In fact, a proton is 1,837 times heavier than an electron. Electrons are found in *energy levels* around the nucleus. All atoms have protons and neutrons in their nuclei except the simplest type of hydrogen, which only has one proton and no neutrons. The chart below compares electrons, protons, and neutrons in terms of charge and mass.

proton - a positively-charged particle found with neutrons in the nucleus of an atom

electron - a low-mass particle with a negative charge that occupies energy levels in space around an atom's nucleus

neutron - an uncharged particle found in the nucleus of an atom which has a mass about equal to the mass of a proton

charge - a fundamental electrical property of matter that can be positive, negative, or zero

nucleus - the mass at the center of an atom that contains protons and neutrons

	Occurrence	Relative charge	Mass (g)	Relative mass
Electron	Found outside nucleus in energy levels	−1	9.109×10^{-28}	1
Proton	Found in all nuclei	+1	1.673×10^{-24}	1,837
Neutron	Found in almost all nuclei (*exception:* most H nuclei)	0	1.675×10^{-24}	1,839

The volume of an atom
The size of an atom is determined by how far the electrons are from the nucleus. The electrons define a region of space called the *electron cloud*. The diameter of an atom is really the diameter of the electron cloud, which is about 10^{-10} meters. The diameter of the nucleus is 100,000 times smaller than the diameter of the atom itself, or about 10^{-15} meters (Figure 10.4). As a comparison, if an atom were the size of a football stadium, the nucleus would be the size of a pea, and the electrons would be like a few gnats flying around the stadium at high speed.

Size and structure of the atom

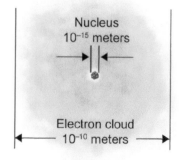

Nucleus
10^{-15} meters

Electron cloud
10^{-10} meters

Figure 10.4: *The overall size of an atom is the size of its electron cloud. The nucleus is much smaller in comparison.*

Fundamental forces and atoms

Electromagnetic forces
Electrons are bound to the nucleus by **electromagnetic force**. This fundamental force of attraction is between the positively-charged protons and the negatively-charged electrons. Because of Newton's first law, the electrons do not fall into the nucleus, because they have inertia. An electron orbiting the nucleus tends to move in a straight line, but the attractive force of the nucleus keeps it from doing so (Figure 10.5). An analogy is Earth orbiting the Sun. Gravity creates a force that pulls Earth toward the Sun. Earth's inertia causes it to orbit the Sun rather than fall into it. While electrons do not move in circular orbits, the analogy is approximately correct and explains their behavior.

Strong nuclear force
Because of electromagnetic force, all of the positively-charged protons in the nucleus *repel* each other. What holds the nucleus together? There is another fundamental force that is even stronger than the electromagnetic force. We call it the **strong nuclear force**. This force attracts neutrons and protons to each other and works only at extremely small distances of 10^{-15} meters. The presence of neutrons helps the attraction from the strong nuclear force counteract the protons' repulsive electromagnetic force so that the nucleus stays together. In most stable atoms, there is at least one neutron for every proton in the nucleus. Even though it only acts over tiny distances, the strong nuclear force is the strongest force known (Figure 10.6).

Weak force
There is another nuclear force called the *weak force*. The weak force is weaker than both the electromagnetic force and the strong nuclear force. If you leave a single neutron outside the nucleus, the weak force eventually causes it to break down into a proton and an electron. The weak force does not play an important role in a stable atom, but comes into action in certain special cases when atoms break apart (*i.e.*, a nuclear reaction called beta decay).

Gravity
The force of gravity inside the atom is much weaker even than the weak force. It takes a relatively large mass to create enough gravity to make a significant force. We know that particles inside an atom do not have enough mass for gravity to be an important force on the scale of atoms. But there are many unanswered questions. Understanding how gravity works inside atoms is an unsolved mystery in science.

electromagnetic force - a force created by electric charge or magnetism or both
strong nuclear force - the force that holds protons and neutrons together in the nucleus of an atom

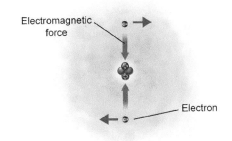

Figure 10.5: *Inertia makes electrons move in a straight line, but since they are also attracted to the positive protons, they end up moving around the nucleus.*

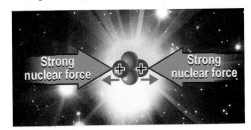

Figure 10.6: *When enough neutrons are present, the strong nuclear force compensates for the repulsion between the positively-charged protons and keeps the nucleus bound together. The strong nuclear force is the strongest-known force in the universe.*

Historical development of understanding fundamental forces

Building understanding You have just read about the four fundamental forces. Below, you will read about scientists who contributed to our understanding of these forces.

Measuring gravitational force Henry Cavendish (1731–1810), a British scientist, was the first to measure the gravitational force between two masses. Cavendish used a device called a *torsion balance* (Figure 10.8). The balance was designed by John Mitchell (1724–1793), an English geologist, who died before he could use it. Cavendish's original idea was to measure Earth's density. Using the results of his experiments, other scientists were able to accurately determine the mass of Earth and *G*, the universal gravitational constant (Figure 10.7).

The torsion balance A simple example of how a torsion balance works is shown in Figure 10.8. Think of hanging a meter stick from a string so it is horizontal with its scale visible. Imagine there are small lead spheres on the ends of the stick. Then, imagine that you roll in two giant lead spheres so the two hanging spheres and the two on the floor are the four corners of a square as shown. What will gravitational force do to the hanging meter stick? It will make the stick "torque," or rotate, a little because the mass of the small spheres will be attracted to the mass of the giant spheres. Using extreme care in his experimentation, Cavendish measured this very small rotation.

Measuring electromagnetic force The unit of electric charge is the *coulomb* (C). The name is chosen in honor of Charles-Augustin de Coulomb (1736–1806), a French physicist who succeeded in making the first accurate measurements of the electromagnetic forces between charges in 1783. Coulomb used a kind of torsion balance to measure these forces, too. Ironically, Mitchell's idea to use a torsion balance to measure Earth's density was inspired by Coulomb's work!

Discovering the strong nuclear force and the weak force Theoretical physicist Hideki Yukawa (1907–1981) was the first Japanese to receive a Nobel Prize. He won the award in 1949 for his theory of the strong nuclear force. This theory predicted the *meson*, an elementary particle that was later discovered. A theory about the existence of the weak force was first proposed by Enrico Fermi (1901–1954), an Italian physicist who worked on the first nuclear reactor and its applications. Fermi's theory was based on his observations of beta decay, which you will read about in Section 10.3.

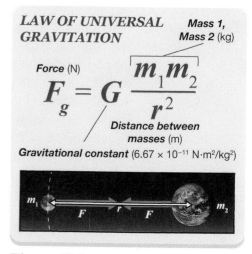

Figure 10.7: *The formula for the law of universal gravitation uses the gravitational constant, G.*

$$F_g = G \frac{m_1 m_2}{r^2}$$

LAW OF UNIVERSAL GRAVITATION — Force (N), Mass 1, Mass 2 (kg), Distance between masses (m), Gravitational constant (6.67×10^{-11} N·m²/kg²)

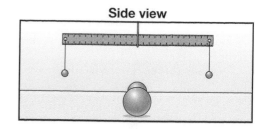

Side view

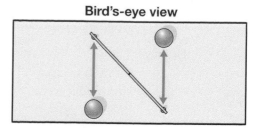

Bird's-eye view

Figure 10.8: *A torsion balance.*

How are atoms of each element different?

Atomic number   How is an atom of one element different from an atom of another element? The atoms of different elements contain different numbers of protons in the nucleus. Because the number of protons is so important, it is called the **atomic number**. The atomic number of an element is the number of protons in the nucleus of every atom of that element. Each element has a unique atomic number. For example, an atom with six protons is the element carbon. An atom with only one proton in its nucleus is the element hydrogen.

*Atoms of the same element always have
the same number of protons.*

Isotopes   All atoms of the same element have the same number of protons in the nucleus. However, atoms of the same element may have different numbers of neutrons in the nucleus. **Isotopes** are atoms of the *same* element that have *different* numbers of neutrons. The number of protons in isotopes of an element is the same.

The isotopes of carbon   Figure 10.9 shows three ways to make atoms of carbon. Most carbon atoms have six protons and six neutrons in the nucleus. However, some carbon atoms have seven or eight neutrons. They are all carbon atoms because they all contain six protons, but they are different *isotopes* of carbon. The isotopes of carbon are called carbon-12, carbon-13, and carbon-14. The number after the name is called the *mass number*. The **mass number** of an isotope tells you the number of protons plus the number of neutrons.

Mass number = number of protons + number of neutrons

What if there are too many neutrons?   Almost all elements have one or more isotopes that are *stable*. "Stable" means the nucleus stays together. Under certain conditions, the nucleus of an atom becomes unstable if it contains too many or too few neutrons compared to the number of its protons. If the nucleus is unstable, it can form new elements or isotopes. Carbon has two stable isotopes, carbon-12 and carbon-13. Carbon-14 is *radioactive* because it has an unstable nucleus. An atom of carbon-14 eventually changes itself into an atom of nitrogen-14. This process, called *radioactive decay*, is discussed further in Section 10.3.

atomic number - the number of protons in an atom

isotopes - forms of the same element that have diffewrent numbers of neutrons and different mass numbers

mass number - the total number of protons and neutrons in the nucleus of an atom

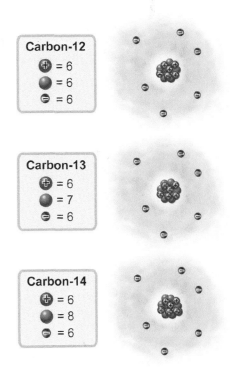

Figure 10.9: *Three isotopes of carbon.*

Atomic mass

Units of atomic mass The atomic mass of an atom is usually given in *atomic mass units* (amu). One amu is 1.66×10^{-27} kg, which is one-twelfth ($\frac{1}{12}$) the mass of a carbon-12 atom. To determine the mass of a single atom, you multiply the atomic mass in amu by 1.66×10^{-27} kg/amu. For example, an "average" lithium atom has a mass of 1.15×10^{-26} kg ($6.94 \times 1.66 \times 10^{-27}$ kg/amu). This is a very small mass compared to the mass of every day objects!

Atomic mass Elements in nature are usually a mixture of isotopes. For example, the element lithium has an atomic mass of 6.94. That does *not* mean there are 3 protons and 3.94 neutrons in a lithium atom! On average, 94 percent of lithium atoms are lithium-7 and 6 percent are lithium-6 (Figure 10.10). The average atomic mass of lithium is 6.94 because of the *weighted average* of the mixture of isotopes.

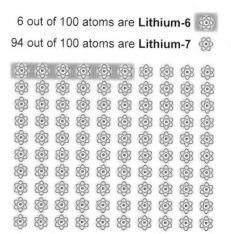

6 out of 100 atoms are **Lithium-6**

94 out of 100 atoms are **Lithium-7**

Figure 10.10: *Naturally-occurring elements have a mixture of isotopes.*

Identifying the number of particles in a nucleus

How many neutrons are present in an aluminum atom that has an atomic number of 13 and a mass number of 27?

1. **Looking for:**   You are asked to find the number of neutrons.

2. **Given:**   You are given the atomic number and the mass.

3. **Relationships:**   Use the formula: ***protons + neutrons = mass number***.

4. **Solution:**   Solve the equation for neutrons: neutrons = mass number − protons
Substitute and solve: neutrons = 27 − 13 = 14   The aluminum atom has 14 neutrons.

Your Turn:

a. How many neutrons are present in a magnesium atom (atomic number 12) that has a mass number of 25?

b. Find the number of neutrons in a calcium atom (atomic number 20) that has a mass number of 42.

(Answers are listed at the end of the chapter.)

10.1 Section Review

1. Name the three subatomic particles. Describe the location and charge of each particle.
2. What force holds (a) an electron in an atom and (b) the nucleus together? List the scientists who contributed to discovering these forces.
3. One atom has 12 protons and 12 neutrons. Another has 13 protons and 12 neutrons. Are they the same or different elements? Why?

10.2 Quantum Theory and the Atom

Have you ever seen a neon light? Inside the glass tube, there is an element in the gaseous phase, such as neon, argon, or krypton. When the right amount of energy is added, the atoms emit light that we can see. Neon emits red light when energized. Other elements emit other colors. Each element emits a characteristic color of light. Why? In this section, you will learn how the colors of light given off by atoms tell scientists a lot about the inside of the atom.

The spectrum

The spectrum Light is given off when electricity passes through a gas. This is how fluorescent bulbs and neon signs work. If you look through a prism at the light given off by a pure element, you see that the light does not include all colors. Instead, you see a few very specific colors, and the colors are different for different elements (Figure 10.11). This characteristic pattern of colors is called a **spectrum**. The colors of clothes, paint, and everything else around you come from this property of elements to emit or absorb light of only certain colors.

Spectrometers and spectral lines Each individual color is called a **spectral line** because each color appears as a line in a **spectrometer**. A spectrometer is a device that breaks light into its different colors. The diagram shows a spectrometer made with a prism. The spectral lines appear on the screen on the right.

Energy and color Light is a form of energy. The amount of energy depends on the color of the light. Red light has lower energy and blue light has higher energy. Green and yellow light have energy between that of red and blue. The fact that atoms only emit certain colors of light tells us that something inside an atom can only have certain values of energy. Light is given off by electrons, and this is how scientists first discovered the energy levels in an atom.

spectrum - the characteristic pattern of colors emitted by a pure substance

spectral line - each individual line of color appearing in a spectrometer

spectrometer - a device that breaks light into its component colors

Hydrogen

Helium

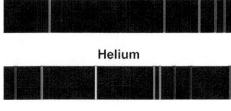

Lithium

Figure 10.11: *When light from energized atoms is directed through a prism, spectral lines are observed. Each element has its own distinct pattern of spectral lines.*

Quantum theory and the Bohr atom

Neils Bohr   Light is emitted by electrons as they are accelerated, or as they change their energy. Danish physicist Neils Bohr (1885–1962) proposed the concept of energy levels to explain the spectrum. When an electron moves from one energy level to another, the atom gives up the energy difference between the two levels. The energy comes out as different colors of light. The specific colors of the spectral lines correspond to the differences in energy between the energy levels. The energy in atoms changes in little jumps which Bohr called *quanta*. For electrons, it's an all-or-nothing jump between energy levels that releases quantities of energy as colors of light.

> **quantum theory** - the theory that describes the behavior of matter and energy on the atomic scale

Explaining spectral lines   When a hydrogen atom absorbs energy from electricity, an electron moves to a higher energy level (Figure 10.12). That is *how* the atom absorbs the energy, by "promoting" electrons to higher energy levels. The atom emits the energy when the electron falls back to a lower energy. The emitted energy comes out as light with a color proportional to the energy difference between the level where the electron started and where it ended up. The diagram below shows how the spectral lines of hydrogen come from electrons falling from the 3rd, 4th, 5th, and 6th energy levels, down to the 2nd energy level.

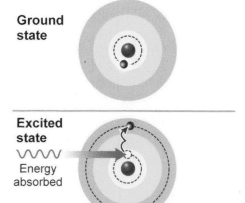

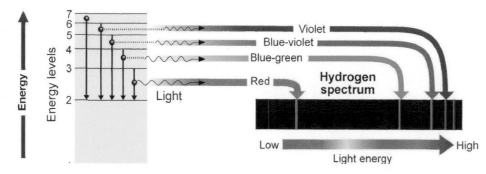

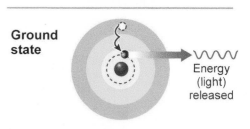

Figure 10.12: *When the right amount of energy is absorbed, an electron in a hydrogen atom jumps to a higher energy level—an excited state. When the electron falls back to lower energy—the ground state—it releases the same amount of energy it absorbed. The energy comes out of the atom as light of a specific color.*

Light can be thought of as a particle   The Bohr atom led to a new way of thinking about energy in atomic systems. A *quanta* is a quantity of something that cannot be divided any smaller. One electron is a quanta of matter, because you can't split an electron. **Quantum theory** says that when a particle, such as an electron, is confined to a small space inside an atom, the energy, momentum, and other variables of the particle become quantized and can only have specific values.

The quantum model of the atom

Quantum theory and probability Quantum theory says that when things get very small, on the size of atoms, matter and energy do *not* obey Newton's laws or other laws of *classical* physics. At least the classical laws are not obeyed in the same way as with larger objects, like a baseball.

The quantum model of the atom In 1925, Erwin Schrödinger (1887–1961) proposed the quantum model of the atom we still use today. The quantum atom still has all the protons and neutrons in its nucleus. However, the electron is thought of as a "fuzzy" cloud of negative charge called a **quantum state** rather than as a particle moving around the nucleus. The cloud is a three-dimensional shape that depends on the electron's energy level and its location within its energy level. For example, the second energy level has eight quantum states, one for each of the eight electrons the level can hold. Figure 10.13 shows the shapes of these eight quantum states. These shapes are important because they determine the shape of molecules the atom forms.

The Pauli exclusion principle According to the quantum model, two electrons can never be in the same quantum state at the same time. This rule is known as the *Pauli exclusion principle* after Wolfgang Pauli (1900–1958). The exclusion principle is why an electron cannot fall to a lower energy level if that level is already filled by other electrons. Once all the quantum states in the first energy level are occupied, the next electron has to go into a higher energy level.

Two electrons can never be in the same quantum state in the same atom at the same time.

Planck's constant The "smearing out" of particles into fuzzy quantum states becomes important when size, momentum, energy or time become comparable in size to *Planck's constant*. Planck's constant (h) has the value 6.6×10^{-34} joule·seconds. The units are energy × time which are the same as distance × momentum. If you measure the momentum of an electron in a hydrogen atom and multiply it by the size of the atom, the result is about 1×10^{-34} joule·seconds. This is comparable to Planck's constant and is why quantum theory must be used to describe this electron rather than Newton's classical laws of physics.

quantum state - the specific values of energy and momentum which are allowed for a particle as described by quantum theory

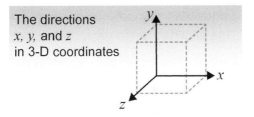
The directions x, y, and z in 3-D coordinates

The eight quantum states in the second energy level

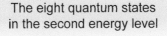
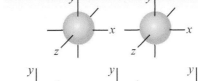
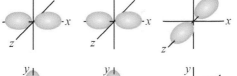
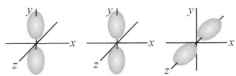

Figure 10.13: *The three-dimensional shapes of the eight quantum states in the second energy level.*

The uncertainty principle

The uncertainty principle
If an electron is spread out into a quantum state, how can you locate its exact position in an atom? You can't! The work of German physicist Werner Heisenberg (1901–1976) led to the **uncertainty principle**. According to the uncertainty principle, a particle's position, momentum, energy, and time can never be precisely known in a quantum system.

Understanding the uncertainty principle
The uncertainty principle arises because the quantum world is so small. In the quantum world, light energy comes in tiny bundles. Each bundle of energy is called a **photon**. When you see a car, your eye collects trillions of photons that bounce off the car. Photons are so small compared with a car that the car is not affected by their motion. To "see" an electron you also have to bounce a photon of light off of it or interact with the electron in some way (Figure 10.14). Because the electron is so small, even a single photon moves it and changes its motion. That means the moment you use a photon to locate an electron, you push it so you no longer know precisely how fast it is going. In fact, any process of observing in the quantum world changes the very system you are trying to observe. The uncertainty principle works because measuring any variable disturbs the others in an unpredictable way.

The meaning of the uncertainty principle
The uncertainty principle has some very strange implications. In the quantum world, anything that *can* happen, *does* happen. Put more strongly, unless something is specifically *forbidden* from happening, it *must* happen. For example, suppose you could create a particle out of nothing, then make it disappear again. Suppose you could do this so fast that it was within the energy and time limit of the uncertainty principle. You could break the law of conservation of energy if you did it quickly enough and in a very small space. *Physicists believe this actually happens.* They believe that the so-called "vacuum" of space is not truly empty when we consider details so small the uncertainty principle prevents us from seeing them. There is experimental evidence that supports the belief that particles of matter and *antimatter* are continually popping into existence and disappearing again, out of pure nothing. This implies that the vacuum of empty space may have energy of its own, even when there is absolutely no ordinary matter or energy present. You will read about antimatter in Chapter 11.

> **uncertainty principle** - it is impossible to precisely know a particle's position, momentum, energy, and time in a quantum system all at the same time
>
> **photon** - the smallest quantity of light energy

An electron is moving.

To see the electron, you must bounce a photon of light off it.

When you receive the photon, you know where the electron *was*, but the photon disturbed it, so you don't know its speed and direction any more.

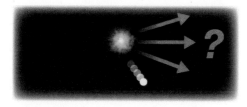

Figure 10.14: *The act of observing anything in the quantum world means disturbing, in unpredictable ways, the very system you are trying to measure.*

Probability and quantum theory

Predicting the behavior of particles in a system
According to Newton's laws, if you throw a ball, you can calculate exactly where the ball will be at every moment of its motion. Because electrons are so tiny, this type of calculation is not possible. Instead, quantum theory uses *probability* to predict the behavior of large numbers of particles in a system.

> **probability** - the science of describing the chance of an event or events to occur

The meaning of probability
Probability describes the chance for getting each possible outcome of a system. If you toss a penny, there are two ways it can land, either heads up or tails up. With a single penny, there is a 50 percent probability of getting heads, and a 50 percent probability of getting tails. Suppose you flip 100 pennies and record the number of heads. You repeat this experiment 100 times and graph your results (Figure 10.15). The graph tells you that there is a 5.5 percent chance that you will get exactly 50 heads out of 100 coin tosses. If you repeated the experiment 1,000 times you would expect 55 experiments to come up with exactly 50 heads and 50 tails. While you can never accurately predict the outcome of one toss of the penny, you *can* make accurate predictions about a collection of many tosses.

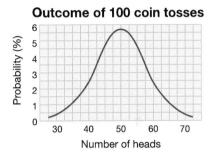

Figure 10.15: *The probability for the outcome of 100 tosses of a penny.*

The wave function
In quantum theory, each quantum of matter or energy is described by its *wave function*. The wave function mathematically describes how the probability for finding a particle is spread out in space (Figure 10.16). If you observe a trillion identical electrons, you can say with great precision how many will be found at that place. But quantum theory still cannot tell you where any *individual* electron is exactly located. Because of its basis in probability, quantum theory can only make accurate predictions about the behavior of large systems with many particles.

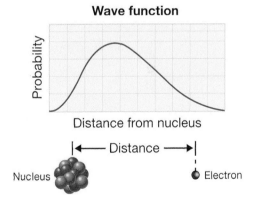

Figure 10.16: *The wave function describes how the probability of finding an electron is spread out in the space around the nucleus.*

10.2 Section Review

1. Describe how the colors in a spectrum from an atom are different from those in a rainbow.
2. Why does light from atoms show spectral lines?
3. How many electrons can fit in the same quantum state in the same atom?
4. What is probability?

10.3 Nuclear Reactions

If left alone, an atom of uranium eventually turns into an atom of lead. This *radioactive decay* is one example of a **nuclear reaction**. Nuclear reactions change the nucleus of an atom. In this section, you will read how this happens.

Nuclear reactions are different than chemical reactions

Nuclear versus chemical   Because they affect the nucleus itself, nuclear reactions can change one element into a different element. Nuclear reactions can also change an isotope into a different isotope of the same element. Remember, isotopes of the same element have the same number of protons but different numbers of neutrons in the nucleus. By comparison, chemical reactions do *not* change the types of atoms. Chemical reactions only rearrange atoms into different compounds.

Nuclear reactions involve more energy   Nuclear reactions involve much more energy than chemical reactions. The energy in a nuclear reaction is much greater because nuclear reactions involve the strong nuclear force, the strongest known force in the universe. Chemical reactions involve electrical forces. The electrical force acting on an electron far from the nucleus is much weaker than the strong force acting on a proton or neutron *inside* the nucleus. A comparison between nuclear and chemical reactions is shown in Figure 10.17.

Mass and energy in nuclear reactions   The *total* amount of mass and energy is conserved in nuclear reactions. Sometimes this sum is referred to together as *mass-energy*. This is because in nuclear reactions mass undergoes a conversion to energy. For example, if you could take apart a nucleus and separate all of its protons and neutrons, the separated protons and neutrons would have more mass than the nucleus does all together. The mass-to-energy conversion is not like the way potential energy can be converted to kinetic energy. Rather, when energy is released, mass is decreased in a proportion, according to Einstein's formula ($E = mc^2$). The formula tells us that the amount of energy (E) is found by multiplying the mass (m) by speed of light (c) squared. The energy released during a nuclear reaction can be calculated if we know the amount by which the mass of the nucleus is reduced. You'll learn more about this relationship, called *mass-energy equivalence*, in Chapter 11.

nuclear reaction - a reaction that changes the nucleus of an atom and which may change the element into another element or into an isotope of the same element

Chemical reactions	Nuclear reactions
What part of the atom is involved?	
Outer electrons	Nucleus (protons and neutrons)
What changes?	
Atoms are rearranged into new molecules but the atoms stay the same.	Atoms can change into atoms of a different element or isotopes of the same element.
How much energy is involved?	
A small amount	A large amount

Figure 10.17: *Comparing nuclear and chemical reactions.*

Nuclear reactions and energy

Energy of the nucleus
Protons and neutrons are attracted by the strong nuclear force and release energy as they come together. The more energy that is released, the lower the energy of the resulting nucleus. The energy of the nucleus depends on the mass and atomic number. The nucleus with the lowest energy is iron-56 with 26 protons and 30 neutrons—the lowest point on the graph shown. Protons and neutrons combined into nuclei of carbon or uranium have higher energy so they appear higher on the graph.

Nuclear energies are very large
The graph compares the energy of the nucleus in 1 kilogram of matter for elements 2 (helium) through 92 (uranium). Each dot on the graph represents one of these elements. The units of energy are hundreds of trillions (10^{12}) of joules per kilogram of material! Nuclear reactions often involve such huge amounts of energy, as protons and neutrons are rearranged to form different nuclei. A nuclear reaction *releases* energy when it rearranges protons and neutrons to make a new nucleus that is lower in energy on the graph (Figure 10.18). A nuclear reaction *uses* energy when the protons and neutrons form a nucleus that is higher in energy on the graph.

Energy of the Nucleus vs. Atomic Number
Relative values with reference to iron-56 (Fe^{56}) with energy set at 0 J/kg

1 kg of protons and neutrons arranged as uranium nuclei

1 kg of protons and neutrons arranged as iron nuclei

+ 130 trillion joules!

Figure 10.18: *A nuclear reaction that changed 1 kg of uranium into 1 kg of iron would release 130 trillion J of energy.*

Fusion reactions

Writing nuclear reactions In a nuclear reaction, each atom is represented using *isotope notation*. In this notation, the element symbol is given along with its mass number and atomic number as shown in Figure 10.19.

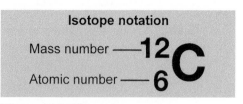

Figure 10.19: *Isotope notation*

Fusion reactions Fusion reactions (the combining of atomic nuclei) release energy if the final nucleus has lower energy than the initial nuclei (Figure 10.20, bottom). A kilogram of carbon-12 contains 104 trillion joules (104 TJ) of nuclear energy according to the graph. A kilogram of magnesium-24 has 48 TJ of nuclear energy. And, 56 TJ are released if the protons and neutrons in a kilogram of carbon-12 are rearranged to make a kilogram of magnesium-24 nucleus. The fusion reaction to make magnesium from carbon would actually go through a series of steps, but the end result would be the same release of energy. (*Note*: The products of a fusion reaction may have slightly less mass because energy has been released and conserved according to mass-energy equivalence, Einstein's formula, $E = mc^2$.)

Fusion reactions need very high temperatures Positively-charged nuclei repel each other. Two nuclei must be very close for the attractive strong nuclear force to overcome the repulsive electric force. One way to make two nuclei get close is to make the temperature very high. At very high temperatures, kinetic energy forces two nuclei together with such force that they almost touch. This allows the strong force to take over and initiate a fusion reaction. The hydrogen fusion reactions in the core of the Sun occur at a temperature of about 15 million degrees Celsius.

Density and fusion power A single fusion reaction makes a lot of energy for a single atom. But, a single atom is so tiny! To produce enough power to light a single 100-watt bulb, 10^{14} fusion reactions per second are required. The density of the atoms must be large enough to get a high rate of fusion reactions, too.

Fusion in the Sun Stars like the Sun make energy from fusion reactions because the core of a star is both very hot and very dense. The density at the core of the Sun is so high that a tablespoon of material weighs more than a ton! The primary fusion reaction that happens in the Sun combines hydrogen nuclei to make helium, converting two protons and two electrons into two neutrons along the way. All of the energy reaching Earth from the Sun comes ultimately from these fusion reactions in the Sun's core.

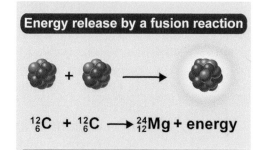

$$^{12}_{6}C + ^{12}_{6}C \longrightarrow ^{24}_{12}Mg + energy$$

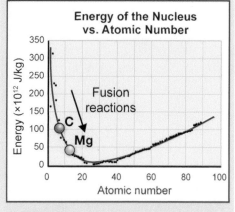

+104 TJ	Energy of carbon (C) nucleus
− 48 TJ	Energy of magnesium (Mg) nucleus
+ 56 TJ	Energy released by fusion of carbon into magnesium

Figure 10.20: *A fusion reaction releases energy if the product nucleus is lower on the graph than the combining nuclei.*

Fission reactions

Fission reactions
For elements heavier than iron, breaking the nucleus up into smaller pieces (fission) releases nuclear energy (Figure 10.21, top). For example, a kilogram of uranium-235 (atomic number 92) has about 123 trillion joules (TJ) of nuclear energy. A fission reaction splits the uranium nucleus into two pieces. Both atoms have a lower atomic number, and are lower on the graph (Figure 10.21, bottom). The fission of a kilogram of uranium into the isotopes molybdenum-99 and tin-135 releases 98 TJ. (*Note*: The products of a fission reaction have slightly less mass because energy has been released and conserved according to mass-energy equivalence given by Einstein's formula, $E = mc^2$).

Fission is triggered by neutrons
A fission reaction typically starts when a neutron hits a nucleus with enough energy to make the nucleus unstable. Fission breaks the nucleus into two smaller atoms and often releases one or more extra neutrons. Some of the energy released by the reaction appears as gamma rays and some as kinetic energy of the smaller nuclei and the extra neutrons.

Chain reactions
A **chain reaction** occurs when the fission of one nucleus triggers fission of many other nuclei. In a chain reaction, the first fission reaction releases two or more neutrons. Those two neutrons hit two other nuclei and cause fission reactions that release more neutrons. The process continues, and the number of neutrons increases rapidly. The increasing number of neutrons causes more nuclei to have fission reactions and releases enormous amounts of energy. The fission chain reaction of uranium is how nuclear power plants produce nuclear energy, which ultimately generates the electricity we use.

Radioactive materials
The products of fission usually have too many neutrons to be stable and are **radioactive**. Radioactive means the nucleus continues to change by ejecting protons, neutrons, or other particles. A radioactive nucleus may also change a neutron into a proton and an electron, or vice-versa. Both molybdenum-99 and tin-135 are radioactive. Radioactive atoms can be dangerous because they continue to give off energy, some for a long time. The term *nuclear waste* means used fuel and other products of nuclear reactors that contain radioactive isotopes such as molybdenum-99 and tin-135.

> **chain reaction** - occurs when the fission reaction of a single atom triggers more nuclear reactions and results in an increasing release of nuclear energy
>
> **radioactive** - describes atoms which are unstable and spontaneously change into other atoms by the emission of particles and/or energy from the nucleus

Energy release by a fission reaction

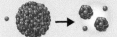

$^{1}n + ^{235}_{92}U \longrightarrow ^{99}_{42}Mo + ^{135}_{50}Sn + (2 \times ^{1}n) + \text{energy}$

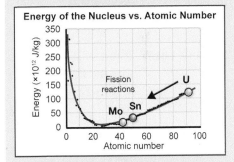

+123 TJ	Energy of uranium (U) nucleus
− 25 TJ	Average energy of nuclei of molybdenum (Mo) and Tin (Sn)
+ 98 TJ	Energy released by fission of uranium into Mo and Sn

Figure 10.21: *Fission releases energy because the uranium nucleus is higher in energy than tin (Sn) or molybdenum (Mo).*

Radioactivity and radiation

Radioactive decay If an atomic nucleus is unstable, it undergoes a type of nuclear reaction called **radioactive decay**. The word *decay* means to "break down." In radioactive decay, the nucleus of an atom spontaneously breaks down and emits subatomic particles and/or radiation. The three most common types of radioactive decay are described here (Figure 10.22, Figure 10.23).

Alpha decay In **alpha decay**, the nucleus ejects two protons and two neutrons. Look at the periodic table. You can see that two protons and two neutrons are the nucleus of a helium-4 atom. Alpha radiation is actually fast-moving helium-4 nuclei. When alpha decay occurs, the atomic number is reduced by two because two protons are removed. The atomic mass is reduced by four because two neutrons go along with the two protons. For example, uranium-238 undergoes alpha decay to become thorium-234.

Beta decay **Beta decay** occurs when a neutron in the nucleus splits into a proton and an electron. The proton stays in the nucleus, but the high-energy electron is ejected and is called *beta radiation*. During beta decay, the atomic number increases by one because one new proton is created. The mass number stays the same because neutrons and protons both have a mass number of 1. By studying beta decay, Enrico Fermi came up with the theory of weak force.

Gamma decay **Gamma decay** is how the nucleus gets rid of excess energy. In gamma decay, the nucleus emits a high-energy photon, but the number of protons and neutrons stays the same. The nucleus decays from a state of high energy to a state of lower energy. Gamma ray photons are energetic enough to break apart other atoms, making them dangerous to living things. Gamma radiation requires heavy shielding for humans working with it. Alpha and beta decay are often accompanied by gamma radiation from the same nucleus.

Radiation The word *radiation* means the flow of energy through space. There are many forms of radiation. Light, radio waves, microwaves, and x-rays are forms of electromagnetic radiation. The energy in alpha and beta radiation comes from moving particles. Radiation is dangerous when it has enough energy to break chemical bonds in molecules. Ultraviolet light, gamma rays, and x-rays are forms of radiation that can be harmful to living things in large doses.

radioactive decay - the spontaneous changing of the nucleus of atoms through the release of radiation

alpha decay - radioactive decay that results in an alpha particle—a helium nucleus—being emitted from the nucleus of an atom

beta decay - radioactive decay that results in a beta particle—an electron—being emitted from the nucleus of an atom

gamma decay - a process by which the nucleus of an atom emits a gamma-ray radiation

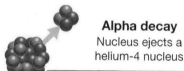

Alpha decay
Nucleus ejects a
helium-4 nucleus

Protons	Decrease by 2
Neutrons	Decrease by 2
Atomic number	Decreases by 2
Mass number	Decreases by 4

Figure 10.22: *Alpha decay. Information about beta and gamma decay appears on the next page.*

The periodic table

The periodic table organizes the elements according to how they chemically combine with other elements. The table is organized in order of increasing atomic number. All atoms of the same element have the same atomic number, which indicates the number of protons in each atom (Figure 10.24). The lightest element, hydrogen, is at the upper left. The heaviest (118), an artificially-produced element, is on the lower right.

Beta decay

Nucleus converts a neutron to a proton and an electron, ejecting the electron.

Protons	Increase by 1
Neutrons	Decrease by 1
Atomic number	Increases by 1
Mass number	Stays the same

Periodic Table of the Elements

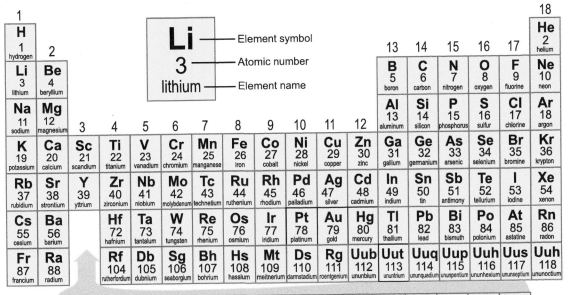

Gamma ray

Gamma decay

Nucleus emits gamma radiation and lowers its energy.

Protons	Stays the same
Neutrons	Stays the same
Atomic number	Stays the same
Mass number	Stays the same

Figure 10.23: *Beta and gamma decay*

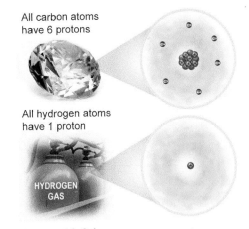

All carbon atoms have 6 protons

All hydrogen atoms have 1 proton

Figure 10.24: *The atomic number indicates how many protons are in the nucleus of an atom.*

Half-life

Chance and radioactivity
Americium-241 is a radioactive isotope used in household smoke detectors. If you look at an individual americium-241 atom, it would be impossible to predict when it would decay. However, if you have a large collection of americium atoms, the *rate* of decay becomes predictable. For americium-241, it is known that half of the atoms in the sample decay in 458 years. Therefore, 458 years is the *half-life* of americium-241. The **half-life** is the time it takes for half of the atoms in a sample of a radioactive element sample to decay.

> **half-life** - the length of time it takes for half of any sample of a radioactive isotope to change into other isotopes (or elements)

The half-life of carbon-14
Every radioactive element has a different half-life, ranging from fractions of a second to millions of years, depending on the specific isotope. For example, the half-life of carbon-14 is about 5,700 years. If you start out with 200 grams of carbon-14, 5,700 years later only 100 grams will still be carbon-14. The rest will have decayed to nitrogen-14 (Figure 10.25). If you wait another 5,700 years, half of the 100 remaining grams of carbon-14 will decay, leaving 50 grams of carbon-14 and 150 grams of nitrogen-14. Wait a third interval of 5,700 years, and you will be down to 25 grams of carbon-14. *One half of the atoms decay during every time interval of one half-life.*

Figure 10.25: *Half of the carbon-14 turns into nitrogen-14 every half-life. The half-life of carbon-14 is 5,700 years.*

The half-life of different isotopes varies greatly
Uranium-238 has a half-life of 4.5 billion years. It was created in the nuclear reactions of forming stars, the remains of which condensed to form the solar system. We can still find uranium-238 on Earth because the half-life is so long. The isotope fluorine-18 has a half-life of 1 hour, 50 minutes. This isotope is used in medicine. Hospitals have to make it when they need it because it decays so quickly. Any natural fluorine-18 decayed billions of years ago. Carbon-15 has a half-life of 2.4 seconds. Scientists who make carbon-15 in a laboratory have to use it immediately.

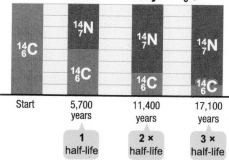

Radioactive decay series
Most radioactive materials decay in a series of reactions involving more than one reaction. For example, radon gas comes from the decay of naturally-occurring uranium in the soil (Figure 10.26). Radon itself decays into lead in a chain reaction of three alpha decays and two beta decays. Radon is a source of indoor air pollution in some houses that do not have adequate ventilation. Many people test for radon before buying a house.

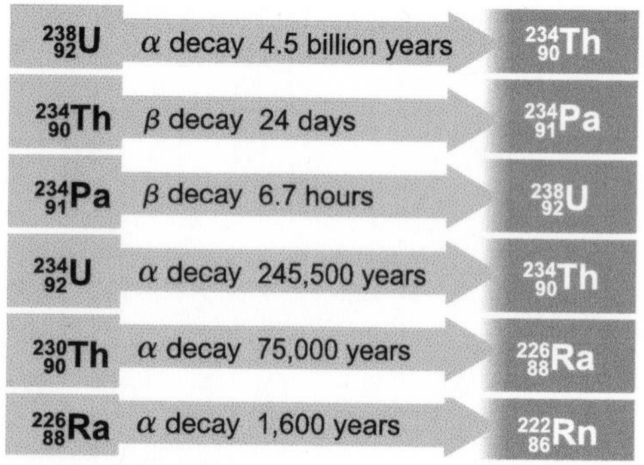

Figure 10.26: *A series of radioactive reactions produces radon-222 gas.*

Applications of nuclear reactions

Carbon dating   Living things contain a large amount of carbon. The isotope carbon-14 is used by archeologists to determine age. We find this isotope in the environment because it is constantly being produced in the upper atmosphere by cosmic rays—high energy particles from the Sun and elsewhere in the universe. The ratio of carbon-14 to carbon-12 in the environment is a constant that is determined by the balance between production and decay of carbon-14. As long as an organism is alive, it constantly exchanges carbon with the environment. Therefore, the ratio of carbon-14 to carbon-12 in the organism stays the same as in the environment.

How carbon dating works

$\blacksquare$ $_{6}^{12}C$

$\square$ $_{6}^{14}C$

Ratio of $_{6}^{12}C$ to $_{6}^{14}C$

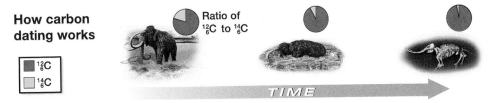

TIME

Why carbon dating works   When a living organism dies, it stops exchanging carbon with the environment. All the carbon-12 in the organism remains because it is a stable isotope. Almost no new carbon-14 is created because most cosmic rays do not reach the ground. As the carbon-14 decays, the ratio of carbon-14 to carbon-12 slowly gets smaller with age. By measuring this ratio, an archeologist can tell how long it has been since the material was alive. Carbon dating works reliably up to about 10 times the half-life, or 57,000 years. After 10 half-lives, there is not enough carbon-14 left to measure accurately. Also, carbon dating only works on material that has once been living, such as bone or wood.

Nuclear medicine   Nuclear medicine involves giving patients radioactive drugs for certain illnesses, including certain cancers. These drugs are administered orally or intravenously. For example, radioactive iodine-131 is given to patients who have for hyperthyroidism or thyroid cancer because the thyroid gland readily absorbs all forms of iodine. As iodine-131 undergoes beta decay, the radiation causes cell damage and death in the diseased tissue. The use of radioactive iodine is a way to permanently treat hyperthyroidism.

How a smoke detector works

Smoke detectors contain a tiny amount of americium-241, a radioactive isotope that emits alpha radiation. When an alpha particle hits a molecule of air, it knocks off an electron, ionizing an air molecule. The positive ion and negative electron are collected by positively- and negatively-charged metal plates attached to a battery in the smoke detector. The flow of ions and electrons creates a tiny electric current that is measured by the electronics of the smoke detector.

When smoke is in the air, the smoke particles interrupt the flow of ions and electrons. The electric current collected by the metal plates drops. The circuit in the smoke detector senses the drop in current and sounds the alarm.

Nuclear power

Sun power is nuclear power
All life on Earth depends on the energy produced by the fusion reactions that occur in the Sun. For example, plants rely on sunlight to photosynthesize and make sugars. Animals and people, in turn, eat plant products like fruits, vegetables, and grains. By eating these plant products, we are eating the Sun's energy! Additionally, our fossil fuels derived from the remains of plants and animals can be attributed to the Sun's energy. All of this energy on which we depend is related to a nuclear reaction in which hydrogen isotopes are fused together to make helium.

Can we produce energy like the Sun?
The interior of the Sun, where fusion takes place, has a temperature of about 15 million degrees Celsius. On Earth, we would need to generate about 100 million degrees Celsius to create fusion of hydrogen to produce energy. This high temperature is necessary to overcome the difficulty of forcing positively charged protons together. Given this fact, is fusion a possible energy source for humans? Not currently. It would take too much energy to actually produce the energy for human needs. However, because fusion reactions produce little waste, scientists are studying this kind of nuclear reaction to see if there are economical ways to produce energy using fusion.

Nuclear power is produced by fission
Currently, nuclear power is produced using fission. Nuclear power plants include reactors in which fission is used to produce heat to generate steam for running turbines. In a power plant that uses fossil fuels, heat is used to generate steam for running turbines by burning fossil fuels. In turn, the turbines generate electricity for homes and businesses (Figure 10.27).

Nuclear reactors produce hazardous nuclear waste
Almost all of our energy generation produces some harmful waste products. Burning coal and oil creates waste gases that contribute to global climate change and acid rain. Nuclear reactors produce relatively few harmful emissions related to global climate change, but they do produce *nuclear waste*.

What is nuclear waste?
The radioactive element in nuclear reactor fuel is uranium. When a uranium atom breaks up, giving off energy, some of the resulting lighter atoms are also radioactive and remain radioactive for a long time. Substances that are radioactive are extremely harmful to living things. The particles and energy emitted from radioactive elements can cause diseases like cancer.

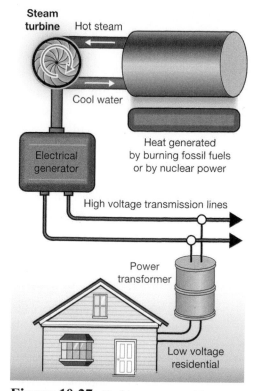

Figure 10.27: *Turbines are used in power plants to generate electricity for homes and businesses.*

How much energy comes from nuclear reactors? The world gets nearly 15 percent of its energy for electricity production from nuclear power. The United States gets about 19 percent of its energy for electricity from nuclear fission reactors. Other energy sources include coal, natural gas, oil, and hydroelectric dams. France is one of the countries that is most dependent on nuclear power. About 75 percent of the electricity generated in France comes from nuclear fission. Using nuclear power, France is able to meet the energy needs of its citizens and sell power to neighboring countries, too.

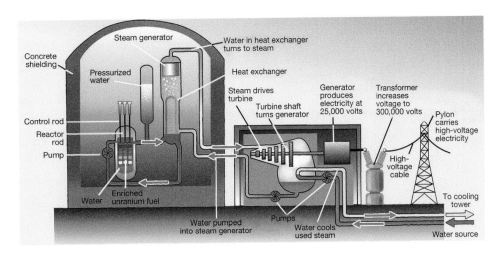

The challenge of storing nuclear waste

For years, the proposed permanent storage location for highly radioactive nuclear waste has been Yucca Mountain, Nevada. This location is 90 miles from Las Vegas. However, in 2009, the federal government decided that Yucca Mountain was no longer an option. In 2010, President Barack Obama established the Blue Ribbon Commission on America's Nuclear Future to develop a new plan for safely storing nuclear waste. The commission will report its findings in 2012.

Presently, nuclear waste is stored in cooling pools or dry casks at nuclear power plants around the country. Storing nuclear waste is a controversial issue because the waste is radioactive, some of which is usable for making nuclear weapons, and very costly to store. Nuclear scientists and engineers are studying the problems of managing and storing nuclear waste.

10.3 Section Review

1. Sketch a graph showing the energy of the nucleus versus the atomic number. Use the graph to explain what kinds of nuclear reactions release energy.
2. Write the nuclear reaction that represents the alpha decay of uranium-238.
3. If americium-241 has a half life of 458 years, how long do you need to wait until only ¼ of a sample of americium-241 is left?
4. List one advantage and one disadvantage of nuclear power.

Indirect Evidence and Archaeology

Ernest Rutherford located the atom's nucleus through experiments—without ever seeing it directly. Using indirect evidence is also transforming the field of archaeology. Using remote sensing techniques, archaeologists can locate and describe features of ancient civilizations before a shovel ever touches the soil.

Searching for a lost city

American archaeologist Dr. Juris Zarins had long been fascinated by tales of a bustling ancient Arabian city called Ubar. The city is mentioned in Bedouin tales, in Greek and Roman histories, the *Arabian Nights*, and the Koran. Clues in these manuscripts led Dr. Zarins to believe that Ubar thrived for centuries as a crossroad for trade until its decline around 300 CE.

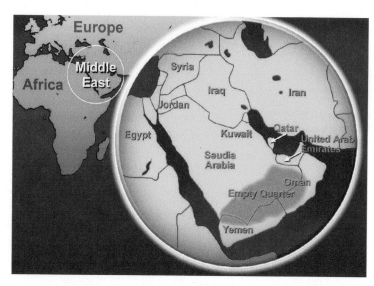

Since then, all traces of the city had vanished, buried in 600-foot tall sand dunes that spread across an area the size of Texas in the southern Arabian peninsula. The area is known as "the empty quarter" and "the sandy sea." How could anyone possibly find a city buried in such a vast, featureless terrain?

Still, Zarins wanted to try. In 1987, he teamed up with American filmmaker and amateur archaeologist Nicholas Clapp to organize an expedition. Knowing it would take several lifetimes to excavate an area that large, they turned to NASA geologist Ron Blom for help. Could space shuttle or satellite imaging reveal anything that would narrow the search?

Hidden pathways revealed

Blom collected images of the region from a space shuttle mission and two satellites. The satellites, known as Landsat, make images from electromagnetic radiation reflected from Earth's surface. The Sun also shines at light wavelengths slightly longer than the human eye can see, called "near infrared" wavelengths. Many landscape features are more distinct at these wavelengths, normally unseen by your eyes.

Centuries of foot travel and camel caravans packed down the desert floor so that 1,700 years later, they still reflected infrared radiation differently than the surrounding terrain. The roads, invisible to the naked eye, showed up clearly in the infrared images. The Landsat images covered a vast area: 30,000 square kilometers. Blom also used close-up images from a

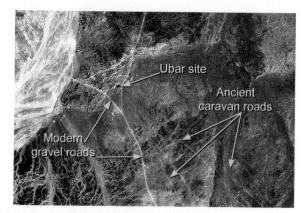

French satellite called SPOT to zoom in on the area where the caravan roads converged. The expedition team, equipped with the infrared "maps," began their search for Ubar at that convergence point—at the eastern edge of the "empty quarter," in the country of Oman.

Ubar rediscovered

The excavation uncovered an octagon-shaped fortress with 10-foot walls and a tall tower at each corner. Pottery fragments from faraway places such as Greece, Rome, and Syria suggested that this had indeed been a major trading center. The city of Ubar, lost for 17 centuries, was found with the help of some remarkable technology.

The Landsat and SPOT satellites Blom used are remote sensing devices. They collect information about Earth from a distant location, without coming into direct contact with the planet or disturbing it in any way.

The infrared images produced using the satellite data are a kind of indirect evidence. Just as nobody has actually seen the inside of an atom, nobody had actually seen the caravan roads to Ubar before the expedition began. Small differences in the way the desert surface reflected the infrared radiation provided clues to the roads' locations.

Transforming archaeology

Other types of remote sensing continue to transform the field of archaeology. Ground-penetrating radar helped the Ubar team find structural features buried up to 20 feet below the surface.

Around the world, archaeologists are experimenting with new methods such as surveying the magnetic properties of the soil, which can help locate iron-containing items buried underneath. They also measure the electrical resistance of the soil. This technique can detect buried brick and stone walls, pavements, shaft tombs, as well as ancient roads, farms, and earthworks, because they are more resistant to

Aerial view of town and sinkhole

current than the surrounding dirt. Microwave radar, used by both space shuttles and satellites, can detect stone walls and other features buried beneath the Earth's surface.

These new methods of gathering indirect evidence are providing archaeologists with something akin to x-ray vision: the ability to collect a wealth of information about a site without ever disturbing the soil.

These new methods save time and resources by narrowing in on the best sites to excavate, and in some places they can even take the place of excavation. Archaeologists can learn a great deal about a site using remote sensing devices. This allows sacred sites to remain untouched while respecting the cultures of other people.

QUESTIONS

1. What is *indirect evidence*?
2. How did a map showing infrared radiation reflected from the desert surface help Dr. Zarins and his team find the lost city of Ubar?
3. Name three benefits of using remote sensing in the field of archaeology.

Chapter 10 Review

Understanding Vocabulary

Select the correct term to complete the sentences.

alpha decay	half-life	quantum state
atomic number	isotopes	quantum theory
atomic theory	mass number	radioactive
beta decay	neutron	radioactive decay
chain reaction	nuclear reactions	spectral lines
charge	nucleus	spectrometer
electromagnetic force	photon	spectrum
electron	probability	strong nuclear force
gamma decay	proton	uncertainty principle

1. Carbon-12, carbon-13, and carbon-14 are _____ of the element carbon.

2. Of the four fundamental forces, the force which is strongest is the _____.

3. The _____ is 1,837 times more massive than the electron while the _____ is 1,839 times more massive than the electron.

4. When an atom's electron falls from an excited state to a lower energy level, light is given off that may be observed as _____.

5. The location of an electron must be described using a(n) _____ because its exact location cannot be specified according to the _____.

6. Fission and fusion reactions are examples of _____, both releasing huge amounts of energy.

7. Of the three most common types of radioactive decay, the process releasing the most massive particle is _____.

Reviewing Concepts

Section 10.1

1. Contrast John Dalton's atomic theory with today's knowledge of the atom.

2. What did Ernest Rutherford discover about the atom with his gold foil experiment?

3. What particles make up the nucleus of the atom?

4. What takes up the most space in an atom, the nucleus or the electron cloud?

5. If the positive charge on protons in the nucleus causes protons to repel each other, why doesn't the nucleus break apart?

6. Compare electrons, protons, and neutrons in terms of size, mass, and charge.

7. Name the scientist(s) credited with the discovery of the electron, the proton, the nucleus, and the neutron.

8. Name the four fundamental forces in the atom in order from strongest to weakest and the scientist responsible for identifying or measuring each.

9. Describe the significance of the atomic number and mass number of an element.

10. What is an isotope? Give an example for isotopes of an element.

11. What is the derivation of the atomic mass unit? What is the value in kilograms and the abbreviation for 1 atomic mass unit?

Section 10.2

12. What is the evidence that an electron's energy is restricted to a specific value?

13. What is a photon?

14. How did Neils Bohr explain spectral lines?

15. Why is probability used to predict the behavior of particles instead of exact calculations?

16. The graph shown might be used to represent the _____ for a specific quantum state of an electron.

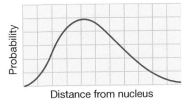

Distance from nucleus

Section 10.3

17. Compare and contrast chemical and nuclear reactions.

18. Compare and contrast fusion and fission reactions.

19. In a chemical reaction, balanced equations are written assuming the law of conservation of mass is strictly obeyed. Can this assumption be made with nuclear reactions?

20. Why is the energy released from a nuclear reaction so much greater than the energy from a chemical reaction?

21. Summarize the three kinds of radioactive decay in the chart below.

Decay	Proton # change	Neutron # change	Ejected particle
Alpha			
Beta			
Gamma			

22. What is the periodic table and how is it organized?

23. What is the half-life of an element?

24. Briefly describe three uses of radioactive isotopes.

25. "All life on Earth depends upon the energy produced by fusion reactions." Briefly explain this statement.

Solving Problems

Section 10.1

1. An atom has seven protons and eight neutrons. What is this atom's atomic number? What is its mass number? What element is this atom?

2. How many neutrons are in a silicon atom with an atomic number of 14 and a mass number of 30?

3. Carbon-12 and carbon-14 have an atomic number of 6. How many protons and neutrons do carbon-12 and carbon-14 have?

4. Find the number of protons in an oxygen atom.

5. An atom has 20 protons and 24 neutrons.

   a. What is this atom's mass number?

   b. What is this atom's atomic number?

   c. What element is this atom?

6. A common isotope of carbon has a mass number of 13. What is the total number of particles in its nucleus?

7. Draw a model of an atom that has five protons, five neutrons, and five electrons. Label the charge of each particle. What element is this?

Section 10.2

8. Atom A gains enough energy to promote an electron from the first energy level to the fourth energy level. Atom B gains enough energy to promote an electron from the third energy level to the fourth energy level. When both electrons fall back to their original energy levels, one atom emits a red photon and the other a green photon. Which atom emits the green photon?

9. If you roll a die once, what is the probability that you will roll a four? If you roll the die 100 times, how many times would you expect to roll a four?

Section 10.3

10. Use the graph below and the "Periodic Table of the Elements" on page 261 to number the elements in a–f in order of increasing energy of their nuclei.

a. carbon (C)

b. iron (Fe)

c. magnesium (Mg)

d. lithium (Li)

e. lead (Pb)

f. krypton (Kr)

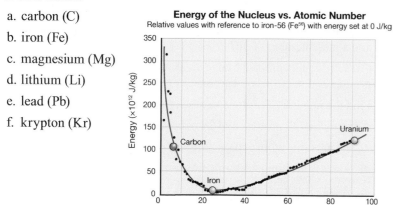

Energy of the Nucleus vs. Atomic Number
Relative values with reference to iron-56 (Fe^{56}) with energy set at 0 J/kg

11. Use the graph above and your knowledge of nuclear reactions to indicate which pairs of atomic nuclei would be most likely to release energy by fission and which would release energy by fusion.

a. helium-4 and carbon-12

b. uranium-235 and strontium-135

c. carbon-12 and carbon-12

12. Radon has a half-life of 3.8 days. How long does it take for 16 g of radon to be reduced to 2 g of radon?

Test Practice

Section 10.1

1. Which subatomic particle has the highest mass?

a. gamma ray

b. electron

c. proton

d. neutron

2. Which is the weakest of the four fundamental forces?

a. gravity

b. weak force

c. electromagnetic force

d. strong nuclear force

3. Who was the first scientist to measure the gravitational force between two objects?

a. Hideki Yukawa

b. John Mitchell

c. Henry Cavendish

d. Charles-Augustin Coulomb

Section 10.2

4. Photons of frequencies corresponding to the colors blue, green, red, and violet are emitted by an atom as electrons fall from the 3rd, 4th, 5th, and 6th levels to the 2nd level. The transition responsible for the emission of a photon with a frequency producing red light is

a. level 3 to 2.

b. level 4 to 2.

c. level 5 to 2.

d. level 6 to 2.

Section 10.3

5. A high energy photon is always emitted in the process of

 a. alpha decay.

 b. beta decay.

 c. gamma decay.

 d. all radioactive decay.

6. According to the graph, the largest amount of energy would be given off from a nuclear change of

 a. carbon nuclei to uranium nuclei.

 b. carbon nuclei to iron nuclei.

 c. uranium nuclei to carbon nuclei.

 d. iron nuclei to carbon nuclei.

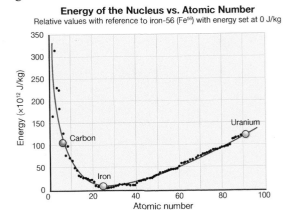

Energy of the Nucleus vs. Atomic Number
Relative values with reference to iron-56 (Fe⁵⁶) with energy set at 0 J/kg

7. Carbon-15 has a half-life of 2.4 s. Starting with 200 g, after 12 s the number of grams of carbon-15 remaining would be

 a. 50.

 b. 25.

 c. 5.

 d. 12.5.

8. The nucleus of an atom becomes unstable when an atom contains

 a. too many neutrons compared to protons.

 b. too many electrons compared to protons.

 c. too many electrons compared to neutrons.

 d. any of the above combinations

Refer to the isotope notation below to answer questions 9 and 10.

$$^{60}_{28}\text{Ni}$$

9. This isotope can be properly identified as

 a. nickel-28.

 b. nickel-32.

 c. nickel-60.

 d. nickel-88.

10. The number protons in this isotope is

 a. 28.

 b. 32.

 c. 60.

 d. 88.

Applying Your Knowledge

Section 10.1

1. Make a poster illustrating models of the atom scientists have proposed since the 1800s. Explain how each model reflects the new knowledge that scientists gained through their experiments. When possible, comment on what they learned about charge, mass, and location of subatomic particles.

2. Research the Bohr model of the atom. Then, choose an atom and make a three-dimensional model of its structure. Choose different materials to represent protons, neutrons, and electrons. Attach a key to your model to explain what each material represents.

Section 10.2

3. Research alternative shapes for the periodic table. Make a poster of one of these alternatives and present the rationale for its shape to the class.

4. The element helium is a light gas that is very rare on Earth. In fact, helium was not discovered on this planet. It was discovered in the Sun, hence the name—in Greek, *helios* means "Sun." Astronomers saw a series of spectral lines in the Sun that did not match any known element on Earth. Helium was first identified from its spectrum of light from the Sun. Researchers were then able to find it on Earth because they knew what to look for. Research and draw the visible spectrum for helium, labeling the wavelength of each spectral line. Rank the spectral lines from highest energy to lowest energy.

Section 10.3

5. Research the possibility of using nuclear fusion as an energy source. Prepare a short report that answers the following questions:

   a. What are the challenges to using nuclear fusion for power?

   b. What are the advantages of using nuclear fusion for power?

   c. What is magnetic confinement fusion and how does it work?

 *Your Turn* **Answers**

Identifying the number of particles in a nucleus (Section 10.1, page 250)

a. 13 neutrons

b. 22 neutrons

Relativity

- In a "black hole," time stops.

- Every particle of matter has an antimatter twin. When matter and antimatter meet, they annihilate each other in a release of pure energy.

- The Sun creates a "warp" in space near it. This space warp results in what we feel as gravity.

The statements above are the essence of some ideas put forth by Albert Einstein, who lived from 1879 to 1955. His name is recognized around the world, and nearly everyone knows that he was a brilliant scientist. What did Albert Einstein discover? What were his greatest contributions to our understanding of science?

Einstein's remarkable discoveries changed our understanding of matter and energy. Once thought to be separate concepts, Einstein's theories show how matter and energy are related and can be turned into one another! This chapter will introduce you to the basic ideas of Einstein's theories of special relativity and general relativity. You will read about the speed of light, antimatter, strange particles, curved space-time, black holes, and the "Big Bang." Is this the stuff of science fiction? The science of Star Trek? Read this chapter to answer some of these interesting questions that probe the edge of our understanding of how the universe works.

KEY QUESTIONS

✔ What does E = mc² mean?

✔ What is the speed limit of the universe?

✔ What is a "black hole"?

VOCABULARY

antimatter	Big Bang	black hole
general relativity	reference frame	speed of light
theory of special relativity	time dilation	

11.1 The Relationship Between Matter and Energy

Before Chapter 10, we discussed matter and energy as related, but separate things. This was how physicists viewed the universe before Einstein, too. Einstein's remarkable discoveries changed all that. Today, we know that matter and energy can be turned into one another! In some ways, you can think of matter as a form of extremely concentrated energy.

Einstein's formula

The meaning of Einstein's formula The formula $E = mc^2$ is probably the most widely recognized formula in the world, even though few people know how to actually *use* the formula. The formula tells you the amount of energy (E) that is released when a mass (m) is completely converted to energy. It also tells you how much mass (m) you can create out of an amount of energy (E).

Mass and energy are equivalent In a nuclear reaction, some mass is converted to energy according to Einstein's formula. The c^2 factor means that even a tiny amount of mass is equivalent to a huge amount of energy. The speed of light (c) is 3×10^8 m/s, so the speed of light squared (c^2) is 9×10^{16} m²/s². This means 1 kilogram of mass is equivalent to 9×10^{16} joules of energy. This is enough energy to drive a powerful sports car for 25,000 years!

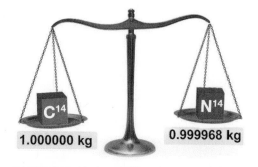

| 1.000000 kg | 0.999968 kg |

Mass difference

$$\begin{aligned} & 1.000000 \text{ kg} \\ - \ & 0.999988 \text{ kg} \\ \hline & 0.000012 \text{ kg} \end{aligned}$$

Energy released

$E = mc^2$
$= (0.000012 \text{ kg})(3 \times 10^8 \text{ m/s})^2$
$= 1.1 \times 10^{12}$ joules

Figure 11.1: *A tiny amount of mass is converted to energy during the radioactive decay of carbon-14.*

> **EINSTEIN'S MASS-ENERGY FORMULA**
>
> Energy (J)——$E = mc^2$—— Speed of light (m/s)
>
> Mass (kg)

Energy in reactions Einstein's formula explains how chemical and nuclear reactions release energy. With chemical reactions, the energy released is relatively small and the difference in mass between reactants and products is too small to measure. With nuclear reactions, the amount of energy is large enough that there is a measurable mass difference (Figure 11.1).

The speed of light

The ultimate speed limit Einstein's theory of relativity says that nothing in the universe can travel faster than the speed of light. Even gravity travels at the speed of light. You may know that it takes light from the Sun 8 minutes and 19 seconds to get to Earth. If the Sun was to vanish, we would still see it in the sky for 8 minutes and 19 seconds. According to Einstein, Earth would also keep moving in its orbit for 8 minutes and 19 seconds, too! Earth would not feel the loss of the Sun's gravity until 8 minutes and 19 seconds passed, because gravity moves at the speed of light, too (Figure 11.2).

> **speed of light** - a universal constant equal to 300 million m/s in a vacuum

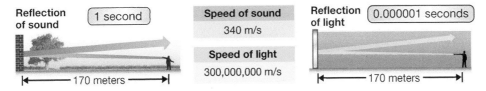

Comparing the speeds of sound and light Imagine shining a flashlight on a mirror that is far away. You don't see the light leave your flashlight, move to the mirror, then come back. But, that is exactly what happens! You don't see light move because it happens so fast. If the mirror was 170 meters away, the light would travel there and back in about one-millionth of a second (0.000001 s). Sound travels much slower than light. If you shout at a wall 170 meters away, you will hear an echo 1 second later. Light travels almost a million times faster than sound.

The speed of light, $c = 3 \times 10^8$ m/s The speed at which light travels through air is 300 million meters per second (it varies slightly in different materials). This is hard to comprehend. Light can travel around Earth 7½ times in 1 second. The **speed of light** is so important in physics that it is given its own symbol, a lowercase c. When you see this symbol, remember that c is 300 million m/s, or 3×10^8 m/s.

The sound of thunder lags the flash of lightning At the point of the lightning strike, the thunder and lightning occur at the same time. The speed of light is so fast that when lightning strikes a few miles away, you see the lightening several seconds before you hear the thunder. At 1 mile away from the lightning strike, the sound of the thunder is already about 5 seconds behind the flash of the lightning.

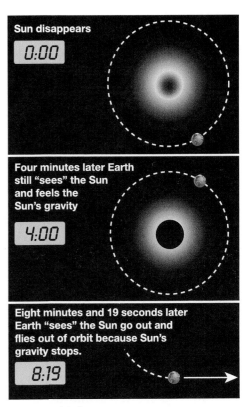

Figure 11.2: *If the Sun was to vanish, Earth would not feel any change for 8 minutes and 19 seconds. This is the time it takes light to get from the Sun to Earth.*

Antimatter

Other particles of matter
Up until the 1930s, scientists were confident that they could explain all the elements with three subatomic particles: protons, neutrons, and electrons. This changed as new developments in technology allowed more sophisticated experiments. The first new thing they discovered was **antimatter**. Then they found other kinds of subatomic particles such as neutrinos. Finally, they discovered that there were *even smaller* particles *inside* protons and neutrons!

Matter and antimatter
Theories in particle physics predict that every particle of matter has an antimatter twin. Antimatter is the same as regular matter, except properties like electric charge are reversed. An antiproton is just like a normal proton except it has a negative charge. An antielectron, also called a *positron*, is like an ordinary electron except that it has positive charge. Some nuclear reactions create antimatter. When matter is created from pure energy, equal quantities of matter and antimatter always appear together.

> **antimatter** - matter which has the opposite charge and other properties from normal matter

Figure 11.3: *A bit of antimatter the size of a grain of sand would release enough energy to power a small city for a week if it combined with an equal amount of normal matter.*

Ordinary matter

	Proton	Neutron	Electron
Charge	+	0	−
Mass (amu)	1.008	1.009	0.0005

Atom — Positive nucleus / Negative electron cloud

Antimatter

	Antiproton	Neutron	Antielectron (positron)
Charge	−	0	+
Mass (amu)	1.008	1.009	0.0005

Antiatom — Negative nucleus / Positive antielectron cloud

Antimatter reactions
When antimatter meets an equal amount of normal matter, both the matter and antimatter are converted to pure energy. Antimatter reactions release thousands of times more energy than ordinary nuclear reactions. If a grain of sand weighing 0.002 kilograms, made of ordinary matter, was to collide and react with a grain of sand made from 0.002 kilograms of antimatter, the resulting explosion would release 400 trillion joules of energy—enough to power a small city for almost a week (Figure 11.3)!

Strange particles

Neutrinos   In Chapter 10, you learned about beta decay, where a neutron turns into a proton and an electron. Although we did not say it then, a *third* particle is also created. This particle is a type of *neutrino*. Neutrinos are lighter than electrons and are very difficult to detect.

Neutrinos are hard to detect   Huge numbers of neutrinos are created by nuclear reactions in the Sun. Every second more than a trillion neutrinos pass right through your body—and you don't feel a thing! That is because neutrinos are not affected by the electromagnetic force or the strong nuclear force. Neutrinos are affected only by the weak force. The weak force is so weak that most neutrinos pass right through Earth without interacting with a single atom. Physicists have built very special experiments to capture and study neutrinos.

Accelerators   Other particles even heavier than the proton and neutron have also been found. We don't see these particles every day because regular protons and neutrons have lower energy than these heavy particles. Since matter tends to find the lowest, most-stable energy levels, ordinary matter tends to become protons and neutrons. Physicists use high-energy accelerators to produce the heavy particles so we can study them (Figure 11.4).

Quarks   Today, we know that protons and neutrons are made of even smaller particles called *quarks*. Quarks come in different types and the lightest two are named the *up quark* and the *down quark*. A proton is made of two up quarks and one down quark. A neutron is made from two down quarks and one up quark (Figure 11.5). All of the heavier particles are made of just six kinds of quarks, named *up*, *down*, *strange*, *charm*, *top*, and *bottom*.

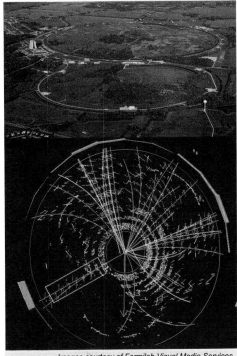

Images courtesy of Fermilab Visual Media Services

Figure 11.4: *Fermilab, near Chicago, is the site of a high-energy particle accelerator. The ring-shaped building in the top photo is 4 miles in circumference! The lower image shows a high-energy collision between particles. Each colored track represents a particle.*

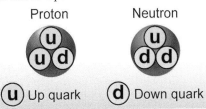

Figure 11.5: *Protons and neutrons are each made of three quarks.*

11.1 Section Review

1. Use Einstein's formula to explain the relationship between mass and energy.
2. Calculate how far light would travel in one year. This distance is called a *light year*.
3. Calculate the energy released by 1 kilogram of matter that is turned into pure energy.
4. Give one difference between antimatter and normal matter.

11.2 Special Relativity

Science fiction writers love to invent "impossible" tricks. For instance, time travel. It may surprise you, but time travel into the future is actually possible. It just takes a lot more energy than we know how to control today. Albert Einstein's theory of special relativity makes a connection between time and space that depends on how fast you are moving.

The relationship between matter, energy, time, and space

The **theory of special relativity** describes what happens to matter, energy, time, and space at speeds close to the speed of light. The fact that light *always* travels at the same speed forces other things about the universe to change in surprising ways. Special relativity does not affect daily life because things need to be moving faster than 100 million m/s before the effects of special relativity become obvious. However, these effects are seen and measured every day in physics labs. Some surprising effects of special relativity are shown in Figure 11.6 and described below.

Time moves slower

1. Time moves more slowly for an object in motion than it does for objects that are not in motion. In practical terms, clocks run slower on moving vehicles compared with clocks on the ground. By moving very fast, it is possible for 1 year to pass on a spaceship while 100 years have passed on the ground. This effect is known as **time dilation**.

Mass increases

2. As objects move faster, their *mass increases*. The closer the speed of an object gets to the speed of light, the more of its kinetic energy becomes mass instead of motion. Matter can never exceed the speed of light because adding energy creates more mass instead of increasing an object's speed.

Distances contract: the speed-of-light problem

3. The length of an object measured by one person at rest will not be the same as the length measured by another person who is moving close to the speed of light. The object does not get smaller or larger, *space itself* gets smaller for an observer moving near the speed of light.

theory of special relativity - a theory by Albert Einstein describing what happens to matter, energy, time, and space at speeds close to the speed of light

time dilation - an outcome of Einstein's theory of special relativity, whereby time runs slower for objects in motion than for objects at rest

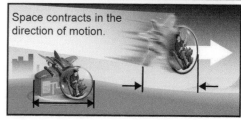

Figure 11.6: *Three ways that relativity describes an object as its speed approaches the speed of light.*

The speed of light problem

How you can be moving and appear at rest The theory of special relativity comes from thinking about light. Einstein wondered what light would look like if you could see it when it wasn't moving. Instead of making the light stop, Einstein thought about moving beside a beam of light at the same speed as light itself. Imagine you could move as fast as light and were traveling right next to the beam from a flashlight. If you looked over, you should see the light beam standing still, *relative to you*. A similar situation occurs when two people are driving on a road side-by-side at the same speed. The two people look at each other and appear *to each other* not to be moving, because both are traveling at the same speed.

The way speeds normally add up A girl on a railroad train, her *frame of reference*, is moving at a speed of 10 m/s. If you are standing on the track, the girl gets 10 meters closer to you every second. Now consider what happens if the girl on the train throws a ball at you at 10 m/s. In 1 second, the ball moves forward on the train 10 meters. The train also moves toward you by 10 meters. Therefore, the ball moves toward you at 20 meters in 1 second. The ball approaches you with a speed of *20 m/s* as far as you are concerned (Figure 11.7).

How you expect light to behave Einstein considered the same problem using light instead of a ball. If the girl on the train was to shine a flashlight toward you, you would expect the light to approach you faster. You would expect the light to come toward you at the speed of the train plus 3×10^8 m/s.

The speed of light does not behave this way That is *not* what happens (Figure 11.8). The light comes toward you at a speed of 3×10^8 m/s *no matter how fast the train approaches you*! This was confirmed in an experiment that was done in 1887 by Albert A. Michelson and Edward W. Morley. They used Earth itself as the "train." Earth moves with an orbital speed of 29,800 m/s. Michelson and Morley measured the speed of light parallel to and perpendicular to Earth's orbital motion. They found the speed to be exactly the same! This result is not what they expected, and was confusing to everyone. Like all unexpected results, it forced people to rethink what they thought they already knew. Einstein's theory of special relativity was the result, and it totally changed the way we understand space and time and explained some events that common sense could not.

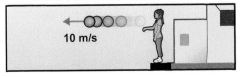
A girl throws a ball at 10 m/s relative to her frame of reference.

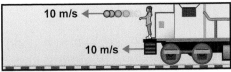
Her frame of reference is moving at 10 m/s.

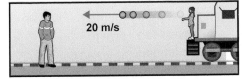
An observer at rest sees the ball approach at 20 m/s.

Figure 11.7: *A ball thrown from a moving train approaches you at the speed of the ball relative to the train plus the speed of the train relative to you.*

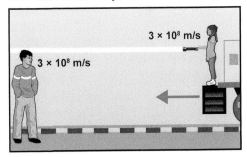

Figure 11.8: *The speed of light appears the same to all observers, independent of their relative motion.*

Speed, time, and clocks

Einstein's thinking

With this new idea that the speed of light is the same for all observers, Einstein thought about what this meant for everything else in physics. One of the strangest results of special relativity is that time itself changes, depending on the motion of an observer. Einstein's conclusion about the flow of time is totally revolutionary, and completely changed our understanding of how nature works.

A light clock on a spaceship

Einstein thought about a clock that measures time by counting the trips made by a beam of light going back and forth between two mirrors (Figure 11.9). The clock is on a moving spaceship. A person standing next to the clock sees the light go back and forth straight up and down. The time it takes to make one trip is the distance between the mirrors divided by the speed of light.

How the light appears on the ground

To someone who is not moving, the path of the light is not straight up and down. The light appears to make a zigzag because the mirrors move with the spaceship (Figure 11.10). The observer on the ground sees the light travel a longer path. This would not be a problem, *except that the speed of light must be the same to all observers, regardless of their motion.*

The paradox

Suppose it takes light 1 second to go between the mirrors. The speed of light must be the same for both observers, yet the person on the ground sees the light move a longer distance! How can this be?

Time itself must be different for a moving object

The only way to explain this is that *1 second on the ground is not the same as 1 second on the spaceship.* The speed of light is the distance traveled divided by the time taken. If 1 second of "ship time" is longer than 1 second of "ground time," then the problem is resolved: Both people measure the same speed for light of 3×10^8 m/s. The difference is that 1 second of "ship time" is *longer* than 1 second of "ground time."

Time slows down close to the speed of light

The fact that the speed of light is constant means *time slows down for objects in motion, including people.* If you move fast enough, the change in the flow of time is enormous. For a spaceship traveling at 99.9 percent of the speed of light, 22 years pass on Earth for every year that passes on the ship. The closer the spaceship's speed is to the speed of light, the slower time flows.

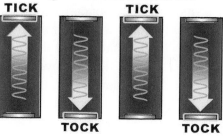

A light clock counts trips of light between two mirrors.

Figure 11.9: *A light clock measures time by measuring the how long it takes a pulse of light to move between two parallel mirrors.*

In the ship the light goes straight up and down.

A stationary observer sees the light zigzag following the motion of the mirrors.

Figure 11.10: *A light pulse moves straight up and down in a light clock in the spaceship. But, the same light pulse moving relative to an observer who is not moving traces out a zigzag path.*

The twin paradox

Proof of time dilation
The idea that moving clocks run slower is difficult to believe. Before Einstein's theory of special relativity, time was always considered universal. One second was 1 second, no matter where you were or what you were doing. After Einstein, we realized this was not true. The rate of time passing for two people depends on their relative motion.

Atomic clocks
One of the most direct measurements of this effect was done in the early 1970s by synchronizing two precise atomic clocks. One was put on a plane and flown around the world. The other was left on the ground. When the flying clock returned home, the clocks were compared. The clock on the plane measured less time than the clock on the ground. The difference agreed precisely with special relativity.

The twin paradox
A *paradox* is a situation that does not seem to make sense. A well-known thought experiment in relativity is known as the *twin paradox*. The story goes like this: Two twins are born on Earth. They grow up, and one of the twins becomes an astronaut. The other twin chooses a different career.

Traveling into the future
The astronaut twin goes on a mission into space. The space ship moves very fast, near the speed of light. Because of traveling at this high speed, the clocks on the ship, including the twin's biological clock, run much slower than the clocks on Earth. Upon returning from a 2-year (ship time) trip, the astronaut is 2 years older than when she left. However, her twin brother is 20 years older now! In essence, the astronaut twin has traveled 18 years into the future by moving near the speed of light (Figure 11.11).

2010: One twin leaves, one twin stays. Both are 23 years old.

The astronaut twin goes near the speed of light for 2 years of her time.

2030: Astronaut twin returns only 2 years older, but her brother is 20 years older.

Figure 11.11: *Relativity allows a kind of "time travel" into the future, if you can move at speeds near the speed of light!*

11.2 Section Review

1. According to special relativity, what three things happen at speeds close to 3×10^8 m/s?
2. Which person experiences a "longer second," a person who is in motion or a person who is standing still?
3. You are standing on the ground beside a train track. A person on the train throws a ball at you at a speed of 20 m/s relative to the train. If the train is moving toward you at 30 m/s, what is the speed of the ball relative to you?
4. Explain how you could travel into the future.

11.3 General Relativity

Einstein's theory of **general relativity** describes gravity in a very different way than Newton's law of universal gravitation does. According to Einstein, the presence of mass changes the shape of space-time itself. In general relativity, an object in orbit is moving in a straight line through curved space. The curvature of space itself causes a planet to move in an orbit. The force we call gravity is an effect created by the curvature of space and time.

The equivalence of acceleration and gravity

Different perspectives on the same motion
Imagine a boy and girl who jump into a bottomless canyon, where there is no air friction. On the way down, they throw a ball back and forth. If the girl looks at the boy, she sees the ball go straight to him. If the boy looks at the girl, he sees the ball go straight to her, with a slight curve due to gravity. However, an observer watching them fall sees the ball follow a curved zigzag path back and forth (Figure 11.12). Who is correct? What is the real path of the ball?

The boy and girl perceive no gravity
Both are correct *from their frame of reference*. Imagine enclosing the boy and girl in a windowless box falling with them. From inside their box, they see the ball go back and forth. To the boy and girl in the box, the ball follows the exact same path it would *if there were no gravity*.

The reverse situation
Next, imagine the boy and girl are in the same box throwing the ball back and forth in deep space, *where there is no gravity*. This time the box is accelerating upwards. When the boy throws the ball to the girl, the ball does not go straight to her, but drops in a parabola toward the floor. This happens because the floor is accelerating upward and pushing the girl with it. The girl moves up while the ball is moving toward her. But, from her perspective she sees the ball go down. To the girl the path of the ball is a parabola *exactly like it would be if there was a force of gravity pulling it downward.*

Reference frames
In physics, the box containing the boy and girl is called a **reference frame**. Everything they can do, measure, or see is inside their reference frame. *No experiment the boy or girl do inside the box can tell whether they are feeling the force of gravity or they are in a reference frame that is accelerating.*

> **general relativity** - Einstein's theory in which gravity is an effect created by the curvature of space-time
>
> **reference frame** - a perspective from which the position and motion of a system can be described

How it appears to a stationary observer

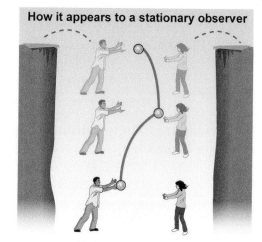

How it appears to them in their reference frame

Reference frame

Figure 11.12: *How the path of the ball appears to an outside observer and in the accelerating reference frame of the boy and girl.*

Curved space-time

Light and the equivalence principle   Earlier in this chapter, special relativity was introduced, which says that the speed of light is the same for all observers, whether they are moving or not. This equivalence of acceleration and gravity must also be true for experiments that measure the speed of light. In order to meet both these conditions, Einstein deduced two strange things which must also be true.

1. Space itself must be curved.
2. The path of light must be deflected by gravity, even though light has no mass.

Flat space   To understand what we mean by curved space, consider rolling a ball across a sheet of graph paper. If the graph paper is flat the ball rolls along a straight line. A flat sheet of graph paper is like "flat space." In flat space, parallel lines never meet, and all three angles of a triangle add up to 180 degrees. Flat space is what you would consider "normal."

Curved space   A large mass, like a star, curves space nearby. Figure 11.13 (middle) shows an example of a graph made of rubber, which holds a large mass. The large mass has created a "well" on the graph; notice the curved lines. If you roll a ball along this graph, its path bends as it rolls near this place where the graph is stretched by the mass. From directly overhead, the graph grid still looks like squares. If you look straight down on the graph, the path of the ball appears to be deflected by a force pulling it toward the large mass. You might say the ball "felt" a force of gravity which deflected its motion. You would be right. This effect of curved space is identical to the force of gravity.

Orbits and curved space   In fact, close to a source of gravity, straight lines become curved lines. A planet moving in an orbit is actually moving in a straight line through curved space. This is a strange way to think of it, but all of the experimental evidence indicates it is the accurate way to think. The event that made Einstein famous was his prediction that light from distant stars should be bent by the curvature of space near the Sun. Physicists were skeptical because, according to Newton's law of gravitation, light is not affected by gravity. In 1919, careful observations were made of the light from a star seen near the Sun during a solar eclipse. Einstein was proven to be right!

Straight line in flat space

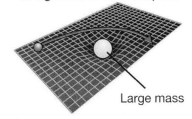

Straight line in curved space

Large mass

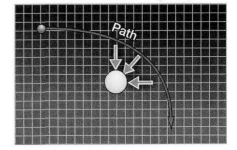

Observed force of gravity

Figure 11.13: *Large amounts of mass cause space to become curved. An object following a straight path in curved space bends the same way as if it were acted on by the force we call gravity.*

Black holes

General relativity predicts black holes

One of the strangest predictions of general relativity is the existence of *black holes*. To understand a **black hole**, consider a rocket trying to leave Earth. If the rocket does not go fast enough, Earth's gravity pulls it back. The minimum speed a rocket needs to escape a planet's gravity is called the *escape velocity*. The stronger the force of gravity, the faster the escape velocity needed.

The escape velocity of a black hole

If gravity becomes strong enough, the escape velocity can reach the speed of light. A black hole is an object with such strong gravity that its escape velocity equals or exceeds the speed of light. When the escape velocity equals the speed of light, nothing can get out because nothing can go faster than light. In fact, even light cannot get out. The name *black hole* comes from the fact that no light can get out, so the object appears "black." Because Earth's escape velocity is much less than the speed of light, light easily escapes its gravity (Figure 11.14).

Black holes are extremely compact matter

To make a black hole, a very large mass must be squeezed into a very tiny space. For example, to make Earth into a black hole, you would have to squeeze the mass of the whole planet down to the size of a marble as wide as your thumb. For a long time, nobody took black holes seriously because they seemed so strange that they could not actually be real.

We see black holes by what is around them

But then astronomers started finding them! You might think it would be impossible to see a black hole—and it is. But, you *can* see what happens

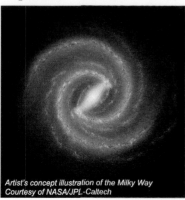

Artist's concept illustration of the Milky Way Courtesy of NASA/JPL-Caltech

around a black hole. When an object falls into a black hole, it loses so much energy that a fraction of its mass turns into energy. Any matter that falls into a black hole gives off so much energy it creates incredibly "bright" (intense) radiation as it falls in. Because of this radiation, astronomers believe our own Milky Way Galaxy has a huge black hole at its center. The Milky Way's central black hole is believed to have a mass more than a million times the mass of our Sun.

black hole - a compact, astronomical object with such strong gravity that its escape velocity is equal to or exceeds the speed of light

Earth image courtesy NASA

Figure 11.14: *On Earth, light travels in nearly straight lines because Earth's escape velocity is much less than the speed of light.*

The Big Bang

The Milky Way Galaxy   When we look out into space with powerful telescopes, we see stars of our own Milky Way Galaxy. The Milky Way contains about 200 billion stars distributed in a gigantic spiral. Some of the stars are like the Sun. Some are hotter, some are cooler, some older, some younger. Just recently we have discovered that many stars have planets.

The universe   Beyond our galaxy with its 200 billion stars are other galaxies. We can see billions of galaxies, many of them as full of stars as our own. This is the universe on its largest scale. When we look at these distant galaxies, we observe an astounding fact: All the galaxies are moving away from each other! The farther away they are from us, the faster they are moving. *This means the entire universe is expanding.*

An expanding universe implies a beginning   If the universe is expanding, then it must have been smaller in the past. It seems reasonable to ask how small was the early universe? And, how long has it been since the universe was small? The best evidence indicates that the age of the universe is about 13 billion years, plus or minus a few billion years (Figure 11.15). This is roughly three times older than the age of the Sun. This age for the universe agrees with other estimates, such as the ages of the oldest stars we can see.

The Big Bang   It also appears that the universe was once very small, possibly smaller than a single atom. Sixteen billion years ago a cataclysmic explosion occurred and the universe started growing from a tiny point into the incredible vastness we now see. In jest, someone called this beginning the "**Big Bang**" and the name stuck. At this time, we have no idea why the Big Bang happened or what came before the Big Bang.

> **Big Bang** - a theory of the origin of the universe in which the universe was once smaller than an atom and began to expand after a huge explosion

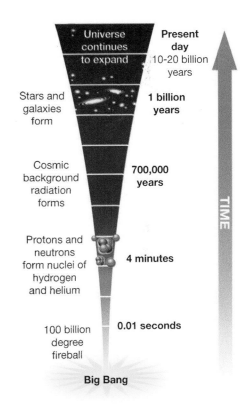

Figure 11.15: *A time line of the history of the universe.*

11.3 Section Review

1. How does general relativity explain gravity?
2. Describe your reference frame. Is it moving? If so, moving relative to what?
3. What is a black hole?
4. What is the Big Bang?

Traveling Faster Than Light

Have you ever watched a science-fiction program and wondered how your heroes can travel from galaxy to galaxy, crossing the universe in mere days? Such a feat would require travel at speeds faster than the speed of light. However, a major assumption of special relativity is that matter cannot travel faster than the speed of light. Some physicists are looking for loopholes in the laws of physics in the hope that one day, science fiction will become reality.

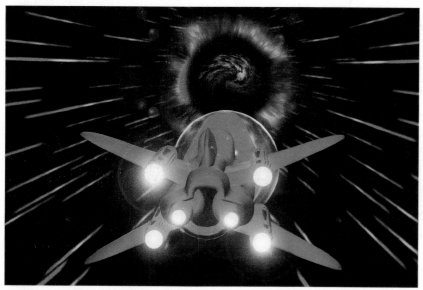

A long, long way from home

Why do we need to travel faster than light to explore the universe in person? Consider that Alpha Centauri, the star closest to the Sun, is 4.2 light years away—that's about 42 trillion kilometers.

The space shuttle travels at about 17,700 kilometers per hour. At that speed, it would take over 150,000 years to reach Alpha Centauri. At light speed with time dilation, it would take only about 2.3 years. As you can see, faster-than-light-speed travel has its benefits.

A shortcut through the universe

One idea being explored to bypass the light-speed barrier involves Einstein's concept that space can be distorted into structures called wormholes. A wormhole is a space-time distortion that is like a corridor connecting areas of space that are far away. Just as hallways in your school lessen the time needed to get to each of your classes, wormholes significantly reduce the amount of time needed to travel across the universe. Imagine walking through a wormhole in your classroom onto the surface of a planet in another galaxy!

Although scientists predict that wormholes occur naturally, they are unsure about their stability and how to control them. Wormholes also present a particular concern to physicists. They require unheard of amounts of energy to create. Creating space-time distortions, like wormholes, also requires a very unusual form of energy called negative energy. It has been estimated that to produce even a tiny wormhole would require an amount of negative energy that equals the entire energy output that a star produces over its 10-billion-year life span.

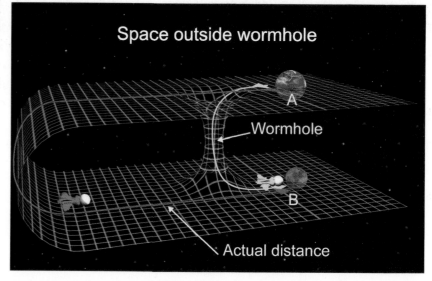

Space outside wormhole

What is negative energy?

Imagine removing all of the matter in your classroom. What's left? You would be in a vacuum containing only energy. You can imagine removing all the energy in the forms we know. Then, you have truly nothing except "nothing." Well, according to some new theories in quantum mechanics, this "nothing" actually has some energy that is the energy of space-time itself. Negative energy means lower energy than the energy of empty space-time. Some recent evidence suggests that negative energy may really exist.

A warped idea

Most theories that predict faster-than light travel involve negative energy, including *warp drive*. Warp drive is often compared with the moving sidewalks found in many airports. There is a limit to how fast you can walk, just like objects are not able to travel faster than light. However, you can move faster if you are on a portion of the moving sidewalk if the floor itself moves. The warp-drive concept is based on expanding space-time behind the spaceship and contracting it in front. The result is that a portion of space-time moves, pushing the spaceship forward.

A job for physicists

Physicists are studying both the possibilities of exceeding light speed and the many challenges it presents. They use their extensive knowledge of the laws of physics to bring this dream closer to reality.

Although they face many obstacles and uncertainties, scientists believe the possibilities of success create hope that future generations might solve many mysteries of our universe by actually going there.

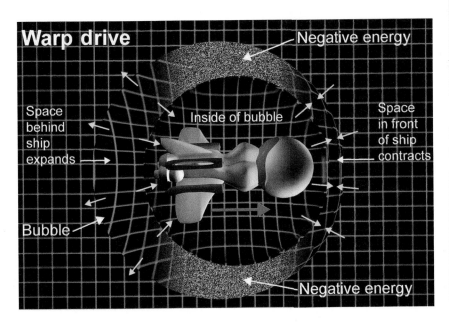

Warp drive

Negative energy

Space behind ship expands

Inside of bubble

Space in front of ship contracts

Bubble

Negative energy

QUESTIONS

1. Which theory predicts that faster-than-light travel is impossible?
2. What is the major obstacle to traveling faster than light?
3. What are some differences between wormholes and warp drive?
4. How is warp drive like a moving sidewalk?

Chapter 11 Review

Understanding Vocabulary

Select the correct term to complete the sentences.

antimatter	general relativity	speed of light
Big Bang	reference frame	time dilation
black hole	special relativity	

1. One of the most important quantities in modern physics, represented by the letter c, is the _____.

2. A positron is the _____ "twin" of the electron.

3. The effect described by Einstein's theory of special relativity that causes time to run slower for moving objects is named _____.

4. The path of light passing the Sun is altered by the curvature of space according to Einstein's theory of _____.

5. A rocket cannot travel fast enough to exit a _____.

Reviewing Concepts

Section 11.1

1. According to Einstein's formula, how are mass, energy, and the speed of light related?

2. What is the speed of light and why is it such an important concept in physics?

3. What is antimatter? What happens when antimatter meets an equal amount of normal matter?

4. What are quarks? In terms of quarks, what is the difference between a proton and a neutron?

Section 11.2

5. According to the theory of special relativity, why can't matter exceed the speed of light?

6. How is the speed of light coming toward you from a moving object different from the speed of a ball being thrown toward you from a moving object? Which theory did this difference lead scientists to?

7. Explain why time slows down at speeds close to the speed of light.

8. What is time dilation? How did scientists prove that it was true using atomic clocks?

9. Describe the twin paradox.

Section 11.3

10. How does the theory of general relativity describe the effects of gravity differently than the law of universal gravitation?

11. What are the effects of a large mass, like a star, on space? What are its effects on the path of light?

12. How would you make a black hole?

13. According to the big bang theory, how did the universe begin? What is happening to the universe?

Solving Problems

Section 11.1

1. In a nuclear reaction, only a small fraction of mass is converted into energy. Suppose 0.1 kg of uranium is converted into energy in a nuclear reaction. How much energy is produced?

2. The Sun produces 3.8×10^{26} J of energy per second. How much mass does the Sun lose each second?

3. Mars is 228 million km from the Sun. If the Sun suddenly burned out, how long would it take for Mars to be affected?

4. In 1969, Neil Armstrong and Buzz Aldrin were the first humans to land a lunar module on the Moon, 384,400 km from Earth. You may have heard Armstrong's famous phrase, spoken when he stepped out of the module onto the moon's surface: "That's one small step for man, one giant leap for mankind." When he spoke, he was not heard immediately on Earth because of the Moon's distance. How long did it take the radio waves to travel to Earth so that those words could be heard by millions of listeners? (*Hint*: Radio waves travel at the speed of light.)

Section 11.2

5. You are standing on a bicycle path. A person on a bike throws a ball at you at a speed of 10 m/s relative to the bike. If the bike is moving toward you at 5 m/s, what is the speed of the ball relative to you?

6. Two clocks are set at identical times. One is placed on a plane and travels around the world. The other remains stationary on the ground. When the plane lands and the two clocks are compared, how would the times on the clocks compare?

7. Suppose you could travel to another galaxy and back at speeds near the speed of light. Why would it be risky to make a doctor's appointment for 9:00 a.m., Earth time, one month after your departure?

Section 11.3

8. Imagine looking down on a large star with an approaching light ray as shown below. Draw the path of the light ray as it travels past the star. Explain why the light ray follows the path you drew.

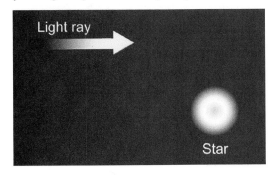

Test Practice

Section 11.1

1. Scientists believe a proton is constructed from which combination of quarks?

   a. one up and one down

   b. two down and one up

   c. two up and one down

   d. one strange and one bottom

Use the diagram and information below to answer questions 2 and 3.

Jupiter is 7.8×10^8 km (780,000,000 km) from the Sun. The speed of light is 3×10^5 km/s (300,000 km/s).

2. If the Sun was to vanish, it would take _____ minutes before an observer on Jupiter would see the Sun go out.

   a. 1. 6.3×10^{-6}

   b. 1.7×10^{-2}

   c. 4.3×10^{1}

   d. 3.8×10^{12}

3. If the Sun was to vanish, it would take _____ seconds before Jupiter would fly out of orbit because the gravitational force between Jupiter and the Sun disappeared.

   a. 2.3×10^{14}

   b. 2.6×10^{3}

   c. 1.0×10^{0}

   d. 3.8×10^{-4}

4. If you converted 3 kg of matter completely into energy, how much energy would you create?

   a. 9×10^8 J

   b. 3×10^{16} J

   c. 9×10^{16} J

   d. 2.7×10^{17} J

Section 11.2

5. Traveling at 2×10^8 m/s, you shine a light at your friend who is standing still. He would measure the speed of the approaching light as

   a. 2×10^8 m/s.

   b. 2.8×10^8 m/s.

   c. 3×10^8 m/s.

   d. 3.2×10^8 m/s.

6. Which of the following are effects of special relativity?

   a. Time runs slower for moving objects.

   b. Mass decreases as an object gets closer to the speed of light.

   c. Space gets larger for an object moving near the speed of light.

   d. All of the above.

7. A 15-year-old student-astronaut leaves Earth traveling toward the center of the Milky Way Galaxy. It takes 20 years (as measured on Earth) at close to the speed of light. If she returns to Earth after 20 years, her biological age would be _____ years.

   a. less than 35

   b. 35

   c. greater than 35

   d. not enough information given

Section 11.3

8. According to Einstein's theory of general relativity, gravity is an effect created by

   a. the Big Bang.

   b. the Milky Way Galaxy.

   c. a black hole.

   d. the curvature of space.

9. The Big Bang is the name given to the

   a. process that is causing super novas at the center of the Milky Way Galaxy.

   b. huge explosion marking the origin of the universe.

   c. nuclear reactions occurring in the Sun.

   d. sound created as matter enters a black hole at the speed of light.

10. According to scientists' best estimates, the age of the universe is _____ years.

   a. 10–20 million

   b. 100–200 million

   c. 10–20 billion

   d. 100–200 billion

11. The background against which measurements of motion and position are made is

   a. special relativity.

   b. general relativity.

   c. a black hole.

   d. a reference frame.

Applying Your Knowledge

Section 11.1

1. In 1989, the space probe Voyager II reached the planet Neptune and began sending images of the planet back to Earth. Assuming these radio waves had to travel 4.0×10^9 km, how long did it take, in minutes, before astronomers received the signals from Voyager II?

2. How have our ideas about matter changed over the past 2,500 years?

   a. Use this book and the Internet to research how our ideas about matter have changed over the past 2,500 years.

   b. Create a timeline that shows the major discoveries and important events that have led to current theories about matter. Make a poster of your timeline with illustrations.

   c. Include dates, people, and a brief description of each event.

   d. Make up a future event about matter that could change our ideas even more. Be creative!

Section 11.2

3. The year 1905 completely changed the field of physics. Many of the new theories and discoveries were published by Albert Einstein during that year. Research these groundbreaking discoveries and theories made by Einstein and write a brief report on them.

4. Explain each statement below:

   a. If an intelligent being on a planet that is billions of miles from Earth has a powerful telescope, could the being observe events that happened long ago on Earth, such as the ice age?

   b. Imagine that space travel at near-light speed is possible. Space travelers could travel into Earth's future as far as they wished, but they could never travel back in time to the Earth time they left.

Section 11.3

5. The Big Bang is the dominant scientific theory about the origin of the universe. Research the scientific evidence for the Big Bang. Prepare a short report that describes the different types of evidence, who discovered them, and how they were discovered.

Unit 5 ELECTRICITY

Electric Circuits

Suppose you have a stationary bicycle that is connected to a light bulb so that when you pedal the bicycle, the energy from the turning wheels lit the bulb. How fast would you have to pedal to generate enough electrical energy to light the bulb? You might be surprised at how fast you have to pedal to do something that seems so simple. Some science museums have interactive exhibits like this bicycle-powered light bulb to help people appreciate and understand how much energy is needed to accomplish everyday tasks.

What would your life be like without electricity? You can probably name at least a dozen aspects of your morning routine alone that would change if you didn't have electricity. Do you know how electrical circuits work? Do you know what voltage and current mean? This chapter will give you the opportunity to explore electricity, electrical circuits, and the nature of electrical energy. Electricity can be powerful and dangerous, but when you know the basic facts about how electricity works, you can use electricity safely and with confidence.

VOCABULARY

ampere	electric current	resistance
battery	electrical symbol	resistor
circuit diagram	insulator	semiconductor
closed circuit	multimeter	switch
conductor	Ohm's law	volt
electric circuit	open circuit	voltage

KEY QUESTIONS

✓ Are there electrical circuits in the human body? What about in other animals?

✓ Why is the shock from a household electrical outlet more dangerous if your skin is wet?

✓ What are semiconductors, and what common household items contain them?

12.1 Electric Circuits

What would your life be like without electricity? Look around. You can probably see at least 10 things that use electricity. Do you know what electricity is and how it works? Devices that use electricity have things in common that you will study in this section.

> **electric current** - the flow of electric charge

Electricity

What is electricity? Electricity is made up of charged particles that carry energy from one place to another. The flow of electric charge is called **electric current**. Electric current is what makes an electric motor turn or an electric stove to heat. Electric current comes from the motion of electrons or other charged particles. This chapter and the next will explain some practical uses of electricity. The third chapter in this unit will deal with electricity at the atomic level.

Electric current It can be hard to understand how electric current works because you cannot see it. For this reason, electric current is often compared to water current. Electric current can carry energy and do work, and so can a current of water. For example, a waterwheel turns when a current of water exerts a force on it (Figure 12.1). A waterwheel can be connected to a machine such as a loom for making cloth, or to a millstone for grinding wheat into flour. Before electricity was available, waterwheels were used to supply energy to many machines. Today, the same tasks are done using energy from electric current. Glance out a window and you might see wires carrying electric current into buildings. Once electricity reaches a building, can you think of at least 10 things that use the energy supplied by the electric current?

Electricity can be powerful and dangerous Electric current can carry a great deal of power. For example, an electric saw can cut wood much faster than a hand saw. An electric motor the size of a basketball can do as much work as five horses, or 15 people. Electric current can be dangerous, too. Touching an electric wire through which current is flowing can result in serious injury. The more you know about electricity, the easier it is to use it with safety and confidence.

Figure 12.1: *A waterwheel uses the force of flowing water to run machines.*

Electric circuits

Electricity travels in circuits
An **electric circuit** is a complete path through which electricity travels. A good example of a circuit is the one in an electric toaster. Bread is toasted by a heater that converts electrical energy to heat. The toaster circuit has a switch that turns on when the toaster's handle is pushed down. With the switch on, electric current enters through one prong of the plug from the wall socket and goes through the toaster heater and out the other prong.

Wires are like pipes for electricity
Wires in electric circuits are similar in some ways to water pipes in a house (Figure 12.2). Wires act like pipes for electric current. Electric current enters the house on a supply wire and leaves on a return wire. The big difference between wires and water pipes is that you cannot get electricity to leave a wire the way water can leave a pipe. If you cut a water pipe, the water flows out. If you cut a wire, the electric current stops immediately.

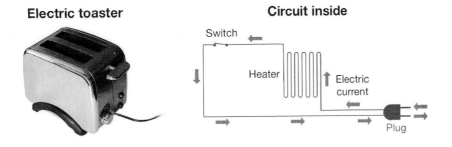

Examples of circuits in nature
Circuits are not confined to appliances, wires, and devices built by people. The first experience humans had with electricity was in the natural world. These are some examples of natural electrical circuits:

- The nerves in your body form an electrical circuit that carries messages from your brain to your muscles and other parts of the body.
- The tail of an electric eel makes a circuit when it stuns its prey with a jolt of electricity.
- An electric circuit with a large amount of energy is formed when lightning carries electric current between clouds and the ground.

> **electric circuit** - a complete path through which electricity travels

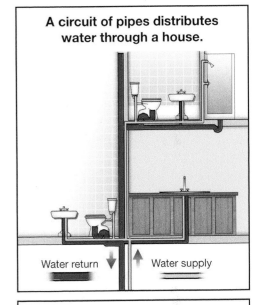

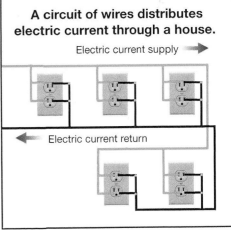

Figure 12.2: *Comparing "circuits."*

Circuit diagrams and electrical symbols

Circuit diagrams   Circuits consist of wires and electrical parts such as batteries, light bulbs, and switches. When a circuit is designed, drawings are made to show how the parts are connected. Electrical drawings are called **circuit diagrams**. In a circuit diagram, **electrical symbols** are used to represent each part of the circuit. Electrical symbols are easier to draw than realistic illustrations of circuit parts.

Electrical symbols   A circuit diagram describes a working circuit. The electrical symbols used in circuit diagrams are standardized. Anyone familiar with electricity can build the circuit by looking at the diagram. Figure 12.3 shows some common parts of a circuit and their electrical symbols. Study the illustration that shows an actual circuit and its circuit diagram. Can you match the real parts to their symbols? The switch is open in the circuit diagram, but closed in the photograph. Closing the switch in the real circuit completes the circuit to light the bulb.

> **circuit diagram** - a drawing that uses symbols to represent each part of an electrical circuit
>
> **electrical symbol** - a symbol used for the parts of an electrical circuit in circuit diagrams
>
> **resistor** - a device that controls or uses the energy carried by an electric current

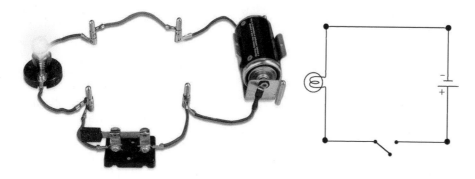

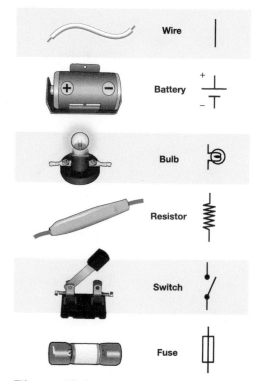

Figure 12.3: *These electrical symbols are used when drawing circuit diagrams.*

Resistors   A **resistor** is an electrical device that uses or controls the energy carried by electric current. In many circuit diagrams, any electrical device that uses energy is shown with a resistor symbol. A light bulb, heating element, speaker, or motor can be drawn with a resistor symbol. In this book, we will use the light bulb symbol to represent a light bulb in a circuit, and the resistor symbol when using a fixed resistor from the electric circuit kit.

Open and closed circuits

Batteries All electric circuits must have a source of energy. Circuits in your home get their energy from power plants that generate electricity. Circuits in flashlights, cell phones, and cameras get their energy from batteries. Some calculators have solar cells that convert energy from the Sun or other sources of light into electrical energy. Of all the types of circuits, those with batteries are the easiest to understand. We will focus on battery circuits for now and will eventually learn how other types of circuits work.

Open and closed circuits It is necessary to turn light bulbs, radios, and other devices used in circuits on and off. One way to turn off a device is to stop the current by "breaking" the circuit. Electric current can only flow when there is a complete and unbroken path throughout the circuit. A circuit with no breaks is called a **closed circuit** (Figure 12.4). A light bulb will light only when it is part of a closed circuit. Opening a switch or disconnecting a wire "breaks" the circuit and stops the current. A circuit with a break in it is called an **open circuit**.

Switches **Switches** are used to turn electricity on and off. Flipping a switch to the "off" position creates an open circuit by making a break in the wire. The break stops the current from flowing in the circuit. Flipping a switch to the "on" position closes the break. The current flows again to supply energy to the light bulb, camera, or other device.

Breaks in circuits A switch is not the only way to make a break in a circuit. Incandescent light bulbs, like the ones used in the electric circuit kit, burn out when the thin, glowing wire in the bulb breaks. This creates an open circuit and explains why a burned-out bulb cannot light.

> **closed circuit** - a circuit with no breaks in which charge flows
>
> **open circuit** - a circuit with a break in which charge can't flow
>
> **switch** - a device used to open and close a circuit

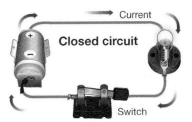

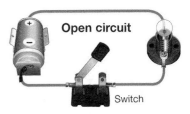

Figure 12.4: *There is current in a closed circuit but not in an open circuit.*

Figure 12.5: *What does the circuit diagram for this circuit look like?*

12.1 Section Review

1. List one way electric current is similar to water current and one way it is different.
2. Draw a circuit diagram for the circuit shown in Figure 12.5.
3. What is the difference between an open circuit and a closed circuit? Which has a lit bulb?

12.2 Current and Voltage

Current is what carries energy in a circuit. Like water current, electric current only flows when there is a difference in energy between two locations that are connected. Water flows downhill from higher gravitational potential energy to lower energy. Electric current flows from higher electrical potential energy to lower electrical potential energy. Electrical *voltage* is a measure of the difference in electrical potential energy between two places in a circuit. Differences in voltage cause electric currents to flow.

ampere - the unit of electric current

Current

Measuring electric current
Electric current is measured in units called **amperes** (A), or amps for short. The unit is named in honor of Andre-Marie Ampere (1775–1836), a French physicist who studied electricity and magnetism. A small battery-powered flashlight bulb uses about half an amp of electric current.

Figure 12.6: *A battery's electrical symbol.*

Positive and negative battery terminals
Examine a battery and you will find a positive and a negative end. The positive end on a AA, C, or D battery has a raised bump, and the negative end is flat. In a circuit diagram, a battery's electrical symbol uses a long line to show the positive end and a short line to show the negative end (Figure 12.6).

Current in equals current out
Electric current from a battery flows out of the positive end and returns back to the negative end. An arrow is sometimes used to show the direction of current on a circuit diagram (Figure 12.7). In most electric circuits, negative charge flows, so you would think the current arrows in Figure 12.7 would show a negative to positive direction. It is practical and conventional, however, to describe current as flowing from positive to negative, or from high voltage to low voltage. The amount of electric current coming out of the positive end of the battery must always be the same as the amount of current flowing into the negative end. You can picture this by imagining a tube filled with steel balls. When you push one ball into the tube, one ball comes out the other end. The rate at which the balls flow in equals the rate at which they flow out.

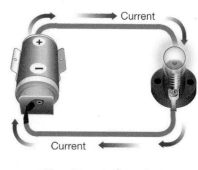

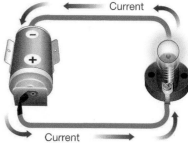

Figure 12.7: *Conventional current direction shows current moving from positive to negative, or high voltage to low voltage.*

Voltage

Energy and voltage

Voltage is a measure of electric potential energy, just as height is a measure of gravitational potential energy. Voltage is measured in **volts** (V). Like other forms of potential energy, a voltage difference means there is energy that can be used to do work. How are voltage and current different? Current is what actually flows and does work. Voltage differences provide the energy that causes current to flow (Figure 12.8).

> **voltage** - a measure of electric potential energy
> **volt** - the unit of voltage
> **multimeter** - an instrument that measures current, voltage, and resistance

What voltage means

A voltage difference of 1 volt allows 1 amp of current to do 1 joule of work in 1 second. You know that the work done per unit of time is called power, and 1 joule per second equals 1 watt of power. Therefore, *voltage is the power per amp of current that flows*. Every amp of current flowing out of a 1.5-V battery carries 1.5 watts of power. The voltage in your home electrical system is 120 volts, which means each amp of current carries 120 watts of power. The higher the voltage, the more power is carried by each amp of electric current.

Measuring voltage

A *voltmeter* measures voltage. A more useful meter is a **multimeter**, which can measure voltage or current, and sometimes resistance. To measure voltage, the meter's probes are touched to two places in a circuit or to a battery's poles. The meter shows the voltage difference between the poles.

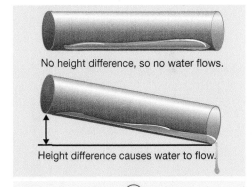

No height difference, so no water flows.

Height difference causes water to flow.

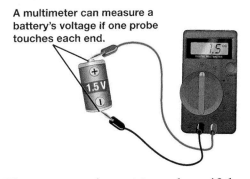

A multimeter can measure a battery's voltage if one probe touches each end.

The meter reads zero volts if both probes are connected at the same end.

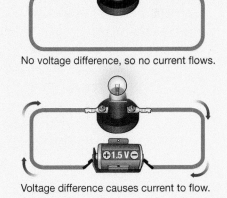

No voltage difference, so no current flows.

Voltage difference causes current to flow.

Meters measure voltage differences

The meter reads *positive* voltage if the red positive probe is at a higher voltage than the black probe. The meter reads negative when the black probe is at the higher voltage. The meter reads voltage *differences* between its probes. If both probes are connected to the same place, the meter reads zero.

Figure 12.8: *A height difference causes water to flow in the pipe. A voltage difference causes current to flow in the circuit.*

Batteries

Batteries   A **battery** is a device that transforms chemical energy into electrical energy. A battery uses chemical energy to create a voltage difference between its two terminals. When current leaves a battery, it carries energy. The current gives up its energy as it passes through a resistor, such as a light bulb. The bulb transforms the current's electrical energy into light and heat energy. The current returns to the battery, where it gets more energy. You can think of the current as a stream of marching particles, each carrying a bucket of energy. A 1.5-volt battery allows the marchers to carry 1.5 joules out of the battery every second, which produces a power of 1.5 watts.

> **battery** - a device that transforms chemical energy into electrical energy and moves the current in a circuit

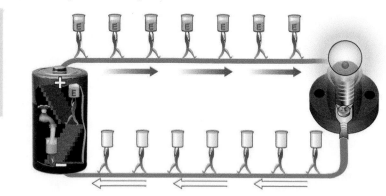

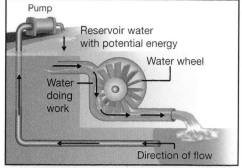

Batteries are like pumps   Two water-filled reservoirs connected by a pump is a good analogy for a battery in a circuit (Figure 12.9). The pump pulls the water to a higher level, giving it potential energy. The water current can flow back down and turn the waterwheel. In a battery, chemical reactions provide a voltage difference to give energy to the current. The current then flows through the circuit, carrying the energy to light the bulb. The current gets a "refill" of energy each time it passes through the battery, for as long as the battery's energy lasts.

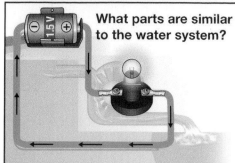

Figure 12.9: *The water pump creates a potential energy difference so falling water can do work. Likewise, a battery in a circuit creates a voltage difference so current can flow and do work.*

Battery voltage   The voltage of a battery depends on how the battery is made. Household zinc-carbon batteries are 1.5 volts each. Lead-acid batteries, like those used in cars, are usually 12 volts. Different voltages can also be made by combining multiple batteries. A flashlight that needs 4.5 volts to light its bulb uses three 1.5-volt batteries.

Measuring current in a circuit

Measuring current   Electric current can be measured with a multimeter, but the meter is not used the same way as when you measure voltage. To measure current, the current must pass *through* the meter. For example, Figure 12.10 shows a circuit with a battery and bulb. The meter has been inserted into the circuit to measure current. The current comes out of the positive end of the battery, and passes through the bulb and the meter and back. The meter in the diagram measures 0.37 amps of current. Some electrical meters, called ammeters, are designed specifically to measure only current.

Setting up the meter   When using a multimeter, remember to set its dial to measure the type of current in your circuit. Multimeters can measure two types of electric current, called *alternating current* (AC) and *direct current* (DC). You will learn about the difference between alternating and direct current in a later chapter. For circuits with light bulbs and batteries, you must set your meter to read direct current, or DC.

Protecting the meter   The meter can be damaged if too much current passes through it. The meter used with your electric circuit investigations has a *fuse* inside. A fuse is a fast-acting switch that opens a circuit if it detects too much current. Some fuses "burn out," and must be replaced. Others, called *circuit breakers*, "trip," break the circuit, and have to be reset, but do not generally have to replaced. To avoid "blowing a fuse," be sure there is a resistor in the circuit when you measure current, and make the meter part of the circuit (Figure 12.11).

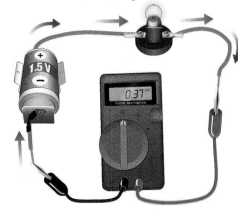

Measuring current

Figure 12.10: *A multimeter can be used to measure current in a circuit.*

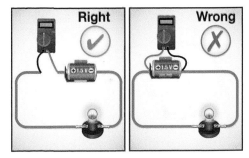

Figure 12.11: *When measuring current, make the meter part of the circuit.*

12.2 Section Review

1. List the unit names and unit abbreviations for current and voltage.
2. When does a meter display a reading of 0 volts?
3. What does a 1.5-V battery give to each amp of current in a circuit?
4. What actually *flows* and *does work* in an electric circuit? Explain.
5. Draw a circuit diagram in which a meter is used to measure current.

12.3 **Resistance and Ohm's Law**

You can apply the same voltage to different circuits and different amounts of current will flow. For example, when you plug in a desk lamp, the current through it is 1 amp. If a hair dryer is plugged into the same outlet, the current through the hair dryer is 10 amps. For a given voltage, the amount of current that flows depends on the *resistance* of the circuit.

> **resistance** - a measure of how much current flows in a circuit for a given voltage

Electrical resistance

Current and resistance **Resistance** is the measure of how strongly an object "resists" current flowing through it. A copper wire has low resistance and can easily carry a large current. A material with a high resistance, such as a rubber band, carries a very small current that is difficult to measure.

A water analogy The relationship between electric current and resistance can be compared to water flowing from the open end of a bottle (Figure 12.12). If the bottle opening is small, the resistance is high and there is a small flow of water. The same thing happens in an electric circuit. If there is a high resistance in the circuit, very little electric current will flow. If the bottle opening is large, the resistance is low, and there is a large flow of water. Likewise, if there is not much resistance in an electric circuit, a large electric current can flow.

Resistance in circuits Every device that uses electrical energy adds resistance to a circuit. The more resistance the circuit has, the lower the current. For example, if you string several light bulbs together, the resistance in the circuit increases and the current decreases. This makes each bulb dimmer than a single bulb would be.

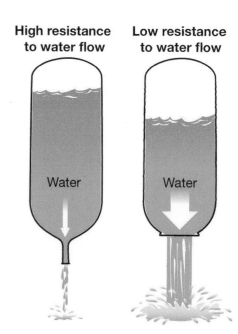

High resistance to water flow   **Low resistance to water flow**

Figure 12.12: *Higher resistance results in low water flow. Lower resistance results in greater water flow.*

One bulb
Single resistance
Full current

Two bulbs
Twice the resistance
Half the current

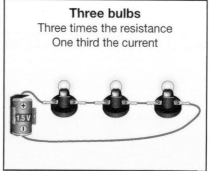
Three bulbs
Three times the resistance
One third the current

Measuring resistance

The ohm   Electrical resistance is measured in units called **ohms**. This unit is abbreviated with the Greek letter *omega* (Ω). When you see Ω in a sentence, think or read "ohms." For a given voltage, the greater the resistance, the lower the current. If a circuit has a resistance of 1 ohm, then a voltage of 1 volt causes a current of 1 amp to flow.

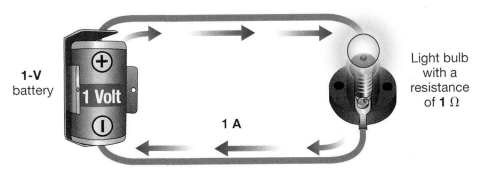

1 volt creates a current of 1 amp through a resistance of 1 ohm

1-V battery

1 Volt

1 A

Light bulb with a resistance of 1 Ω

Figure 12.13: *A multimeter can be used to measure the resistance of a device that has been removed from the circuit.*

Resistance of wires   The wires used to connect circuits are made of metals that have low resistance, such as copper or aluminum. The resistance of wires is usually low compared with other devices in a circuit. You can ignore wire resistance when measuring or calculating the total resistance in the circuits we will study. The exception is when there are large currents. If the current is large, the resistance of wires may be important.

Measuring resistance   You can use a multimeter to measure the resistance of wires, light bulbs, and other devices (Figure 12.13). Remove the device from the circuit. Then, set the dial on the multimeter to the resistance setting and touch the probes to each end of the device. The meter will display the resistance in ohms (Ω), kilo-ohms (× 1,000 Ω), or mega-ohms (× 1,000,000 Ω).

How resistance is measured

A multimeter contains a battery with a fixed voltage. When the fixed voltage is applied to a device, the meter measures the resulting current and calculates the resistance. For example, suppose you want to measure the resistance of a light bulb. You would remove it from the circuit so a precise amount of voltage can be applied to it by the meter's battery. This will give an accurate resistance value. If you leave the bulb in the circuit, the circuit current will interfere with the meter's resistance reading.

Ohm's law

Ohm's law The current in a circuit depends on the battery's voltage and the circuit's resistance. Voltage and current are *directly* related. Doubling the voltage doubles the current. Resistance and current are *inversely* related. Doubling the resistance halves the current. These two relationships form **Ohm's law**. Ohm's law states that current is directly related to voltage and inversely related to resistance. The table shows how to find any of the three values.

> **Ohm's law** - states that the current is *directly* related to the voltage and *inversely* related to the resistance

OHM'S LAW

Current (amps, A) $I = \dfrac{V}{R}$ **Voltage** (volts, V)

Resistance (ohms, Ω)

Equation	gives	if you know
$I = V \div R$	current (*I*)	voltage and resistance
$V = I \times R$	voltage (*V*)	current and resistance
$R = V \div I$	resistance (*R*)	voltage and current

Applying Ohm's law Ohm's law shows how resistance is used to control the current. If the resistance is low, then a given voltage will result in a large amount of current. Devices that need a large amount of current typically have lower resistance. This allows the device to get the current it needs.

➕ ➖ ✖ ➗ **Using Ohm's Law**

A toaster oven has a resistance of 12 ohms and is plugged into a 120-volt outlet. How much current in amps does it use?

1. **Looking for:**   You are asked for the current in amps.

2. **Given:**   You are given the resistance in ohms and the voltage in volts.

3. **Relationships:**   Ohm's law: $I = \dfrac{V}{R}$

4. **Solution:**   Substitute the values for *V* and *R*: $I = \dfrac{120 \text{ V}}{12 \text{ Ω}} = 10 \text{ A}$

Your Turn:

a. A laptop computer uses a 24-volt battery. If the computer's circuits have a total resistance of 16 ohms, how much current does it use?

b. A toy car's motor needs 2 amps of current to work properly. If the car uses four 1.5-volt batteries, what is the motor's resistance?

(Answers are listed at the end of the chapter.)

The resistance of common objects

Resistance matches operating voltage

The resistance of electrical devices can vary from as little as 0.001 ohms to over a million ohms. Every electrical device is designed with a resistance that causes the right amount of current to flow when the device is connected to the proper voltage. For example, a 100-watt light bulb has a resistance of 145 ohms. When connected to 120 volts from a wall socket, the current is 0.83 amps and the bulb lights (Figure 12.14). If you connect the same light bulb to a 1.5-volt battery, it will not light. According to Ohm's law, the current is only 0.01 amps when 1.5 volts is applied to a resistance of 145 ohms. This amount of current will not light the bulb. All electrical devices are designed to use the "right" amount of current only when connected to a specific voltage value.

The resistance of skin

Electrical outlets are dangerous because you can get a fatal shock by touching the wires inside. So, why can you safely handle a 9-volt battery? Ohm's law explains this. The typical resistance of dry skin is 100,000 ohms or more. According to Ohm's law, 9 V ÷ 100,000 Ω is only 0.00009 amps. This is not enough current to be harmful. On average, nerves in the skin can feel a current of about 0.0005 amps. You can get a dangerous shock from 120 volts from a wall socket because that is enough voltage to force 0.0012 amps (120 V ÷ 100,000 Ω) through your skin, and you can certainly feel that.

Water lowers skin resistance

Wet skin has much lower resistance than dry skin. Because of the lower resistance, the same voltage will cause even more current to pass through your body when your skin is wet. The combination of water and 120-volt electricity is dangerous. The high voltage and lower resistance make it possible for large, perhaps even fatal, amounts of current to flow.

Resistance can vary

The resistance of many electrical devices varies with temperature. For example, the amount of resistance a light bulb contributes to a circuit increases as its temperature increases, due to the current running through it. Devices that have a variable resistance like this are referred to as *non-ohmic*, because you cannot use Ohm's law to predict the current when there is a changing resistance (Figure 12.15). The small light bulbs in your circuit kit are non-ohmic, so you will use *fixed* resistors to apply Ohm's law to your simple circuits.

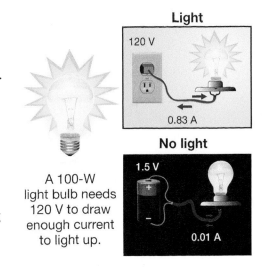

A 100-W light bulb needs 120 V to draw enough current to light up.

Figure 12.14: *A light bulb designed for use in a 120-volt household circuit does not light when connected to a 1.5-volt battery.*

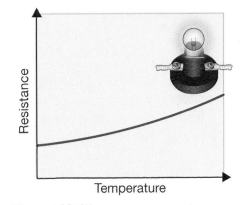

Figure 12.15: *The resistance of some materials, such as light bulb filaments, increases as their temperature increases. A light bulb is non-ohmic for this reason.*

Conductors and insulators

Conductors   Current passes easily through some materials, such as copper, which are called *conductors*. A **conductor** can *conduct*, or carry, electric current. The electrical resistance of wires made from conductors is low. Most metals are good conductors.

Insulators   Other materials, such as rubber, glass, and wood, do not allow current to pass easily through them. These materials are called **insulators**. An insulator is a material that does not conduct electric current well, because it opposes or slows the flow of current.

Semiconductors   The electrical conductivities of some materials is between that of conductors and insulators. These materials are called **semiconductors** because their ability to carry current is higher than an insulator but lower than a conductor. Computer chips, televisions, and portable radios are among the many devices that use semiconductors. Silicon is a semiconductor commonly used in making computer chips. There is an area south of the San Francisco Bay area in California called Silicon Valley. It is called Silicon Valley because many internet, semiconductor, and computer companies are located there.

Comparing materials   No material is a perfect conductor or insulator. Some amount of current will always flow in any material if a voltage is applied to it. Even a good conductor such as copper has some resistance. Figure 12.16 compares the resistances of various conductors, semiconductors, and insulators.

Applications of conductors and insulators   Both conductors and insulators are necessary materials in technology. For example, a wire has one or more conductors on the inside and an insulator on the outside and sometimes between the conductors. A computer cable might have 20 or more conductors, each separated from the others by an insulator. This insulation prevents the conductors from being exposed to the current and voltage carried by the other conductors.

> **conductor** - a material with low electrical resistance such as copper or aluminum
>
> **insulator** - a material with high electrical resistance such as plastic or rubber
>
> **semiconductor** - a material with electrical conductivity between that of conductors and insulators

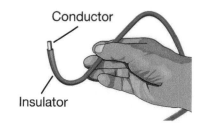

Electrical properties	Category	Example materials
High conductivity **Low resistance** ↑	Conductors	• silver • gold • copper • aluminum • tungsten • iron
	Semiconductors	• carbon • germanium • silicon
↓ **Low conductivity** **High resistance**	Insulators	• air • paper • ice • glass • rubber • plastic (most)

Figure 12.16: *Comparing the conduction and resistance of various materials.*

Resistors

Resistors are common   As you have read, resistors are used to control the current in circuits. They are found in many common electronic devices such as computers, televisions, telephones, and stereos.

Fixed resistors   There are two main types of resistors: fixed and variable. Fixed resistors have a resistance that cannot be changed. If you have ever looked at a circuit board inside an electronic device, you may have seen fixed resistors. In some simple electronic devices, resistors are small, skinny cylinders or rectangles with colored stripes on them. The resistors are too small for written labels on which to indicate their resistance values. Instead, the resistors are coded with colored stripes that indicate the resistance (Figure 12.17).

Variable resistors   Variable resistors, also called *potentiometers*, can be adjusted to have a resistance within a certain range. If you have ever turned a dimmer switch or volume control, you have used a potentiometer. When the resistance of a dimmer switch increases, the current decreases, and the bulb gets dimmer. Inside a potentiometer is a circular resistor and a sliding contact called a wiper (Figure 12.18). If the circuit is connected at A and C, the resistance will vary depending on the location of the wiper (B). Turning the dial changes the resistance between A and C from 0 to 10 ohms. This may also change the current or voltage in the circuit.

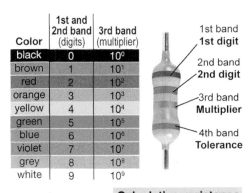

Color	1st and 2nd band (digits)	3rd band (multiplier)
black	0	10^0
brown	1	10^1
red	2	10^2
orange	3	10^3
yellow	4	10^4
green	5	10^5
blue	6	10^6
violet	7	10^7
grey	8	10^8
white	9	10^9

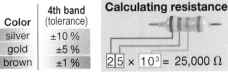

Color	4th band (tolerance)
silver	±10 %
gold	±5 %
brown	±1 %

Calculating resistance

$2\ 5 \times 10^3 = 25{,}000\ \Omega$

Figure 12.17: *The color code for resistors.*

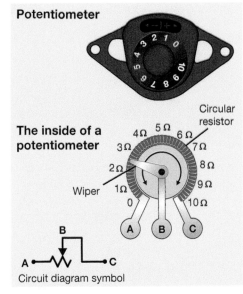

Figure 12.18: *The resistance of this potentiometer can vary from 0 to 10 ohms.*

12.3 Section Review

1. What happens to the current if a circuit's resistance increases? What happens to the current if the voltage increases instead?
2. List the units used to measure resistance, voltage, and current. Then give the abbreviation for each unit.
3. A hair dryer uses a current of 10 A when plugged into a 120-V outlet. What is the resistance of the hair dryer?
4. Classify each of the following as a conductor, semiconductor, or insulator: air, gold, silicon, rubber, aluminum.

The Shocking Truth: You are Wired!

Did you know that there are electric circuits in your body? Obviously, they aren't the kind made from batteries, bulbs, and wires—and there certainly isn't anything like lightning flashing around in there. However, there are electric circuits of a different type inside your body, and you couldn't survive without them.

Withdrawal reflexes

Have you ever accidentally touched a hot stove? The first thing you do is pull your hand back quickly—without even thinking about it.

A withdrawal reflex like this happens because electrical signals are sent through the nerve network in your body. When you touch a hot stove, nerve endings in your fingers send a signal to nerves in your spinal cord. From the spinal cord, the signal is transferred to nerve fibers that control muscles in your hand and arm, causing them to contract, and jerking your hand away from the stove. All of this happens in a split second!

Neurons

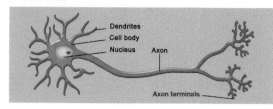

Your nervous system uses specialized cells called *neurons* to transfer electrical signals from one part of your body to another. A neuron has three basic parts: the cell body; a long, thin *axon*; and finger-like projections called *dendrites*.

Battery circuits versus body circuits

Unlike the components of the electric circuits you built in class, most neurons don't touch one another. Instead, as the electrical signal reaches the end of the axon, a chemical called a *neurotransmitter* is released. The chemical is picked up by receptors on the next neuron's dendrites. The dendrites then activate their own cell body to continue sending the signal along the axon.

Electricity in your home works because negatively-charged electrons in the wires are free to carry the electrical current. This doesn't happen in the electric circuits of your body. Instead, the electrical current is carried by positively-charged ions.

How does a nerve impulse work?

When a neuron is at rest, the inside of the cell membrane is electrically negative. A nerve impulse is transmitted in this sequence:

1. An outside stimulus, like touching a hot stove, causes the neuron's cell membrane to open tiny channels that let positively-charged ions into the cell. One area inside of the neuron is now positively charged relative to the outside.

2. In a type of chain reaction, depolarization occurs along the entire neuron. As downstream channels open to let positive ions in, the previously-depolarized areas let positive ions back out. As the ions leave, the membrane once again becomes negatively charged compared with the outside, as it was before the outside stimulus occurred.

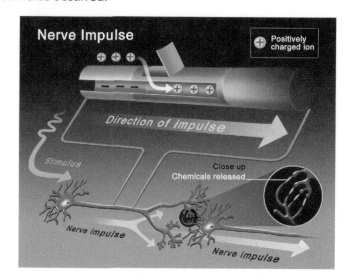

3. The nerve impulse continues from neuron to neuron, across the gaps, called synapses, between neurons, like a row of falling dominoes. The positive ions move in and out of one neuron, and at the gap between neurons, a chemical neurotransmitter is released to allow the depolarization to continue along the next neuron. In this way, nerve impulses or messages are conducted from one area of the body to another.

In a split second, your muscle receives the message to contract and pull your hand away from the source of heat. It all happens because of the flow of charged ions. Your nervous system and your muscles are controlled by electrical impulses; some of them can move around 250 miles per hour!

Withdrawal reflexes are just one of many actions in your body that happen as a result of electrical signals. Your emotions, decisions, and physical actions all happen when nerve impulses transmit electrical signals through neurons in your brain, spinal cord, and body.

What makes your heart beat?

Did you know that electrical signals cause your heart to beat? There is specialized electrical tissue in your heart called the *sinoatrial node*.

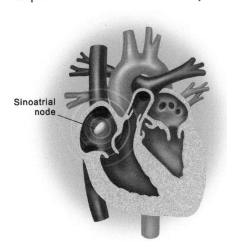

Sinoatrial node

This specialized group of cells releases positive ions that carry an electrical message to muscle cells all over the heart. This stimulates the heart to contract and pump blood throughout the body. People often refer to heart contractions as the "heartbeat."

For your heart to pump blood effectively, it must beat regularly in a rhythmic pattern. The sinoatrial node is usually very good at sending rhythmic electrical impulses to the muscle cells, so the contractions happen steadily and regularly. However, if the sinoatrial node needs extra help, a surgeon can implant an artificial device, called a *pacemaker*, to regulate the electrical impulses.

If you have ever seen doctors working in an emergency room on television or in a movie, you have probably seen a device called a *defibrillator*. A defibrillator uses an electric current to start a patient's heart to beat again after a heart attack or other trauma. Small, portable defibrillators are now being placed in schools, airports, and other public buildings. These devices have saved many lives by allowing trained people to help heart attack victims before paramedics arrive.

Electricity and living things

Many processes inside you and other living things depend on electric circuits. Most organisms keep this "shocking truth" to themselves, but not the electric eel! These South American river fish can stun unsuspecting prey with a 500-volt, 1-amp electric current generated through a flow of positive ions in specialized abdominal organs.

QUESTIONS

1. Compare and contrast battery and bulb circuits with the circuits of your nervous system. How are they alike? How are they different?

2. Why would someone need to have an artificial pacemaker implanted?

3. What do defibrillators do, and why are they now available in some public places?

4. There are hundreds of organisms that, like the electric eel, use electricity for more than just internal body processes. Do an Internet search. Choose two of the animals (other than the electric eel), name them, and write a brief description of how much electricity they produce and how they use it.

Chapter 12 Review

Understanding Vocabulary

Select the correct term to complete the sentences.

ampere	electrical symbols	resistance
battery	insulator	resistor
circuit diagram	multimeter	semiconductor
closed circuit	ohm	switch
conductor	Ohm's law	volt
electric circuit	open circuit	voltage
electric current		

1. _____ is what flows and carries energy in a circuit.

2. A(n) _____ has a break in it, so there is no current.

3. _____ explains the relationship between current, voltage, and resistance in a circuit.

4. _____ is the difference in the amount of energy carried by current at two points in a circuit.

5. Wires in a circuit are made of a material that is a(n) _____, such as copper.

6. A(n) _____ has a higher resistance than a(n) _____.

Reviewing Concepts

Section 12.1

1. Give one example of a circuit found in nature and one example of a circuit created by people.

2. Why are symbols used in circuit diagrams?

3. Draw the electrical symbol for each of the following devices.
   a. battery
   b. resistor
   c. switch
   d. wire

4. List three devices that could be a resistor in a circuit.

5. List two sources of energy that a circuit might use, and give an example of a circuit that uses each type.

6. Will a bulb light if it is in an open circuit? Explain.

7. Is flipping a switch the only way to create an open circuit? Explain.

Section 12.2

8. The direction of electric current in a circuit is away from the _____ end of the battery and toward the _____ end.

9. How are voltage and energy related?

10. A voltage of 1 volt means 1 _____ of _____ does 1 _____ of work in 1 second.

11. Explain how a battery in a circuit is similar to a water pump.

12. What are the differences between a multimeter, a voltmeter, and an ammeter?

13. Suppose you have a closed circuit containing a battery and a bulb. Why must you first create a break in the circuit before using an ammeter to measure the current?

Section 12.3

14. The greater the resistance in a circuit, the less the _____.

15. A circuit contains one light bulb and a battery. What happens to the total resistance in the circuit if you replace the one light bulb with a string of four identical bulbs? Why?

16. What does it mean to say that current and resistance in a circuit are inversely related?

17. What does it mean to say that current and voltage in a circuit are directly related?

18. According to Ohm's law, the current in a circuit increases if the _____ increases. The current decreases if the _____ increases.

19. A battery is connected to a light bulb, creating a simple circuit. Explain what will happen to the current in the circuit if
   a. the bulb is replaced with a bulb having a higher resistance.
   b. the bulb is replaced with a bulb having a lower resistance.
   c. the battery is replaced with a battery having a greater voltage.

20. Why does a light bulb's resistance increase if it operates for a long period of time?

21. Why can you safely handle a 1.5-V battery without being electrocuted?

22. What is the difference between a conductor and an insulator?

23. Why is it important to always have dry hands when working with electric circuits?

24. Explain why electrical wires are made of copper covered in a layer of rubber insulation.

25. What is a semiconductor?

26. Classify each of the following as a conductor, semiconductor, or insulator.

    a. ice

    b. plastic

    c. carbon

    d. iron

    e. glass

    f. silver

27. What is the difference between a fixed resistor and a variable resistor?

28. What is another name for a variable resistor?

Solving Problems

Section 12.1

1. Draw a circuit diagram of a circuit with a battery, three wires, a light bulb, and a switch.

Section 12.2

2. What voltage would the electrical meter show in each of these diagrams?

    a.    b.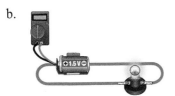

3. Which of these diagrams shows the correct way to measure current in a circuit?

    a.    b.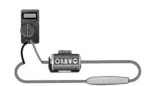

4. A portable radio that runs on 1.5-V batteries needs 6 V to work properly. How many batteries does it use?

Section 12.3

5. What happens to the current in a circuit if the *resistance* triples? What happens to the current if the *voltage* triples?

6. A hair dryer draws a current of 10 A when plugged into a 120-V outlet. What is the resistance of the hair dryer?

7. A television runs on 120 V and has a resistance of 60 Ω. How much current does it use?

8. A digital camera uses one 6-V battery. The circuit that operates the flash and takes the pictures has a resistance of 3 Ω. What is the current in the circuit?

9. The motor in a toy car has a resistance of 3 Ω and needs 1.5 A of current to run properly.

    a. What battery voltage is needed?

    b. How many 1.5-V batteries would the car require?

10. Find the current in each of these circuits.

    a.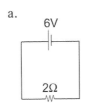
    6V
    2Ω

    b.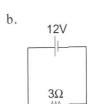
    12V
    3Ω

    c.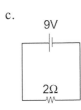
    9V
    2Ω

11. Household circuits in the United States operate at 120 V. Circuit breakers and fuses commonly break such a circuit if the current is greater than 15 A. What is the minimum amount of resistance needed in a circuit to prevent the circuit breaker from tripping?

12. A flashlight bulb has a resistance of about 6 Ω. It works in a flashlight with two 1.5-V batteries. How much current is in the flashlight's circuit when the bulb is lit?

Test Practice

Section 12.1

1. Which of the following will light the bulb?

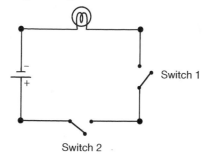

Switch 1

Switch 2

   a. switches 1 and 2 both closed

   b. switches 1 and 2 both open

   c. switch 1 open and switch 2 closed

   d. switch 1 closed and switch 2 open

2. Which of the following devices is used to create an open circuit?

   a. switch

   b. bulb

   c. battery

   d. resistor

3. Which device in a circuit has the most similar function to a bulb?

   a.   b.   c.   d.

   a. battery

   b. switch

   c. resistor

   d. wire

Section 12.2

4. Which device in a circuit transforms chemical energy into electrical energy?

   a. wire

   b. bulb

   c. meter

   d. battery

5. The battery in a circuit is changed from 1.5 V to 4.5 V. What happens to the power in the circuit?

   a. It increases.

   b. It decreases.

   c. It does not change.

   d. It stops.

6. What does voltage measure?

   a. current

   b. gravitational potential energy

   c. electrical potential energy

   d. the flow of charge

Section 12.3

7. What is the current of a circuit with a resistance of 3 Ω and a voltage of 6 V?

    a. 0.5 A

    b. 2 A

    c. 9 A

    d. 18 A

9. What is the voltage of the battery in the circuit shown below?

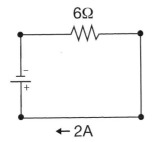

6Ω

← 2A

    a. ⅓ V

    b. 3 V

    c. 8 V

    d. 12 V

10. Which material would be classified as a conductor?

    a. silicon

    b. glass

    c. water

    d. air

11. Four blocks with the same dimensions are made of different materials. Which block has the highest resistance?

    a. copper

    b. silver

    c. glass

    d. aluminum

Applying Your Knowledge

Section 12.1

1. Write a paragraph explaining how your life would be different if electricity didn't exist.

2. Research Benjamin Franklin's experiments with electricity. Make a poster that describes one of his experiments.

Section 12.2

3. Brain and nerve cells communicate through the movement of charged chemicals that create electrical currents. Some conditions, such as epilepsy, occur because these currents are sometimes present when they shouldn't be. Research electrical currents in the body and problems that occur when the body's circuits don't work properly.

4. Ask an adult to show you the circuit breaker or fuse box in your home. Does it contain circuit breakers or fuses? How many?

5. There are many different kinds of batteries in use today. Do research to answer following questions.

 a. Are all 1.5-V household batteries the same on the inside?

 b. Why can some 1.5-V batteries be recharged and used over and over again?

 c. Which type of batteries is used in portable electronics such as cell phones and laptop computers?

6. Do an experiment in which you determine whether more-expensive household batteries last longer than cheaper ones. Why is it important to test the batteries in the same electrical device and to use it in the same way each time?

Section 12.3

7. Look on the back or underside of different appliances in your home to find information about the current and voltage each uses. Find two appliances that list the current and voltage. Calculate the resistance of each appliance.

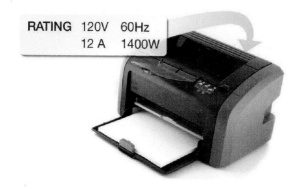

RATING 120V 60Hz
        12 A   1400W

 ***Your Turn* Answers**

Using Ohm's law (Section 12.3, page 304)

 a. 1.5 A

 b. 3 Ω

Electrical Systems

You may recognize the abbreviations AC and DC. There is a classic rock music group called AC/DC that has helped to make the acronym famous. Did you know that in the late 1800s, a major disagreement over the use of AC and DC methods for transmitting electricity erupted between two famous inventors?

Thomas Edison favored the direct current (DC) method of moving electrical energy from electrical generation stations to homes and buildings. George Westinghouse argued that the alternating current (AC) method worked better. The feud became quite public, as each inventor tried to win support. The DC method works well over short distances, like between buildings in a densely-populated city. AC works well over long distances, but uses higher voltages than DC technology. Edison used some morbid methods for demonstrating his views of the danger involved with high-voltage electrical transmission that used his opponent's AC method.

Which inventor won the AC/DC debate? Does the United States rely on AC or DC technology for transmitting electrical energy? In this chapter, you will find out how our country distributes electricity, and what the difference is between AC and DC current. You will also learn how electricity is "purchased" and paid for, as well as how simple electrical circuits are constructed and how they work.

VOCABULARY

alternating current	Kirchoff's current law	series circuit
direct current	Kirchoff's voltage law	short circuit
electrical power	parallel circuit	voltage drop
kilowatt-hour		

KEY QUESTIONS

✓ *Why do some strings of holiday lights go out when one bulb is removed?*

✓ *What is a "short circuit," and why can it be dangerous?*

✓ *Why do most wall sockets have three holes?*

13.1 Series Circuits

We use electric circuits for thousands of things, from flashlights to computers, cars, and satellites. There are two basic ways circuits can be built to connect electrical devices. The two types of circuits are called *series* and *parallel*. Series circuits have only one path for the current. Parallel circuits have branching points and multiple paths for the current. This section discusses series circuits. You will learn about parallel circuits in the next section.

series circuit - an electric circuit that has only one path for the current

What is a series circuit?

A series circuit has one path A **series circuit** is an electric circuit that has only one path for current. All the circuits you have studied so far have been series circuits. Three bulbs, a battery, and a switch connected in a loop form a series circuit. The current is the same in each identical bulb, so they are equally bright.

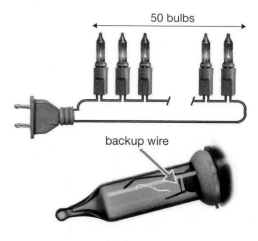

Holiday lights If there is a break at any point in a series circuit, the current will stop everywhere in the circuit. Inexpensive strings of holiday lights are wired with the bulbs in series. These "mini" bulbs are rated at 2.5 volts each. With 50 bulbs wired in series, the string operates properly when plugged into a 120-volt outlet. Each bulb will get 2.4 volts (120 volts ÷ 50 bulbs). If you remove one of the bulbs from its socket, the whole string of bulbs will go out. However, if a bulb's filament burns out, but the bulb is still in the socket, the string will stay lighted. How does this work? Mini bulbs have a special backup wire to carry the current when a filament breaks (Figure 13.1). As long as the burned-out bulb is still in the socket, the series circuit will not be broken. The current can travel through the backup wire, called a *shunt*.

Figure 13.1: *Each mini bulb in a strand of 50 has a backup wire inside called a shunt. If one bulb's filament burns out, current can still flow through the backup wire to keep the rest of the bulbs lit.*

Current and resistance in a series circuit

Use Ohm's law You can use Ohm's law to calculate the current in a circuit if you know the voltage and resistance. If you are using a battery, you know its voltage. If you know the resistance of each device in a circuit, you can find the total resistance by adding up the resistances of the device.

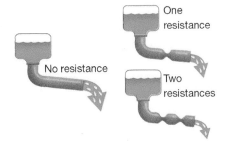

One resistance

No resistance

Two resistances

Adding resistances Think of adding resistances as pinching a water hose (Figure 13.2). Each pinch adds some resistance. The total resistance is the sum of the pinches. Likewise, the total resistance of a series circuit is the sum of its resistances.

Figure 13.2: *Adding resistors in a circuit is like adding pinches in a hose.*

ADDING RESISTANCES IN SERIES

$$R_{total} = R_1 + R_2 + R_3 + \ldots$$

Total resistance (Ω) *Individual resistances* (Ω)

Ignoring resistances Everything has some resistance, even wires. However, the resistance of wire is often small compared with the resistance of other circuit devices. We can ignore the wire's resistance in the circuits we build and analyze.

Calculating current

A series circuit contains a 12-V battery and three bulbs with resistances of 1 Ω, 2 Ω, and 3 Ω. What is the current in amps?

1. *Looking for:* You are asked for the current in amps.

2. *Given:* You are given the voltage in volts and resistances in ohms.

3. *Relationships:* Series resistance: $R_{total} = R_1 + R_2 + R_3$ Ohm's law: $I = V/R$

4. *Solution:* $R_{total} = 1\ \text{W} + 2\ \text{W} + 3\ \text{W} = 6\ \text{W}$ $I = (12\ \text{V})/(6\ \text{W}) = 2\ \text{A}$

Your Turn:

a. A string of five lights is connected to a 9-V battery. If each bulb has a resistance of 2 Ω, what is the current?

b. A series circuit operates with a 6-V battery and has two 1-W resistors. What is the circuit current?

(Answers are listed at the end of the chapter.)

Energy and voltage in a series circuit

Energy changes forms
Energy cannot be created or destroyed. The devices in a circuit convert electrical energy into other forms of energy. The rate of energy transfer that takes place is called *power*, and is measured in watts (W). Each device in a circuit requires power. As a result, the *voltage in the circuit is lowered after passing through each device that uses power.* This is known as a voltage drop. A **voltage drop** is a reduction of electrical energy by an electrical device as current passes through it.

Charges lose their energy
Consider a circuit with three bulbs and two batteries. The total voltage is 3 volts. Each amp of current leaves the battery with the ability to transfer energy at a rate of 3 watts. Each bulb changes one third of the power into light and heat. Because the first bulb uses 1 watt, the voltage drops from 3 volts to 2 volts as the current flows through it. The current in a series circuit is the same everywhere. So, as the power gets used, the voltage drops.

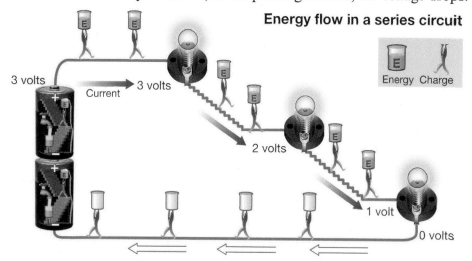

Energy flow in a series circuit

Voltage
If the three bulbs are identical, each gives off the same amount of light and heat. Each uses the same amount of power. A meter will show the voltage drop from 3 volts to 2 volts to 1 volt, and finally down to 0 volts after the last bulb. After passing through the last bulb, the current returns to the battery where it is given more energy and the cycle starts over.

> **voltage drop** - a reduction of electrical energy by an electrical device as current passes through it

Batteries and cells

A D-battery and a D-cell refer to the same thing. The terms *battery* and *cell* are often used interchangeably. However, technically there is a difference between batteries and cells. Cells are the building blocks of batteries. AAA, AA, C, and D batteries each contain a single 1.5-volt cell. A chemical reaction inside a cell supplies electric current to devices connected to it.

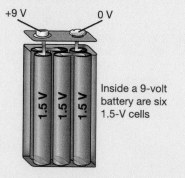

Inside a 9-volt battery are six 1.5-V cells

A 9-volt battery like the kind used in smoke detectors contains six tiny 1.5-volt cells connected in series. Each cell adds 1.5 volts to the total voltage.

Voltage drops and Ohm's law

Voltage drops Each separate bulb or resistor in a series circuit creates a voltage drop. The voltage drop for a bulb is measured by connecting a multimeter's leads on each side of the bulb (Figure 13.3). The greater the voltage drop, the greater the amount of power used per amp of current flowing through the bulb.

> **Kirchoff's voltage law** - the sum of the voltage drops in a series circuit must equal the circuit's total voltage

Ohm's law The voltage drop for a resistance is determined by Ohm's law in the form $V = IR$. The voltage drop (V) equals the current (I) multiplied by the resistance (R) of the device. In the circuit illustration, each bulb has a resistance of 1 ohm, so each has a voltage drop of 1 volt when 1 amp flows through the circuit.

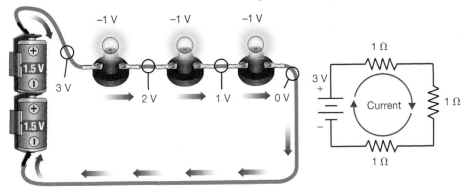

Each resistance drops the voltage

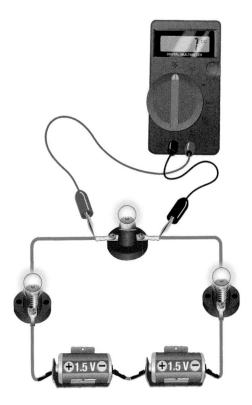

Energy conservation The law of conservation of energy applies to a circuit. Over the entire circuit, the power used by all the bulbs must equal the power supplied by the battery. **Kirchhoff's voltage law** states that the sum of the voltage drops must equal the circuit's total voltage. Gustav Robert Kirchhoff (1824–1887) was a German physicist.

Figure 13.3: *Using a multimeter to measure the voltage drop for a bulb in a circuit.*

Applying Kirchhoff's law In the circuit above, three identical bulbs are connected in series to two 1.5-volt batteries. The total resistance of the circuit is 3 ohms. The current flowing in the circuit is 1 amp ($I = 3\ \mathrm{V} \div 3\ \Omega = 1\,\mathrm{A}$). Each bulb creates a voltage drop of 1 volt ($V = IR = 1\ \mathrm{A} \times 1\ \Omega = 1\,\mathrm{V}$). The total of all the voltage drops is 3 volts, which is the circuit's total voltage.

Solving series circuit problems

Unequal resistances   Ohm's law is especially useful in series circuits where the devices do *not* have the same resistance. A device with a larger resistance has a greater voltage drop. However, the sum of all the voltage drops must still add up to the battery's voltage. The example below shows how to find the voltage drops in a circuit with two different light bulbs.

⊕ ⊖ ⊗ ⊘ **Calculating voltage drops**

The circuit shown here contains a 9-V battery, a 1-Ω bulb, and a 2-Ω bulb. Calculate the circuit's total resistance and current. Then, find each bulb's voltage drop.

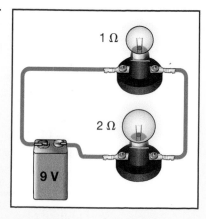

1. **Looking for:**   You are asked for total resistance and current, and bulb voltage drops.

2. **Given:**   You are given the battery's voltage and the resistance of each bulb.

3. **Relationships:**   Total resistance in a series circuit: $R_{total} = R_1 + R_2$
   Ohm's law: $I = V/R$ and $V = IR$

4. **Solution:**   Calculate the total resistance: $R_{total} = 1\ \Omega + 2\ \Omega = 3\ \Omega$
   Use Ohm's law to calculate the current:
   $I = (9\ \text{V})/(3\ \Omega) = 3\ \text{A}$
   Use Ohm's law to find the voltage for the 1-Ω bulb:
   $V = (3\ \text{A})(1\ \Omega) = 3\ \text{V}$
   Use Ohm's law to find the voltage for the 2-Ω bulb:
   $V = (3\ \text{A})(2\ \Omega) = 6\ \text{V}$

Your Turn:

a. The battery in the circuit is replaced with a 12-volt battery. Calculate the new current and bulb voltage drops.

b. A 12-V battery is connected in series with a 1-Ω and a 5-Ω bulbs. What is the voltage for each bulb?

(Answers are listed at the end of the chapter.)

13.1 *Section Review*

1. What do you know about the current at different points in a series circuit?
2. Three bulbs are connected in series with a battery and a switch. Do all of the bulbs go out when one bulb is removed? Explain.
3. What happens to a circuit's resistance as more resistors are added in series?
4. A series circuit contains a 9-volt battery and three 1-Ω bulbs. What is the voltage drop for each bulb?

13.2 **Parallel Circuits**

It would be a problem if your refrigerator went off when you turned out the light! That is why houses are wired with parallel circuits instead of series circuits. Parallel circuits provide each device with a separate path back to the power source. This means each device can be turned on and off independently of the others. It also means that each device receives the full voltage of the power source without voltage drops from other devices.

> **parallel circuit** - an electric circuit with more than one path or branch
>
> **Kirchoff's current law** - the total current entering a circuit branch must equal the current leaving the branch

What is a parallel circuit?

Parallel branches   A **parallel circuit** is a circuit with more than one path for the current. Each path in the circuit is sometimes called a *branch*. The current through a branch is also called the *branch current*. The current supplied by the battery in a parallel circuit splits at one or more branch points.

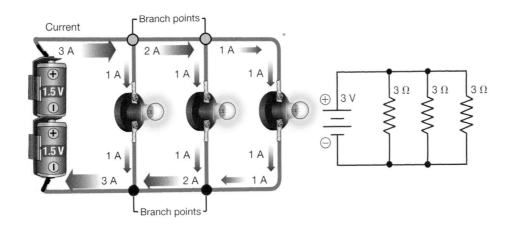

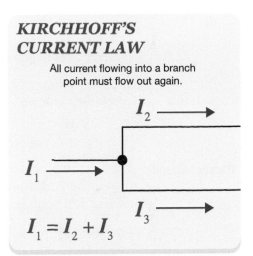

KIRCHHOFF'S CURRENT LAW

All current flowing into a branch point must flow out again.

$$I_1 = I_2 + I_3$$

Figure 13.4: *The total current entering a branch point in a circuit must equal the current leaving the branch point.*

Example: three bulbs in parallel   All of the current entering a branch point must exit the branch point. This rule is known as **Kirchhoff's current law** (Figure 13.4). For example, the image above shows three identical light bulbs connected in parallel. The circuit has two branch points where the current splits (green dots). There are also two branch points where the current comes back together (black dots). You measure the branch currents and find each to be 1 amp. The current supplied by the battery is the sum of the three branch currents, or 3 amps. At each branch point, the current entering is the same as the current exiting.

Voltage and current in a parallel circuit

Parallel circuit of two bulbs with different resistances

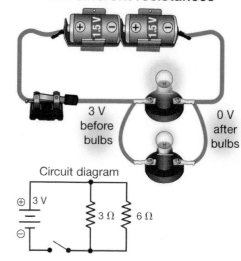

Each branch has the same voltage The voltage is the same anywhere along the same wire in a circuit. This is true as long as the resistance of the wire itself is very small compared to the rest of the circuit. If the voltage is the same along a wire, then the *same voltage appears across each branch of a parallel circuit*. This is true even when the branches have different resistances (Figure 13.5). Both bulbs in this circuit get 3 volts from the batteries since each is connected back to the batteries by wires without any other electrical devices in the circuit.

The voltage is the same for each branch of a parallel circuit.

Parallel circuits have two advantages over series circuits:

1. Each device in a parallel circuit has a voltage drop equal to the full battery voltage.
2. Each device in a parallel circuit may be turned off without stopping the current in the other circuit devices.

Figure 13.5: *The voltage for each branch of a parallel circuit is the same, regardless of the resistance in that branch.*

Parallel circuits in homes Parallel circuits allow you to turn off one lamp without all of the other lights in your home going out. They also allow you to use many appliances at once, each at full voltage.

Current in branches Each branch in a parallel circuit has the same voltage. Therefore, the current in a branch is determined by the branch resistance and Ohm's law, $I = V/R$ (Figure 13.6). The greater the resistance of a branch, the smaller its current. Each branch works independently. The current in one branch does not depend on the current in other branches.

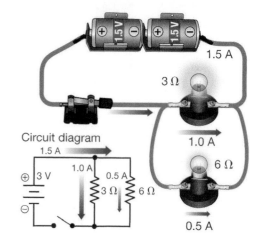

Total current The total current in a parallel circuit is the sum of the currents in each branch. The only time branches have an effect on each other is when the total current is more than the battery or wall outlet can supply. If the branches in a circuit try to draw too much current, the battery voltage will drop and less current will flow.

Figure 13.6: *The current in each branch depends on the branch resistance. The current may be different for each branch.*

Resistance in parallel circuits

More branches means more current In series circuits, adding extra resistance increases the total resistance of the whole circuit. The opposite is true in parallel circuits. Adding resistance in parallel provides another path for current, and *more* current flows. When more current flows at the same voltage, the total resistance of the circuit must *decrease*.

Similarity to checkout lines A similar result occurs in the check-out area of a grocery store. If only one register is open, every person must pass through the same lane, and the rate of people leaving the store is slow. If a second register opens, half of the people can pass through each lane. The average amount of time each person has to spend waiting in line can be cut in half: The total flow of people from the store is higher.

The formula for adding parallel resistances The formula shown below allows you to calculate the total resistance in a parallel circuit. At the end of the chapter, you will see that all the outlets in your home are connected in parallel. Every device you plug in adds a parallel resistance and draws more current.

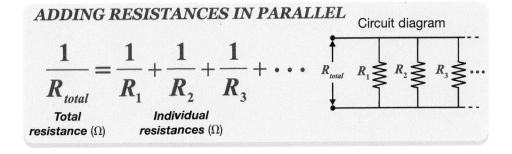

ADDING RESISTANCES IN PARALLEL

$$\frac{1}{R_{total}} = \frac{1}{R_1} + \frac{1}{R_2} + \frac{1}{R_3} + \cdots$$

Total resistance (Ω)   Individual resistances (Ω)

Circuit diagram

Example of a parallel circuit Figure 13.7 shows a parallel circuit with three 3-Ω bulbs. The voltage is 3 volts. To find the total resistance, use the formula for adding resistances in parallel as shown above. Three 3-Ω resistors in parallel create a total resistance of 1 Ω. This happens because every new path in a parallel circuit allows more current to flow for the same voltage. The resistance of the whole circuit decreases. To find the circuit's total current, use Ohm's law, $I = V/R$. Substituting values gives 3 V divided by 1 Ω, which equals 3 A.

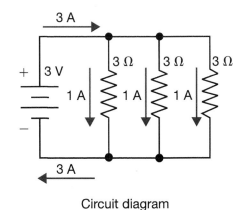

Circuit diagram

Figure 13.7: *A parallel circuit with three equal resistances divides the total current into three equal currents.*

Calculating the resistance of a parallel circuit

A circuit contains a 2-ohm resistor and a 4-ohm resistor in parallel. Calculate the total resistance of the circuit.

1. You are asked for the resistance.
2. You are given the type of circuit and branch resistances.
3. Use the rule for parallel resistances.
4. Solve:

$$\frac{1}{R_{total}} = \frac{1}{2\Omega} + \frac{1}{4\Omega} = \frac{3}{4\Omega}$$

$$R_{total} = \frac{4}{3}\Omega \approx 1.33\,\Omega$$

Calculating current and resistance in a parallel circuit

More branches mean less resistance In series circuits, adding an extra resistor increases the total resistance of the circuit. The opposite is true in parallel circuits. Adding a resistor in a parallel circuit provides another independent path for current. More current flows for the same voltage so the total resistance is *less*.

   Calculating current and resistance in parallel circuits

Calculate the total resistance, total current, and current in each branch for the circuit shown.

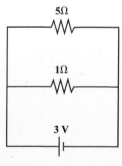

1. **Looking for:**   You are asked for total resistance, total current, and each branch current.

2. **Given:**   You are given the resistance of each branch and the total voltage.

3. **Relationships:**   Formula for parallel resistance: Ohm's law:

4. **Solution:** $R_{total} = 5/6\ \Omega = 0.83\ \Omega$

   $I_{total} = (3\ \text{V})/(0.83\ \Omega) = 3.6\ \text{A}$

   $I_{1\text{-}ohm} = (3\ \text{V})/(1\ \Omega) = 3\ \text{A}$

   $I_{5\text{-}ohm} = (3\ \text{V})/(5\ \Omega) = 0.6\ \text{A}$

Your Turn:

a. The electrical outlets in Jonah's living room are on one parallel circuit. The circuit breaker cuts off the current if it exceeds 15 amps. Will the breaker trip if he uses a light (240Ω), a stereo (150 Ω), and an air conditioner (10Ω) all at the same time?

b. Will the circuit breaker trip if Jonah also turns on a computer which has a resistance of 60Ω?

c. What is the total resistance and current in a parallel circuit containing a 12-V battery, a 3-Ω resistor, and a 4-Ω resistor?

(Answers are listed at the end of the chapter.)

Short circuits, circuit breakers, and fuses

Heat and wires   When electric current flows through a resistance, some of the power carried by the current becomes heat. Toasters and electric stoves are designed to use electric current to make heat. Although the resistance of wires is low, it is not zero, so wires heat up when current flows through them. If too much current flows through too small a wire, the wire overheats and may melt or start a fire.

Short circuits   A **short circuit** occurs when a branch in a circuit has very low resistance. A short circuit can be created accidentally by making a parallel branch with a wire (Figure 13.8). A copper wire may have a resistance as low as 0.001 ohm. Ohm's law states that with a resistance this low, 1.5 volts from a power source could result in a current of 1,500 amps! A short circuit is dangerous because currents this large can melt wires.

Parallel circuits in homes   Appliances and electrical outlets in homes are connected in many parallel circuits. Each circuit has its own fuse or circuit breaker that stops the current if it exceeds a safe amount, usually 15 or 20 amps (Figure 13.9). If you turn on too many appliances in one circuit at the same time, the circuit breaker or fuse cuts off the current. To restore the current, you must first disconnect some or all of the appliances. You reset the circuit breaker switch. In older electrical systems, you had to replace a blown fuse. Fuses are still used in some car electrical systems and in electrical devices such as multimeters.

> **short circuit** - occurs when a circuit branch has a very low resistance, creating a large current

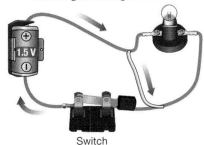

Short circuit
A large amount of current passes through the short circuit branch. Almost no current goes through the bulb.

Switch

Figure 13.8: *A short circuit is created when there is a parallel branch of very low resistance.*

Circuit breaker from a home

Fuse from an automobile

Figure 13.9: *Electrical systems use circuit breakers or fuses to open circuits if the current gets too high.*

13.2 Section Review

1. Is the voltage for each branch of a parallel circuit the same? Explain.
2. Is the current in each branch of a parallel circuit the same? Explain.
3. Why do home electrical systems use parallel wiring?
4. What happens to the total current in a parallel circuit as more branches are added? Why?
5. What is the total resistance of two 12-ohm resistors in parallel? What is the total resistance for three 12-ohm resistors in parallel?

13.3 Electrical Power, AC, and DC Electricity

Look at a stereo, hair dryer, or other household appliance. You may find a label giving its power in watts. In this section, you will learn what the power ratings on appliances mean, and how to figure out the electricity costs of using various appliances.

Electrical power

A watt is a unit of power **Electrical power** is measured in watts, just like mechanical power you studied in a previous chapter. Electrical power is the rate at which electrical energy is changed into other forms of energy such as heat, sound, or light. Anything that "uses" electricity is actually converting electrical energy into some other type of energy. The watt is an abbreviation for 1 joule per second. A 100-watt light bulb uses 100 joules of energy *every second* (Figure 13.10).

The three electrical quantities We have now introduced three important electrical quantities:

Current (*I*)	Current is a moving charge that carries power in a circuit. Current is measured in amperes (A).
Voltage (*V*)	Voltage measures the difference in energy carried by charges at two points in a circuit. A difference in voltage causes current to flow. Voltage is measured in volts (V). One volt can also be thought of as 1 watt per amp of current.
Resistance (*R*)	Resistance measures the ability of a device to resist current. Resistance is measured in ohms (Ω). One amp of current flows if a voltage of 1 V is applied to a resistance of 1 Ω.

Paying for electricity Electric bills sent out by utility companies don't charge by the amp, volt, or ohm. Electric companies charge for the energy you use. Electrical appliances in your home are rated by another unit—the *watt*. Most appliances have a label that lists the number of watts or kilowatts used. You may have purchased 60-watt light bulbs, a 1,000-watt hair dryer, or a 1,200-watt toaster oven. The amount you owe the utility company depends on how many watts each appliance uses and the amount of time each is used during the month.

Figure 13.10: *One watt equals 1 joule per second.*

Calculating power in a circuit

Calculating power One volt is the same as 1 watt per amp. To calculate power in an electric circuit you multiply the voltage by the current. To calculate the power of a device in a circuit, multiply the voltage drop of the device by the current.

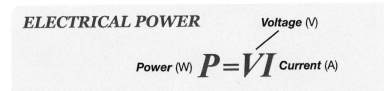

ELECTRICAL POWER   **Voltage** (V)

Power (W) $P = VI$ **Current** (A)

RATING 120V 60Hz
12 A   1400W

Figure 13.11: *Most appliances have a label that lists their power usage in watts.*

Watts and kilowatts Most electrical appliances have a label that lists their power usage in watts (Figure 13.11) or kilowatts. The *kilowatt* is used for large amounts of power. One kilowatt (kW) equals 1,000 watts. Another common unit of power, especially on electric motors, is the horsepower. One horsepower is 746 watts. The range in power for common electric motors is from 1/25th of a horsepower (about 30 watts) for a small electric fan to 1 horsepower (746 watts) for a garbage disposal.

Equation	gives	if you know
$P = I \times V$	power (P)	current and voltage
$I = P \div V$	current (I)	power and voltage
$V = P \div I$	voltage (V)	power and current

 **Calculating power**

A 12-volt battery is connected in series to two identical light bulbs. The current in the circuit is 3 amps. Calculate the power output of the battery in watts.

1. *Looking for:*   You are asked for the power in watts supplied by the battery.

2. *Given:*   You are given the battery voltage in volts and current in amps.

3. *Relationships:* $P = VI$

4. *Solution:* $P = (3\ A)(12\ V) = 36\ W$

Your Turn:

a. A 12-volt battery is connected in parallel to the same light bulbs used in the example. The current through each bulb is now 6 amps. Find the battery's power output.

b. The label on the back of a television states that it uses 300 watts of power. How much current flows when it is plugged into a 120-volt outlet?

(Answers are listed at the end of the chapter.)

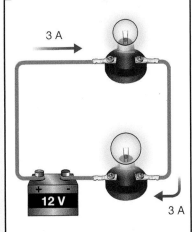

3 A

12 V

3 A

Paying for electricity

Kilowatt-hours
Utility companies charge customers for the number of **kilowatt-hours** (kWh) used each month. One kilowatt-hour means that a kilowatt of power has been used for 1 hour. A kilowatt-hour is not a unit of power but a unit of *energy*. A kilowatt-hour is a relatively large amount of energy, equal to 3.6 million joules. If you leave a 1,000-watt hair dryer on for 1 hour, you have used 1 kilowatt-hour of energy. You could also use 1 kilowatt-hour by using a 100-watt light bulb for 10 hours. The number of kilowatt-hours used equals the number of kilowatts multiplied by the number of hours the appliance was used.

Electricity Bill

1,300 kWh
× $0.14
——————
$182.00

kilowatt-hour - 1 kilowatt or 1,000 watts of power used per hour

Appliance	Power (watts)
Electric stove	3,000
Toaster	1,200
Hair dryer	1,000
Television	250
Video game console	170
Light	100
Small fan	50
Clock radio	10

Figure 13.12: *Typical power usage of some common appliances.*

You pay for kilowatt-hours
Electric companies charge for kilowatt-hours used during a period of time, often a month. Your home is connected to a meter that measures the total number of kilowatt-hours used. A meter reader checks it monthly or a newer-model meter transmits the data to the utility. If you know the cost per kilowatt-hour, you can estimate the cost of operating any electrical appliance.

 Calculating electricity costs

How much does it cost to run a television and a video game console for 2 hours? Use Figure 13.12 and a cost of $0.15 per kWh.

1. *Looking for:* You are asked for the cost to run a television and video game console for 2 hours.

2. *Given:* You are given the time, the power, and the price per kilowatt-hour.

3. *Relationships:* 1 kilowatt = 1,000 watts   number of kilowatt-hours = (kilowatts used) x (hours appliances are used)

4. *Solution:* $250\,\text{W} + 170\,\text{W} = 420\,\text{W}; 420\,\text{W} = 0.42\,\text{kW} \times 2\,\text{hr} = 0.84\,\text{kWh} \times \dfrac{\$0.15}{\text{kWh}} = \$0.13$

Your Turn:

a. At $0.15 per kilowatt-hour, what is the cost of running a hair dryer for 20 minutes each day for 7 days? (*Hint:* 1 h = 60 min.)

b. At $0.15 per kilowatt-hour, what is the cost of running a clock radio for 24 hours?

(Answers are listed at the end of the chapter.)

Alternating (AC) and direct (DC) current

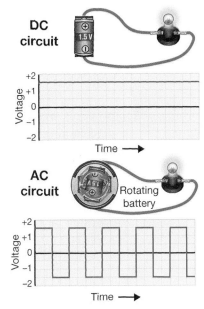

Direct current   The current from a battery is always in the same direction: from the positive to the negative end of the battery. This type of current is called **direct current** or DC. Although the letters *DC* stand for "direct current" the abbreviation DC is used to describe both voltage and current. A DC voltage is one that stays the same as time passes. The terminal that is positive stays positive and the terminal that is negative stays negative. Your experiments in the lab use DC since they use batteries.

Alternating current   The electrical system in your house uses **alternating current** or AC. Alternating current constantly switches direction. You can theoretically create alternating current with a battery if you keep reversing the way it is connected in a circuit (Figure 13.13). In the electrical system used in the United States, the current reverses direction 60 times per second. It would be hard to flip a battery this fast!

A DC current or voltage stays the same as time passes.

An AC current reverses direction 60 times per second in the United States power grid.

Figure 13.13: *Direct current is in one direction, but alternating current reverses.*

Electricity in other countries   For large amounts of electricity, we use alternating current because it is easier to generate and to transmit over long distances. All the power lines you see overhead carry alternating current. Other countries also use alternating current. However, in many other countries, the current reverses itself 50 times per second rather than 60, and wall sockets are at a different voltage. When visiting other countries, you often need special adapters to use electrical appliances made for use in the United States.

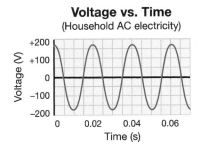

Voltage vs. Time
(Household AC electricity)

Peak and average voltages   The 120-volt AC (VAC) electricity used in homes and businesses alternates between peak values of +170 V and −170 V (Figure 13.14). This kind of electricity is called 120 VAC because +120V is a type of *average* positive voltage and −120V is a type of *average* negative voltage. AC electricity is usually described by this average voltage, not the peak voltage.

Figure 13.14: *The voltage from your wall outlets varies from +170 V to −170 V.*

Electricity, power, and heat

How do you get more power?

How do you get more power when you need it? From the power formula, $P = VI$, we can see that increasing voltage or current will increase power. The problem with raising voltage is that the electricity in a standard wall outlet is 120 volts and is hard to change. Some appliances, like dryers and stoves, use 240 volts, which is more dangerous, so 120 volts is used for most electrical appliances.

Higher power usually means more current

The most common way to get higher power is to use more current. However, heat becomes a problem when wires carry large currents. A wire's voltage drop equals the current multiplied by the wire's resistance ($V = IR$). Because a wire's resistance is small, the voltage drop is usually small enough to be ignored. But if there is a large current, there can be a significant voltage drop. Remember, power is voltage multiplied by current. In a wire, this power is converted into heat. A small amount of heat can safely be transferred away from the wire by conduction or convection. Too much heat could melt the wire or start a fire.

Reducing heat in electrical wires

Wires are made in different sizes to carry different amounts of current. A large diameter wire has less resistance and can safely carry more current than a smaller, thinner wire. A 12-gauge wire is thicker than a 14-gauge wire and can carry more current (Figure 13.15). You should always use the right wire for the current that is flowing. This includes extension cords, which you may use without thinking about whether they are safe or not. Extension cords are made with 18-gauge wire, 16-gauge, 14-gauge, and 12-gauge wire.

Length and resistance

The length of a wire also affects its resistance. The longer a wire is, the more resistance it has. Think about moving around your school. You can move through a short, crowded hallway quickly. It takes longer to move down a long, crowded hallway.

Check your extension cords for safety

All extension cords are rated for how many amps of current they can carry safely. *Always* check to see if the extension cord can carry *at least* as much current as the connected device uses. For example, the average circular saw needs 15 amps of current. You should use a 14- or 12-gauge heavy-duty extension cord for the circular saw (Figure 13.15). Many fires have been caused by using the wrong extension cord.

Extension cords are made from multiple wires woven together

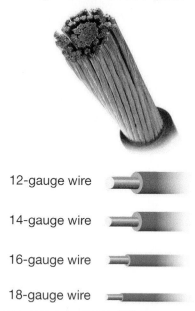

12-gauge wire

14-gauge wire

16-gauge wire

18-gauge wire

Wire gauge	Current (amps)
12	20
14	15
16	10
18	7

Figure 13.15: *The larger the gauge of a wire, the smaller its diameter, and the smaller the amount of current the wire can carry safely.*

Electricity in homes and buildings

Circuit breaker panel The 120-VAC electricity comes into a normal home or building through a circuit breaker panel. The circuit breakers protect against wires overheating and causing fires. Each circuit breaker protects one parallel circuit which may connect many wall outlets and switches.

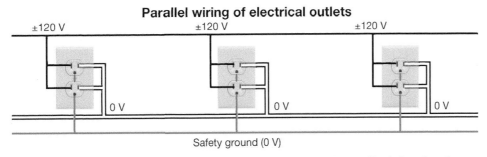

Parallel wiring of electrical outlets

±120 V   ±120 V   ±120 V

0 V   0 V   0 V

Safety ground (0 V)

Hot, neutral, and ground wires Each wall socket is connected to three wires. One wire, called the "hot" wire, carries 120 volts AC. The neutral wire stays at 0 volts. When you plug something in, current flows in and out of the hot wire, and back through the neutral wire. A third wire is connected to the ground (0 V) near your house. The ground wire is for safety. If there is a short circuit in an appliance, the current flows through the ground wire instead of through you.

Ground fault interrupt (GFI) outlets Locations near water in kitchens and bathrooms are required to have ground fault interrupt (GFI) outlets (Figure 13.16). A GFI outlet has a circuit that compares the current flowing in and out on the hot wire and back on the neutral wire. If everything is working properly, the two currents are equal. If they are different, some current must be flowing to another path, such as through your hand. If this happens, the GFI immediately breaks the circuit. GFI outlets give excellent protection from electric shocks.

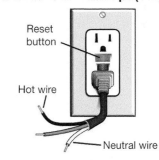

Ground fault interrupt (GFI) outlet

Reset button

Hot wire

Neutral wire

Figure 13.16: *A ground fault interrupt outlet is found in bathrooms and kitchens where water may be near electricity.*

13.3 Section Review

1. How is an appliance's power related to the amount of energy it uses?
2. How many watts or joules are a horsepower, kilowatt, and kilowatt-hour?
3. What does the electric utility company charge you for each month?
4. What is the difference between direct current and alternating current?

Plugged In: The Future of Transportation?

Most of the vehicles on US roads today are powered by gasoline. But, concerns about global climate change, rising oil prices, and dependence on imported oil have spurred automotive engineers to look for alternatives. Some of the most promising new technologies involve "plugging in"—connecting our vehicles to the electricity grid.

The trouble with gasoline engines

Gasoline is an energy-dense fuel and is easy to transport. These two advantages pushed gasoline-powered internal combustion engines to the technology forefront in the early 20th century. At that time, oil was inexpensive and global climate change was not yet understood.

But, the efficiency of a gasoline engine is only about 13 percent. This means that when the car is in motion, it uses only about 13 percent of the available energy from a tank of gas. The rest is lost as heat.

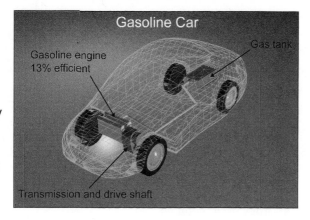

Gasoline Car

Gasoline engine 13% efficient

Gas tank

Transmission and drive shaft

All-electric cars

Compared to gasoline-powered cars, electric motors are very efficient. About 80 percent of the energy stored in the batteries is converted to kinetic energy that moves the car. While on the road, electric cars produce no emissions. But, there are some problems. While a typical gasoline-powered car can store enough energy in the tank to go about 400 kilometers, electric car batteries can store only enough energy to go about 100 to 160 kilometers. Then, they need to be recharged.

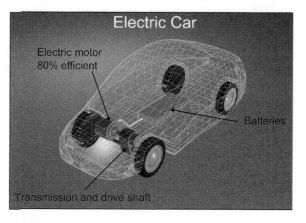

Electric Car

Electric motor 80% efficient

Batteries

Transmission and drive shaft

Recharging takes time. With a standard US 120-volt outlet, recharging takes 8 to 14 hours. You can cut that time in half if an electrician installs a 220/240-volt dedicated outlet in your garage, those used with many electric clothes dryers and stoves.

But what if you don't have a garage? Can urban dwellers with on-street parking, renters, and others without plug-in capacity still drive an all-electric car? Not yet, but there are proposals to place solar rechargers in workplace parking lots. Another idea being discussed is to create a system where drivers could swap spent batteries for fresh ones, or plug in their cars at charging stations. Drivers would buy "miles" from a company that owns the batteries and charging stations, just like you buy "minutes" from a mobile phone company.

Another drawback to the electric car is that it's only as "green" as the power plant producing the electricity. If you live in a region of the United States where natural gas is the dominant power-plant fuel, your electric car will be responsible for 40 percent less carbon dioxide emission than a gas-electric hybrid. But, if your electricity comes from a coal-burning power plant, your car will be responsible for about the same amount of carbon dioxide emission as a gas-electric hybrid. However, the hybrid would still produce less carbon dioxide than even the most efficient gasoline-powered car.

Plug-in hybrid vehicles

What if you would like to drive an electric vehicle, but want to be able to drive more than 100–160 kilometers without plugging in? Several automobile makers are introducing plug-in hybrids to meet that need. Plug-in hybrids run exclusively on batteries for the first 65 kilometers. That is far enough to get 75 percent of Americans to and from work every day. For longer trips, a small gasoline engine generates electricity to extend the vehicle's range to about 480 kilometers. The power generated is sent to the electric motor, with the excess energy going to recharge the batteries. In a plug-in hybrid, the gasoline engine only generates electricity; it does not move the wheels.

Standard gas-electric hybrids

For those who can't or don't want to plug in their cars, a standard gas-electric hybrid car provides better fuel efficiency and lower emissions than a gasoline-powered car. The electric motor increases the car's overall efficiency to about 26 percent by using electricity to transfer energy within the system.

In a standard gas-electric hybrid, the gasoline engine and electric motor work together to accelerate the car. This allows for a smaller, more-efficient gasoline engine. Every time a standard car slows

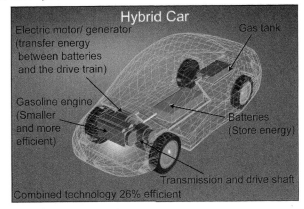

Hybrid Car
Electric motor/ generator (transfer energy between batteries and the drive train)
Gas tank
Gasoline engine (Smaller and more efficient)
Batteries (Store energy)
Transmission and drive shaft
Combined technology 26% efficient

down, kinetic energy is lost as the brakes heat up. In contrast, the hybrid's electric motor operates as a generator during braking. When the car slows down, kinetic energy is converted to electrical energy that charges the batteries. Then, to speed up the car, the electric motor converts energy stored during braking into kinetic energy.

Gas-electric hybrid cars do not produce as many pollutants as standard cars of comparable size because the engine is smaller and uses less gasoline. Also, when a gas-electric hybrid car comes to a stop, the engine automatically shuts off to save gas. When it is time to go again, the car turns again. At very low speeds, as when driving in city traffic, the electric motor runs the car instead of the gas engine, reducing tailpipe emissions and frequent engine starting and stopping.

Hybrid technology is just a beginning

The gas-electric hybrid is only one of the many types of more efficient motor-powered vehicles that are being developed today. Driving this development is an interest in decreasing our use of fossil fuels for transportation. In the meantime, since we all need to travel and often use gasoline-powered vehicles, how can you reduce your use of fossil fuels so that you save money and reduce pollution? Here are some options: Share rides, take public transportation, and drive a medium-sized or small car that has a high gas-mileage rating.

QUESTIONS

1. Who would benefit more from driving a gas-electric hybrid rather than a gasoline-powered car: someone who does mostly city driving or someone who does mostly highway driving? Explain.

2. Analyze the transportation needs of a driver you know. How far does this person travel on an average day? What is the ratio of city to highway miles? Where is the car parked overnight? Using this information, recommend the best type of vehicle to meet the driver's needs.

3. Find examples of all-electric, plug-in hybrid, and gas-electric hybrid vehicles on the market today. Look in newspapers and magazines and on the Internet to find information about production and sale of these vehicles. Can you determine which is having the greatest environmental impact? Why or why not?

Chapter 13 Review

Understanding Vocabulary

Select the correct term to complete the sentences.

alternating	kilowatt	parallel circuit
direct	kilowatt-hour	series circuit
electrical power	Kirchhoff's current law	short circuit
horsepower	Kirchhoff's voltage law	voltage drop

1. A(n) _____ contains only one path for the current.

2. There is a(n) _____ across each resistance in a series circuit when current is flowing.

3. _____ states that all the current entering a point in a parallel circuit must also leave that point.

4. A(n) _____ contains multiple paths or branches for the current.

5. The _____ is a unit used by electric utility companies to measure the electrical energy your home uses each month.

6. Electrical appliances in your home use _____ current.

Reviewing Concepts

Section 13.1

1. Draw a circuit diagram for a circuit containing a battery and two bulbs in series.

2. Is the current at every point in a series circuit the same? Explain.

3. One of the bulbs burns out in a string of lights. What happens to the current in the circuit? What happens to the other bulbs?

4. Explain how to calculate the total resistance of a series circuit.

5. As more bulbs are added to a series circuit, what happens to the resistance of the circuit? What happens to the brightness of the bulbs?

6. Explain Kirchhoff's voltage law.

Section 13.2

7. What is a parallel circuit?

8. Draw the circuit diagram for a circuit containing two bulbs in parallel.

9. What does Kirchhoff's current law say about the current entering any point in a circuit?

10. Each branch in a parallel circuit has the same _____.

11. List two advantages of parallel circuits over series circuits.

12. Does the wiring in your home connect the appliances in series or parallel? How could you prove this?

13. What happens to the total resistance of a parallel circuit as more branches are added? Why?

14. How do you calculate the total resistance of two resistances that are wired in parallel?

15. What is a short circuit?

16. Why can short circuits be dangerous?

Section 13.3

17. A light bulb has a power of 60 W. Explain what this means in terms of energy and time.

18. Explain how to calculate the power of an electrical appliance.

19. What is the meaning of the kilowatt-hour?

20. What is the difference between direct current and alternating current?

21. How frequently does the alternating current used in the United States reverse direction?

22. Do thinner or thicker wires have more resistance? Why?

23. Do longer or shorter wires have more resistance? Why?

24. Why can it be dangerous to connect several extension cords to make one long cord?

Solving Problems

Section 13.1

1. A series circuit contains 5-Ω, 3-Ω, and 8-Ω resistors. What is the total resistance of the circuit?

2. A circuit contains a 9-V battery and two identical bulbs. What is the voltage drop across each?

3. A circuit contains a 12-V battery and two 3-Ω bulbs in series. Draw a circuit diagram and use it to find the current in the circuit and the voltage drop across each bulb.

4. A circuit contains a 12-V battery and three 1-Ω bulbs in series. Draw the circuit diagram and find the current in the circuit.

5. Calculate the total resistance of each circuit shown below. Then, calculate the current in each.

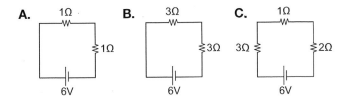

6. A circuit contains two 1-Ω bulbs in series. The current in the circuit is 1.5 A. What is the voltage provided by the batteries?

7. A circuit contains two identical resistors in series. The current is 3 A, and the batteries have a total voltage of 24 V. What is the total resistance of the circuit? What is the resistance of each device?

Section 13.2

8. Find the amount and direction of the current through point P in each of the circuits shown below.

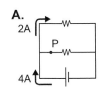

9. Find the following for each of the three circuits shown:
   a. the voltage across each resistor
   b. the current through each resistance (*Hint*: Use Ohm's law.)
   c. the total current in the circuit
   d. the total resistance of the circuit

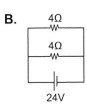
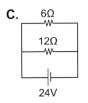

10. A parallel circuit contains a 6-V battery and two 6-Ω bulbs.
    a. Draw the circuit diagram for this circuit.
    b. Calculate the current through each branch.
    c. Calculate the total current.
    d. Use Ohm's law to calculate the total resistance of the circuit.
    e. Use the formula for combining parallel resistors to calculate the total resistance of the circuit.

11. A parallel circuit contains a 24-V battery, a 4-Ω bulb and a 12-Ω bulb.
    a. Draw the circuit diagram for this circuit.
    b. Calculate the current through each branch.
    c. Calculate the total current in the circuit.
    d. Use Ohm's law to calculate the total resistance of the circuit.
    e. Use the formula for combining parallel resistors to calculate the total resistance of the circuit.

12. Find the unknown quantity in each of the circuits shown.

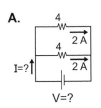
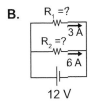
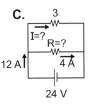

Section 13.3

13. Calculate the power of each of the following appliances when plugged into a 120-V outlet.

   a. an iron that uses 10 A of current

   b. a stereo that uses 2 A of current

   c. a light bulb that uses 0.5 A of current

14. Calculate the current each of the following appliances uses when plugged into a 120-V outlet.

   a. a 100-W computer

   b. a 1,200-W microwave

   c. a 30-W radio

15. A portable MP3 player requires 1.5 A of current and has a power of 15 W. What is the voltage of the rechargeable battery it uses?

16. A flashlight contains a 6-W bulb that uses 2 A of current. How many 1.5-V batteries does it use?

17. Alex uses a 1,000-W heater to heat his room.

   a. What is the heater's power in kilowatts?

   b. How many kilowatt-hours of electricity does Alex use if he runs the heater for 8 hours?

   c. If the utility company charges $0.15 per kilowatt-hour, how much does it cost to run the heater for 8 hours?

18. You watch a movie on 300-W television for two hours.

   a. What is the television's power in kilowatts?

   b. How many kilowatt-hours of electricity did you use?

   c. If the utility company charges $0.15 per kilowatt-hour, how much did it cost to watch the movie?

Test Practice

Section 13.1

1. _____ states that the sum of the voltage drops in a series circuit must equal the circuit's total voltage.

   a. Ohm's law

   b. Ampere's law

   c. Coulomb's law

   d. Kirchhoff's law

2. The current for the circuit is:

   a. 0.5 Ω.

   b. 2 Ω.

   c. 0.5 A.

   d. 2 A.

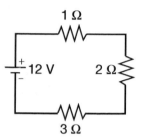

3. A series circuit contains a 3-V battery and three identical light bulbs. What is the voltage drop for each light bulb?

   a. 1/3 V

   b. 1 V

   c. 3 V

   d. 9 V

4. If the current in the circuit is 1.5 A, what is the battery voltage?

   a. 4 V

   b. 6 V

   c. 9 V

   d. 12 V

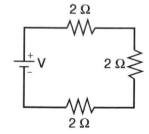

Section 13.2

5. Which formula is used for calculating the total resistance (R_{total}) when given the individual resistances (R_1, R_2, R_3...) in a parallel circuit?

    a. $R_{total} = R_1 + R_2 + R_3 +...$

    b. $R_{total} = 1/R_1 + 1/R_2 + 1/R_3 +...$

    c. $1/R_{total} = 1/(R_1 + R_2 + R_3 +...)$

    d. $1/R_{total} = 1/R_1 + 1/R_2 + 1/R_3 +...$

6. What is the current at point A?

    a. 2 A

    b. 6 A

    c. 8 A

    d. 10 A

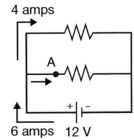

4 amps

6 amps   12 V

7. What is the total current in this circuit?

    a. 2 A

    b. 6 A

    c. 12 A

    d. 24 A

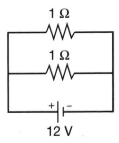

1 Ω

1 Ω

12 V

8. Calculate the total resistance of this circuit.

    a. 1 1/3 Ω

    b. 2 Ω

    c. 4 Ω

    d. 6 Ω

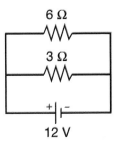

6 Ω

3 Ω

12 V

Section 13.3

9. A stereo uses 2 A of current when plugged into a 120-V outlet. What is its power?

    a. 240 W

    b. 200 W

    c. 120 W

    d. 60 W

10. Kilowatt-hours is a unit of

    a. power.

    b. current.

    c. energy.

    d. voltage.

11. You watch a 10-hour science fiction movie marathon. The power rating of your television is 300 W and your utility company charges $0.15 per kilowatt-hour. How much did it cost to watch the marathon?

    a. 4.5¢

    b. 20¢

    c. 45¢

    d. $450

12. How much current is used by a 2,400-W electric oven operating on a 120-V circuit?

    a. 2 A

    b 20 A

    c. 200 A

    d. 2,000 A

Applying Your Knowledge

Section 13.1

1. Some appliances contain components that are connected in series. For example, many microwave ovens have a light that turns on while the microwave is running. Look around your house and see how many appliances you can find that use series circuits.

Section 13.2

2. A car contains a warning bell that turns on if you open the door while the key is in the ignition. The bell also turns on if you open the door while the headlights are on. A single circuit with three switches and a a bell can be built to ring in both cases. Figure out how the circuit is designed. Draw a circuit diagram that shows your solution.

3. Many circuits contain resistors in series and in parallel. Apply what you have learned about circuits to find the total resistance of each of the circuits below.

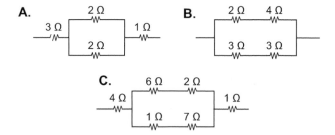

Section 13.3

4. Look at the back or underside of appliances in your home. Find the power ratings of three appliances. Calculate the amount of current each appliance draws when plugged into a 120-V outlet.

5. Choose an appliance with a known power rating that you use frequently, such as a clock radio, stereo, or light.

   a. Calculate its power rating in kilowatts.

   b. Determine the amount of time you use the appliance in one day.

   c. Calculate the number of kilowatt-hours of energy the appliance uses in one day.

   d. Calculate the number of kilowatt-hours of energy it uses in one year.

   e. Find out the cost of electricity in your home for one year.

   f. Calculate the cost of running the appliance for one year.

 *Your Turn* **Answers**

Calculating current (Section 13.1, page 317)

a. 0.9 A

b. 3 A

Calculating voltage drops (Section 13.1, page 320)

a. 4 A, 4 V for 1-Ω bulb, 8 V for 2-Ω bulb

b. 2 V, 10 V

Calculating current and resistance in parallel circuits (Section 13.2, page 324)

a. No. The total current is 13.3 A, so the circuit breaker will not trip.

b. Yes. The additional current is 2 A, so the total is 15.3 A.

c. 1.7 Ω and 7 A

Calculating power (Section 13.3, page 327)

a. 144 W

b. 2.5 A

Calculating electricity costs (Section 13.3, page 328)

a. $0.35

b. $0.04 (rounded to nearest cent)

Electrical Charges and Forces

Benjamin Franklin's famous kite experiment has been referred to many times, even though it is not known when, or if, he even actually did the experiment at all. The major question of the day was "Is lightning an electrical phenomenon?" Back in the mid-1700s, the longest spark that could be generated was about 1-inch long, so it was not obvious that powerful lightning bolts could be similar to the small sparks seen in laboratory experiments.

Popular legend explains that Franklin attached a metal key to the end of a kite string and flew the kite in a lightning storm. Because he knew the experiment would be dangerous, he most likely attached a second silk string to the key that insulated him from the electrical charges, and held onto that string. He did not do his experiments during the peak of the storm, but chose to fly the kite as the storm was beginning to form. He noticed, according to an account written several years later, that he did receive a shock when he touched his knuckle to the metal key. He determined that lightning exhibited the same properties as small static electricity sparks, and he was correct!

In this chapter, you will read how atoms are ultimately responsible for electrical charges. In an earlier chapter, we found that all atoms contain positive and negative charges. Now, you will see that these charges are the very same ones that allow us to benefit from generating, conducting, and using electricity.

KEY QUESTIONS

✓ **What is the actual source of current in a household electrical system?**

✓ **After you rub a balloon on your dry hair, why can you then place the balloon on a wall without it falling, but not to a metal doorknob?**

✓ **How does a defibrillator work, and what does it have to do with electricity?**

VOCABULARY

capacitance	Coulomb's law	polarized
capacitor	electroscope	static electricity
coulomb	farad	superconductor

14.1 Electric Charge and Current

In Chapter 12 and Chapter 13, we looked at how electricity is used and measured. Amps, volts, and ohms describe most of what you need to know to use electricity safely. However, we did not discuss what electricity *is* on the atomic level. What is current? What is it that can flow through solid metal? Why can an electric motor do the work of two horses?

coulomb - the unit of electric charge

Positive and negative charge

The cause of electric current   Virtually all the matter around you has electric charge because all atoms contain electrons (–) and protons (+). Electrons have negative charge and protons have positive charge. The electrons and protons are held tightly in atoms and are unable to separate from each other. However, in electrical conductors, such as copper, some electrons are free to move around. These mobile electrons are the real cause of electric current.

Like charges repel and unlike charges attract   Whether two charges attract or repel depends on whether they are the same or opposite. A positive and a negative charge will attract each other. Two positive charges will repel each other. Two negative charges will also repel each other. The force between charges is shown in Figure 14.1.

Charge is measured in coulombs   The unit of charge is the **coulomb** (C). The name was chosen in honor of Charles Augustin de Coulomb (1736–1806). Coulomb was a French physicist who performed the first accurate measurements of the force between charges. One coulomb is a *large* amount of charge. A single proton has a charge of only 1.602×10^{-19} coulombs. An electron has the same charge, but it is negative: -1.602×10^{-19} coulombs.

Two types of charge   Electric charge, like mass, is a fundamental property of matter. An important difference between mass and charge is that there are two types of charge, which we call positive and negative. We know there are two kinds because electric charges can attract or repel each other. As far as we know, there is only one type of mass. All masses *attract* each other through gravity. We have never found masses that repel each other.

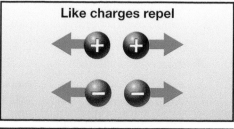

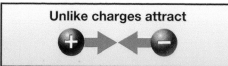

Figure 14.1: *The direction of the forces on charges depends on whether the charges are alike or opposite.*

Static electricity

Neutral objects Matter contains trillions of charged electrons and protons because matter is made of atoms. Neutral atoms have equal numbers of electrons and protons. The forces from positive charges are canceled by negative charges in the same way that +1 and −1 add up to 0. Because ordinary matter has zero net charge, most matter acts as if there is no charge at all. An object with a net charge of zero is described as being *electrically neutral*. A pencil, a textbook, and even your body are electrically neutral, at least most of the time.

Charged objects An object is *charged* when its net charge is *not* zero. If you have ever felt a shock when you have touched a doorknob (Figure 14.3) or removed clothes from a dryer, you have contacted a charged object. An object with more negative than positive charge has a net negative charge (Figure 14.2). If it has more positive than negative charge, the object has a net positive charge. The net charge is also called *excess* charge because a charged object has an excess of either positive or negative charges.

Static electricity and charge A tiny imbalance in either positive or negative charge on an object is the cause of **static electricity**. If two neutral objects are rubbed together, the friction can pull some electrons from one object and put them temporarily on the other. This is what happens to clothes in the dryer and to your socks when you walk on a carpet. The static electricity you feel when taking clothes from a dryer or scuffing your socks on a carpet typically results from an excess charge of less than one-millionth of a coulomb.

What causes shocks You get a shock because excess charge of one type strongly attracts the opposite charge and repels like charge. When you walk across a carpet on a dry day, your body picks up excess negative charge. If you touch a neutral doorknob, some of your excess negative charge moves to the doorknob. Because the doorknob is a conductor, the charge flows quickly. The moving charge makes a brief, intense electric current between you and the doorknob. The shock you feel is the electric current created as some of your excess negative charge transfers to the doorknob (Figure 14.3).

> **static electricity** - a buildup of positive or negative charge consisting of isolated motionless charges, such as those produced by friction

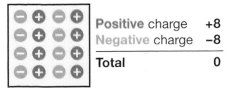

This object is neutral.

Positive charge	+8
Negative charge	−8
Total	0

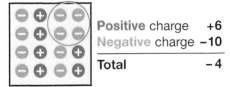

This object is charged.

Positive charge	+6
Negative charge	−10
Total	−4

Figure 14.2: *A neutral object has an equal number of positive and negative charges.*

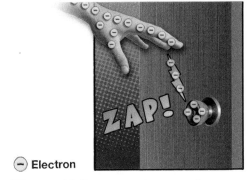

⊖ **Electron**

Figure 14.3: *The shock you get from touching a doorknob on a dry day comes from a tiny imbalance of charge.*

Coulomb's law

The strength of electric forces   Electric forces are strong. A millimeter cube of carbon the size of a pencil point contains about 77 coulombs of positive charge and the same amount of negative charge. Suppose you could separate all these positive and negative charges by a distance of 1 meter. The attractive force between them would be 50 thousand billion newtons. This is the weight of about 3 thousand million cars. All this force from the charge in a pencil point (Figure 14.4)! The large forces between charges is the reason objects are electrically neutral.

More charge means more force   The force between two charges depends on the charge and the distance. The force is directly proportional to each object's charge. The greater the charge, the stronger the force. Doubling the charge of one object doubles the force. Doubling the charge of both objects quadruples the force (Figure 14.5, top).

Less distance means more force   The force is inversely proportional to the square of the distance between the charges (Figure 14.5, bottom). The electric force get stronger as charges move closer and weaker as they move apart. Doubling the distance makes the force one-fourth as strong ($1 \div 2^2$). The force is one-ninth as strong ($1 \div 3^2$) at three times the distance.

Coulomb's law   **Coulomb's law** explains the relationship between the amount of each charge (q_1 and q_2), the distance between their centers (r), and the electrical force (F_E). The constant k relates the distance and charges to the force. Coulomb's law is similar in form to Newton's law of universal gravitation.

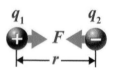

$$\text{Electric Force (N) } F_E = k \frac{q_1 q_2}{r^2} \begin{array}{l}\text{Charges (C)}\\ \\ \text{Distance (m)}\end{array}$$

COULOMB'S LAW

Constant (9×10^9 N·m²/C²)

Action-reaction pairs   The force between two charges acts along a line joining their centers. As required by Newton's third law of motion, the forces on each charge make an action-reaction pair. They are equal in strength and opposite in direction.

> **Coulomb's law** - states that the attraction or repulsion between two electric charges is inversely related to the square of the distance between them

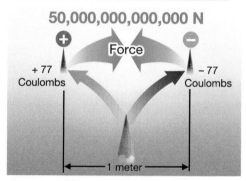

Figure 14.4: *If you could separate the positive and negative charge in a pencil point by 1 meter, the force between the charges would be 50 thousand billion newtons!*

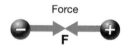

Doubling one charge doubles the force

Doubling both charges multiplies the force by 4

Doubling the distance reduces the force to 1/4 its original strength

Figure 14.5: *How the electric force changes with charge and distance.*

Electrostatics

What is electrostatics?
Electrostatics is the part of physics that studies the forces created by unmoving charges. Suppose you remove a length of plastic from a roll of plastic wrap. Because of electrostatic forces, the plastic tends to cling to itself before you can get it to cling to a glass bowl.

Electrostatics and photocopiers
A photocopier uses electrostatic forces. You place an item face-down on the glass. A bright light scans the item to be copied. An electrical "shadow" or image forms on a rotating belt. Tiny *charged* particles of powdered ink called *toner* are attracted to the image on the belt. A sheet of paper feeds into the machine and is given a strong electrical *charge*. When the paper moves near the image belt, the toner particles are attracted to the charged paper. In this way, the image is transferred from the belt to the paper. The inked paper passes through two rollers that fuse the ink to the paper. Finally, the copy comes out of the machine with an image of the original.

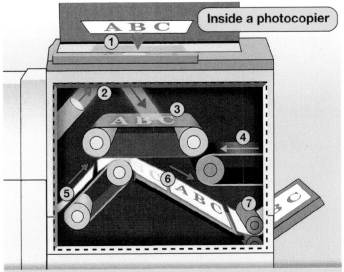

Inside a photocopier

1. Place item on glass 2. Light scans document
3. Electrical image forms on belt 4. Electrically charged toner is placed on belt's image 5. Paper feeds into copier and is given electrical charge 6. Paper's charge attracts toner particles from belt
7. Inked paper passes through rollers to fuse ink

 Using Coulomb's law

Two steel marbles are each given a net charge of one-thousandth (0.001) of a coulomb. Calculate the size of the force on the marbles, in newtons, if they are held 2 meters apart.

1. *Looking for:*   You are asked for the electric force in newtons.

2. *Given:*   Two charges (0.001 C each) and the distance in meters.

3. *Relationships:* $F_E = k\dfrac{q_1 q_2}{r^2}$

4. *Solution:* $F_E = \left(9 \times 10^9 \text{ N} \cdot \text{m}^2/\text{C}^2\right)\dfrac{(0.001 \text{ C})(0.001 \text{ C})}{(2 \text{ m})^2} = 2,250 \text{ N}$

Your Turn:

a. Calculate the size of the force if the marbles are held 4 meters apart.

b. Calculate the size of the force between 3-columb and 4-columb charges 500 meters apart.

(Answers are listed at the end of the chapter.)

The electroscope

Electrons and static electricity   Since electrons are small, light, and on the outside of atoms, almost all electrical effects are caused by moving electrons. A negatively-charged object has an excess of electrons. A positively-charged object is missing some electrons. Electric forces are so strong that a "charged" object is really almost completely neutral. A tiny excess of charge, smaller than one part in a million, is enough to cause the "static electricity" effects we observe.

Charge spreads out in a conductor   Electrons in a conductor are free to move around. If a conductor has an excess of electrons, they repel each other with strong forces. The repelling forces cause the electrons to move as far away from each other as they can get. That means excess electrons spread out evenly over the surface of any conductor and flow along the conductor wherever they can get farther away from each other.

Parts of an electroscope   The force between charges can be observed with an **electroscope**. An electroscope contains two very thin "leaves" of metal that can swing from a central rod connected to a metal ball (Figure 14.6, top). Charges can flow freely between the ball and the leaves. An insulator holds the rod in place and keeps charges from getting to the outside of the electroscope.

Charging an electroscope   Suppose a positively-charged rod touches the metal ball of an electroscope. Some negative electrons are attracted to the rod. The metal ball and leaves of the electroscope are left with a net positive charge. Since both leaves have the same positive charge, the leaves repel each other and move apart.

Testing an unknown charge with an electroscope   Once an electroscope is charged, it can be used to test other charged objects. The leaves move farther apart if another positively-charged rod is brought near the metal ball. This happens because the positive rod attracts some negative electrons from the leaves toward the ball, increasing the positive charge on the leaves. If a negatively-charged rod is brought near the ball, the opposite effect occurs. A negatively-charged rod repels negative electrons from the ball onto the leaves where they neutralize some of the positive charge. The positive charge on the leaves is reduced and the leaves move closer together (Figure 14.6, bottom).

electroscope - an instrument used to detect charged objects

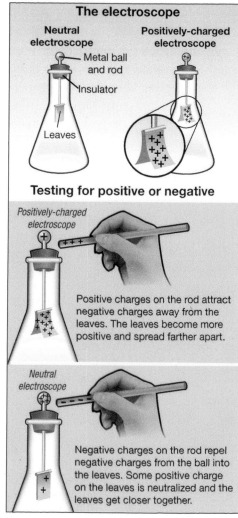

Figure 14.6: *You can use an electroscope to observe electric forces.*

Static electricity, charge polarization, and induction

Charging by friction If you rub a balloon on your dry hair, you can place it on a wall but not on a metal doorknob. When the balloon and your hair are rubbed together, electrons are transferred from your hair to the balloon. This is called *charging by friction*. Objects charged by this method will attract each other. The balloon gains electrons, so it has a negative net charge. Your hair loses electrons, so it has a net positive charge. The balloon and your hair attract each other.

Polarization When the balloon is held against a wall, electrons inside atoms near the wall's surface are repelled toward the far side of each atom. The wall's atoms become **polarized**—one end positive, the other negative (Figure 14.7). The balloon is both attracted to the positive side of each atom and repelled by the negative side. The attractive force is stronger because the positive side of each atom is closer to the balloon than the negative side. The balloon "sticks" to the wall.

Conductors If the balloon is brought toward a doorknob or other conductor, it doesn't stay. Electrons in the doorknob can move freely, so they repel to the opposite side of the doorknob as the negative balloon approaches. The side of the doorknob near the balloon becomes positively charged. The balloon first attracts the doorknob. But when the two touch, some of the balloon's excess electrons move onto the doorknob because it is a conductor. When the doorknob gains electrons, it becomes negative—like the balloon—and they repel.

Charging by induction *Charging by induction* is a method of using one object to charge another without changing the net charge on the first (Figure 14.8). Suppose you hold a negative balloon close to an electroscope. The balloon repels the electroscope's electrons, so they move down into the leaves. If you touch the ball, "*grounding*" the electroscope, electrons are repelled onto your finger. If you remove your finger, the electroscope is left with a net positive charge.

polarized - describes the separation of positive and negative charge in an object's atoms

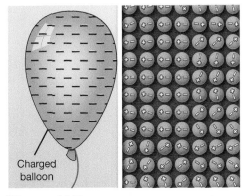

Figure 14.7: *A negative balloon sticks to a neutral wall.*

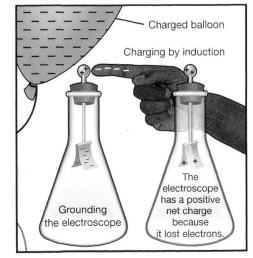

Figure 14.8: *When a balloon charges the electroscope through induction, the charge on the balloon is not disturbed.*

14.1 Section Review

1. Explain how there can be charge inside matter, yet the matter is electrically neutral.
2. According to Coulomb's law, what happens to the force between two charges if the distance between them is tripled?
3. When you charge a balloon by friction, why can it stick to a wall but not to a doorknob?

14.2 Electric Current, Resistance, and Voltage

Earlier, you read that electric current is what flows and does work. We can now say current is the *movement* of electric charge. Electric charge is always there, but it may not be moving. Current flows when charges move. One amp is a flow of 1 coulomb per second. Higher current means more charge flows per second. For example, a current of 10 amps means that 10 coulombs of charge flow every second.

Charge and current

Current is the flow of charge Electric current is the flow of charge. If the current in a wire is 1 amp, 1 coulomb of charge passes by a point in the wire in 1 second. The unit *amp* is a shorter way of saying "coulomb per second."

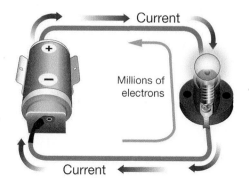

Figure 14.9: *Conventional current versus electron flow.*

> *If the current in a wire is 1 amp, 1 coulomb of charge passes by a point in the wire in 1 second.*

Positive and negative Benjamin Franklin first used the terms *positive* and *negative* to describe charge. He believed electricity was a type of fluid. He thought positive objects had too much and negative objects had too little of the fluid. According to Franklin's theory, a positive object's extra fluid naturally flowed toward a negative object. The flow would stop when each had the right amount and became neutral.

The direction of current Because of Franklin's work, the direction of electric current is defined as going *from positive to negative*. Long after Franklin's work, scientists discovered that current in wires is the flow of *electrons*. The direction in which electrons move in a circuit is *from negative to positive*, opposite the way current was defined earlier (Figure 14.9).

Current is from positive to negative We still define current as going from positive to negative. For ordinary electric circuits it does not matter that negative electrons are really moving the other way. In a conductive liquid such as salt water, both positive and negative charges can move to create current. No matter what the sign of the moving charges, conventional current is defined as moving from positive voltage to negative voltage.

Positive and negative history

Image courtesy of NOAA.

The terms *positive* and *negative* were first used by Benjamin Franklin (1706–1790). After coining the terms, Franklin theorized that electricity is a result of the presence of a single fluid in different amounts. Although scientists no longer believe that electricity is caused by different kinds of fluids, the words *positive* and *negative* are still used to describe the two types of charge.

The source of current

Electron motion   In a conducting metal like copper, the atoms of copper bond together by sharing electrons. In some ways, a solid piece of copper acts like a single large molecule. Some of the electrons can move freely anywhere within the copper. The copper atoms (⊕) with the remaining electrons are bonded together and stay fixed in place.

If a copper wire is not connected to a battery, the free electrons move around at high speeds. They have no net motion because as many move one way as the other way. However, the free electrons move energy very effectively, so metals are good conductors of heat as well as electricity.

Drift velocity   If a battery is connected to a copper wire, the free electrons are attracted to the battery's positive terminal and repelled by its negative terminal. However, the electrons do not move directly from one end of the wire to the other because of the copper atoms present. Instead, the electrons bounce off the atoms while slowly making their way toward the positive end of the battery. A force created by the battery voltage causes a slow electron "drift" in one direction, in addition to the electrons' random bouncing (Figure 14.10). This *drift velocity* is what creates electrical current. The bouncing transfers some energy from the drifting motion to the fixed copper atoms. This explains why wires "heat up" when current is passed through them.

The source of current-carrying electrons   With a 1.5-volt battery, the drift velocity is only a few millimeters per second. So why does the bulb light up instantly? The electrons carrying current in a wire *do not come from the battery*. Current flows because the voltage from a battery makes electrons move *that are already in the wire*. This is why a light bulb goes on as soon as you flip the switch. A copper wire contains many electrons bouncing randomly. Without an applied voltage, as many electrons bounce one way as the other. There is no net flow of electrons and no electrical current. When a voltage is applied, *all* of the free electrons in the wire start drifting, including those already in the bulb.

No voltage
Electrons have only random motion
No average current

Applied voltage
Electrons have random motion plus small drift velocity
Current flows

⊕ Fixed atom   ⬅—⚫ Mobile electron

Figure 14.10: *When a voltage is applied to a wire, electrons slowly drift while randomly colliding with atoms in the wire.*

Conductors and insulators

Insulators The electrons in insulators are not free to move—they are tightly bound inside atoms (Figure 14.11). The atoms in insulators are fixed in place, and so are their electrons. Insulators have very high resistance because there are no free electrons to carry current.

Semiconductors A semiconductor has some free electrons, but not nearly as many as a conductor. Semiconductors have a resistance value between conductors and insulators. The diagram below shows a model of the atoms and electrons in conductors, semiconductors, and insulators. The arrows on the electrons show the direction of their drift velocity but not of their random bouncing.

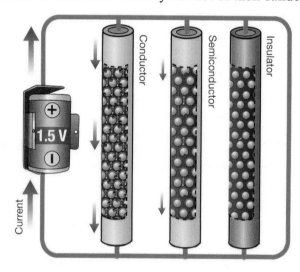

superconductor - a material that becomes a conductor with zero resistance at very low temperatures

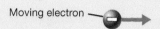

Electrical current is usually carried by moving electrons; atoms stay fixed in place.

In an insulator, the electrons are tightly bound to atoms and cannot move.

In a conductor, the electrons come free and can move to create electrical current. Since electrons are negative, they move in the opposite direction to the current.

Figure 14.11: *In a conductor, some of an atom's electrons are free to move. In an insulator, all of the electrons are tightly bound to their atoms.*

Superconductors Some materials become **superconductors** when they are cooled to very low temperatures. For example, the metal alloy niobium-zirconium becomes a superconductor at −262°C. A superconductor carries electrical current with *zero resistance*. A current in a loop of superconducting wire will flow forever without an energy source! An electric motor made with superconducting wires would be far more efficient than one made with copper wires. Physicists are searching for superconductors that work at room temperatures so that expensive cooling equipment is unneeded. Claims for the discovery of such materials are so far unfounded.

Voltage and charge

Current and voltage   Earlier you learned that current flows in response to differences in voltage. If one point in a circuit is at 3 volts and another is at 0 volts, current will flow toward the point at 0 volts and away from the point at 3 volts. Now, you know that current is actually moving charge. How do we understand voltage in terms of charges?

A volt is a joule per coulomb   Voltage measures electrical potential energy *per unit of charge*. One volt is 1 joule per coulomb. That means 1 coulomb of charge that moves through a difference of 1 volt gains or loses 1 joule of potential energy. The charge *loses* 1 joule if it goes from higher voltage to lower voltage. This is what happens in a device that uses energy, like a light bulb. The charge *gains* 1 joule if it moves from lower voltage to higher voltage. This is what happens inside a battery. A battery transforms chemical energy to electrical energy (Figure 14.12).

Joules or watts?   This updated definition of a volt is really the same as the earlier one. In terms of charge, 1 volt is 1 joule per coulomb. But, 1 amp is 1 coulomb per second, and 1 watt is 1 joule per second. If you work through the units as shown using this information, you can see that 1 joule per coulomb of charge is exactly the same as 1 watt per amp of current.

$$\text{Volt} = \frac{\text{Watt}}{\text{Amp}} = \frac{\dfrac{\text{Joule}}{\text{Second}}}{\dfrac{\text{Coulomb}}{\text{Second}}} = \frac{\dfrac{\text{Joule}}{\text{Second}}}{\dfrac{\text{Coulomb}}{\text{Second}}} = \frac{\text{Joule}}{\text{Coulomb}}$$

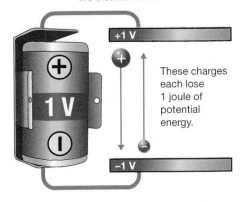

A charge does work, and loses potential energy when it moves in the direction of the the electric force.

These charges each lose 1 joule of potential energy.

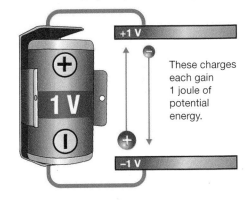

Work must be done on a charge to move it against the direction of the electric force, so the charge gains potential energy.

These charges each gain 1 joule of potential energy.

Figure 14.12: *A charge of 1 coulomb can either gain or lose 1 joule of energy by moving across a voltage difference of 1 volt.*

14.2 Section Review

1. Why is conventional current flow defined as moving from positive to negative when current in a wire is actually a flow of electrons from negative to positive?
2. If electron drift velocity is so slow, why does a bulb light immediately upon closing a switch?
3. What is it about an insulator's atoms that causes it to have such high resistance?
4. What is a volt in terms of joules and coulombs?

14.3 Capacitors

So far, the circuits you have studied have contained only wires, batteries, switches, and resistors, such as bulbs. In these circuits, the current stops immediately when the source of voltage is removed. This section discusses a device called a *capacitor* which stores charge. If the voltage is removed from a circuit containing a capacitor, the current keeps going for a while, until all the capacitor's stored charge has flowed out. Almost all electric appliances, including televisions, cameras, and computers, use capacitors in their circuits. Capacitors are a useful tool for investigating the relationship between electric charge, voltage, and current.

capacitor - a device that stores electric charge by keeping positive and negative charges separated

A capacitor is an energy-storage device

A capacitor stores energy   A **capacitor** is a device that stores electrical energy by keeping positive and negative charges separated. The simplest type of capacitor is made of two parallel conducting "plates" with an insulator between them. Both plates of the capacitor are neutral (zero net charge) to begin with. Energy is stored in the capacitor by transferring electrons from one plate to the other. The greater the number of electrons transferred, the greater the amount of stored energy. The plate that gains electrons gets a net negative charge. The plate that loses electrons gets an equal but opposite net positive charge.

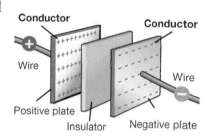

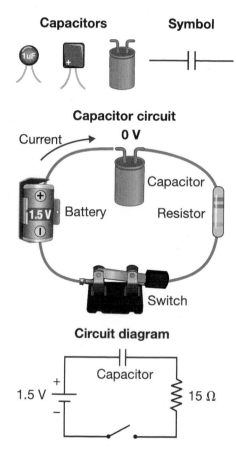

Using a capacitor's stored energy   Once a capacitor's plates are charged, it has a voltage and can drive current in a circuit. A capacitor is connected just like a battery (Figure 14.13). (Its electronic symbol is similar to a battery's, too, but *not* the same.) The positive plate attracts free electrons, and the negative plate repels them. This creates a voltage, and current flows out of the capacitor from positive to negative just as it would with a battery. Eventually the positive plate has gained enough electrons for it to be neutral and the negative plate has lost all of its excess electrons. The current stops and the voltage of the capacitor drops to zero. A camera flash uses a capacitor in this way. When you press the button to take a picture, you close the circuit between the flash and a charged capacitor. The current is large, so the capacitor's energy is converted very quickly in a flash.

Figure 14.13: *A simple circuit with a resistor, capacitor, switch, and battery.*

Charging a capacitor

Equal and opposite charges We say a capacitor is *charged* when one of its plates has a positive net charge and the other has a net negative charge. The amount of charge on each plate is the same, but opposite in sign. Suppose one plate has a charge of +2 coulombs and the other has a charge of −2 coulombs. We say this capacitor's charge is 2 coulombs. However, the net charge of the *whole* capacitor is zero no matter how many electrons are transferred between the plates.

A battery can charge a capacitor A capacitor can be charged by connecting it to a battery or another voltage source. In Figure 14.14, a capacitor, bulb, battery, and switch are connected in series. The capacitor starts with zero charge and has zero voltage across its terminals. When the switch is closed, current flows and the capacitor builds up a charge separation on its plates. As the capacitor charges, a voltage develops across its terminals. The voltage keeps increasing until the capacitor has the same voltage as the battery. At this point, the capacitor has stored as much charge as it can from the battery.

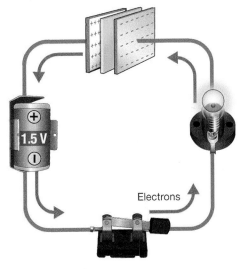

Figure 14.14: *A battery can be used to charge a capacitor.*

Current and voltage while charging a capacitor The bulb is bright at first, but gradually dims and then goes out. The current in the circuit starts high and decreases over time. The current decreases because the battery voltage attracts negative charge to one side of the capacitor. The negative charge attracts an equal amount of positive charge to the other side. As charge "builds up" in the capacitor, it creates a voltage difference between the two terminals of the capacitor. Charge continues to fill up the capacitor until the capacitor voltage is equal and opposite to the battery voltage.

Current and voltage change with time As the capacitor charges, the current in the circuit decreases. This is because the current flow is proportional to the voltage difference between the battery and the capacitor. As the voltage on the capacitor increases, the circuit's voltage difference decreases and so does its flow of current. The graphs in Figure 14.15 show how the current and voltage change together in the circuit.

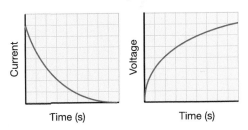

Figure 14.15: *How current and voltage change over time while a capacitor charges.*

Voltage of a charged capacitor A fully-charged capacitor has equal amounts of positive and negative charge. Because both kinds of charge are present but separated, a capacitor develops a voltage across its two terminals, like a battery. The voltage across a fully-charged capacitor is equal and opposite to the voltage applied to the circuit.

Capacitance

Voltage and charge
The amount of charge a capacitor will hold before the current stops depends on the voltage of the source that charges it. Voltage is what pushes the electrons onto the negative plate and pulls them from the positive plate. The higher the voltage, the greater the amount of charge on the capacitor when the current stops.

Measuring capacitance
The amount of charge a capacitor will hold also depends on its **capacitance**. Capacitance is the measure of a capacitor's ability to store charge. It is measured in **farads** (F). A 1-farad capacitor attached to a 1-volt battery holds 1 coulomb of charge. A 2-farad capacitor attached to the same battery holds 2 coulombs of charge.

Microfarads
A coulomb is a huge amount of charge. Most capacitors hold much less than a coulomb of charge and they have capacitances that are only a fraction of a farad. For this reason, capacitances are often measured in microfarads. One microfarad is 1×10^{-6} farad. A capacitor that supplies energy to a point-and-shoot camera flash has a capacitance of about 200 microfarads and holds 0.02 coulombs of charge.

Factors determining capacitance
The capacitance of a capacitor depends on three factors (Figure 14.16):

1. The greater the area of a capacitor's plates, the more charge it can hold, and the larger the capacitance.
2. The insulating material between the plates affects how much charge can be stored in a capacitor.
3. The smaller the separation distance between the plates, the greater the capacitance.

Parallel plates are not practical
Parallel plate capacitors are not practical to use in most devices because they must be large to store enough charge to be useful. If a capacitor's plates and insulating material are made of a flexible material, it can be rolled into the shape of a cylinder (Figure 14.17). This allows each plate to have a large area that fits into a small space.

> **capacitance** - a measure of a capacitor's ability to store charge
>
> **farad** - a unit of capacitance

Three factors determine a capacitor's capacitance

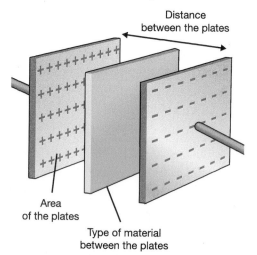

Figure 14.16: *Three factors determine a capacitor's capacitance.*

Capacitors

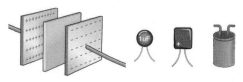

Figure 14.17: *There are many types of capacitors.*

Discharging a capacitor

Discharging a capacitor   A capacitor can be discharged by connecting it to any closed circuit that allows current to flow. A low-resistance circuit discharges the capacitor more quickly because the current is higher. Electrons are quickly removed from the negative plate and added to the positive plate. A capacitor is fully discharged when the two plates are both neutral and the net voltage is zero.

Designing circuits   When using a capacitor that will be charged and discharged, the circuit can be designed to change from charging to discharging with the flip of a switch. In the circuit shown at right, the capacitor charges when the switch is at position A. When it is flipped to position B, the battery is cut off and the capacitor discharges through the light bulb. The bulb dims at a rate that depends on the capacitor's capacitance.

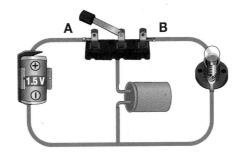

Capacitor safety   If connected in a circuit with a low resistance, a capacitor can discharge very quickly, creating a large amount of current. This can be very useful in devices that require a brief burst of a large amount of current for their operation. However, this can also make such capacitors very dangerous. When working with a capacitor, *never* pick it up by its terminals if it has just been used; you could receive a dangerous shock! It is important to always fully discharge a capacitor when you finish working with it.

14.3 Section Review

1. What is the purpose of the parallel plates in a simple capacitor?
2. Suppose a capacitor is charged by a 1.5-V battery. When will the capacitor have stored as much charge as it can?
3. After a capacitor is fully charged, what happens to its current over time? What happens to its voltage over time?
4. What happens to a capacitor's capacitance if the plate area is increased? Why?
5. Why can capacitors be dangerous?

Defibrillators

If you have ever seen doctors working on television or in a movie, you may have seen a *defibrillator*. A defibrillator uses an electric current to make a patient's heart start beating after a heart attack or other trauma.

A defibrillator uses a capacitor to create a very large current. Before using a defibrillator, a doctor must wait briefly for the capacitor to charge. If a patient's heart doesn't start after one attempt, the voltage across the capacitor is increased. This provides more current to stimulate the heart. Small portable defibrillators are now being placed in schools, airports, and other public buildings. They have saved many lives by allowing trained people to help heart attack victims even before paramedics arrive.

Lightning

Have you ever scuffed your feet across a carpeted floor and then touched a metal doorknob? Zap! You feel a static electric shock, and if the room is dark, you can see a quick flash of light.

The zap happens because contact between your shoes and the carpet transfers some of the carpet atoms' electrons to your shoes. Your body acquires an excess negative charge. When you touch a conducting object like the doorknob, the excess charge moves from your hand to the metal in a flash.

Believe it or not, the same process that caused you to get zapped when you touched the doorknob creates the spectacular lightning displays you see on a stormy evening.

How does lightning get started?

Lightning originates in towering, dark storm clouds. Inside these clouds, charges begin to separate. Scientists still don't really understand how this happens. Some think that collisions between hailstones and ice crystals are responsible, while others speculate that

friction between particles of ice and raindrops causes electrons to be ripped from some of the atoms.

While the mechanism is still a mystery, we do know that the bottom of the cloud acquires an excess negative charge, like your feet after you scuff them on the carpet. Warm updrafts carry the positively-charged particles to the cloud's top.

The buildup of negative charges at the bottom of the cloud repels negative charges in the ground and attracts positive charges. The positively-charged ground surface pulls the cloud's freed electrons downward. On their way down, these electrons crash into air molecules, knocking even more electrons out of place. All of these electrons would continue hurling snowball-like toward the earth, if it weren't for a tug-of-war that begins with the positively-charged particles in the top of the cloud.

The stepped leader

Those positive charges at the top of the cloud tend to pull slower-moving electrons back upward. But remember, as the storm develops, more charges separate in the cloud. Newly-freed electrons pull the slow movers down again. This tug-of-war causes the initial downward path of electrons to move toward the ground in jerky 45-meter sections, or steps. This pathway is called the *stepped leader*.

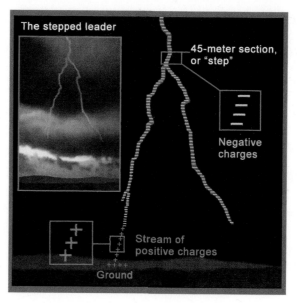

The stepped leader

45-meter section, or "step"

Negative charges

Stream of positive charges

Ground

Sometimes the stepped leader continues all the way down to the ground, but at other times, it will pull a stream of positive charges up to meet it about 100 meters above the ground. The stepped leader moves at about 390 kilometers per second, and takes about five thousandths (0.005) of a second to reach the ground. You can't see the stepped leader without using a special camera, because it moves so quickly and doesn't produce a lot of light.

A wire of plasma

The stepped leader is created as electrons knock other electrons off of air molecules. When these air molecules break apart, you end up with a pathway made of positive ions surrounded by a "sea" of electrons. That's a bit like what you find in a wire made of metal. The stepped leader creates a "wire" of *plasma*—the so-called "fourth" state of matter, made up of ionized gas—in the atmosphere. This plasma wire, with all its freed electrons, conducts electricity extremely well.

The return stroke

Once the stepped leader is connected to the ground, a surge of electrons moves along the plasma wire from cloud to ground, traveling 98,000 kilometers per second! The air glows like a bright fluorescent light. This "return stroke" is the lightning you see.

The return stroke

Plasma "wire" creates path for return stroke

Stepped leader connected to ground

Ground

The return stroke drains the cloud of its freed electrons, but more charges are continually being separated in the cloud. As a result, an average of four lightning bolts in a row zing along a single path. That's why lightning sometimes seems to flicker.

Volts, amps, and lightning

Lightning bolts can deliver between 15 million and 1 billion volts of electricity. Although the flow of charge is very brief, the current has been estimated at about 50,000 amps. That much current can cause a great deal of damage. If a lightning bolt strikes a tree, the sap may boil, and the buildup of vapor pressure can cause the tree to explode.

QUESTIONS

1. Name two ways a lightning bolt is like a static shock.

2. How does the stepped leader process create a "plasma wire" in the atmosphere as a pathway for lightning?

3. Find out how to stay safe during a lightning storm. Create a poster with lightning safety tips.

Chapter 14 Review

Understanding Vocabulary

Select the correct term to complete the sentences.

capacitance	Coulomb's law	polarized
capacitor	electroscope	static electricity
coulomb	farads	superconductor

1. _____ exists when there is an excess of one type of charge on an object.

2. _____ explains the relationship between electric force, charge, and distance.

3. A(n) _____ can be used to tell whether an object has a net charge.

4. A(n) _____ carries electrical current with zero resistance.

5. A(n) _____ is used to store electrical energy by separating charge.

6. Capacitance is measured in _____.

Reviewing Concepts

Section 14.1

1. Protons are _____ charged, and electrons are _____ charged.

2. Like charges _____, and opposite charges _____.

3. What does it mean to say an object is electrically neutral?

4. Is an object's net charge positive or negative if it loses electrons? Why?

5. How many protons are needed to make 1 C of charge?

6. How does the charge of an electron compare to the charge of a proton?

7. Why don't you usually notice electric forces between objects?

8. What two factors determine the amount of electric force between two charged objects?

9. What happens to the electric force between two charges as they are moved closer together?

10. Explain what happens to the force between two protons if each of the following occurs. Consider each one individually.

    a. The distance between them is cut in half.

    b. The distance between them is doubled.

    c. The distance between them is tripled.

    d. One of the protons is replaced with an electron.

    e. The two protons are replaced with two electrons.

11. Compare Coulomb's law to Newton's law of gravitation.

12. Explain what happens inside an electroscope if a positively-charged object is held above it without touching.

13. What happens to the charges in your hair and a balloon if you rub them together? What is this called?

14. Explain how to charge an electroscope positively through induction.

Section 14.2

15. How are the units *ampere* and *coulomb* related?

16. Ben Franklin defined current as going from _____ to _____. Now we know that electrons in a circuit move from _____ to _____.

17. Do all electrons in a wire move to make the current in a circuit?

18. Does a battery supply the electrons to a circuit that create a current? Explain.

19. Why can current easily be created in a conductor but not in an insulator?

20. One volt equals 1 _____ of energy per _____ of charge. A volt is also equal to 1 _____ of power per _____ of current.

Section 14.3

21. What is a capacitor? What are some uses of capacitors?

22. What does it mean to say a capacitor is charged?

23. What happens to the current in a circuit as a capacitor charges? Why?

24. List the three factors that affect a capacitor's capacitance.

Solving Problems

Section 14.1

1. What is the charge of 1,000 electrons, measured in coulombs?

2. Find the net charge of an atom that contains

    a. 5 protons and 3 electrons.

    b. 7 electrons and 6 protons.

    c. 8 electrons and 8 protons.

3. Two charged objects, each with a charge of 2.5×10^{-6} C, are separated by 2 m. Calculate the electric force between the objects.

4. Two charged objects have equal charge. The electric force between the objects is 9 N when they are held 3 m apart. What are the charges of the objects?

Section 14.2

5. Six coulombs of charge pass through a wire in a time of 2 s. What is the current in the wire?

6. A wire carries a current of 2 A. How many coulombs of charge pass through the wire in 10 s?

Section 14.3

7. Draw a circuit diagram containing a 3-V battery, a 12-Ω resistor, a capacitor, and a switch.

8. One plate of a charged capacitor has a charge of –1 C. What is the charge of the second plate? What is the net charge on the whole capacitor?

Test Practice

Section 14.1

1. You rub a balloon on your hair. The balloon gains electrons. Which of the following is a *true* statement?

    a. Your hair is electrically neutral.

    b. Your hair is negatively charged.

    c. Your hair is positively charged.

    d. Your hair and the balloon have the same charge.

2. The electric force between two charges is F. If you double the distance between the two charges, what would the new electric force be?

    a. ¼ F

    b. ½ F

    c. F

    d. $2F$

3. When an electroscope is negatively charged, the two thin "leaves" of metal will

    a. stay together as the negative charges repel each other.

    b. stay together as the negative charges attract each other.

    c. separate as the negative charges repel each other.

    d. separate as the negative charges attract each other.

4. An object is _____ when the positive and negative charges are separated.

    a. neutral

    b. polarized

    c. static

    d. charged

Section 14.2

5. If the current in a wire is 1 A, 1 _____ of charge passes by a point in the wire in 1 s.

   a. farad

   b. coulomb

   c. volt

   d. newton

6. Current in a copper wire is the movement of

   a. electrons.

   b. protons.

   c. atoms.

   d. fluid.

7. Materials where electrons are tightly bound inside atoms are called

   a. conductors.

   b. semiconductors.

   c. superconductors.

   d. insulators.

8. A joule per coulomb is 1

   a. watt.

   b. volt.

   c. amp.

   d. newton.

Section 14.3

9. The graph shows current versus time for

   a. a capacitor charging.

   b. a capacitor discharging.

   c. a conductor charging.

   d. a conductor discharging.

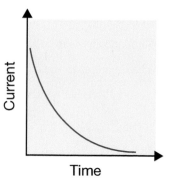

10. Capacitance is measured in

    a. ohms.

    b. coulombs.

    c. farads.

    d. amps.

11. The capacitance of a capacitor is determined by all of the following *except*

    a. the insulating material between the plates.

    b. the area of the plates.

    c. the distance between the plates.

    d. the flexibility of the plate material.

Applying Your Knowledge

Section 14.1

1. Static cling causes clothes to stick together when they come out of the dryer. What kinds of materials seem to stick together the most?

2. Static electricity is more often observed in dry weather than in damp weather. Why do you think this is?

3. How did Coulomb measure the force between electric charges? Research this topic and write a report that gives the answer.

4. Conduct an experiment at home in which you charge an object by friction. You might use a balloon and hair or fleece, polystyrene foam and wool, or plastic and a tissue. Turn on a faucet so a narrow stream of water is created. Hold the charged object near the stream of water. What happens? What do you think is going on? (*Hint*: Water molecules are naturally polarized.)

Section 14.2

5. Research the topic of *superconductivity*. Find out what it is and what applications it may have in the future.

Section 14.3

6. Use the Internet to research capacitors. Describe their applications in different electrical devices.

 *Your Turn* **Answers**

Using Coulomb's law (Section 14.1, page 343)

a. 563 N

b. 432,000 N

Magnetism

Have you ever used a compass? A compass is very handy when you are on an open body of water with no land in sight, and you are trying to make sure you are headed in the right direction. It is also a good idea to have a compass with you if you are hiking. Some automobiles now come equipped with a built-in compass, and some even use more sophisticated Global Positioning System (GPS) technology, which uses satellites rather than magnetic fields to determine direction.

How does a compass work? A simple compass is really nothing more than a lightweight magnet, in the shape of a pointer, that is mounted on a very low-friction pivot point. Earth, with its molten iron and nickel core, acts as though a giant magnet was buried deep inside, with the south pole end of the magnet located at the Geographic North Pole. When you hold a compass in your hand, (and there is no other magnet nearby), the small pivoting magnet in the compass will be attracted by the Geographic North Pole of Earth, and it will "point" north.

In this chapter, you will learn how magnets and magnetic fields work, and you will explore the source of magnetism. As with electricity, the source of magnetism can be traced back to atoms!

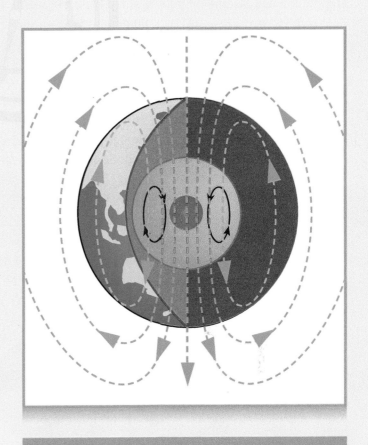

VOCABULARY

compass	magnetic declination	magnetic pole
electromagnet	magnetic domain	permanent magnet
gauss	magnetic field	right-hand rule
hard magnet	magnetic field line	soft magnet
magnetic		

KEY QUESTIONS

✓ *How can a magnet be strong enough to lift a car?*

✓ *What is the biggest magnet on Earth?*

✓ *How does a compass work?*

15.1 Properties of Magnets

Magnetism has fascinated people since the earliest times. We know that magnets stick to steel refrigerator doors and pick up paper clips or pins. They are also found in electric motors, computer disk drives, burglar alarm systems, and many other common devices. This chapter explains magnetic force, some of the properties of magnets, and magnetic materials.

What is a magnet?

Magnets and magnetic materials
If a material is **magnetic**, it has the ability to exert forces on magnets or other magnetic materials. A refrigerator magnet is attracted to the steel in the refrigerator's door or sides. A *magnet* is a material that produces magnetism by itself. *Magnetic materials* are affected by magnets but do not produce magnetism. Iron and steel are magnetic materials that can also be made magnetic.

Permanent magnets
A **permanent magnet** is a material that keeps its magnetic properties even when it is not close to other magnets. Bar magnets, refrigerator magnets, and horseshoe magnets are good examples of permanent magnets.

> **magnetic** - the ability to exert forces on magnets or other magnetic materials
>
> **permanent magnet** - a material that retains its magnetic properties even when no external energy is supplied
>
> **magnetic pole** - north or south; one of the two opposite places on a magnet where the magnetic field is the strongest; all magnets have at least one north pole and one south pole

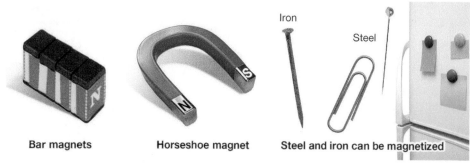

Bar magnets   Horseshoe magnet   Steel and iron can be magnetized

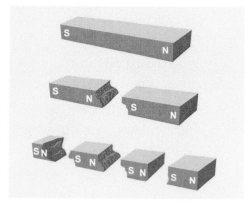

Figure 15.1: *If a magnet is cut in half, each half will have both a north pole and a south pole.*

Poles
The location on a magnet where the magnetic field is the strongest is called a **magnetic pole**. All magnets have two opposite magnetic poles, called the north pole and south pole. If a magnet is cut in half, each half will have its own north and south poles (Figure 15.1). It is impossible to have only a north or south pole by itself. The north and south poles are like the two sides of a coin. You cannot have a one-sided coin, and you cannot have a north magnetic pole without a south magnetic pole.

The magnetic force

Attraction and repulsion   When near each other, magnets exert forces on each other. Two magnets can either attract or repel. Whether the force between two magnets is attractive or repulsive depends on which poles face each other. If two opposite poles face each other, the magnets attract. If two like poles face each other, the magnets repel.

The three interactions between two magnets

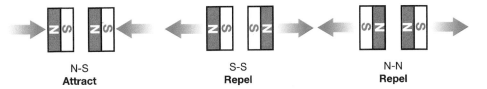

N-S	S-S	N-N
Attract	**Repel**	**Repel**

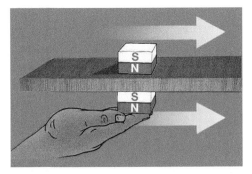

Figure 15.2: *One magnet attracts and can move another magnet even when there is a material like wood between them.*

Most materials are transparent to magnetic forces   Magnetic forces can pass through many materials with no apparent decrease in strength. For example, one magnet can drag another magnet even when there is a piece of wood between them (Figure 15.2). Plastics, wood, and most insulating materials are transparent to magnetic forces. Conducting metals, such as aluminum, also allow magnetic forces to pass through, but may change the forces. Iron, cobalt, and nickel, metals that are near each other on the periodic table, have strong magnetic properties.

Metals with magnetic properties

Fe	Co	Ni
26	27	28
iron	cobalt	nickel

Using magnetic forces   Magnetic forces are used in many applications because they are relatively easy to create and can be very strong. There are large magnets that create forces strong enough to lift a car (Figure 15.3). Small magnets are everywhere. For example, some doors are sealed with magnetic weather stripping that blocks out drafts. There are several patents for magnetic zippers, and many handbags, briefcases, and cabinet doors close with magnetic latches. Many everyday devices rely on magnetic forces to make objects attract or repel one another.

Figure 15.3: *Powerful magnets are used to lift discarded cars in a junkyard.*

The magnetic field

How to describe magnetic forces   Two magnets create forces on each other at a distance much larger than the size of the magnets. How do you describe these forces everywhere around a magnet? One way is with a formula that is similar to Newton's law of universal gravitation. Unfortunately, magnetic forces are more complex than gravity because magnets can attract and repel. Gravity can only attract. Also, magnets have two poles. That means part of the same magnet feels an attracting force and part feels a repelling force.

The test magnet   A convenient way to show the magnetic force around a magnet is with a drawing. The standard drawing shows the force acting on the north pole of an imaginary test magnet. The test magnet is so small that it does not affect the magnetic force. Also, since the test magnet is imaginary, we can let it have only a north pole. Having only one pole makes it easier to visualize the direction of the magnetic forces (Figure 15.4).

Drawing the force   The diagram at the right shows a drawing of the magnetic force around a magnet. The force points away from the north pole because a north pole would be repelled from a north pole. The force points toward the south pole because a north pole magnet would be attracted. How does Figure 15.4 relate to this diagram?

Magnetic field

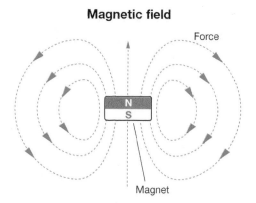

The magnetic field   The drawing also shows what physicists call the **magnetic field**. A *field* in physics is a quantity that has a value at all points in space. A magnet creates a field because it creates a force on other magnets at all points around itself. The interaction between two magnets really occurs in two steps. First, a magnet creates a magnetic field. Then, the magnetic field creates forces on other magnets. In the drawing, the field is represented by the arrows and lines.

> **magnetic field** - the magnetic forces that surround an object at all points in space

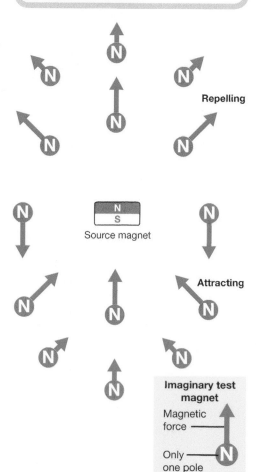

Figure 15.4: *The force on an imaginary test magnet near a source magnet.*

Drawing the magnetic field

Describing magnetic force The magnetic field is a *force field*, because it represents forces at all points in space. Every magnet creates a magnetic field in the space around it. The magnetic field then creates forces on other magnets.

Field lines The magnet that creates a field is called the *source magnet*. In the standard drawing of a magnetic field, the arrows for the imaginary test magnet's field are connected by lines. Each line is called a **magnetic field line**. Magnetic field lines point in the direction of the force on an imaginary north pole test magnet. Magnetic field lines always point from the north to the south pole.

> *Magnetic field lines always point away from a magnet's north pole and toward its south pole.*

Understanding magnetic field lines A field line must start on a north pole and finish on a south pole. You cannot just "stop" a field line anywhere. In the drawing in Figure 15.5, notice that the field lines spread out as they get farther from the source magnet. If field lines are close together, the force is stronger at that location. If field lines are farther apart, the force is weaker. The field lines spread out because the force from a magnet gets weaker as the distance from the magnet increases.

How a magnetic field affects another magnet Figure 15.5 shows how a magnetic field affects another magnet. Magnets A and C feel a net attracting force toward the source magnet. The north pole of magnet A does feel a repelling force, but the south pole of magnet A is closer to the north pole of the source magnet, so the net force is attracting. Magnets B and D feel a twisting force, or torque, because one pole is repelled and the opposite pole is attracted with approximately the same strength.

> **magnetic field line** - one of many lines with arrows used to show the direction of the forces in a magnetic field; magnetic field lines always point away from a magnet's north pole and toward a magnet's south pole

How a magnetic field affects another magnet

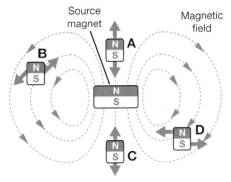

Figure 15.5: *Forces are exerted on both poles of another magnet in a magnetic field.*

15.1 Section Review

1. Is it possible for a magnet to have a south pole without a north pole? Explain your answer.
2. Describe the interaction between each pair of magnetic poles: two north poles; a north and south pole; two south poles.
3. What does the spacing of magnetic field lines mean? Where are forces strongest on a magnet?
4. Give an example of an everyday object that works using magnetic force.

15.2 The Source of Magnetism

Magnets attract and repel each other but only *attract* objects such as steel paper clips and nails. This is related to the objects' atoms. Moving charges, either in an electric current or in the atoms that make up a material, create magnetism. This section takes a closer look at how this happens.

Electromagnets

A coil of wire An **electromagnet** is a magnet created by electric current flowing in wires. A simple electromagnet is a coil of wire wrapped around an iron core (Figure 15.6). When the coil is connected to a battery, current flows and a magnetic field appears around the coil. The iron core "concentrates" the magnetic field created by the current in the coil.

Finding the poles with the right-hand rule The north and south poles of an electromagnet are at each end of the coil. Which end is the north pole depends on the direction of the electric current. When the fingers of your right hand curl in the direction of current, your thumb points toward the magnet's north pole. This method of finding the magnetic poles is called the **right-hand rule**.

Advantages of electromagnets Electromagnets have some advantages over permanent magnets. You can switch an electromagnet on and off by switching the current on and off. An electromagnet's north and south poles are reversed by switching the direction of the current in the coil. The strength of an electromagnet's field can be changed by changing the amount of current in the coil. Electromagnets made of copper wound around iron are also more durable than permanent magnets. For example, neodymium permanent magnets are brittle and break easily.

How electromagnets can be used Electromagnets are used in the mechanisms of some toasters and fire doors. For a toaster, the switch you press down turns on the heating circuit and sends current to an electromagnet. An electromagnet attracts a spring-loaded metal tray to the bottom of the toaster. A timer signals that the bread is done toasting, and the electromagnet's current is cut off. This releases the tray, which pops the bread out of the toaster. Fire doors in office building and school hallways are held open with electromagnets. During a fire (or fire drill), the current to the electromagnets is cut off so that these special doors close to prevent fire and fumes from spreading.

electromagnet - a magnet created by electric current flowing in wires

right-hand rule - a method used to identify the direction of a magnetic field

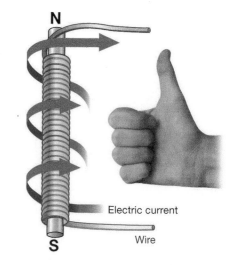

Figure 15.6: *An electromagnet.*

Direction of current

When a wire is connected to a battery, electric current flows out of the positive end of the battery and returns to the negative end.

Building an electromagnet

Wire and a nail   An electromagnet can be made by wrapping wire around an iron nail and connecting it to an electric circuit (Figure 15.7). When current flows in the wire, the nail and coil become magnetic. The direction of current is shown in Figure 15.7. Can you determine which end of the nail is the north pole using the right-hand rule? Where is the north pole if you reverse the connections to the battery, making the current go the opposite direction? (*Note*: In this setup, do not keep the circuit closed longer than a few seconds since the circuit generates heat and will use up the battery's energy quickly.)

Increase the strength of an electromagnet   There are two ways you can make an electromagnetic field stronger:

1. You can add a second battery to increase the current.
2. You can add more turns of wire to the coil around the nail.

Field is proportional to current   The strength of the magnetic field is directly proportional to the amount of current flowing around the nail. If you double the current, the strength of the magnetic field doubles.

Adding turns of wire   Adding turns of wire to a coil increases the field because the magnetic fields around the turns of wire cross and reinforce each other. The effect is proportional to the number of turns. Two turns doubles the strength of the magnetic field. Three turns triples it. The current in the wire, however, remains the same throughout the wire as you add turns.

Resistance   Adding more turns to a coil increases electrical resistance. More turns means a greater length of wire. Resistance increases as the wire's length increases, so more energy is lost as heat. Electromagnets must be designed with this in mind. Using larger-gauge wire also reduces resistance.

Factors affecting the field   The magnetic field of a simple electromagnet depends on three factors: the amount of electric current in the wire, the amount and type of material in the core of the electromagnet, and the number of turns of wire in the coil (Figure 15.8). In more sophisticated electromagnets, the shape, size, and material of the core, and the winding pattern of the coil can be specially designed to control the strength and shape of the magnetic field.

A simple electromagnet

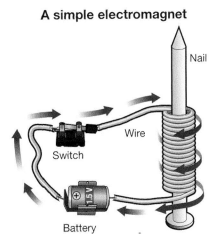

Figure 15.7: *Making an electromagnet from a nail, wire, and a battery.*

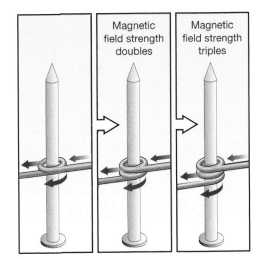

Figure 15.8: *Adding turns of wire increases the magnetic-field strength of an electromagnet.*

Magnetism in materials

Electric currents cause magnetism Once scientists discovered that electric current can make magnetism, they soon realized that all magnetism comes from electric currents. Each electron in an atom behaves like a small loop of current forming its own miniature electromagnet. All atoms have electrons, so you might think that all materials would be magnetic. In reality, we find great differences in the magnetic properties of materials. These differences come from the arrangement of electrons in the atoms of the material.

Diamagnetic materials In many materials, the magnetic fields of individual electrons in each atom cancel each other's magnetic effects. This leaves the whole atom with a zero net magnetic field. Materials made of these kinds of atoms are called *diamagnetic*. Lead and diamond are diamagnetic. However, if you try hard enough, you can see magnetic effects in diamagnetic materials. However, it takes either a *very strong* magnetic field to cause the effects or very sensitive instruments to detect them.

Paramagnetic materials In a *paramagnetic* material, the magnetism of electrons in individual atoms do not cancel each other completely. Paramagnetic materials can show signs of weak magnetism in the presence of a magnet. Aluminum is a paramagnetic material. In an atom of aluminum, the magnetism of individual electrons do not cancel completely. This makes each aluminum atom a tiny magnet with a north and a south pole. However, these aluminum atoms are randomly arranged, so the alignment of the north and south poles changes from one atom to the next. Even a tiny piece of aluminum has trillions of atoms. Solid aluminum is "nonmagnetic" because the *total* magnetic field averages to zero over many atoms (top of Figure 15.9).

Magnetic fields in paramagnetic materials The weak magnetic activity shown by paramagnetic materials can be detected using sensitive instruments. If you hold the north pole of a permanent magnet near aluminum, it attracts the south poles of aluminum atoms nearby. Some atoms change their alignments (Figure 15.9). A weak overall magnetic field is created in the aluminum, so it weakly attracts the external magnet. When the permanent magnet is pulled away, the atoms go back to their random arrangement and the magnetic field disappears.

 Atom

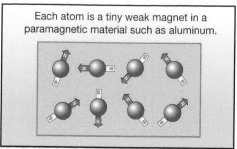

Each atom is a tiny weak magnet in a paramagnetic material such as aluminum.

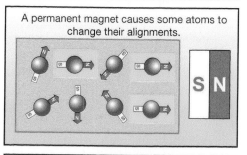

A permanent magnet causes some atoms to change their alignments.

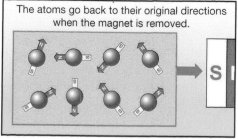

The atoms go back to their original directions when the magnet is removed.

Figure 15.9: *Atoms in a paramagnetic material such as aluminum are tiny magnets. A piece of aluminum is not magnetic because the atoms are arranged in random directions. However, weak magnetic effects can be created when a permanent magnet temporarily changes the orientation of atoms near the surface.*

Ferromagnetic materials

Ferromagnetism A small group of ferromagnetic metals have very strong magnetic properties. Examples of ferromagnetic materials are iron, nickel, and cobalt. Like paramagnetic atoms, the electrons in a ferromagnetic atom do not cancel each other's magnetic fields completely. Unlike paramagnetic atoms, the atoms in a ferromagnetic material align themselves with neighboring atoms in groups. Each group is called a **magnetic domain**. Because atoms in a domain are aligned, their magnetic fields add up. This gives each magnetic domain a relatively strong overall magnetic field.

Why all steel is not magnetic Each domain may contain millions of atoms, but the overall size of a domain is small. For example, there are hundreds of domains in a steel paper clip. Steel is an alloy of iron. The domains in a steel paper clip are randomly arranged, so their magnetic fields cancel each other out (Figure 15.10). That is why a paper clip does not produce a magnetic field all the time.

Aligning domains Ferromagnetic materials have strong magnetism because domains can grow very quickly by "adopting" atoms from neighboring domains. When a magnet is brought near a paper clip, magnetic domains that attract the magnet grow and domains that repel the magnet shrink. The paper clip quickly builds a magnetic field that attracts the magnet, no matter which pole is used (Figure 15.10). When the magnet is pulled away the domains tend to go back to their random orientation and the magnetism goes away.

Hard and soft magnets Permanent magnets are created when the magnetic domains become so well aligned that they stay aligned even after the external magnet is removed. A steel paper clip can be *magnetized* by aligning its magnetic domains to make a weak permanent magnet. This is done by rubbing it with another magnet or by exposing it to a strong magnetic field. Steel is a **soft magnet** because it is easy to magnetize but loses its magnetization easily, too. Heat, hammering, and the presence of other magnets can demagnetize steel. Materials that make better permanent magnets are called **hard magnets**. The domains in hard magnets tend to remain aligned under a variety of conditions. Strong electromagnets are used to magnetize hard magnets.

magnetic domain - a region of a material in which atoms align in the same direction, increasing the magnetic field strength

soft magnet - a magnetic material that is relatively easily magnetized or demagnetized, such as iron

hard magnet - a material in which the magnetic domains remain aligned after being magnetized, making them more difficult to demagnetize

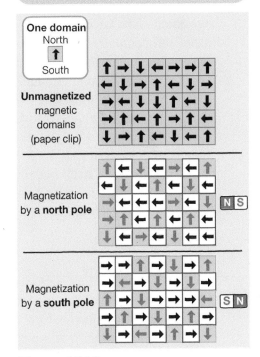

Figure 15.10: *A permanent magnet can temporarily magnetize a paper clip.*

Magnetism in solids

High temperatures destroy magnetism Permanent magnets are created when atoms arrange themselves so they are magnetically aligned with each other. Anything that breaks the alignment destroys the magnetism, so "permanent" magnets are not really permanent. One way to break the alignment is with temperature. The higher the temperature, the more atoms move and become less aligned. Permanent magnets and ferromagnetic materials become demagnetized if the temperature gets too hot. The best magnetic materials are able to retain their magnetism only up to a few hundred degrees Celsius. A permanent magnet can also be demagnetized by being struck or by other stronger magnets.

Liquids and gases Permanent magnetism only exists in solids. There are no liquid or gaseous permanent magnets. Liquids or gases cannot be permanent magnets because the atoms have too much thermal energy to stay aligned with each other.

More about hard and soft magnets The strongest permanent magnets (hard magnets) are made from ceramics containing nickel and cobalt, or the rare earth metal neodymium. Using these materials, it is possible to manufacture magnets that are very small but also very strong and harder to demagnetize than steel magnets. Soft magnets are easy to magnetize with other magnets. You can see both the magnetization and demagnetization of paper clips or small iron nails using a bar magnet (Figure 15.11). If you use the north end of the magnet to pick up a nail, the nail becomes magnetized with its south pole toward the magnet. Because the nail itself becomes a magnet, it can be used to pick up other nails. If you separate that first nail from the bar magnet, the entire chain demagnetizes and falls apart.

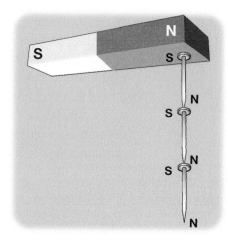

Figure 15.11: *Iron nails become temporarily magnetized when placed near a magnet.*

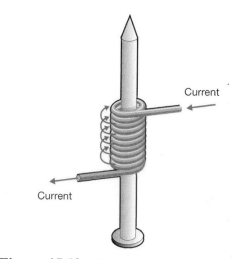

Figure 15.12: *Can you determine the location of the north and south poles of this electromagnet?*

15.2 *Section Review*

1. Use the right-hand rule to identify which end of the nail in Figure 15.12 is the north pole.
2. List two ways to increase the strength of the electromagnet in Figure 15.12.
3. How is magnetism in an electromagnet related to magnetism in a permanent magnet?
4. Explain what happens when a ferromagnetic material is made into a permanent magnet.
5. Are permanent magnets truly permanent? Explain.

15.3 Earth's Magnetic Field

The biggest magnet on Earth is the planet itself. Earth has a magnetic field that has been useful to travelers for thousands of years. Compasses, which contain small magnets, interact with Earth's magnetic field to indicate direction. Certain animals, including migratory birds, can sense Earth's magnetic field and use it for navigation.

compass - a device containing a magnet that interacts with Earth's magnetic field to indicate direction

Discovering and using magnetism

Lodestone   As early as 500 BCE, people discovered how to make a **compass**, a device with a magnet that can be used to indicate direction. For example, during this time, the Greeks observed that one end of a suspended piece of lodestone (made of the mineral magnetite) pointed north and the other end pointed south. Sailors used this lodestone device to navigate.

The Chinese "south pointer"   The invention of the compass was also recorded later in China in 220 BCE. Writings from the Zheng dynasty tell stories of how people would use a "south pointer" when they went out to search for jade, so that they wouldn't lose their way home. The pointer, made of lodestone, looked like a large spoon with a short, skinny handle. When balanced on a plate, the "handle" would align with magnetic south.

The first iron needle compass   By 1088 CE, iron refining had developed to the point that the Chinese were making a small needlelike compass. Shen Kua recorded that a needle-shaped magnet was placed on a reed floating in a bowl of water. Chinese inventors also suspended a long, thin magnet in the air, realizing that the magnet ends were aligned with geographic north and south. Explorers from the Sung dynasty sailed their trading ships all the way to Saudi Arabia using compasses as navigational tools. About 100 years later, a similar design appeared in Europe and soon spread through the civilized world.

Compasses and exploration   By 1200, explorers from Italy were using a compass to guide ocean voyages beyond the sight of land. The Chinese also continued exploring with compasses, and by the 1400s were traveling to the east coast of Africa. The compass, and the voyages it made possible, led to many interactions among cultures.

Some animals have biological compasses

Many animals, including species of birds, frogs, fish, turtles, and bacteria, can sense Earth's magnetic field. Migratory birds are the best known examples. Magnetite, a magnetic mineral made of iron oxide, has been found in bacteria and in the brains of birds. Tiny crystals of magnetite may act like compasses and allow these organisms to sense the small magnetic field of Earth.

Magnetite

How does a compass work?

A compass is a magnet   A compass needle is a magnet that is free to spin (Figure 15.13). The needle spins until it lines up with any magnetic field that is present. The north pole of a compass needle always points toward the south pole of a permanent magnet. This is in the direction of the magnetic field lines. Because the needle aligns with the local magnetic field, a compass is a great way to "see" magnetic field lines (Figure 15.14).

North and south poles   The origin of the terms *north pole* and *south pole* of a magnet comes from the direction that a magnetized compass needle points. The end of the magnet that pointed toward geographic north was called the magnet's north pole and the opposite pole was called south. The names were decided long before people truly understood how a compass needle worked.

Figure 15.13: *A compass is made of a small bar magnet that is able to rotate.*

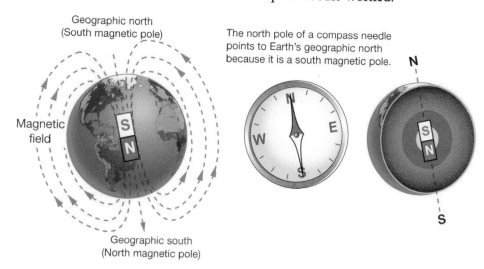

Geographic and magnetic poles   The true *geographic* north and south poles are where Earth's axis of rotation intersects its surface. Earth's *magnetic* poles are defined by the planet's magnetic field. When you use a compass, the north-pointing end of the needle points toward a spot near, but not exactly at, Earth's geographic north pole. That means the *south magnetic pole* of the planet is near the north geographic pole. Earth has a planetary magnetic field that acts as if the core of the planet contained a giant magnet oriented as shown in the diagram.

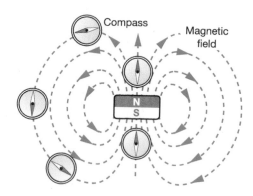

Figure 15.14: *A compass needle lines up with a magnetic field. The red end of the compass needle is the north-pointing end.*

Magnetic declination and "true north"

Magnetic declination
Earth's geographic north pole—called "true north"—and magnetic south pole are not located at exactly the same place. Therefore, a compass does not point *directly* to the geographic north pole. Depending on where you are, a compass will point slightly east or west of true north. The difference between the direction a compass points and the direction of true north is called **magnetic declination**. Magnetic declination is measured in degrees and is indicated on topographical maps.

Finding true north with a compass
Maps like the one shown below often list the declination for an area. For example, suppose you are using this map and want to travel north. You do not simply walk in the direction of your compass needle. To go north, you must walk in a direction 16 degrees *west* of the direction the needle is pointing. Fortunately, many compasses are designed so that you can adjust for magnetic declination.

> **magnetic declination -** the difference between the direction a compass points and the direction of true (geographic) north

Test yourself

The geographic north pole of Earth is really a magnetic south pole. Therefore, the north-pointing end of a compass needle is a magnetic _____ (north or south) pole.

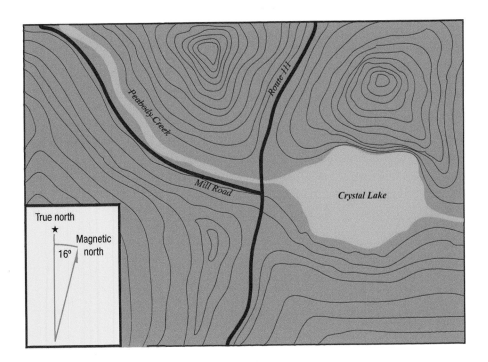

The source of the Earth's magnetism

Earth's magnetic core Earthquake waves reveal that Earth's outer core is made of hot liquid iron and a few other metals. This mixture of metals circulates between the hotter, solid inner core and the surrounding mantle (Figure 15.15). Huge electric currents flowing in the molten iron produce Earth's magnetic field.

The strength of Earth's magnetic field The magnetic field of Earth is weak compared to the field near the ceramic magnets in your classroom. For this reason, you cannot trust a compass to point north if any other magnets are close by. The **gauss** is a unit used to measure the strength of a magnetic field. A small ceramic permanent magnet has a field between 300 and 1,000 gauss (G) at its surface. By contrast, the magnetic field averages about 0.5 G at Earth's surface.

Reversing poles Historical data shows that the strength of Earth's magnetic field and the location of the north and south magnetic poles change over time. Studies of magnetized rocks in Earth's crust provide evidence that the poles have reversed many times over tens of millions of years. The reversal has happened every 500,000 years on average. The last field reversal occurred roughly 750,000 years ago, so Earth is overdue for another switch of the planet's north and south magnetic poles.

The next reversal Today, Earth's magnetic field is losing approximately 7 percent of its strength every 100 years. We do not know whether this trend will continue, but if it does, the magnetic poles will reverse sometime in the next 2,000 years. During a reversal, Earth's magnetic field would not completely disappear. However, the main magnetic field that we use for navigation would be replaced by several smaller fields with poles in different locations until the reversal is complete.

Movements of the magnetic poles The location of Earth's magnetic poles is always changing slowly, even between full reversals (Figure 15.16). In fact, the the magnetic south pole, to which the north end of a compass points, changes daily and is currently moving toward Russia at a rate of tens of kilometers per year. (*Note*: Earth's magnetic south pole is also referred to as the North Magnetic Pole since it is located in the North Pole.)

> **gauss** - a unit used to measure the strength of a magnetic field

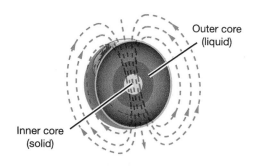

Figure 15.15: *Moving charges in Earth's liquid outer core create its magnetic field.*

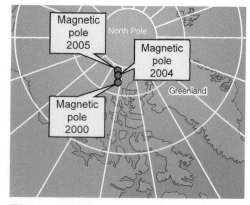

Figure 15.16: *The location of Earth's magnetic pole changes over time. Compass needles point north because they are attracted to Earth's magnetic south pole.*

Magnetism in stars and planets

Planets and moons   Like Earth, other planets in the solar system also have magnetic fields. In the case of Jupiter, the magnetic field is very strong compared to Earth's and was mapped by the Cassini spacecraft. Since the Moon does not have a hot, liquid core, it does not have a magnetic field like Earth. However, the Moon does have a very weak magnetic field that may be related to its formation.

The Sun's magnetic field   Even stars have magnetic fields. The Sun has a strong magnetic field. Like Earth, the Sun also rotates with a "day" of about 25 Earth days. Because the Sun is not solid, different parts of the Sun rotate at different rates. The Sun rotates once every 25 days at its "equator" but takes 35 days to rotate once near its poles. The Sun's uneven rotation twists its magnetic field lines. Every so often, the magnetic field lines become so twisted they "snap" and reconnect themselves. This sudden change causes huge solar storms where great eruptions of hot gas flare up from the Sun's surface (Figure 15.17). The energy released by the Sun's magnetic storms is great enough to disrupt radio and cell phone signals here on Earth. Magnetism also causes sunspots, regions of relative darkness on the Sun's surface.

Energy for the Earth's field   It's very fortunate for life on Earth that we have a strong and relatively stable magnetic field. The Sun's magnetic storms eject enormous amounts of charged particles into space. Most of these particles never reach the surface of our planet because our magnetic field acts as a shield. When these particles first impact our magnetic field, they are deflected and forced to flow around Earth. Eventually they stream off into space. The auroras at the north and south poles are caused by small amounts of these particles that enter the upper atmosphere.

The Sun rotates faster at its equator than at its poles.

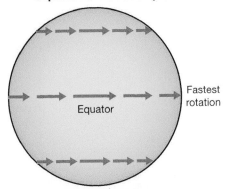

Photo courtesy NASA/NSSDC.

Figure 15.17: *The Sun rotates unevenly because it is not solid, but a ball of hot gas. This twists the Sun's magnetic field resulting in both sunspots and also huge magnetic storms.*

15.3 Section Review

1. Describe one of the early compasses used to indicate direction.
2. How does a compass respond when it is placed in the magnetic field of a bar magnet?
3. What causes Earth's magnetism?
4. Why is Earth's magnetic north pole not at the same location as its geographic north pole?

What is an MRI Scanner?

Has anyone ever told you that you have a magnetic personality? Well, here's a machine with one—an MRI scanner. MRI stands for Magnetic Resonance Imaging—a device that uses magnetism and radio waves to scan all or part of the human body for medical purposes.

Unlike x-rays, which were discovered over 100 years ago, the MRI scanner is a relatively new medical diagnostic tool, having first been used in 1977. The first MRI scanners were very large and intimidating, extremely loud, and slow, with a single scan taking several hours. Fortunately, these machines have come a long way. Although they are still large and loud, they are faster and produce better results in diagnosing illness and injury.

MRIs are especially valuable as diagnostic tools because they are noninvasive. In other words, information about a person's body can be obtained without probing or cutting tissue. You may be wondering how an MRI "sees" inside a human body. This device uses magnetism, radio waves, and a lot of computer power to create images. To understand how the MRI works, let's examine each concept represented in the name of this technology—magnetism, resonance, and imaging.

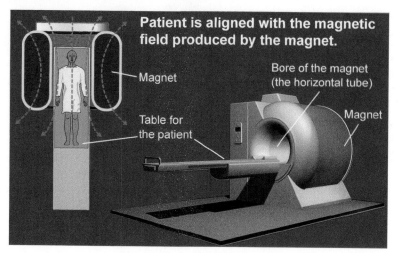

Patient is aligned with the magnetic field produced by the magnet.

Magnet

Bore of the magnet (the horizontal tube)

Table for the patient

Magnet

The role of magnetism

MRIs contain powerful magnets. The strength of common magnets such as ones found in motors or sound speakers ranges from a few hundred to a few thousand gauss. As defined in the chapter, the gauss is a unit used to measure magnetic-field strength. The magnets in MRIs range from 5,000 to 20,000 gauss. Since 10,000 gauss equals 1 *tesla*, this translates to 0.5 to 2.0 teslas. In comparison, the strength of Earth's magnetic field is 0.3 to 0.5 gauss or 3×10^{-4} to 5×10^{-4} teslas.

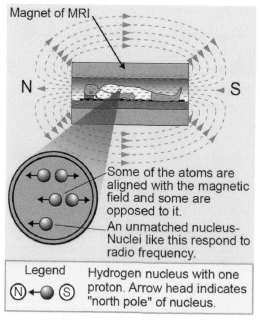

Magnet of MRI

N

S

Some of the atoms are aligned with the magnetic field and some are opposed to it.

An unmatched nucleus- Nuclei like this respond to radio frequency.

Legend — Hydrogen nucleus with one proton. Arrow head indicates "north pole" of nucleus.

N ← ● → S

There are two kinds of magnets used in an MRI. The main magnet creates a very strong magnetic field. The gradient magnets create a changing magnetic field.

The main magnet is used to temporarily "polarize" the nuclei of certain atoms in parts of the body. These atoms become tiny magnets with a north and south pole. This process is similar to how an iron nail can be "magnetized" by rubbing a magnet along its length in one direction. Actually, all substances are capable of becoming internally "polarized" to some extent under the right conditions. This phenomenon is what makes an MRI work.

Some of the nuclei in a certain part of the body line up with the MRI magnetic field and some oppose it. Aligned and opposing nuclei cancel each other. Nuclei that are not cancelled are used to create the MRI image.

The role of the gradient magnets within the main magnet is to locate a particular area of the body to be imaged. The gradient magnets turn on and off quickly and causes changes in the magnetic field where a specific part of the body or a specific plane or "slice" of the body is to be examined. Unlike an x-ray or CT scanner, which can only take scans of one plane at a time, the gradient magnets can image many slices at virtually any angle. This not only produces a detailed picture of that slice, but the slices can be combined to form a two-dimensional (2-D) or three-dimensional (3-D) images.

The role of resonance

The effects of the main magnet and the gradient magnets set up conditions for creating an MRI image using resonance. Resonance describes how an object responds when it receives a pulse of energy at its natural frequency. At its natural frequency, the object oscillates easily or "resonates." For example, if you speak into the sound box of a piano, some of the frequencies that make up your voice will match the natural frequencies of some of the strings, and set them oscillating!

For an MRI, radio waves, oscillating at thousands or even millions of cycles per second, are first produced by the on-off oscillations of an electrical current through a series of coils. The frequency of these oscillations in the radio frequency (RF) part of the electromagnetic spectrum is set to match the natural frequency of the nuclei of common elements found in the body, like hydrogen, carbon, or calcium. When the nuclei of atoms in the body absorb this specific energy, they, too, like the strings in the piano, vibrate as they absorb and release energy.

The nuclei that respond to the RF are removed from their nuclei pairings. The energy they absorb causes them to resonate and change their alignment in the magnetic field. When the RF is turned off, the unmatched nuclei return to their original positions and give off energy. That energy is captured by the MRI and used to make the final image.

Making images

Energy signals that are released by the unpaired nuclei are received by coils and recorded as bits of mathematical data. This data is used to map the density of the particular atoms responding to the RF signal. A computer assembles the data, creates the map, and sends it to either a screen or film. The result is a clear, detailed picture of a part or "slice" of the body. MRIs are commonly used to visualize, diagnose, and evaluate abnormalities in the body due to disease or injury. As MRIs become more advanced, we will be able to use this wonderful application of physics to learn more about how the brain functions, how serious diseases develop and grow within the body, and how best to treat injured bone, tissue, and cartilage.

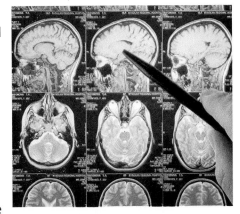

QUESTIONS

1. What is the role of the main magnet in an MRI? What is the role of the gradient magnets?

2. In MRI technology, what resonates as a result of radio waves and helps to produce an MRI scanner image?

3. Imagine you had a choice of getting an MRI, a CAT scan, or an x-ray. Research and describe what each procedure involves. List the pros and cons of each procedure. Which is the least expensive? Which is the most expensive?

4. MRI scanners are very safe devices. However, they do produce very strong magnetic fields that powerfully attract metal objects. Research the precautions that MRI facilities use when these strong magnetic fields are present.

Chapter 15 Review

Understanding Vocabulary

Select the correct term to complete the sentences.

compass	magnetic declination	permanent magnet
diamagnetic	magnetic domains	right-hand rule
electromagnet	magnetic field	soft magnet
ferromagnetic	magnetic poles	magnetic field lines
gauss	paramagnetic	

1. The angular difference east or west of true north as indicated by a compass is known as _____.

2. In a drawing, the spacing of the _____ surrounding a magnet indicates the strength of the magnetic field at a given location.

3. Water, which is weakly repelled in the presence of a strong magnetic field, is considered a(n) _____ material.

4. A needle suspended in a magnetic field that orients itself parallel to the field is an example of a(n) _____.

Reviewing Concepts

Section 15.1

1. What is a magnetic material able to do?

2. Suppose you stick a magnet on the door of your refrigerator. Is the magnet a magnetic material or a permanent magnet? Is the refrigerator door a magnetic material or permanent magnet? Explain.

3. Is it possible to have a south pole without a north pole or a north pole without a south pole? Explain.

4. What happens to a magnet if it is cut in half?

5. Two magnetic north poles _____ each other. Two south poles _____ each other. A north pole and a south pole _____ each other.

6. Can magnetic forces pass through non-magnetic materials?

7. List three uses for magnetism.

8. What describes the magnetic force in the space around a magnet?

9. Draw a bar magnet and sketch the magnetic field lines around it. Include arrows to show the direction of the lines.

10 Magnetic field lines outside a magnet point away from its _____ pole and toward its _____ pole.

11. What information can you get by looking at the spacing of magnetic field lines?

12. What happens to the strength of the magnetic field as you move away from a magnet?

Section 15.2

13. Explain the design of a simple electromagnet.

14. What is the purpose of the core of an electromagnet?

15. Explain how you can use the right-hand rule to determine the location of an electromagnet's poles.

16. What happens to an electromagnet's field if the current is increased?

17. What happens to an electromagnet's field if the direction of the current is reversed?

18. Describe two ways you can increase the strength of an electromagnet without increasing the current.

19. Why is it not always the best idea to increase an electromagnet's strength by simply increasing the current?

20. What advantages do electromagnets have over permanent magnets when used in machines?

21. Are diamagnetic materials magnetic? Why or why not?

22. Are paramagnetic materials magnetic? Why or why not?

23. What happens inside a paramagnetic material if a permanent magnet is brought close to it? What happens when the permanent magnet is removed?

24. List three ferromagnetic materials.

25. What are magnetic domains?

26. Which materials are more strongly magnetic, ferromagnetic or paramagnetic? Why?

27. Describe how to create a permanent magnet from a ferromagnetic material.

28. What is the difference between hard magnets and soft magnets?

29. Which is easier to magnetize, a hard magnet or a soft magnet? Once magnetized, which is easier to demagnetize?

30. List several ways to demagnetize a permanent magnet.

Section 15.3

31. For what purpose did people first use magnetism?

32. Describe the design of two early compasses.

33. Explain why the two ends of a magnet are called "north pole" and "south pole."

34. Is Earth's magnetic north pole at its geographic north pole? Explain.

35. Why does a compass point north?

36. Why is it important to know the magnetic declination in a region where you are using a compass to navigate?

37. How does the strength of Earth's field compare to the strength of the field of average permanent magnets?

38. What material is at the core of Earth?

39. What do scientists believe is the source of Earth's magnetism?

40. What has happened to the strength and location of Earth's magnetic field in the past?

41. If the current trend continues, how long do scientists think it will take for Earth's magnetic poles to reverse again?

Solving Problems

Section 15.1

1. A student knocks a ceramic permanent magnet off her desk, and it shatters when it hits the floor. Copy the broken pieces and label the north and south poles on each one.

2. The diagram below shows the magnetic field in a region. The source of the field is not shown. At which of the labeled points in the diagram is the magnetic field the strongest? At which point is it the weakest? Explain your answers.

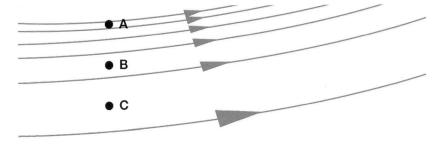

3. Copy this picture of a horseshoe magnet and draw the magnetic field lines around it.

Section 15.2

4. Which picture below shows the correct location of the north and south poles of the electromagnet? Choose A or B and explain how you arrived at your choice.

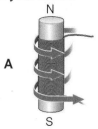

A

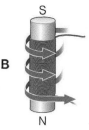

B

5. A permanent magnet attracts a steel pin as shown to the right. The pin has become a soft magnet. Copy the picture then use what you know about magnetism to label the north and south poles of the pin.

6. A strong permanent magnet is brought near a piece of iron. Magnetic domains are created as shown below. Which pole of the permanent magnet is closest to the iron?

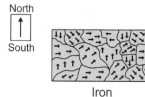

Iron

Permanent Magnet

Section 15.3

7. Suppose Earth's magnetic field were to change so it looks like the picture to the right. If you stand at the marked point, in which direction will your compass needle point? What is the approximate magnetic declination at this point?

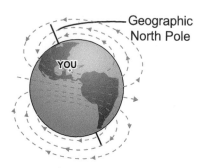

Geographic North Pole

YOU

Test Practice

Section 15.1

1. The picture shows three pairs of permanent magnets. Which pair(s) of magnets will attract one another?

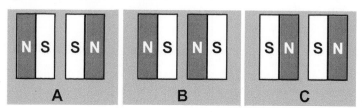

A   B   C

   a. A and B

   b. B and C

   c. A and C

   d. A only

2. The diagram shows the magnetic field that results when a piece of iron is placed between opposite magnetic poles. At which point is the magnetic field strongest?

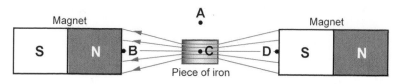

Magnet   Magnet

Piece of iron

   a. A

   b. B

   c. C

   d. D

3. Which best represents the magnetic field surrounding the bar magnet?

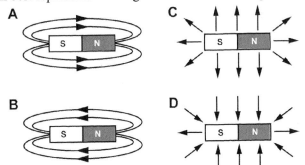

a. A

b. B

c. C

d. D

4. Which of the following best describes a material that is only weakly attracted to a very strong permanent magnet?

a. diamagnetic

b. ferromagnetic

c. paramagnetic

d. nonmagnetic

5. The diagram shows a coil of wire connected to a battery. The north pole of this coil is closest to point

a. A.

b. B.

c. C.

d. D.

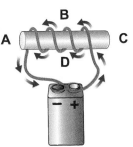

Section 15.2

6. A coil is made from three turns of copper wire. It carries a current of 1 A. As current flows, the coil is surrounded by a magnetic field. The strength of the magnetic field can be increased by

a. increasing the current.

b. inserting an iron core in the coil.

c. adding more turns to the coil of wire.

d. all of the above

7. Permanent magnetism may exist in

a. solids.

b. liquids.

c. gases.

d. all phases of matter.

8. A compass is located at point X near a bar magnet. Which of the following shows the correct direction of the compass needle at X?

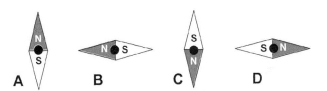

Section 15.3

9. The north magnetic pole of Earth is located closest to

a. just above the equator.

b. the north geographic pole.

c. just below the equator.

d. the south geographic pole.

10. Which of the following would have the weakest magnetic field?

   a. Earth's magnetic field

   b. a classroom permanent ceramic magnet

   c. a classroom permanent iron bar magnet

   d. an electromagnet made from 20 coils of wire carrying 0.5 A surrounding an iron core

Applying Your Knowledge

Section 15.1

1. A story dating back 2,300 years describes Ptolemy Philadelphos's attempt at using magnetism. He had the dome of a temple at Alexandria made of magnetite and tried to suspend a statue of himself in midair. The experiment failed. However, you can use magnetism to suspend a small magnet by building a device like the one shown here. The upper magnet is fixed to the underside of a shelf or table. The lower magnet is connected to a thread. See how far apart you can position the magnets and still have the lower one levitate.

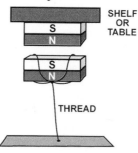

Section 15.2

2. Magnetically levitated or "maglev" trains use electromagnets to raise the train cars above the tracks before the train starts moving. Research where maglev trains are used and how they work.

Section 15.3

3. You can easily build your own compass using a sewing needle, a permanent magnet, a piece of cork or styrofoam, and a dish of water. Rub the magnet many times along the length of the needle, always in the same direction. Float a piece of cork or styrofoam in a cup of water. Place the needle on top of it and give it a gentle spin. When it stops, it will be lined up with Earth's magnetic field.

4. What is the magnetic declination where you live?

Electromagnets and Induction

Electricity and magnetism may not seem very similar to you. You don't get a shock from picking up a magnet! However, you can create magnetism with the electric current in an electromagnet. Why does electric current create magnetism?

In 1819, a teacher named Hans Christian Øersted tried an experiment in front of his students for the first time. He passed electric current through a wire near a compass. To his surprise, the compass needle moved! A few years later, Michael Faraday built the first electric motor. Today, we know electricity and magnetism are two faces of the same basic force: the force between charges. In this chapter, you will see how our knowledge of electricity and magnetism allows us to build both an electric motor and an electric generator. It would be hard to imagine today's world without either of these important inventions.

As you read and study this chapter, you will see that our knowledge of the atom, electricity, and magnetism has come full circle! This chapter will help you understand exactly how the electricity that we use in our homes, schools, and offices is generated. It is actually all about magnets! Isn't that amazing?

VOCABULARY

armature	rotor	transformer
electromagnetic induction	coil	electric motor
	fossil fuel	nonrenewable resource
renewable resource	solenoid	
brushes	commutator	
Faraday's law of induction	generator	

KEY QUESTIONS

✓ *Why are there magnets in an electric motor?*

✓ *How is the electricity generated that powers all of the appliances in your home?*

✓ *What is the purpose of a transformer that is connected a power line?*

16.1 Electric Current and Magnetism

For a long time, people believed electricity and magnetism were unrelated. As scientists began to understand electricity, they searched for relationships between electricity and magnetism. In 1819, Hans Christian Øersted, a Danish physicist and chemist, placed a compass needle near a wire in a circuit. When a switch in the circuit was closed and current flowed, the compass needle moved just as if the wire were a magnet. We now know that magnetism is created by the motion of electric charge, and that electricity and magnetism are two forms of the same basic force.

The effect of current on a compass

An experiment with a wire and compasses   Magnetism is created by moving charges. Electric current is made of moving charges (electrons), which creates the magnetic field around a current-carrying wire. Consider the following experiment: A straight wire is connected to a battery and a switch. The wire passes through a board with a hole in it as shown. An array of compasses surrounds the hole.

Magnetism is created by moving charges.

Compasses react to electric current   When the switch is open, no current flows, and the compass needles point north (Figure 16.1). As soon as the switch is closed, current flows, and the needles form a circle (see graphic below). The needles point in a circle as long as there is current in the wire. If the current stops, the needles return to pointing north again. If the current is reversed in the wire, the compass needles form a circle again, but in the opposite direction.

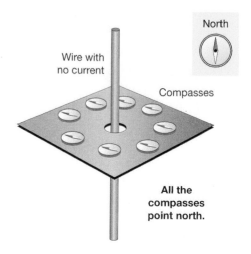

Figure 16.1: *When there is no current in a wire, all of the compass needles point to Earth's magnetic north pole.*

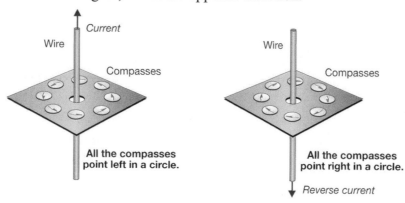

The magnetic field of a straight wire

The magnetic field of a wire

The experiment with the compasses shows that a wire carrying electric current creates a magnetic field around it. The magnetic field lines are concentric circles with the wire at the center of the circles. The direction of the field depends on the direction of the current in the wire.

Using the right-hand rule

To find the direction of the magnetic field, you can use the *right-hand rule*. When your thumb is in the direction of the current, the fingers of your right hand wrap in the direction of the magnetic field. (*Note*: This way of using the right-hand rule is different from how you used it in Section Chapter 15, but both ways give you information about the direction of the magnetic field.)

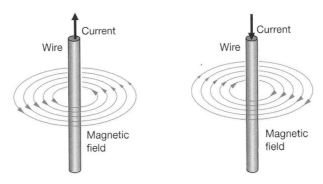

The strength of the field

The strength of the magnetic field near the wire depends on two factors:

1. The strength is directly proportional to the current, so doubling the current doubles the strength of the field.

2. The field strength is inversely proportional to the distance from the wire. The field gets stronger as you move closer to the wire. Decreasing the distance to the wire by half doubles the strength of the field.

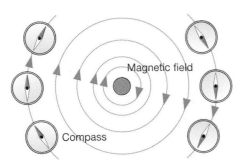

Near a straight wire, the north pole of a compass needle feels a force in the direction of the field lines. The south pole feels a force in the opposite direction. As a result, the needle twists to align its north-south axis along the circular field lines.

Electrical wiring

There is a magnetic field around all wires that carry current. So, why don't you notice magnetic fields created by electrical wiring in your house?

For starters, a single straight wire and the resulting magnetic field is weak and gets even weaker the farther you are from the wire. Also, the wires in your home are actually made of two parallel wires inside a rubber covering. At any instant, the current in one wire is moving opposite to the current in the other wire. Each creates a magnetic field, but the fields are in opposite directions so they cancel each other out.

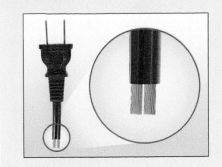

The magnetic fields of loops and coils

Making a strong magnetic field from current   The magnetic field around a single ordinary wire carrying a safe amount of current is too small to be of much use. However, there are two clever ways to make strong magnetic fields from reasonable currents in small wires.

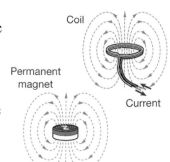

Coil

Permanent magnet

Current

> **coil** - a current-carrying wire made into loops
> **solenoid** - a coil of wire that acts as an electromagnet when current passes through it

1. Parallel wires placed side-by-side can be bundled together. Ten wires, each with 1 amp of current, create 10 times as strong a magnetic field as 1 wire carrying 1 amp.

2. A wire can be looped into a **coil** so the magnetic field is concentrated at the center. A coil's magnetic field is the same shape as the field of a circular permanent magnet.

Coiling wires   When a wire is made into a coil, the total magnetic field is the sum of the fields created by the current in each individual loop. By wrapping a wire around into a coil, the current can be "reused" as many times as there are turns in the coil. A coil with 50 turns of wire carrying 1 amp creates the same magnetic field as a single-wire loop with 50 amps of current. Virtually all electrical machines use coils because it is much easier and safer to work with 1 amp of current than to work with 50 amps of current.

Coils and solenoids   A coil concentrates the magnetic field at its center. When a wire is bent into a circular loop, field lines on the inside of the loop squeeze together. Field lines that are closer together indicate a higher magnetic field. Field lines on the outside of the coil spread apart, making the average field lower outside the coil than inside. The most common form of electromagnetic device is a coil with many turns called a **solenoid** (Figure 16.2).

Where coils are used   A simple electromagnet made of a nail with wire wrapped around it (see Section 15.2) is one example of a solenoid. Solenoids and other coils are also used in speakers, electric motors, electric guitars, and almost every kind of electric appliance that has moving parts. Coils are the most efficient way to make a strong magnetic field with the least amount of current, which is why coils are found in so many electric appliances.

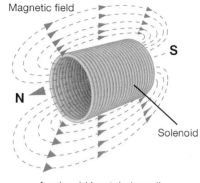

Magnetic field

N

S

Solenoid

A solenoid is a tubular coil of wire with many turns.

Figure 16.2: *A solenoid is a tubular coil of wire with many turns.*

Magnetic forces and electric currents

The force between two coils Two coils carrying electric current exert forces on each other, just as magnets do. The forces can be attractive or repulsive depending on the direction of current in the coils (Figure 16.3). If the current is in the same direction in both coils, they attract. If the currents are in opposite directions, they repel.

Observing the force between wires Two straight wires have a similar effect on each other. When the current is in the same direction in both wires, they attract each other. If the currents go in opposite directions, the wires repel each other. For the amount of current in most electric circuits, the forces are small but can be detected. For example, if the wires are one meter long and each carries 100 amps of current, the force between them is 0.1 newtons when they are 1 centimeter apart.

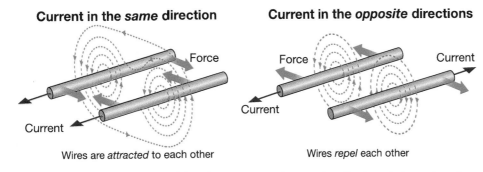

Current in the *same* direction **Current in the *opposite* directions**

Force / Current / Current / Force / Current / Current

Wires are *attracted* to each other   Wires *repel* each other

Permanent magnets The magnetic fields created by the currents in a pair of wires interact and cause the force between the wires. A similar effect can be seen with a current-carrying wire in a magnetic field created by a permanent magnet. The wire can attract or repel a permanent magnet just as it can attract or repel the magnetic field created by another wire.

16.1 Section Review

1. Why does a compass change direction when it is near a current-carrying wire?
2. What is the shape of the magnetic field created by a current-carrying wire?
3. How can you increase the magnetic field created by a wire? How can you change the direction of the field?
4. Do the two wires inside an appliance cord attract or repel each other? Why?

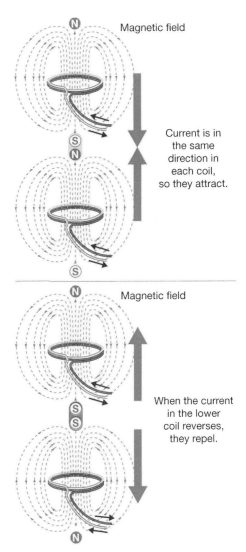

Magnetic field

Current is in the same direction in each coil, so they attract.

Magnetic field

When the current in the lower coil reverses, they repel.

Figure 16.3: *Two coils attract if their currents are in the same direction. The coils repel if their currents are in opposite directions.*

16.2 Electric Motors

Permanent magnets and electromagnets work together inside electric motors and generators. In this section, you will learn about how an electric motor works. The motor's key mechanism is the ability of an electromagnet to reverse its north and south poles. By changing the direction of electric current, the electromagnet attracts and repels other magnets in the motor, causing the motor's shaft to spin. **Electric motors** convert electrical energy into mechanical energy.

> **electric motor** - a machine that converts electrical energy into mechanical energy
>
> **rotor** - a rotating disk found in an electric motor or generator

Using magnets to spin a disk

A spinning disk with magnets Imagine you have a disk that can spin on an axis at its center. Around the edge of the disk are several magnets. You have arranged the magnets so their north and south poles alternate and face away from the axis. You hold another magnet which is not attached to the disk. You can make the disk spin by moving the magnet you're holding close to the disc's edge (Figure 16.4).

Reversing the magnet To keep the disk spinning, you need to reverse the magnet you're holding as soon as the disk magnet that was attracted passes by. That way, you first attract the disk magnet, and then reverse your magnet to repel it. Then, you attract the next disk magnet on the rotor. You make the disk spin by using your magnet to alternately attract and repel the magnets on the disk.

Knowing when to reverse the magnet The disk is called the **rotor** because it can rotate. The key to making the rotor spin smoothly is to reverse your magnet when the disk is at the right place. You want the reversal to happen just as each magnet in the rotor passes by. If you reverse too early, you will repel the magnet in the rotor backward before it reaches your magnet. If you reverse too late, you attract the magnet backward after it has passed. For it to work best, you need to change your magnet from north to south just as each magnet on the rotor passes by.

Using a magnet to spin a rotor

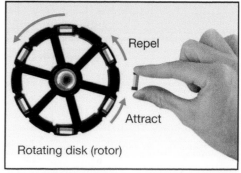

Repel

Attract

Rotating disk (rotor)

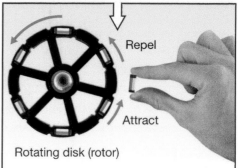

Repel

Attract

Rotating disk (rotor)

Figure 16.4: *Using a single magnet to spin a disk of magnets. Reversing the magnet in your fingers attracts and repels the magnets in the rotor, making it spin.*

How the electromagnets in a motor operate

How electromagnets are used in electric motors In a working electric motor, an electromagnet replaces the magnet you reversed with your fingers. The switch from north to south is done by reversing the electric current in the electromagnet. The sketch below shows how an electromagnet switches its poles to make the rotor keep turning.

commutator - the device that switches the direction of electrical current in the electromagnets of an electric motor

First, the electromagnet repels magnet A and attracts magnet B.

Then, the electromagnet switches so it repels magnet B and attracts magnet C.

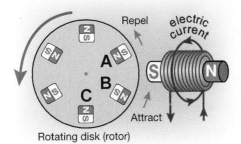

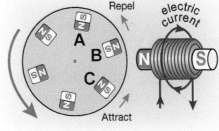

Rotating disk (rotor)

The commutator is a kind of switch Just as with the magnet you reversed, the electromagnet must switch from north to south as each rotor magnet passes by to keep the rotor turning. The device that makes this happen is called a **commutator**. As the rotor spins, the commutator reverses the direction of the current in the electromagnet. This makes the electromagnet's field facing the disk change from north to south, and then back again. The electromagnet attracts and repels the magnets in the rotor, and the motor turns.

The three main parts of an electric motor

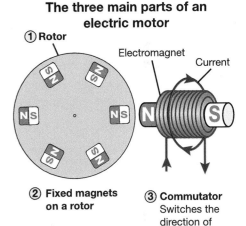

① Rotor

Electromagnet

Current

② Fixed magnets on a rotor

③ Commutator Switches the direction of current in the electromagnet at the right time

Figure 16.5: *An electric motor has three main parts.*

Three things you need to make a motor All types of electric motors must have three parts (Figure 16.5). They are:

1. A rotating part (rotor) with magnets that have alternating poles.
2. One or more fixed magnets around the rotor.
3. A commutator that switches the direction of the current in the electromagnets back and forth to keep the rotor spinning.

AC motors Motors that run on alternating current (AC) electricity are easier to make because the current switches direction all by itself—a commutator isn't needed. Almost all household appliances, industrial electrical machines, and power tool motors use AC motors. Their motors use electromagnets for both the rotating and fixed magnets.

How a battery-powered electric motor works

Inside a small electric motor
The picture below shows a small, battery-powered electric motor and what it looks like inside with one end of its case removed. The permanent magnets are on the outside, and they stay fixed in place.

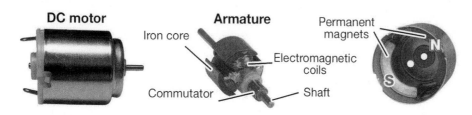

DC motor   Armature

Iron core   Permanent magnets

Electromagnetic coils

Commutator   Shaft

> **armature** - the rotating part of an electric motor that includes the rotor and electromagnets
>
> **brushes** - allow current to flow into the coil of an electric motor

Electromagnets and the armature
The electromagnets are in the rotor, and they turn. The rotating part of the motor, including the electromagnets, is called the **armature**. It has three electromagnets that correspond to the three coils (Figure 16.6).

How the switching happens
The wires from each of the three coils are attached to three metal plates that form the commutator at the end of the armature. As the rotor spins, the three plates come into contact with the positive and negative **brushes**. Electric current passes through the brushes into the coils. The metal plates rotate past the brushes, switching the poles of the electromagnets by reversing the positive and negative connections to the coils. The turning electromagnets are attracted and repelled by the permanent magnets and the motor turns. For example, in Figure 16.6, the coil that is labeled with the south pole is being repelled by the permanent magnet on the right and attracted by the permanent magnet on the left. When that coil passes the permanent magnet on the left, its south pole becomes a north pole. As a result, it switches from being attracted to being repelled by the permanent magnet on the left. This mechanism for switching poles keeps the rotor spinning.

16.2 Section Review

1. Explain how you can use a permanent magnet to make a rotor spin.
2. How do the magnetic poles in an electromagnet reverse?
3. List the three main parts every electric motor must have.

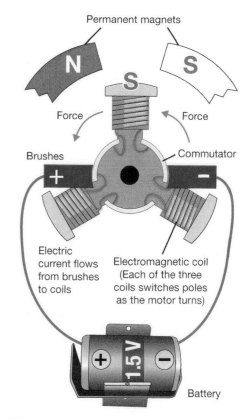

Permanent magnets

N   S

Force   Force

Brushes   Commutator

Electric current flows from brushes to coils

Electromagnetic coil (Each of the three coils switches poles as the motor turns)

1.5 V

Battery

Figure 16.6: *A simple, battery-powered motor has three electromagnets.*

16.3 Electric Generators and Transformers

Motors transform electrical energy into mechanical energy. Electric generators do the opposite. They transform mechanical energy into electrical energy. Generators are used to create the electricity that powers all of the appliances in your home. In this section, you will learn how generators produce electricity.

electromagnetic induction - the process of using a moving magnet to create a current in a conductor

Electromagnetic induction

Magnetism and electricity An electric current in a wire creates a magnetic field. The reverse is also true. If you move a magnet near a coil of wire, an electric current is *induced* in the coil. The word *induce* means "to cause to happen." The process of using a moving magnet to create an electric current is called **electromagnetic induction**. A moving magnet induces electric current to flow in a circuit.

Symmetry in physics Many laws in physics display *symmetry*. In physics, symmetry means that a process works in both directions. Earlier in this chapter, you read that moving electric charges create magnetism. The symmetry is that changing magnetic fields also cause electric charges to move, which creates a current. Many physical laws display symmetry of one form or another.

Making current flow Figure 16.7 shows an experiment demonstrating electromagnetic induction. In the experiment, a magnet can move in and out of a coil of wire. The coil is attached to a meter that measures the electric current. When the magnet moves into the coil of wire, *as the magnet is moving*, electric current is induced in the coil and the meter swings to the left. The current stops when the magnet stops moving.

Reversing the current When the magnet is pulled out again, *as the magnet is moving*, current is induced in the opposite direction. The meter swings to the right as the magnet moves. Again, the current stops when the magnet stops moving.

Current flows only when a magnet is moving Current is produced only if the magnet is moving, because a changing magnetic field is what creates the current. Moving magnets induce current because they create changing magnetic fields. If the magnetic field is not changing, such as when the magnet is stationary, the current is zero.

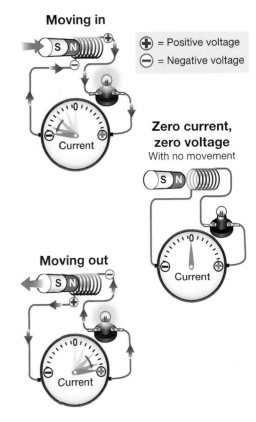

Figure 16.7: *A moving magnet produces a current in a coil of wire. A voltage is induced by the magnetic field.*

Faraday's law of induction

When current is induced Do you think a big current will flow in a coil if you wave a magnet around far away from the coil? If you guessed no, you are right. The coil has to be close enough that the magnetic field from the magnet passes *through* the coil. The induced current depends on the amount of the magnetic field actually passing through the coil. Adding an iron core helps direct the magnetic field through the coil.

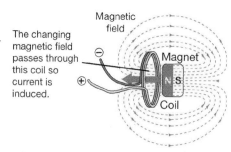

The changing magnetic field passes through this coil so current is induced.

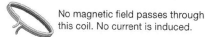

No magnetic field passes through this coil. No current is induced.

> **Faraday's law of induction** - the voltage induced in a coil is directly proportional to the rate of change of the magnetic field through the coil

Induced voltage Current flows because a voltage difference is created between the ends of the coil. A moving magnet, like the one shown above, produces a voltage difference between the ends of the wires that make the coil. If the wires were connected, current *would* flow. When the wires are disconnected you see the voltage difference instead. Because the currents can be quite small, in experiments it is easier to measure the induced voltage instead of the current.

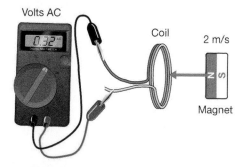

Faraday's law The voltage (energy) produced and the current induced depend on how *fast* the magnetic field through the coil changes. Michael Faraday (1791–1867), an English physicist and chemist, was first to explain it. He experimented with moving magnets and coils and discovered **Faraday's law of induction**. Faraday's law says the induced voltage is proportional to the *rate of change* of the magnetic field through the coil. If the magnetic field does not change, no voltage is produced even if the field is very strong.

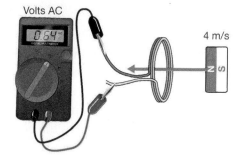

Figure 16.8: *A moving magnet produces a voltage difference between the ends of the wires. Current is induced and flows when the wires are connected.*

Induced current, work, and energy As a magnet is pushed through a coil of wire, current is induced to flow and voltage develops. The induced current in the coil makes its own magnetic field that tries to push the magnet back out again. If you push a north pole into a coil, the coil itself will develop a repelling north pole from the induced current. If you pull the magnet back out again, the coil will reverse its current, making a south pole that attracts your magnet. Either way, you have to push the magnet in or out, doing work, to supply the energy that makes current flow (Figure 16.8). This is another example of conservation of energy.

Generating electricity

A simple generator A **generator** converts mechanical energy into electrical energy using Faraday's law of induction. Most large generators use some form of rotating coil in a magnetic field (Figure 16.9). You can also make a generator by rotating magnets past a stationary coil as shown below. As the disk rotates, first a north pole and then a south pole pass the coil. When a north pole is approaching, the current flows in one direction. After the north pole passes and a south pole approaches, the current flows in the opposite direction. As long as the disk is spinning, there is a changing magnetic field through the coil, and electric current is created.

> **generator** - a device that converts kinetic energy into electrical energy using Faraday's law of induction

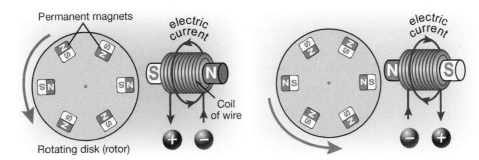

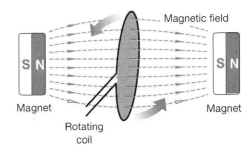

Figure 16.9: *Current is created when a coil rotates in a magnetic field.*

Alternating current The generator shown above generates AC electricity. The direction of the current is one way when the magnetic field is becoming "more north" and the opposite way when the field is becoming "less north." It is impossible to make a situation where the magnetic field keeps increasing forever. Eventually, the field stops increasing and starts decreasing. Therefore, the current and voltage alternates. The electricity transmitted to homes in the United States is produced by AC generators.

Energy for generators The electrical energy created by a generator is not created from nothing. Energy must continually be supplied to keep the rotating coil or magnetic disk turning. In hydroelectric generators, falling water turns a *turbine* which spins a generator to produce electricity. Windmills can generate electricity in a similar way. Other power plants use gas, oil, or coal to heat steam to high pressures. The steam then spins the turbines that convert the chemical energy stored in the fuels into electrical energy (Figure 16.10).

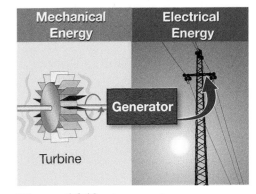

Figure 16.10: *A power plant generator contains a turbine that turns magnets inside loops of wire, generating electricity. Some other form of energy must be continually supplied to turn the turbine.*

Producing and transporting electricity

One way to produce electricity

Hoover Dam is a hydroelectric plant near Las Vegas, Nevada (Figure 16.11). Towering more than 200 meters above the Colorado River, this gigantic concrete structure is known as one of the greatest engineering projects in the world. Hoover Dam is called a hydroelectric plant because it converts the energy of falling water into electricity. Using the potential energy of water is one way to produce electricity. What are other ways?

Starting at the power plant

To find out how electricity is produced and transported, let's trace the energy pathway. Electricity is supplied by a power plant. Many power plants use a form of fossil fuel—coal, oil, or natural gas—as an energy source. Water, nuclear energy, wind, and solar energy can also be used as energy sources. In a power plant that uses coal, the heat produced from burning coal is used to boil water. The steam from the boiling water turns a turbine. The turbine turns a generator which produces electricity. The electricity is transported to homes and businesses through a network of wires, often called "the grid."

Electricity is carried by wires

The graphic below shows how energy is transformed throughout the process of generating and transporting electricity from a power plant that uses fossil fuels. With each transformation (green arrows), some energy is lost to the system in the form of heat (red arrows).

Hoover Dam | Turbines in the Hoover Dam

Figure 16.11: *The Hoover Dam has a power plant that uses water to turn turbines that produce electricity.*

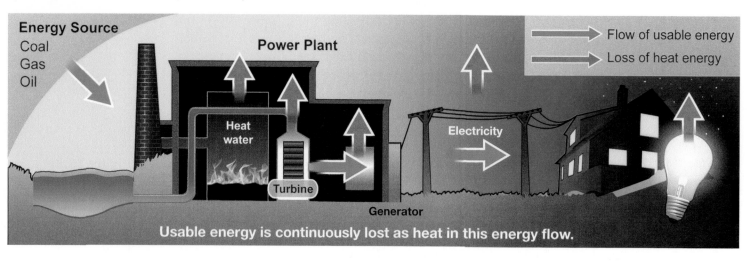

Electricity from different resources

To produce electricity, you need an energy resource. Energy resources are divided into two categories: nonrenewable and renewable.

Nonrenewable resources A **nonrenewable resource** is not replaced as it is used. Any **fossil fuel** is an good example of nonrenewable resource. Fossil fuels are found in Earth's crust. They are called fossil fuels because they were formed hundreds of millions of years ago by processes acting on dead plants and animals. The three major fossil fuels are coal, oil (also called petroleum), and natural gas.

Problems with using fossil fuels to generate electricity Since they are not replaced as they are used, nonrenewable resources will be too scarce to produce the electricity we need. Besides being nonrenewable, fossil fuels pose additional problems. Burning fossil fuels produces sulfur oxide emissions that reduce air quality. Carbon dioxide is also produced when fossil fuels are burned. Because carbon dioxide has increased in Earth's atmosphere since the 1800s, our planet is experiencing global climate change. Global climate change is the increase of average temperature due to increased concentrations of carbon dioxide and other gases in the atmosphere. This warming trend has led to glacial melting and an increase in volume of Earth's oceans. As a result, the sea level has been rising. These consequences, and the possibility of global climate change, are causing scientists and governments to look to renewable resources for producing electricity.

Renewable resources A **renewable resource** can be replaced naturally in a relatively short period of time. Falling water, energy from the Sun, wind energy, and geothermal energy are examples of renewable resources that can be used to produce electricity. Other examples include burning solid waste and biomass (plant matter) in place of fossil fuels (Figure 16.12). In 2009, 8 percent of the total amount of resources used for electricity production was renewable. In 2008, renewable resources represented 7 percent of the total energy used. A current trend in the United States is an increase each year in renewable energy consumption, but an overall decrease in total energy consumption.

nonrenewable resource - a natural resource that is not replaced as it is used

fossil fuel - substances found in Earth's crust that were formed over millions of years from the remains of dead organisms

renewable resource - a natural resource that can be replaced

Renewable Resources Used for U.S. Electricity Production, 2009

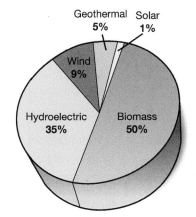

Data are from the U.S. Energy Information Administration.

Figure 16.12: *Types of renewable resources used for energy production in 2009 and their percentages.*

Geothermal, biomass, and hydroelectric energy

Geothermal reservoirs Iceland is a country of contrasts. Glaciers cover 11 percent of Iceland, yet there are also many places where molten rock is close to the surface. At these hot spots, where geothermal reservoirs are located, wells have been drilled to tap into the hot water. Geothermal power plants use Earth's internal heat energy, in the form of water or steam, to produce electricity. Iceland produces most of its electricity from geothermal energy. Geothermal power plants can be found all over the world, including Alaska, Hawaii, and some western parts of the United States.

Biomass Biomass is organic material from plants or animals. For thousands of years, people have used wood, a type of biomass, for space and water heating. Now, new technology allows farmers to grow crops, such as corn, specifically to be used for biomass energy. Biomass can also come from municipal waste, industrial waste, or agricultural and forestry activities. In waste-to-energy plants, renewable solid waste is burned to produce steam, which is used to generate electricity. Biomass, such as harvested corn, can even produce liquid transportation fuels (biofuels) such as ethanol and biodiesel. Plants used to make biomass can be grown over and over, so biomass is considered a renewable resource. Burning biomass does produce carbon dioxide—a gas associated with global climate change—but as living plants, the biomass originally consumed carbon dioxide during its growth process.

Hydroelectric As mentioned earlier, a hydroelectric plant uses energy from falling water to generate electricity (Figure 16.13). The two most common types of hydroelectric power plants are water *impoundment* using a dam, and *pumped storage*. An impoundment facility dams up river water and stores it in a reservoir. The water falls from the reservoir and turns a turbine, which spins a generator and produces electricity. Instead of holding back river water in a reservoir, a pumped storage facility actively pumps water from a lower reservoir to a higher reservoir during off-peak or low-demand hours. The water is then release back to the lower reservoir during high-demand hours. Again, the energy of the falling water is used to generate electricity.

From biomass to electricity

The McNeil generating station in Burlington, Vermont, uses waste wood from forestry and used wooden shipping pallets to produce electricity. In 1989, a natural-gas-burning system was added to the plant. The heat energy from the combustion of both wood and gas is fed into the same boiler. This unique power plant has been fully operational since 2000. Some interesting McNeil station facts:

- turbine speed: 3,600 rpm
- pressurized steam temperature: 950°F
- wood usage: 76 tons per hour
- gas usage: 550,000 cubic feet per hour
- full capacity: 50 megawatts (enough electricity for almost the entire city of Burlington, Vermont)

Figure 16.13: *A dam is part of a hydroelectric impoundment facility.*

Electricity and power

A watt is a unit of power   Electrical power is measured in watts, just like mechanical power. Recall that electrical power is the rate at which electrical energy is changed into other forms of energy such as heat, sound, or light. Anything that "uses" electricity is actually converting electrical energy into some other type of energy. The watt (W) is an abbreviation for 1 joule per second (J/s). A 100-watt light bulb uses 100 joules of energy every second. Figure 16.14 shows some typical power ratings for common devices.

Kilowatt-hours   Utility companies charge customers for the number of kilowatt-hours (kWh) used each month. One kilowatt-hour means that 1 kilowatt of power has been used for 1 hour. A kilowatt-hour is not a unit of power but a unit of energy, like a joule. A kilowatt-hour is a relatively large amount of energy, equal to 3.6 million joules. If you leave a 1,000-watt hair dryer on for 1 hour, you have used 1 kilowatt-hour of energy. You could also use 1 kilowatt-hour by using a 100-watt light bulb for 10 hours. The number of kilowatt-hours used equals the number of kilowatts multiplied by the number of hours the appliance was turned on. Electric companies charge for kilowatt-hours used monthly. Your home is connected to a meter that keeps track of the energy or kilowatt-hours used.

Save money on electricity   How can you save money on your household's electric bill? Use less electrical energy, of course! There are many simple things you can do to use less electricity. When added up, these simple things can mean many dollars of savings each month, which adds up to a large amount of money over a one-year period. What can you do? Make sure your windows seal properly when they are closed. Turn off lights when you are not using them. Switch off electronic equipment that uses standby power. Also, you can ask your electric utility company to send an energy consultant to your home to give suggestions on how to conserve electricity. Some utility companies can install devices in homes that allows them to control electricity usage, too.

Electricity Bill
1,300 kWh
× $0.14
$182.00

Appliance	Power (watts)
Electric Stove	3,000
Electric heater	1,500
Toaster	1,200
Hair dryer	1,000
Iron	800
Washing machine	750
Television	300
Light bulb	100
Small fan	50
Clock radio	10

Figure 16.14: *Typical power usage of some common appliances.*

Transformers

Electricity is distributed at high voltage From the perspective of physics, it makes sense to distribute electricity from a generator to homes using high voltage. For example, most main power lines on a city street carry AC current at 13,800 volts. Power is current times voltage, each amp of current provides 13,800 watts of power. The problem is that you would *not* want your wall outlets to be at 13,800 volts! With a voltage this high, plugging in your appliances would be dangerous.

Electric power transformers A **transformer** steps down or decreases a higher voltage to a lower voltage. Transformers are useful because they efficiently change voltage and current with little loss of power. The voltage of your wall outlet is a much safer 120 volts. A transformer can take 1 amp at 13,800 volts from the power lines outside and convert it to 115 amps at 120 volts (Figure 16.15). The total electrical power remains the same: 13,800 V × 1 A = 120 V × 115 A.

Transformers operate by electromagnetic induction A transformer uses electromagnetic induction, similar to a generator. Figure 16.15 shows what a transformer looks like inside its protective case. You may have seen one inside a doorbell or an AC adapter. The input to the transformer is connected to the *primary* coil. The output of the transformer is connected to the *secondary* coil. The coils are wound around an iron or iron-like alloy core. The core concentrates the magnetic field lines through the centers of the coils.

How a transformer works Consider the transformer between the outside power lines and your house:

1. The primary coil is connected to outside power lines. Current in the primary coil creates a magnetic field through the secondary coil. The primary coil's field is shown by the magnetic field lines (green arrows) in the core in Figure 16.16.

2. The current in the primary coil changes constantly because it is *alternating current*.

3. As the current changes, so does the strength and direction of the magnetic field through the secondary coil.

4. The changing magnetic field through the secondary coil induces current in the secondary coil. The secondary coil connects to your home's wiring.

> **transformer** - a device that increases or decreases the voltage from a power source

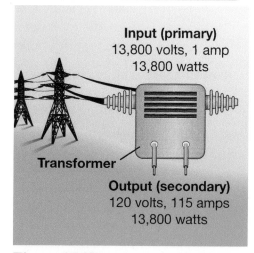

Input (primary)
13,800 volts, 1 amp
13,800 watts

Transformer

Output (secondary)
120 volts, 115 amps
13,800 watts

Figure 16.15: *A high-power transformer reduces the voltage, which keeps the power constant.*

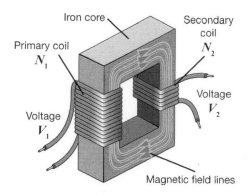

Iron core

Secondary coil N_2

Primary coil N_1

Voltage V_2

Voltage V_1

Magnetic field lines

Figure 16.16: *A transformer contains coils wrapped around an iron-like core.*

Voltage relationships for a transformer

The number of turns is important Transformers work because there are different number of turns in the coils. The strength of an electromagnet's magnetic field, induced voltage, and induced current all depend on the number of turns (Figure 16.17). In the same changing magnetic field, a coil with 100 turns produces 10 times the voltage of the induced current as a coil with 10 turns.

Voltage and current With fewer turns than the primary, the secondary coil also has lower induced voltage than the voltage applied to the primary coil. In this case, voltage is stepped down. With more turns than the primary coil, the secondary coil has greater induced voltage than the voltage applied to the primary coil and the voltage is stepped up. Because of energy conservation, the power (voltage × current) is the same for both coils (neglecting resistance).

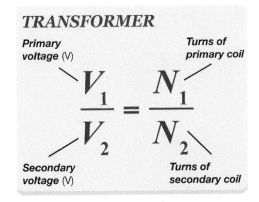

TRANSFORMER

Primary voltage (V)   Turns of primary coil

$$\frac{V_1}{V_2} = \frac{N_1}{N_2}$$

Secondary voltage (V)   Turns of secondary coil

Figure 16.17: *The relationship between voltage and the number of turns in a transformer.*

Changing voltage with a transformer

A cell-phone AC adapter reduces the 120 V AC to the 6 V DC needed by the phone's battery. If the primary coil has 240 turns, how many turns must the secondary coil have?

1. *Looking for:*   You are asked for the number of turns of the secondary coil.

2. *Given:*   You are given the voltage of each coil and the number of turns of the primary coil.

3. *Relationships:* $\dfrac{V_1}{V_2} = \dfrac{N_1}{N_2}$

4. *Solution:* $\dfrac{120\ V}{6\ V} = \dfrac{240\ turns}{N_2}$ $N_2 = 12\ turns$

Your Turn:

a. A transformer has a secondary coil with 20 turns and a primary coil with 200 turns. What is the secondary voltage if the primary voltage is 120 volts?

b. A secondary coil has 112 turns. How many turns must the primary coil have if it reduces 13,800 volts to 120 volts?

(Answers are listed at the end of the chapter.)

16.3 Section Review

1. Explain Faraday's law of induction.

2. What is the purpose of a transformer?

Michael Faraday

Despite little formal schooling, Michael Faraday rose to become one of England's top research scientists of the 19th century. He is best known for his discovery of electromagnetic induction, which made possible the large-scale production of electricity in power plants.

Michael Faraday was born in Surrey, England, in 1791, the son of a blacksmith. When he was five, his family moved to London, where his parents paid a local schoolmistress to teach him rudimentary reading, writing, and arithmetic. Unfortunately, Michael's father contracted a lung disease which was exacerbated by the city's polluted air. He was frequently unable to work. By the time he was 10, Michael's parents could no longer afford to send him to school, or even provide enough food for their four children. Michael had to take a job as an errand-boy for a book binder. He walked all over London, delivering newspapers, and upon his return, he cleaned the shop.

At age 14, Faraday was offered a position as a book binder's apprentice. He would spend seven years learning the trade, and afterward he could open his own shop. Faraday enjoyed reading the materials he was asked to bind, and found himself mesmerized by scientific

papers that outlined new discoveries. He used his meager savings to buy some basic laboratory equipment so that he could try out some of the electricity experiments.

A wealthy client of the book binder noticed this voracious young reader and gave him some tickets to hear Humphrey Davy, a prominent British chemist, give a series of lectures to the public. Faraday was fascinated by Davy's work and took detailed notes at each lecture. It was 1812, and Faraday was almost finished with his book binding

apprenticeship. He enjoyed the work, but nothing had ever sparked his interest like Davy's lectures.

Faraday knew that without a strong education, it was unlikely that he would ever find work as a scientist. But, he had a bold idea. He bound his notes from the lectures—all 386 pages—and sent them to Davy along with a letter asking him for a job. Davy wrote back that he was impressed

Painting of Faraday working in his laboratory at the Royal Institution

with Faraday's "great zeal, power of memory, and attention." But he had no paid position to offer him. Several months later, however, Davy hired Faraday as a chemistry laboratory assistant at the Royal Institution, London's top scientific research facility.

Despite his lack of formal training in science or math, Faraday was an able assistant and soon began independent research in his spare time. In the early 1820s, he discovered how to liquefy chlorine and became the first to isolate benzene, an organic solvent with many commercial uses. Faraday was also interested in electricity and magnetism. After reading about the work of Hans Christian Ørsted, the Danish physicist and chemist, Faraday repeated Ørsted's experiments and used what he learned to build a machine that used an electromagnet to cause rotation—the first electric motor.

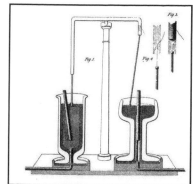

Drawing of Michael Faraday's experiment demonstrating electromagnetic rotation

Next, he tried to do the opposite–use a magnet to cause an electric current. He tried wrapping coils of copper wire around various bar magnets. No matter how many coils he used, or how powerful the magnet, he could not generate electric current. In 1831, he tried bending a soft iron bar into a circle. He wrapped a coil of copper wire around one side of the iron

Faraday's induction ring

circle and connected it to a battery. This, he knew, would turn the iron circle into an electromagnet. Then, he wrapped a second wire coil around the opposite side of the circle. This wire was attached to a galvanometer, which measures current. To his surprise, the galvanometer did measure current—but only for the moment when he connected or disconnected the first wire from the battery. Faraday realized he needed a *changing* magnetic field to induce current. Over the next three months, he found that he could induce a steady current by moving a bar magnet in and out of a coil of wire, or by spinning a disc of copper between the poles of a horseshoe magnet. This was the first electric generator.

Drawing of Faraday disk, the first electric generator

Faraday's discovery is called *electromagnetic induction*, and it is used by power plants to generate electricity even today. Faraday first developed the concept of a field to describe magnetic and electric forces, and used iron filings to demonstrate magnetic field lines. He also conducted important research in electrolysis and invented a voltmeter. He was interested in finding a connection between magnetism and light, too. In 1845, he discovered that a strong magnetic

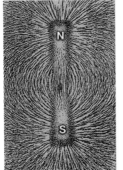

Iron filings around magnet showing magnetic field lines

field could rotate the plane of polarized light. Today, this is known as the Faraday effect.

Faraday was a teacher as well as a researcher. When he became director of the Royal Institution laboratory in 1825, he instituted a popular series of Friday Evening Discourses. Here paying guests—including Prince Albert, Queen Victoria's husband—were entertained with demonstrations of the latest discoveries in science. He also instituted the Christmas Lectures for Children, which continue to this day.

Detail of a lithograph of Michael Faraday delivering a Christmas lecture at the Royal Institution

Photo of Michael Faraday in 1860

Faraday continued his work at the Royal Institution until just a few years before his death in 1867. Two units of measure have been named in his honor: the farad, a unit of capacitance, and the faraday, a unit of charge.

QUESTIONS

1. Name two ways that Michael Faraday's work affects your life in the 21st century.

2. Use iron filings and a magnet to demonstrate magnetic field lines, or prepare a simple demonstration of electromagnetic induction for your class.

Induction ring photo: :© DK Limited/CORBIS

Chapter 16 Review

Understanding Vocabulary

Select the correct term to complete the sentences.

armature	electric generator	rotor
brushes	electric motor	solenoid
coil	electromagnetic induction	transformer
commutator	Faraday's law of induction	

1. An electromagnet device made using a nail surrounded by a coil is an example of a(n) _____.

2. All electric motors are made from three basic parts: stationary magnet(s), _____, and _____.

3. The mechanical energy of moving magnets is transformed into electrical energy by a(n) _____.

4. When a laptop computer is plugged into an electrical outlet, a(n) _____ in the plug reduces the outlet's 120 volts to the 19 volts needed by the computer's battery.

Reviewing Concepts

Section 16.1

1. How is magnetism created?

2. What exists in the region around a wire that is carrying current and that exerts a force on another current-carrying wire?

3. Explain how the right-hand rule can help you determine the direction of the magnetic field lines around a current-carrying wire.

4. What effect does increasing the current in a wire have on its magnetic field?

5. What effect does reversing the direction of the current in a wire have on the magnetic field?

6. What happens to the magnetic field as you move farther away from a current-carrying wire?

7. Why do we not use a single wire with a large current to create a strong magnetic field?

8. What is the advantage of using a coil to create a magnetic field?

9. Why don't we usually notice the force between the current-carrying wires in an extension cord?

Section 16.2

10. A motor turns _____ energy into _____ energy.

11. Why is it necessary to use at least one electromagnet in a motor instead of only permanent magnets?

12. What is the purpose of the commutator in a motor?

13. Why must the direction of the current in a motor's electromagnets be switched repeatedly?

14. List the three main parts of an electric motor.

Section 16.3

15. What happens as you move a magnet toward a coil of wire?

16. If you hold a magnet still near a coil of wire, will a current be induced? Explain your answer.

17. State Faraday's law of induction in your own words.

18. Why does a spinning coil near a magnet produce alternating current rather than direct current?

19. What is the magnitude of the voltage provided by most electrical outlets in homes and buildings in the United States?

20. The voltage of the electricity in outside power lines is much higher than the voltage of the electricity in buildings. How is the voltage reduced?

21. The primary and secondary coils in a transformer have different voltages and currents but the same _____.

22. A certain transformer has more turns in its secondary coil than in its primary coil. Does the transformer increase or decrease voltage?

Solving Problems

Section 16.1

1. Copy the diagram of the wire shown and draw the magnetic field lines in the region around the wire. Don't forget to include arrows to show the field's direction.

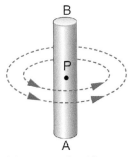

2. What happens to the strength of the magnetic field near a wire if you double the current? Triple the current? Quadruple the current?

3. Copy the diagram of the coil shown to the right and draw the magnetic field in the region around it. Don't forget to include arrows to show the field's direction.

4. Explain how each of the following would affect the current produced by a magnet moving toward a coil of wire.

   a. a stronger magnet

   b. moving the magnet toward the coil at a faster speed

   c. reversing the magnet's motion so it moves away from the coil

   d. adding more turns of wire to the coil

   e. moving the magnet's south pole toward the coil

   f. adding a second light bulb to the circuit

5. Decide whether each pair of wires or coils will attract or repel.

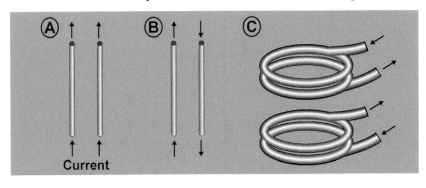

Section 16.2

6. At a certain instant, the electromagnet in the motor shown below has its north pole facing the rotor that holds the permanent magnets. In which direction is the rotor spinning?

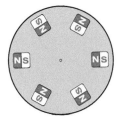 

7. The rotor in the motor below is spinning clockwise. Is the direction of the current in the electromagnet from A to B or from B to A? Why?

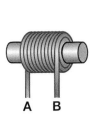 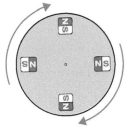

Section 16.3

8. A transformer has 1,000 turns in its primary coil and 50 turns in its secondary coil.

   a. If the voltage in the secondary coil is 120 V, what voltage is in the primary coil?

   b. If the voltage in the primary coil is 120 V, what voltage is induced in the secondary coil?

9. A laptop computer uses a rechargeable 24-V battery. A transformer is used to convert an electrical outlet's 120 V AC to 24 V DC.

   a. If the primary coil has 500 turns, how many turns must the secondary coil have?

   b. If the current in the primary coil is 1 A, what is the current in the secondary coil? (*Hint:* First, calculate the power.)

Test Practice

Section 16.1

1. The picture shows a current-carrying coil. Toward which point is the magnetic field inside the coil directed?

   a. A

   b. B

   c. C

   d. D

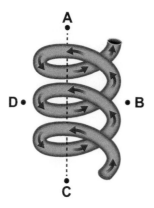

2. The diagram shows the magnetic field around point P at the center of a straight piece of current-carrying wire. The direction of the current flow is

   a. from A to B.

   b. from B to A.

   c. from P into the page.

   d. from P out of the page.

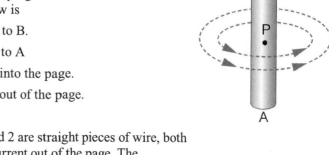

3. Wires 1 and 2 are straight pieces of wire, both carrying current out of the page. The wires are 1 m apart. As a result of the magnetic fields associated with the wires, wire 1 will experience a force directed toward point

   a. A.

   b. B.

   c. C.

   d. D.

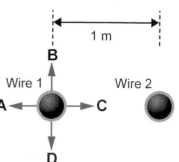

Section 16.2

4. The part of an electric motor responsible for reversing the direction of the current in the electromagnets of the motor is the

   a. armature.

   b. rotor.

   c. commutator.

   d. brush.

5. A device used to transform mechanical energy to electrical energy is a

   a. rotor.

   b. motor.

   c. generator.

   d. transformer.

Section 16.3

6. A transformer is designed to step 220 V to 2,200 V. If the primary coil has 200 turns, how many turns are on the secondary?

   a. 20

   b. 200

   c. 1,000

   d. 2,000

7. A transformer has 2 A of current and 120 V in its primary coil. If the current in the secondary coil is 0.5 A, what is the voltage induced in the secondary coil?

   a. 480 V

   b. 120 V

   c. 60 V

   d. 30 V

8. The device best represented by the diagram is

   a. an induction coil.

   b. a motor.

   c. a generator.

   d. a transformer.

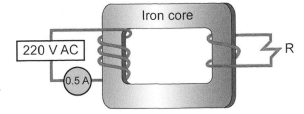

9. The picture shows a solenoid that is free to rotate around an axis at its center, C. The solenoid is placed between two magnets' opposite poles. The direction of the current is shown by the arrow.

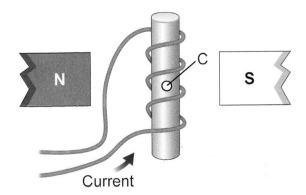

While the current flows in the direction shown, the solenoid will

   a. remain motionless.

   b. vibrate back and forth.

   c. turn clockwise.

   d. turn counterclockwise.

Applying Your Knowledge

Section 16.1

1. Speakers use electromagnets and permanent magnets to create sound from electric currents. Research how electromagnets are used to produce the vibrations that create the music you listen to.

Section 16.2

2. The first motors were built to run on direct current. However, direct current could not be easily transmitted over long distances. In the late 1800s, Nikola Tesla invented a motor that ran on alternating current. Research Tesla's life and his invention of the AC motor.

Section 16.3

3. Suppose you have a transformer that provides a secondary voltage four times as great as the primary voltage. You have a cell phone that uses a 6-V battery. Could you use a 1.5-V battery and the transformer to power the phone? Explain.

4. A bicycle-light generator is a device you place on the wheel of your bike. When you turn the wheel, the generator powers a light. When you stop, the light goes out. Explain how you think the generator makes electricity.

Generator

5. A clever inventor claims to be able to make an electric car that makes its own electricity and never needs gas. The inventor claims that as the car moves, the wind generated by the motion spins a propeller. The propeller turns a generator that makes electricity to power the car.

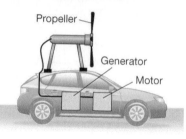

Propeller

Generator

Motor

Do you believe this car would work? Why or why not? (*Hint*: Think about conservation of energy.)

6. Some electric toothbrushes contain rechargeable batteries that are charged by placing the toothbrush on a plastic charging base. Both the bottom of the toothbrush and the base are encased in plastic, so there is no physical connection between the circuits in the toothbrush and the base. How do you think the battery in the toothbrush gets charged?

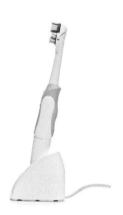

 *Your Turn* **Answers**

Changing voltage with a transformer (Section 16.3, page 399)

a. 12 V

b. 12,880 turns

Fields and Forces

"Use the force, Luke" is a well-known quote from a very popular film series, which you have probably seen at least once. The force field in the movie is only imaginary, but real force fields do exist and are very important in physics. Gravity, electricity, magnetism, and other important physical phenomena all depend on real force fields. All forces exist in what we call "fields." In fact, you are in a virtual sea of fields right now. You are surrounded by light fields, electric fields, magnetic fields, sound fields, and, of course, a gravitational field.

A group of scientists, physicians, and engineers formed a group in 1978 called the Bioeletromagnetics Society. Bioeletromagnetics is the study of how electromagnetic fields affect biological systems. With at least one-third of the US population using cell phones, some researchers are exploring how the radio frequency fields that exist around cell phone antennas might affect cell phone users. Some studies in Sweden have shown some possible links between cell phone usage and increased headaches and fatigue. However, no studies have been able to conclusively show serious harmful affects of cell phone usage.

KEY QUESTIONS

✓ *How does the force of gravity get from the Sun to Earth?*

✓ *If all masses exert gravity on all other masses, why don't you feel the gravitational pull from your textbook?*

✓ *How can electrical appliances, lightning, and even static electricity interfere with the operation of sensitive electronics?*

VOCABULARY

electric field	gravitational field	shielding
field	intensity	source charge
force field	inverse square law	

17.1 Fields and Forces

In previous chapters, you have read about forces. Some forces come from electricity or magnetism. Other forces come from pressure, motion, or gravity. What we have *not* discussed is how forces *actually act*. What carries the influence of a force from one place to another? How does the force of gravity due to the Sun act on Earth? How does the electrical force from a battery travel through a wire to cause current to flow everywhere in the wire? This chapter will answer these and other questions by discussing the concept of a *field*.

field - the physical phenomena responsible for how forces are transmitted from one object to another everywhere in space

What is a field?

An example   Think about listening to music from a portable stereo. You can hear the music for a long distance away from the stereo. However, the farther away you go, the softer the music gets. If you keep moving away, you will eventually reach a distance where you can no longer hear the music at all. How do you describe the loudness of the music all around the stereo?

Definition of a field   In physics, a **field** is a physical phenomena that has a value everywhere in space. The loudness has a value everywhere around the stereo. That means you can describe the loudness with a field. Figure 17.1 (top) shows what the sound-intensity or loudness field might look like near a stereo. The circular lines represent places where the loudness is equal. Another way to represent the loudness is with a graph. The graph in Figure 17.1 (bottom) shows the loudness of the sound in decibels (dB). At a distance of 120 meters, the sound has a loudness of 10 decibels, which is about the same loudness as hearing a whisper from 1 meter away.

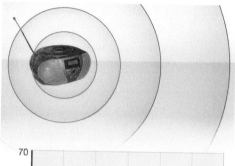

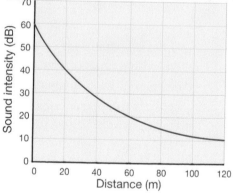

Figure 17.1: *The sound-intensity field near a stereo.*

You hear the field, not the stereo itself   If you were to switch the stereo off, a person listening from far away may not be instantly aware of this. That is because the person standing far away does not hear the stereo directly. Instead, the person hears the sound field created by the stereo. This may seem like an unimportant detail, but it turns out to be fundamental to physics.

We experience fields, not their sources   *All* interactions between matter and energy occur by way of fields. Sound is a form of energy. The sound-intensity field describes precisely how much sound energy a listener hears in any given place. Like sound from the stereo, we only experience the fields created by things, not the things themselves.

Fields and energy

Fields are everywhere All of space is filled with fields. In fact, many different fields can occupy the same space. You are constantly immersed in fields, including radio and television broadcasts, microwaves, light, electricity, and gravity. There are fields everywhere (Figure 17.2)!

Fields contain energy Any field is a form of energy that is distributed through space. You can easily show that a magnetic field has energy because it can exert force over distance, or do work, on another magnet. The stronger the field, the more energy is stored in the field. Where does the energy come from?

Energy must come from somewhere The energy in the field of an electromagnet comes from the current in the wires. But what about a permanent magnet? Permanent magnets are not magnetic early in the manufacturing process because their atoms are randomly oriented. Powerful electromagnets are used to magnetize permanent magnets. The initial magnetization process is the source of the energy that creates the magnetic field of a permanent magnet.

Fields and forces Fields create forces when they interact with matter. The force holding you to your chair comes from the gravitational field of Earth interacting with the matter in your body. You do not fall *through* the chair because electrons in the atoms of the chair repel electrons in atoms in *you* through electric fields.

You can add fields of the same type Fields of the same kind can be added or subtracted. You can use two magnets to force a compass needle to point in any direction you wish. Figure 17.3 illustrates the effects of a permanent magnet and an electromagnet on a compass. The compass responds to the *total* magnetic field at its position. The total magnetic field is the sum of the magnetic fields from each magnet plus the magnetic field of Earth itself.

Adding forces from fields of different types 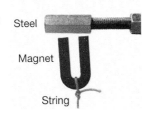 The total force acting on a body is the sum of all forces from all fields that are present. This photograph shows a small magnet that is being held up by a magnetic field. Forces from several fields act on the magnet, including gravity, magnetism, and the electric fields holding the atoms of the string together.

Figure 17.2: *Some of the fields that pass through you all the time.*

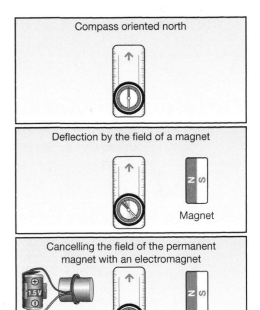

Figure 17.3: *The field from an electromagnet can either cancel the field from a permanent magnet or add to it.*

The inverse square law

Intensity   Your hear only the sound energy that falls on the small area of the opening to your ear. This area is about 1 square centimeter (1 cm²). Because the conversion of electricity to sound is only 1 percent efficient, a 100-watt stereo puts out a sound power of 1 watt. As the sound spreads out, that single watt is spread over more and more area, and loudness decreases. Close to the stereo, 0.01 watts are captured by the small opening of your ear. The **intensity**—the number of watts per unit area—reaching your ear is 0.01 watts per square centimeter. Because the power spreads out, far away from the stereo the intensity drops so that the same square centimeter of your ear captures *less* than 0.01 watt of power (Figure 17.4).

The ear
All the sound energy you hear must pass through about 1 cm² near the opening to the ear.

The inverse square law   The strength of a field decreases the farther you get from the source and follows the inverse square law. The **inverse square law** states that a field decreases as the square of the distance from the source of the field increases.

Fields and the inverse square law   Many fields follow an inverse square law, including electricity and gravity as well as light. Magnetism is an exception because all magnets have two opposite poles, not just one. The magnetic field decreases much faster than an inverse of the square of distance (Figure 17.4). The north and south poles cancel each other out as you move farther from the magnet.

An example   To see how the inverse square law works, look at the diagram below. The light intensity around a bulb is described by the number of watts per square meter of area. At a radius of 1 meter, 8 watts of light fall on a 1-meter-square area. The light intensity is 8 W/m². The intensity at 2 meters is one-fourth the intensity at 1 meter or 2 W/m². Increasing the distance by a factor of 2 reduces the intensity by a factor of 2^2 or 4. Tripling the distance from 1 to 3 meters would reduce the intensity by a factor of 3^2 or 9. The intensity at 3 meters would be $^8/_9$ or about 0.9 W/m².

> **intensity** - the field strength at a certain point in space
>
> **inverse square law** - describes a quantity that varies inversely with the square of the distance

Comparing Force vs. Distance

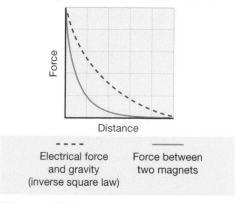

- - - - Electrical force and gravity (inverse square law)

──── Force between two magnets

Figure 17.4: *The force from a magnet decreases faster than an inverse square of the distance. This is because all magnets have two opposite poles, not just one.*

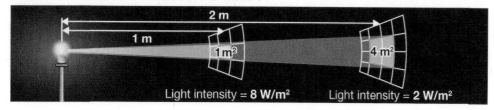

2 m

1 m

1 m²

4 m²

Light intensity = **8 W/m²**   Light intensity = **2 W/m²**

The speed of a field

Some questions for thought When you bring a magnet close to another magnet, how fast does the first magnet experience the other's force? Does the force from one magnet reach the other instantly, no matter what the distance is between them? The answers come from thinking about the interaction in two steps. First, the magnet creates a magnetic field. Second, the magnetic field creates forces on other magnets.

The speed of light The magnetic field exerts a force of one magnet on another at the speed of light (Figure 17.5). The speed of light is 300 million m/s, so it takes only a tiny fraction of a second for the force to be exerted by one magnet on another when the distance is a few meters. However, when the distance is large the time delay is also large. If a giant magnet was to suddenly appear at the center of the Milky Way galaxy, we would not experience its force for thousands of years.

Nothing is instantaneous Nothing travels instantly from one place to another. Not force, not energy, and not even information! This applies to light, electricity, gravity, sound, and any other form of energy you can think of. All interactions are carried by fields, and the fastest that any field can spread is the speed of light.

Time delays due to field speed When you make a cell phone call, information like your number and the number you are calling is coded in pulses of energy. The information spreads as an electromagnetic field that expands at the speed of light (Figure 17.6). Since light can circle Earth 7½ times in 1 second, there is not much time delay. However, talking to a space craft is another story! It takes 35 minutes for light to travel from Earth to Jupiter when the planets are at their closest distance. That is one reason why it is so difficult to control distant space craft. It would take 35 minutes for a Jupiter space craft's signal to reach Earth and another 35 minutes for it to return which is a 70-minute round-trip.

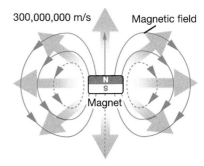

Figure 17.5: *The magnetic field moves outward at 300 million m/s, causing a magnetic force to be exerted on objects.*

Figure 17.6: *Information carried by a field cannot travel faster than the speed of light.*

17.1 Section Review

1. Name three quantities that are described by fields.
2. How does the intensity of a light bulb compare at 30 meters away and at 10 meters away?
3. If the Sun were to vanish instantly, would Earth immediately fly out of its orbit? Explain why or why not.

17.2 Gravity

When Newton first proposed the law of universal gravitation, he was quoted as saying, "Though I have calculated its effect, exactly *how* gravity operates is still a mystery." He realized that it did not make sense that gravity should instantly transmit forces between planets regardless of their distance. The idea of a field had not yet been thought of during Newton's time. Therefore, his law of gravitation described the strength and direction of the force of gravity, but not how the force got from one body to the next.

> **gravitational field** - a force field created by mass and acting on mass
>
> **force field** - a distribution of energy in space that exerts a force on objects in it, including magnetic fields, gravitational fields, and electrical fields

The gravitational field

Mass creates the gravitational field   Like the force exerted by a magnet, the force of gravity comes from a field. The **gravitational field** is created by mass. All mass creates a gravitational field. However, gravity is a relatively weak force, and it takes a planet-sized mass to create a field strong enough to exert a significant force.

The gravitational interaction between two masses occurs in two steps. First, mass creates a gravitational field. Second, the gravitational field exerts forces on other masses (Figure 17.7).

The mass of Earth creates a gravitational field.

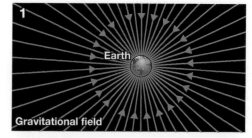

The gravitational field around Earth

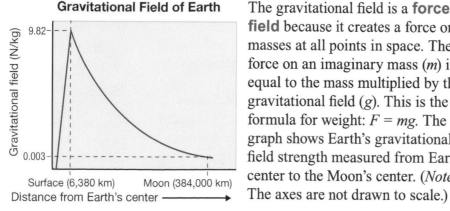

Gravitational Field of Earth

Gravitational field (N/kg)

9.82 –

0.003 –

Surface (6,380 km)   Moon (384,000 km)

Distance from Earth's center ⟶

The gravitational field is a **force field** because it creates a force on masses at all points in space. The force on an imaginary mass (*m*) is equal to the mass multiplied by the gravitational field (*g*). This is the formula for weight: $F = mg$. The graph shows Earth's gravitational field strength measured from Earth's center to the Moon's center. (*Note*: The axes are not drawn to scale.)

The gravitational field exerts a force on the Moon.

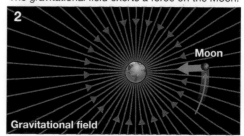

Fields and relativity   The idea of the gravitational field is an important part of Einstein's theory of relativity. In Chapter 11, you learned that the gravitational field is caused by distortions in space and time created by massive objects. This is why gravity can bend light even though light has no mass.

Figure 17.7: *Gravitational force acts in two steps. For example, (1) Earth creates a gravitational field, and (2) the Moon feels a force from the gravitational field that causes it to orbit Earth.*

The gravitational field of planets and stars

Gravity is a vector The gravitational field is a vector field because a gravitational force has a direction at all points in space. Like the magnetic field, you can draw field lines to show the direction of the gravitational field. The field lines represent the force acting on an imaginary test mass. The field lines point toward the center of a large mass, such as Earth (Figure 17.8).

Calculating the field

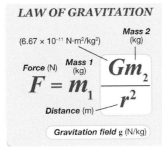

LAW OF GRAVITATION

$$F = m_1 \frac{Gm_2}{r^2}$$

Force (N) — Mass 1 (kg)
(6.67 × 10⁻¹¹ N·m²/kg²) — Mass 2 (kg)
Distance (m)

Gravitation field g (N/kg)

The formula for Newton's law of gravitation, first presented in Chapter 5, can be rearranged. The strength of the gravitational field (g) is given by the quantity, Gm_2/r^2. If we know the mass and radius of a planet, we can use this quantity to calculate the strength of gravity on that planet. The example problem illustrates how to find g for single objects like a planet or ball.

  Calculating the gravitational field of Mars

The planet Mars has a mass of 6.4×10^{23} kg and a radius of 3.4 million m. Calculate the value of g on the surface of Mars.

1. *Looking for:*   Value of g in **N/kg**

2. *Given:*   Mass in kilograms and radius in meters

3. *Relationships:* $g = Gm_2/r^2$ where $G = 6.67 \times 10^{-11}$ **N·m² / kg²**

4. *Solution:* $g = (6.67 \times 10^{-11}$ **N·m² / kg²**$)(6.4 \times 10^{23}$ **kg**$) / (3.4 \times 10^6$ **m**$)^2$
    $= 3.7$ **N/kg compared to Earth's 9.8 N/kg**

Your Turn:

a. Calculate the gravitational field at the surface of a 1-kilogram ball with a radius of 0.10 meters.

(Answers are listed at the end of the chapter.)

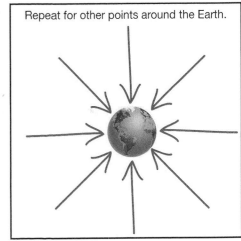

Choose a point to begin. Draw a vector showing the direction of the force of gravity at that point.

Earth

Repeat for other points around the Earth.

Figure 17.8: *Field lines show the direction of the force an object would feel if placed in any location around Earth.*

17.2 Section Review

1. If Earth were to vanish instantly, would the Moon immediately fly out of its orbit or would there be a time delay? Explain.

2. Why don't you feel gravity between ordinary objects such as yourself and a bowling ball?

17.3 **The Electric Field**

In Chapter 14, you learned that electric charges exert forces on each other. Unlike charges attract, and like charges repel. You also learned about Coulomb's law, which describes the strength of the force between two charges. Coulomb's law is one of the fundamental relationships in the universe because atoms are held together by the electrical attraction between positively-charged protons and negatively-charged electrons. Like gravity, the force between electric charges is carried by a field, called the electric field.

electric field - a force field created by the forces between electric charges

Drawing the electric field

Direction of an electric field   By convention, we draw the **electric field** to represent the force on an imaginary positive test charge. Because it is imaginary, the test charge itself does not change the electric field. The electric field therefore points *toward* negative charges and *away* from positive charges (Figure 17.9). Because of this convention, a positive charge placed in an electric field will feel a force in the direction of the field. A negative charge will feel a force opposite the direction of the field. This is shown in the diagram below.

Field lines   As we did with magnetic and gravitational fields, we use field lines to make a diagram of the electric field around one or more charges. Electric field lines follow the direction of the force on a positive test charge. The strength of the electric field is shown by the spacing of the field lines. The field is strong where the field lines are close together and weak where the lines are far apart.

The field lines show the force on a positive test charge.

Field lines always point away from positive charge and toward negative charge.

The spacing of the lines indicates the strength of the electric field.

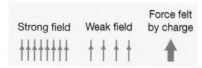

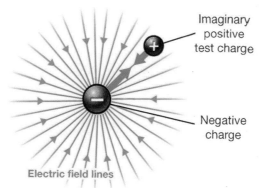

Electric field lines

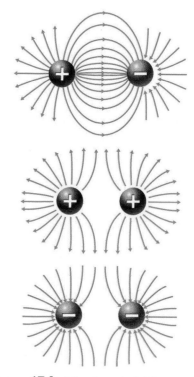

Figure 17.9: *The electric field around two or more charges can be found by imagining the force on an imaginary positive test charge at nearby points.*

Calculating the electric field

Electric field strength The strength of the electric field determines the amount of force exerted by a charge on another charge. The object that creates the field is called the **source charge** (q_1). The charge you place to test the force is the test charge. The force (F) on the test charge is equal to the amount of charge (q_2) multiplied by the electric field (E), or $F = q_2 E$. As we did with gravity, we can rewrite Coulomb's law so that the electric field is a separate quantity in the formula (Figure 17.10).

Units of electric field For gravity, the strength of the field is in newtons per kilogram (N/kg) because the field describes the amount of force per kilogram of mass. For the electric field, the strength is in *newtons per coulomb* (N/C) for a similar reason. The electric field describes the amount of force per *coulomb of charge*. For example, a 10-column test charge exerts 10 times as much force as a 1-column charge.

Volts per meter The electric field can also be written in more practical units. Remember, 1 volt is 1 joule per coulomb. A joule is equal to a newton·meter. By combining the relationships between units, you can prove that 1 newton per coulomb is the same as *1 volt per meter*. This is a prescription for how to make an electric field in the laboratory. A voltage difference of 1 volt over a space of 1 meter makes an electric field of 1 V/m. That same field exerts a force of 1 newton on a 1-coulomb test charge (Figure 17.11). Note that in Figure 17.11, the 1-volt battery is hypothetical.

Current in a wire We can now explain how the voltage from a battery causes current to flow in a wire. Once the wire is connected, an electric field spreads very rapidly through the wire. The field spreads much faster than the movement of the electrons. Electrons throughout the wire begin moving and carrying current as soon as the electric field exerts a force on them. The electrons move slowly, at their drift velocity. The field, however, moves at nearly the speed of light so it penetrates the entire wire almost instantaneously.

> **source charge** - the charge that creates an electric field

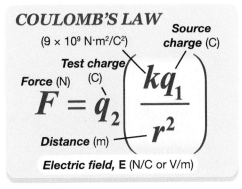

Figure 17.10: *Coulomb's law can be rewritten so that electric field and test charge appear as separate quantities.*

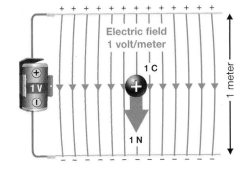

Figure 17.11: *A voltage difference of 1 volt across a distance of 1 meter makes an electric field of 1 volt per meter. This creates a force of 1 newton on a 1-coulomb test charge.*

The force on a charge in an electric field

The force on electrons in a wire　The force on a charge is equal to the charge in coulombs multiplied by the electric field in volts per meter (Figure 17.12). Like any force, the force from the electric field accelerates the charge on which it is acting. Inside a copper wire carrying current, the electric field exerts a force on the free electrons, accelerating them in the direction of the field. Why don't the electrons move faster and make the current go higher? An electron only accelerates for a short distance before it collides with a copper atom. The electron bounces off and is accelerated for another short distance before it bounces off another atom. This is why the constant force from the electric field results in a constant drift velocity for electrons. Similarly, an object travels with a constant speed when the applied force equals the force of friction.

How to make an electron-beam accelerator　An electric field is produced by any voltage difference across any insulating space, such as air or a vacuum. Many electrical devices use electric fields created in this way. For example, suppose voltage is created across a metal plate and screen (Figure 17.13). The plate repels electrons and the screen attracts them. Because the screen has holes, many of the electrons pass through it. Because a force is exerted on the electrons between the plate and screen, this device is an *accelerator* for electrons. With such a device, electrons in a beam can easily move at speeds exceeding 1 million meters per second.

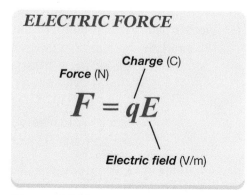

ELECTRIC FORCE

$$F = qE$$

Force (N)　Charge (C)

Electric field (V/m)

Figure 17.12: *The force on a charge in an electric field is equal to the charge in coulombs multiplied by the field strength in volts per meter.*

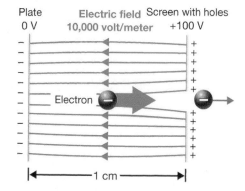

Figure 17.13: *An electric field between a plate and a screen makes an accelerator for charged particles like electrons.*

 **Calculating the electric force on a raindrop**

A raindrop has a static charge of 0.0001 C. In a thunderstorm, the raindrop experiences an electric field of 1,000 V/m. What would be the force on the drop?

1. Looking for:	Force in newtons
2. Given:	Charge in coulombs and electric field in volts per meter
3. Relationships:	$F = qE$
4. Solution::	$F = (0.0001\ \text{C}) \times (1,000\ \text{V/m}) = 0.1\ \text{N}$

Your Turn:

a. What is the force on a 0.005-C charge in an electric field of 300 V/m?

(Answers are listed at the end of the chapter.)

Electric shielding

Conductors can block electric fields In a conductor, charges are free to move under the influence of any electric field. When a circular conductor is placed in an electric field, a very interesting thing happens. If the field is positive, negative charges move toward it until the field in the conductor is neutralized. If the field is negative, electrons move away, leaving enough positive charge behind to neutralize the field in the conductor. *On the inside of the conductor, the field is zero!*

> **shielding** - materials that reduce or block electric fields

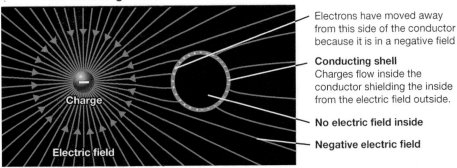

The shielding effect of a conductor

Electrons have moved away from this side of the conductor because it is in a negative field

Conducting shell
Charges flow inside the conductor shielding the inside from the electric field outside.

No electric field inside

Negative electric field

Charge

Electric field

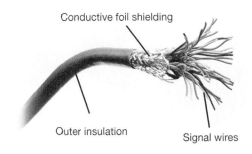

Computer network cable

Conductive foil shielding

Outer insulation

Signal wires

Figure 17.14: *Computer network cables have a conducting foil shield to keep out unwanted electric fields that could cause interference.*

Shielding out electrical interference Electric fields are created all around us by electric appliances, lightning, and even static electricity. These stray electric fields can interfere with the operation of computers and other sensitive electronics. Many electrical devices and wires that connect them are enclosed in conducting metal shells to take advantage of the **shielding** effect. For example, if you unwrap a computer network wire, you will find smaller wires wrapped by aluminum foil. The aluminum foil is a conductor and shields the wires inside from electrical interference (Figure 17.14).

17.3 Section Review

1. Draw the electric field around a negative charge. Do the field lines point toward or away from the charge?
2. What is the force on a 1-coulomb charge in an electric field of 1 volt per meter?
3. Why is electric shielding important?

Space Weather is Magnetic

"Today's high will be 24°C with clear skies and sunshine. And it looks like the magnetic storm that is on its way will affect our local electric power grid! More on this after a station break."

This fictional weather report includes information about space weather. The extent to which space weather affects Earth is actively investigated by scientists. Aiding this research is the Advanced Composition Explorer (ACE) satellite launched by NASA in 1997.

The ACE orbits one of a few unique points in space at which the gravitational pull on the satellite by Earth

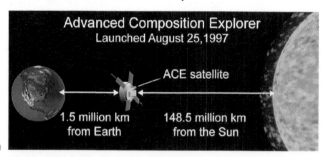

Advanced Composition Explorer
Launched August 25, 1997

ACE satellite

1.5 million km from Earth

148.5 million km from the Sun

and the Sun exactly cancel each other. For ACE, the center of its orbit is a point that is 148.5 million kilometers from the Sun and 1.5 million kilometers from Earth. At this location, the ACE is far enough from Earth so that it is not affected by the planet's magnetic field.

Storming Earth's atmosphere

The Sun emits more than heat and light. The solar wind travels at 400 km/s and is composed of electrically-charged particles. The solar wind comes from the Sun's outer surface and is so hot that the Sun's gravity cannot hold on to it. Evidence of solar wind comes from the tails of comets. A comet's tail acts like a "wind sock" and shows that there is a continuous flow of particles from the Sun.

The ACE collects data on solar wind particles and provides 1-hour advanced warnings of magnetic storms—events when solar wind is particularly intense due to massive solar eruptions. Magnetic storms can damage communications satellites orbiting Earth and cause

electrical currents to flow through and overwhelm electric power grids on the ground. Potential consequences are disrupted radio, television, and telephone signals, and possible loss of electricity for homes and businesses. For example, on March 13, 1989, a major magnetic storm caused a blackout in Quebec, Canada, that affected 6 million people. Magnetic storms also affect the flight of spacecraft and can be hazardous to astronauts. If an astronaut performed a space walk during a magnetic storm, the exposure to space radiation would be more than a million times greater than the dose of radiation we experience daily on Earth!

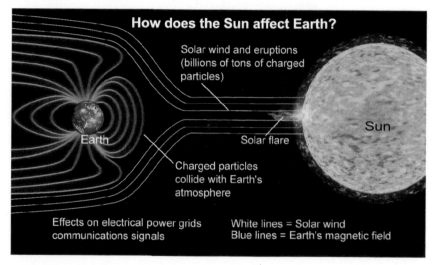

How does the Sun affect Earth?

Solar wind and eruptions (billions of tons of charged particles)

Earth

Solar flare

Sun

Charged particles collide with Earth's atmosphere

Effects on electrical power grids communications signals

White lines = Solar wind
Blue lines = Earth's magnetic field

Gigantic magnetic spots

Solar wind and magnetic storms are associated with sunspots. Sunspots occur when magnetic fields—caused by the movement of gas within the Sun—break the Sun's surface. The spots, which are cooler than surrounding areas, appear dark because they give off less light than the gases around them. The magnetic field in a sunspot may be 5,000 times stronger than Earth's magnetic field.

Sunspot

Sunspots were observed by many early astronomers such as Galileo. In fact, Galileo harmed his eyesight by looking at the Sun using a telescope. Remember, you should never look directly at the Sun. A safe method for viewing the Sun is to project its image onto a white surface using a telescope or binoculars. When the Sun is observed in this way, you can see the sunspots as dark areas. Although the areas look small, they can be as large as Earth.

Occasionally, large "loops" of gas can be seen jumping up from groups of sunspots and extending far out into space. These are most easily observed during eclipses. Sometimes loops from different sunspot regions connect and become solar flares. The flares release such large amounts of heat and light that the solar wind intensifies and causes magnetic storms.

Sun activity in 11-year cycles

Not surprisingly, the occurrence of solar flares is related to the number of sunspots. The number of sunspots varies over an 11-year period known as the sunspot cycle. Scientists speculate that there is a relationship between the sunspot cycle and variations in our global climate. Two decades of satellite research have shown that at times of high sunspot activity, the amount of energy that reaches the edge of Earth's atmosphere increases slightly. However, only through further research will scientists be able to say how the sunspot cycle affects the global climate.

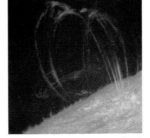

Image courtesy of NASA

After a peak in the sunspot cycle, the Sun emits billions of tons of gas referred to as coronal mass ejections (CMEs). As the gas leaves the Sun's surface, its "magnetic skin" is shed as well. The result is that the Sun's magnetic field lines are reoriented, and the build up of new CMEs begins. CMEs can also cause magnetic storms on Earth.

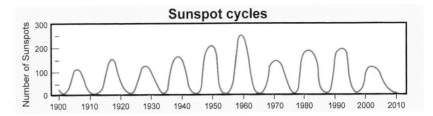

Sunspot cycles

Magnetism shields Earth

Earth's magnetic field lines protect the planet from solar wind. The field lines, which exert force on moving charges, trap the electrical charges in the solar wind and force them to move along the field lines, particularly at the poles. When the charged particles encounter the upper atmosphere, they cause atmospheric atoms to emit light. The lights—called auroras—appear above the horizon in the night sky.

Auroras are a mild effect of solar wind. Magnetic storms are a dramatic form of space weather. Scientists are very interested in predicting these storms since they can seriously disrupt our daily activities that rely on electrical systems. For this reason, scientists pay close attention to space weather. You can keep up with solar activity and how it affects Earth by getting a daily space weather report at the NASA-sponsored site www.spaceweather.com.

QUESTIONS

1. Why is it important to have a satellite like the ACE in space? Research the ACE at http://www.srl.caltech.edu/ACE.

2. How can astronauts be protected from space radiation?

3. When are magnetic storms most likely to happen?

4. When will the next sunspot peak occur?

Chapter 17 Review

Understanding Vocabulary

Select the correct term to complete the sentences.

electric field	gravitational field	shielding
field	intensity	source charge
force field	inverse square law	

1. The _____ states that a field decreases as the square of the distance from the source of the field increases.

2. A(n) _____ creates a force on masses at all points in space.

3. Materials that cause a(n) _____ effect, reduce or block electric fields.

4. A charge that creates an electric field is called a(n) _____ .

5. A force field created by the forces between electric charges is called a(n) _____ .

Reviewing Concepts

Section 17.1

1. Interactions between _____ and _____ occur through fields.

2. List three types of fields that are affecting you right now.

3. What is stored in a field?

4. Why does a sound get softer as you move away from its source?

5. In what units is intensity measured?

6. What does it mean to say a field follows an inverse square law?

7. Do all fields follow an inverse square law? Explain.

Section 17.2

8. Anything with _____ creates a gravitational field.

9. Why don't we notice the gravitational fields created by all of the objects around us?

10. What happens to the strength of Earth's gravitational field as you move away from Earth's surface?

11. Explain how you feel Earth's gravity even when you jump off the ground and are not directly touching the Earth.

12. In what units are gravitational fields measured?

13. In what direction do the gravitational field lines around Earth point?

Section 17.3

14. A(n) _____ charge in an electric field feels a force in the direction of the field. A(n) _____ charge feels a force in a direction opposite the field.

15. What determines the strength of a charge's electric field at a point?

16. What two pieces of information can you get by looking at field lines?

17. What does the spacing of electric field lines tell you about the field strength?

18. In what units is electric field strength measured? (*Hint*: There are two possible answers.)

19. What makes free electrons move through a wire in a circuit? Use the idea of electric fields in your answer.

20. Why are many electrical wires enclosed in a metal covering?

Solving Problems

Section 17.1

1. The light intensity 1 m away from a bulb is 2 W/m². What is the intensity 2 m away?

2. You stand 4 m away from a light and measure the intensity to be 1 W/m². What will the intensity be at 2 m from the light?

Section 17.2

3. Gravitational fields follow an inverse square law. Suppose you weigh 600 N when you are on Earth's surface. How much would you weigh if you move away from Earth so that you double your distance from its center?

4. Jupiter has a mass of 1.9×10^{27} kg and a radius of 7.15×10^7 m. Calculate the strength of Jupiter's gravitational field at its surface.

5. Jupiter's moon Io has a mass of 8.94×10^{22} kg and a radius of 1.82×10^6 m. Calculate the strength of the gravitational field on Io's surface.

6. Use Newton's law of gravitation to show that Earth's gravitational field has a strength of 9.8 N/kg.

Section 17.3

7. Draw the electric field for each of the following.

    a. a single proton

    b. a single electron

    c. a proton a small distance away from an electron

    d. the region between two oppositely-charged plates

8. The electric field in a region is shown below. At which marked point is the electric field the strongest? At which point is it the weakest?

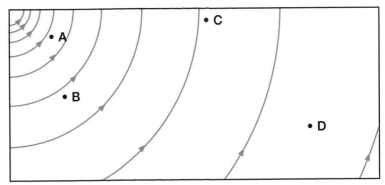

9. The electric field strength in a region is 2,000 N/C. What is the force on an object with a charge of 0.004 C?

10. What is the strength and direction of the force on each charge shown?

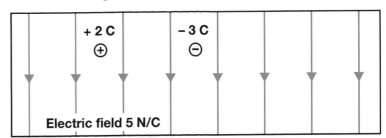

Test Practice

Section 17.1

1. Which of the following fields does *not* follow an inverse square law?

   a. gravitational

   b. electric

   c. magnetic

   d. light

2. The distance between two masses is multiplied by three. The gravitational force between them is

   a. 1⅓ times as great.

   b. 2 times as great.

   c. 9 times as great.

   d. 8 times as great.

3. What is the maximum speed of a cell phone call between New York City and Los Angeles?

   a. the speed of sound

   b. the speed of light

   c. instantaneous

   d. depends on the service provider

Section 17.2

4. Planet X has a mass of 4.33×10^{22} kg and a radius of 1.85×10^{6} m. What is the gravitational field strength at its surface? ($G = 6.67 \times 10$-11 N·m²/kg²)

   a. 8.44×10^{-1} N/kg

   b. 1.56×10^{6} N/kg

   c. 2.34×10^{16} N/kg

   d. 1.27×10^{10} N/kg

5. Which diagram best represents the lines of gravitational field surrounding Earth?

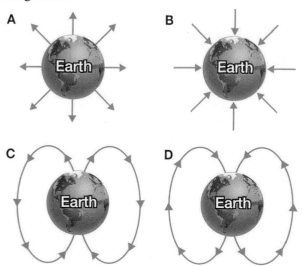

Section 17.3

6. Which diagram best represents the field near a positively-charged body?

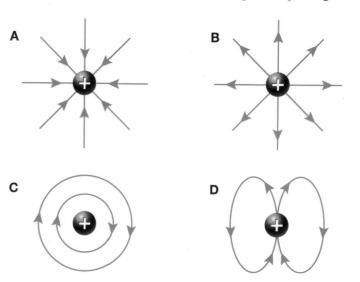

7. Two charged spheres are shown in the diagram. Which combination of charges produce the electric field shown?

    a. A positive and B negative

    b. A negative and B positive

    c. A and B both negative

    d. A and B both positive

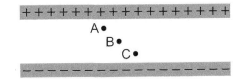

8. This diagram represents two charged parallel plates. How does the electric field strength compare at locations A, B, and C?

    a. The field strength is greatest at A.

    b. The field strength is greatest at B.

    c. The field strength is greatest at C.

    d. The field strength is the same at all locations.

9. This diagram shows two parallel metal plates A and B connected to a voltage source. What is the approximate electric field strength between the two plates?

    a. 400 N/C

    b. 500 N/C

    c. 600 N/C

    d. 4,000 N/C

10. What force is applied to an electron in an electric field of 518 V/m?

    a. 8.29×10^{21} N

    b. 3.24×10^{21} N

    c. 5.18×10^{2} N

    d. 8.29×10^{-17} N

Applying Your Knowledge

Section 17.1

1. Are some types of fields vectors while others are scalars, or are all fields the same? Explain using examples.

2. Fields cannot travel faster than the speed of light. List some examples of fields that travel slower than the speed of light and fields that travel at the speed of light.

3. Use the idea of intensity to explain why it is not a good idea to put your ear directly up to a loud stereo speaker.

4. If the Sun was to suddenly vanish, how long would it take for us to notice?

Section 17.2

5. A planet's gravitational field is represented with the letter g and is measured in N/kg. When you studied free fall, you measured g in m/s². Show that the two units are equivalent.

6. Suppose you could double Earth's mass without changing its size. What would happen to the strength of the gravitational field? What would happen to Earth's gravitational field if you doubled the radius but kept the mass at its current value?

Section 17.3

7. Research particle accelerators. How are they designed, and what are they used for?

 Your Turn Answers

Calculating the gravitational field of Mars (Section 17.2, page 413)

a. 6.7×10^{-9} N/kg

Calculating the electric force on a raindrop (Section 17.3, page 416)

a. 1.5 N

Unit 7 VIBRATIONS, WAVES, AND SOUND

Harmonic Motion

People often create habits that are repetitive because some repetitive motions have regular, comfortable rhythms. Babies like the feel of the back-and-forth motion of a rocking chair. It often puts them to sleep. We see back-and-forth motion in many situations. Earth spins on its axis every 24 hours. Maybe this is why we are often comfortable with motions that have regular rhythms.

A swing, the pendulum of a grandfather clock, and a rocking chair all have this kind of motion. Motion that repeats is called *harmonic motion*. Offered a choice of sitting in a stationary chair or a rocking chair, you might pick the rocking chair. Rocking back and forth can be more fun than sitting still!

Harmonic motion includes motion that goes around and around. Earth orbiting the Sun, a planet spinning on its axis, and a moving Ferris wheel are all examples of this kind of harmonic motion.

Objects or systems that make harmonic motions are called oscillators. Think about where you see oscillators or oscillating systems at home or in school. Look around your classroom. Where do you see oscillators? Where do you see back-and-forth motion or motion that goes around and around?

VOCABULARY

amplitude	hertz	periodic force
cycle	natural frequency	phase
damping	oscillation	resonance
frequency	oscillator	restoring force
harmonic motion	period	vibration

KEY QUESTIONS

✓ *How is Earth part of harmonic motion systems?*

✓ *What does it mean when two oscillators are "out of phase"?*

✓ *How does a guitar use natural frequency to make notes?*

18.1 Harmonic Motion

The forward rush of a cyclist pedaling past you on the street is called *linear motion*. Linear motion gets us from one place to another whether we are walking, riding a bicycle, or driving a car (Figure 18.1). The pedaling action and turning of the cycle's wheels are examples of harmonic motion. **Harmonic motion**, also called *oscillatory motion*, is motion that repeats.

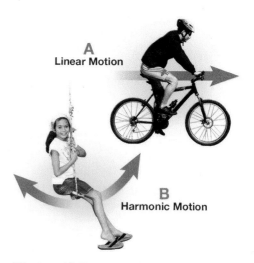

> **harmonic motion -** repeating motion; also called oscillatory motion
>
> **cycle -** a unit of oscillation that repeats

Motion in cycles

What is a cycle? In earlier chapters, we used position, speed, and acceleration to describe motion. For harmonic motion, we need some new ideas that describe the "over-and-over" repetition. The first important idea is the **cycle**. A cycle is a unit of motion that repeats over and over. One complete spin of a bicycle wheel is a cycle and so is one complete turn of the pedals. One full back-and-forth swing of a child on a playground swing is also one cycle (Figure 18.1).

Looking at one cycle A pendulum's cycle is shown in the diagram below. Each box in the diagram is a snapshot of the motion at a different time in the cycle.

The cycle of the pendulum

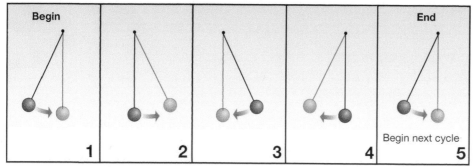

Figure 18.1: *(A) Real-life situations such as riding a bicycle can include both linear motion and harmonic motion. (B) A person swinging on a swing is an example of harmonic motion in action.*

The cycle of a pendulum The cycle starts with (1) the swing from left to center. The cycle continues with (2) from center to right, and (3) back from right to center. The cycle ends at (4), when the pendulum moves from center to left because this brings the pendulum back to the beginning of the cycle. Box (5) is the same as (1) and starts the next cycle. Once a cycle is completed, the next cycle begins without any interruption in the motion.

Where do you find harmonic motion?

Oscillators   The word **oscillation** means a motion that repeats regularly. Therefore, a system with harmonic motion is called an **oscillator**. Harmonic motion can also be called *oscillatory motion*. A pendulum is an oscillator; so is your heart and its surrounding muscles. Our solar system is a large oscillator with each planet in harmonic motion around the Sun. An atom is a small oscillator because its electrons vibrate around the nucleus. The term **vibration** is another word used for back and forth motion. We will use "vibration" for motion that repeats fast and "oscillation" for motion that repeats more slowly.

> **oscillation** - a motion that repeats regularly
>
> **oscillator** - a system that shows harmonic motion
>
> **vibration** - a rapid oscillation

Earth is part of harmonic motion systems

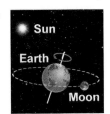

Earth is a part of several oscillating systems. The Earth-Sun system has a cycle of one year, which means Earth completes one orbit around the Sun in a year. The Earth-Moon system has a cycle of approximately 28 days. Earth rotates on its axis once a day, making the 24-hour cycle of day and night. There are also cycles in weather, such as the El Niño Southern Oscillation, an event that involves warmer ocean water and increased thunderstorm activity in the western Pacific Ocean. Cycles are important; the lives of all plants and animals depend on seasonal cycles.

Music   Sound is a traveling vibration of air molecules. Musical instruments and stereo speakers are oscillators designed to create sounds with certain cycles that we enjoy hearing. When a stereo is playing, the speaker cone moves back and forth rapidly (Figure 18.2). The cyclic back-and-forth motion pushes and pulls on air, creating tiny oscillations in pressure. The pressure oscillations travel to your eardrum and cause it to vibrate. Vibrations of the eardrum move tiny bones in the ear setting up more vibrations that are transmitted by nerves to the brain. There is harmonic motion from the musical instrument's sound to the perception of sound by your brain.

Color   Light is the result of harmonic motion of the electric and magnetic fields (Chapter 17). For example, the colors that you see in a painting come from the vibration of electrons in the molecules of paint. Each color of paint contains molecules that oscillate with different cycles to create the colors of light you see (Chapter 21).

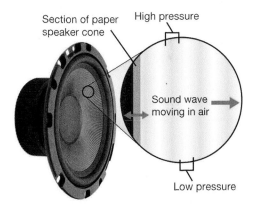

Figure 18.2: *As a speaker cone moves back and forth, it pushes and pulls on air, creating oscillating changes in pressure that we can detect with our ears. The dark blue bands in the graphic represent high-pressure regions and the white bands represent low-pressure regions.*

Describing harmonic motion

Oscillators in communications   Almost all modern communication technology relies on harmonic motion. The electronic technology in a cell phone uses an oscillator that makes more than 100 million cycles each second. When you tune your radio to a station at 101.5 on the FM dial, you are actually setting the oscillator in your radio to 101.5 million cycles per second.

Period is the time for one cycle   The time for one cycle to occur is called the **period**. The cycles of some oscillators always repeat with the same period. This makes harmonic motion a good way to keep time. For example, a clock pendulum with a period of 1 second will complete 60 swings (or cycles) in 1 minute. A clock keeps track of time by counting cycles of an oscillator.

period - the amount of time it takes for one cycle

frequency - the number of cycles per second

hertz - the unit of one cycle per second

A period is the time to complete one cycle of harmonic motion.

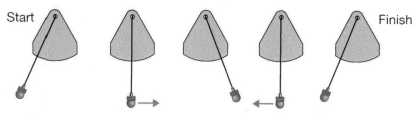

Start   Finish

Frequency is the number of cycles per second   The term **frequency** means the number of cycles per second. FM radio—the *FM* stands for "frequency modulation"—uses frequencies between 87.5 million and 108.0 million cycles per second. Your heartbeat has a frequency between one-half and two cycles per second. The musical note "A" has a frequency of 440 cycles per second. The human voice contains frequencies mainly between 100 and 2,000 cycles per second.

A hertz equals one cycle per second   The unit of one cycle per second is called a **hertz**. You hear music when the frequency of the oscillator in your radio exactly matches the frequency of the oscillator signal being transmitted from the radio station tower (Figure 18.3). A radio station dial set to 101.5 FM receives music broadcast at a frequency of 101,500,000 hertz, or 101.5 megahertz. Your ear can hear frequencies of sound in the range from 20 hertz to between 15,000 and 20,000 hertz. The hertz (Hz) is a unit that is the same in both the English and SI systems of measurement.

Figure 18.3: *For your radio to play a specific station, the frequency of the oscillator in your radio must match the frequency of the oscillator signal being broadcast from the transmission tower used by the radio station.*

Calculating harmonic motion

Frequency is the inverse of period
Frequency and period are inversely related. The period is the time per cycle. The frequency is the number of cycles per time. For example, if the period of a pendulum is 2 seconds, its frequency is 0.5 cycles per second (0.5 Hz).

PERIOD AND FREQUENCY

$$T = \frac{1}{f}$$

Period (s)   Frequency (Hz)

$$f = \frac{1}{T}$$

Period (s)

   Calculating frequency

The period of an oscillator is 15 minutes. What is the frequency of this oscillator in hertz?

1. **Looking for:**   You are asked for the frequency in hertz.

2. **Given:**   You are given the period in minutes.

3. **Relationships:**   Convert minutes to seconds using the conversion factor 1 minute/60 seconds; Use the formula: $f = 1/T$;

4. **Solution:** $15 \text{ minutes} \times \dfrac{60 \text{ s}}{1 \text{ min}} = 900 \text{ s}; f = \dfrac{1}{900 \text{ s}} = 0.0011 \text{ Hz}$

Your Turn:

a. The period of an oscillator is 2 minutes. What is the frequency of the oscillator?

b. How often would you push someone on a swing to create a frequency of 0.20 hertz?

c. *Challenge!* The minute hand of a clock pendulum moves 1/60 of a turn after 30 cycles. What is the period and frequency of this pendulum?

(Answers are listed at the end of the chapter.)

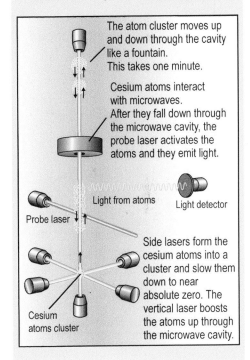

Keeping "perfect" time

One of the world's most accurate clocks is the NIST-F1 Cesium Fountain Atomic Clock in Boulder, Colorado. It keeps time by counting cycles of light waves emitted by a cluster of cesium atoms after they interact with microwaves in a special cavity. This clock is only off by 1 second every 100 million years!

The atom cluster moves up and down through the cavity like a fountain. This takes one minute.

Cesium atoms interact with microwaves. After they fall down through the microwave cavity, the probe laser activates the atoms and they emit light.

Light from atoms   Light detector

Probe laser

Side lasers form the cesium atoms into a cluster and slow them down to near absolute zero. The vertical laser boosts the atoms up through the microwave cavity.

Cesium atoms cluster

Amplitude

Amplitude describes the size of a cycle   The **amplitude** of an oscillator describes the "size" of a cycle. Figure 18.4 shows a pendulum with small amplitude and large amplitude. With mechanical systems (such as a pendulum), the amplitude is often a distance or angle. With other kinds of oscillators, the amplitude might be voltage or pressure. The amplitude is measured in units appropriate to the kind of system you are describing.

How do you measure amplitude?   The amplitude is the maximum distance the oscillator moves away from its *equilibrium* position. For a pendulum, the equilibrium position is hanging straight down in the center. For the pendulum in Figure 18.5, the amplitude is 20 degrees, because the pendulum moves 20 degrees away from center in either direction.

Damping   Friction slows a pendulum down, as it does all oscillators. That means the amplitude slowly gets reduced until the pendulum is hanging straight down, motionless. We use the word **damping** to describe the gradual loss of amplitude of an oscillator. If you wanted to make a clock with a pendulum, you would have to find a way to keep adding energy (through winding or electricity) to counteract the damping of friction.

amplitude - the maximum distance from the equilibrium position in harmonic motion

damping - the gradual loss of amplitude of an oscillator

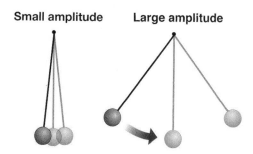

Figure 18.4: *Small amplitude versus large amplitude.*

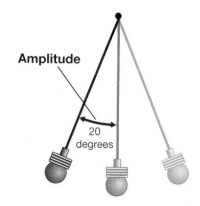

Figure 18.5: *A pendulum with an amplitude of 20 degrees swings 20 degrees away from the center.*

18.1 Section Review

1. Which is the best example of a cycle: a turn of a bicycle wheel or a slide down a ski slope?
2. Describe one example of an oscillating system you would find at an amusement park.
3. What is the relationship between period and frequency?
4. Every 6 seconds a pendulum completes one cycle. What are the period and frequency of this pendulum?

18.2 Graphs of Harmonic Motion

Harmonic motion graphs show cycles (Figure 18.6). Even without seeing the actual motion, you can look at a harmonic motion graph and figure out the period and amplitude. You can also quickly sketch an accurate harmonic motion graph if you know the period and amplitude.

Reading harmonic motion graphs

Repeating patterns   The most common type of graph puts position on the vertical, or y-axis and time on the horizontal, or x-axis. The graph below shows how the position of a pendulum changes over time. The repeating "wave" on the graph represents the repeating cycles of motion of the pendulum.

Finding the period   The pattern of the pendulum in the figure below repeats every 1.5 seconds. This is the period of the pendulum. If you were to cut out any piece of the graph and slide it over 1.5 seconds it would line up exactly. You can tell the period is 1.5 seconds because the graph repeats itself every 1.5 seconds.

Showing amplitude on a graph   The amplitude of harmonic motion can also be seen on a graph. The graph below shows that the pendulum swings from +20 centimeters, to −20 centimeters, and back. Therefore, the amplitude of the pendulum is 20 centimeters. Harmonic motion graphs often use positive and negative values to represent motion on either side of the center position. Zero usually represents the equilibrium point. Notice that zero is placed halfway up the y-axis so there is room for both positive and negative values. This graph is in centimeters, but the motion of the pendulum could also have been graphed using the angle measured relative to the center or equilibrium position.

Typical linear motion graphs

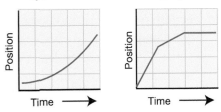

Typical harmonic motion graphs

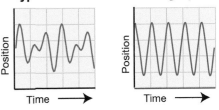

Figure 18.6: *Typical graphs for linear motion (top) and harmonic motion (bottom). Graphs of linear motion do not show cycles. Harmonic motion graphs show repeating cycles.*

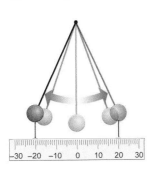

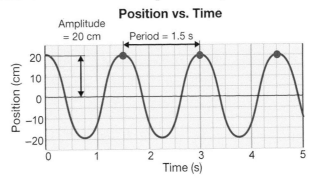

Determining period and amplitude from a graph

Calculating period from a graph   To find the period from a graph, start by identifying one complete cycle. The cycle must begin and end in the same place in the pattern. Figure 18.7 shows how to choose the cycle for a simple harmonic motion graph and for a more complex one. Once you have identified a cycle, you use the time axis of the graph to determine the period. The period is the time difference between the beginning of the cycle and the end. Subtract the beginning time from the ending time, as shown in the example below.

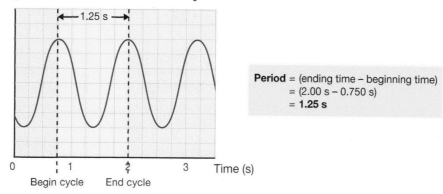

Period = (ending time – beginning time)
= (2.00 s – 0.750 s)
= **1.25 s**

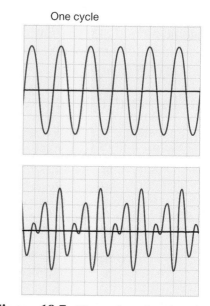

Figure 18.7: *The cycle is the part of the graph that repeats over and over. The yellow shading shows one cycle for each of the graphs above.*

Calculating amplitude from a graph   On a graph of harmonic motion, the amplitude is half the distance between the highest and lowest points on the graph. For example, in Figure 18.8, the amplitude is 20 centimeters. Here is the calculation:

[20 cm − (−20 cm)] ÷ 2 = [20 cm + 20 cm] ÷ 2 = 40 cm ÷ 2 = 20 cm.

AMPLITUDE

$$Amplitude = \frac{1}{2} \left(\begin{array}{c} high \\ point \end{array} - \begin{array}{c} low \\ point \end{array} \right)$$

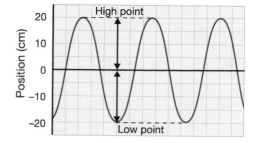

Figure 18.8: *The amplitude is one half the distance between the highest and lowest points on the graph. In this graph of harmonic motion, the amplitude is 20 centimeters.*

Circular motion and phase

Phase How do you describe where a pendulum is in its cycle? Saying the pendulum is at a 10 degree angle is not enough. If the pendulum started at 10 degrees, then it would be at the start of its cycle. If the pendulum started at 20 degrees, it would be part way through its cycle and could be near the start or the end. The **phase** tells you exactly where an oscillator is in its cycle. Phase is measured relative to the whole cycle, and is independent of amplitude or period.

phase - where an oscillator is in its cycle

Each cycle of circular motion is 360° The most convenient way to describe phase is to think in terms of angles and circular motion. Circular motion is a kind of harmonic motion because rotation is a pattern of repeating cycles. Each cycle of circular motion measures 360 degrees. It does not matter how big the wheel is, each full turn is 360 degrees. Because circular motion always has cycles of 360 degrees, *we use degrees to measure phase.*

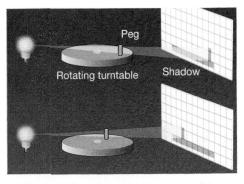

Phase is measured in degrees To see how degrees apply to harmonic motion that is not circular (such as a pendulum), imagine a peg on a rotating turntable (Figure 18.9). A bright light casts a shadow of the peg on the wall. As the turntable rotates, the shadow goes back and forth on the wall (A in Figure 18.9). If we make a graph of the position of the shadow, we get a harmonic motion graph (B). One cycle passes with every 360-degree turn of the turntable. A quarter cycle has a phase of 90 degrees, half a cycle has a phase of 180 degrees, and so on.

One cycle of a rotating turntable

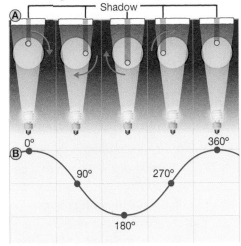

Two oscillators "in phase" The concept of phase is most important when comparing two or more oscillators. Imagine two identical pendulums. If you start them together, their graphs look like the picture below. We say these pendulums are *in phase* because their cycles are aligned. Each is at the same place at the same time.

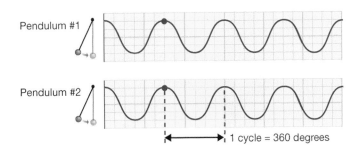

Figure 18.9: *The harmonic motion of a rotating turntable is illustrated by the back-and-forth motion of the shadow of the peg.*

Harmonic motion that is out of phase

Out of phase by 90 degrees   If we start the first pendulum swinging a little before the second one, the graphs look like Figure 18.10. Although, they have the same cycle, the first pendulum is always a little bit ahead in its cycle compared to the second pendulum. Notice that the graph for pendulum 1 reaches its maximum 90 degrees *before* the graph for pendulum 2. We say the pendulums are *out of phase* by 90 degrees, or one-fourth of a cycle (90 degrees is one-fourth of 360 degrees).

Out of phase by 180 degrees   When they are out of phase, the relative motion of oscillators may differ by any fraction of a whole cycle. For example, two oscillators that are 180 degrees out of phase are one-half cycle apart. Figure 18.11 shows that the two pendulums are always on opposite sides of the cycle from each other. When pendulum 1 is all the way to the left, pendulum 2 is all the way to the right. This motion is illustrated on the graph by showing that "peaks" of motion (positive amplitude) for one pendulum match the "valleys" of motion (negative amplitude) for the other.

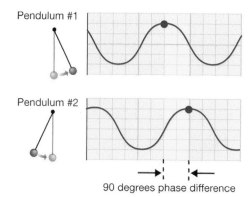

Figure 18.10: *The two pendulums are 90 degrees out of phase.*

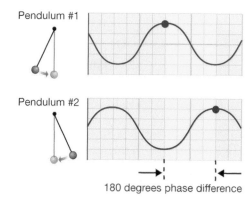

Figure 18.11: *The two pendulums are 180 degrees out of phase.*

18.2 Section Review

1. What is the difference between a graph of linear motion and a graph of harmonic motion?
2. A graph of the motion of a pendulum shows that it swings from +5 centimeters to −5 centimeters for each cycle. What is the amplitude of the pendulum?
3. A pendulum swings from −10 degrees to +10 degrees. What is its amplitude?
4. A graph of harmonic motion shows that one cycle lasts from 4.3 seconds to 6.8 seconds. What is the period of this harmonic motion?
5. A graph of harmonic motion shows that the motion lasted for 10 seconds and completed 5 cycles. What is the period of this harmonic motion?
6. Sketch the periodic motion for two oscillators that are 45 degrees out of phase.
7. If one oscillator was out of phase with another oscillator by 45 degrees, what fraction of a 360-degree cycle would it be out of phase: ⅛, ¼, ½, or ¾?

18.3 **Properties of Oscillators**

Why does a pendulum oscillate? A car on a ramp just rolls down and does not oscillate. What properties of a system determine whether its motion will be linear motion or harmonic motion? You will learn the answers to these questions in this section. You will also learn how to change the period of an oscillator by changing a few important variables.

> **restoring force** - a force that pulls an oscillating system back toward equilibrium

Restoring force and equilibrium

Different kinds of systems   If you set a wagon on a hill and let it go, the wagon rolls down and does not come back. If you push a child on a swing, the child goes away from you at first, but then comes back. The child on the swing shows harmonic motion while the wagon on the hill does not. What is the fundamental difference between the two situations?

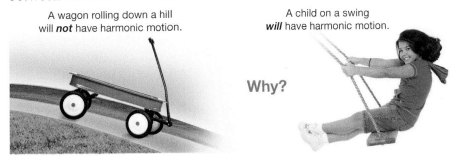

A wagon rolling down a hill will **not** have harmonic motion.

A child on a swing **will** have harmonic motion.

Why?

Equilibrium   Systems that have harmonic motion always move back and forth around a central, or equilibrium position. You can think of equilibrium as the system at rest, undisturbed, with zero net force. A wagon on a hill is *not* in equilibrium because the force of gravity is not balanced by another force. A child sitting motionless on a swing *is* in equilibrium because the force of gravity is balanced by the tension in the ropes.

Restoring forces   Equilibrium is maintained by restoring forces. A **restoring force** is any force that acts to pull a system back toward equilibrium. If the child on the swing is moved forward, gravity creates a restoring force that pulls her back, toward equilibrium. If she moves backward, gravity pulls her forward, back toward equilibrium again (Figure 18.12). Systems with restoring forces are the ones that move in harmonic motion.

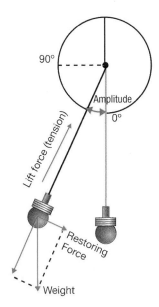

Figure 18.12: *A restoring force keeps a pendulum swinging. The restoring force is related to the weight of the mass and the lift force (or tension) of the string supporting the mass.*

Inertia and mass

Inertia causes an oscillator to go past equilibrium
The restoring force of gravity always pulls a pendulum towards equilibrium. Newton's first law of motion explains why the pendulum doesn't stop at equilibrium. The first law states that an object in motion tends to stay in motion. The pendulum has inertia that keeps it moving forward. Inertia causes the pendulum to overshoot its equilibrium position every time. The result is harmonic motion.

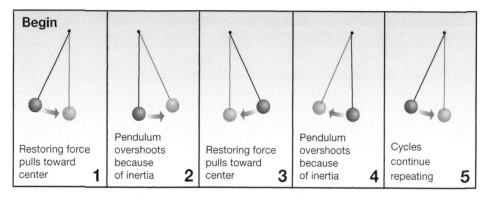

| **Begin** | | | | |
| Restoring force pulls toward center **1** | Pendulum overshoots because of inertia **2** | Restoring force pulls toward center **3** | Pendulum overshoots because of inertia **4** | Cycles continue repeating **5** |

Inertia is common to all oscillators
Systems that oscillate naturally without external energy have some property that acts like inertia and some type of restoring force. Harmonic motion results from the interaction of the two effects: inertia and restoring force.

Increasing mass may increase the period
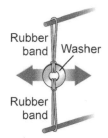

Rubber band Washer
Rubber band

You can make a simple oscillator with a steel washer and two rubber bands as shown here. What happens to the period if you increase the mass by adding more washers? The restoring force from the rubber band is the same. If the mass increases, then by Newton's second law ($a = F/m$) the acceleration decreases proportionally. Therefore, the oscillator moves slower and the period gets longer.

How mass affects the period
Changing the mass of a pendulum does *not* affect its period. That is because the restoring force on a pendulum is created by gravity. Like free fall, if you add mass to a pendulum, the added inertia is equal to the added force from gravity. The acceleration is the same and therefore the period stays the same.

Harmonic motion in machines

Natural harmonic motion results from restoring forces and inertia. However, harmonic motion can also be forced. When a machine is involved, motion can be created using an energy source to push or rotate parts.

Mechanical systems usually do not depend on a restoring force or inertia. For example, the piston of a car engine goes up and down as the crankshaft turns. The piston is in harmonic motion, but the motion is caused by the rotation of the crankshaft and the attachment of the connecting rod. Gasoline provides the energy to keep this harmonic motion system going.

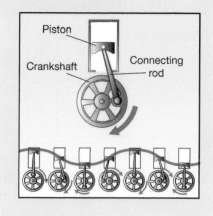

Piston
Crankshaft   Connecting rod

Period and natural frequency

Inertia causes an oscillator to go past equilibrium

A pendulum will have the same period each time you set it in motion. Unless you change the pendulum (such as changing its length), it will always swing with the same period. The **natural frequency** is the frequency (or period) at which a system oscillates naturally. Every oscillating system has a natural frequency.

Why natural frequency is important

Microwave ovens, musical instruments, and cell phones are common devices that use the natural frequency of an oscillator. For example, the strings of a guitar are tuned by adjusting the natural frequency of vibrating strings to match musical notes (Figure 18.13). All objects can oscillate, and that means everything in the universe has a natural frequency. In fact, most objects have several natural frequencies because they can oscillate in different ways.

Natural frequency

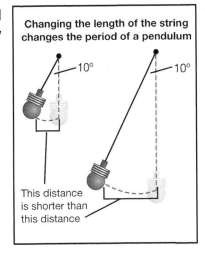

Changing the length of the string changes the period of a pendulum

10°   10°

This distance is shorter than this distance

The natural frequency depends on balancing the restoring force and inertia (mass). Any change that affects this balance will also change the natural frequency. The natural frequency of a pendulum depends on the length of the string. If you make the string longer, the restoring force is spread out over a proportionally-greater distance. The period of the pendulum gets longer. Tuning a guitar changes the natural frequency of a string by changing its tightness or *tension*. Changing the mass changes the natural frequency *only if restoring force is not due to gravity.*

Periodic force

You can keep a swing or pendulum swinging for a long time by pushing it at the right time in each cycle. A force that is repeated over and over is called a **periodic force**. A periodic force has a cycle with an amplitude, frequency, and period just like an oscillator. *To supply energy to an oscillator, you need to use a periodic force.* If you push once per cycle at the right time with a periodic force, the amplitude of the swing increases (Figure 18.14).

natural frequency - the frequency at which a system naturally oscillates

periodic force - an oscillating (repetitive) force

Guitar strings vibrate when plucked

Figure 18.13: *A guitar uses the natural frequency of strings to make musical notes.*

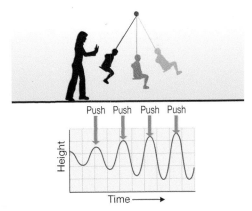

Push Push Push Push

Height

Time

Figure 18.14: *Each push of a swing at the right time increases the amplitude (height) of the swing. Each push is a periodic force.*

Resonance

Force and natural frequency Newton's second law ($a = F/m$) tells you how much acceleration results from a force acting on a mass. While the second law is still true for harmonic motion, there is a new and important difference. Harmonic motion is motion that oscillates back and forth. What happens if the force is periodic and oscillates back and forth too? When you shake one end of a rope up and down in a steady rhythm you are applying a periodic force to the rope (Figure 18.15). The rope behaves very differently depending on the frequency at which you shake it up and down! If you shake it at *just the right frequency* the rope swings up and down in harmonic motion with a large amplitude. If you don't shake it at the right frequency, the rope wiggles around but you don't get the large amplitude *no matter how strong a force you apply*. This is true for swings, too. If you don't push at the right time in the cycle, a swing won't swing (Figure 18.14).

Resonance **Resonance** occurs when a periodic force has the same frequency as the natural frequency of the system. If the force and the motion have the same frequency, each cycle of the force matches a cycle of the motion. As a result, each periodic force cycle adds to the next one and the amplitude of the motion grows. You can think about resonance in three steps: the *periodic force*, the *system*, and the *response*. The response is what the system does when you apply the periodic force. In resonance, the response is very large compared to the strength of the force, much larger than you would expect. Resonance occurs when

- there is a system in harmonic motion, like a swing or a jump rope;
- there is a periodic force, like a push or a shake; and
- the frequency of the periodic force equals the system's natural frequency.

Swings and jump ropes are examples of resonance Both a swing and a jump rope depend on resonance. For example, if you want to get a jump rope going, you shake the ends up and down at the right frequency to get the rope moving with a large amplitude (Figure 18.15). The response is an example of resonance and happens only when the frequency of your periodic force matches the natural frequency of the jump rope.

> **resonance** - occurs when a periodic force has the same frequency as the natural frequency

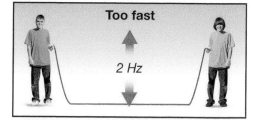

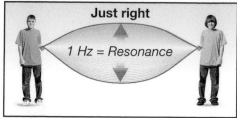

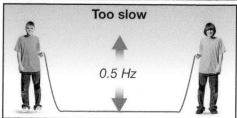

Figure 18.15: *A jump rope is a good way to show resonance. If you shake it at the right frequency, it makes a wave. If the frequency is too fast or too slow, the rope will not make the wave pattern at all.*

Simple oscillators

A mass on a spring You know from experience that springs resist being extended or compressed. Figure 18.16 shows how the restoring force from a spring always acts to return it to equilibrium. A system of a mass on a spring is a simple oscillator. When the spring is compressed, it pushes back on the mass. When the spring is extended, it pulls on the mass. The system is an oscillator because the push-pull of the spring is a restoring force, and the mass supplies the inertia. An example of a mass on a spring is a car and its shock absorbers (springs). Wheels on springs can oscillate up and down over bumps without the whole car having to move up and down. Along with springs, shock absorbers also have high-friction *dampers* that quickly slow any oscillation down. A car that keeps bouncing after going over a bump could have shock absorbers with dampers that are worn out and not providing enough friction.

A vibrating string An example of a *vibrating string* oscillator is a rubber band stretched between two rods (Figure 18.17). If the middle of the rubber band is pulled to the side, it will move back toward equilibrium when it is released. Stretching the rubber band to the side creates a restoring force. When the rubber band is released, inertia carries it past equilibrium and it vibrates. Vibrating strings tend to move much faster than springs and pendulums. The period of a vibrating string can be one-hundredth of a second (0.01 s) or shorter.

Mass on a vibrating string You can modify the rubber band oscillator by adding a bead to the middle of a stretched rubber band (Figure 18.17). The bead adds extra mass to this simple oscillator, which increases its inertia. How would adding a bead to a rubber band change the natural frequency? Notice that gravity is not directly involved in the back-and-forth movement of this oscillator.

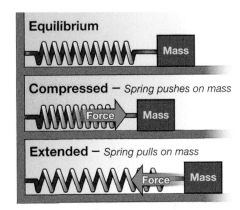

Figure 18.16: *A mass on a spring is an oscillating system. When the spring is compressed, it pushes the mass back to equilibrium. When the spring is extended, it pulls the mass back toward equilibrium.*

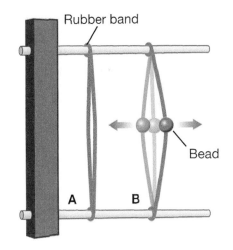

Figure 18.17: *A stretched rubber band is a good example of a vibrating string (A). You can modify this simple oscillator by adding a bead to the rubber band (B).*

18.3 *Section Review*

1. Identify the restoring force for a pendulum, a mass on a spring, and a vibrating string.
2. You change the amplitude of a pendulum from 10 centimeters to 30 centimeters. How does this change affect the period of the pendulum? Justify your answer.
3. Is a person jumping on a trampoline an oscillator? Justify your response.
4. If you wanted to increase the period of a pendulum, how would you change its length?

Skyscrapers and Harmonic Motion

The John Hancock Tower is one of the tallest skyscrapers in New England. This 60-story building is 240.7 meters tall and was completed in 1976. With 10,344 windowpanes, the most striking feature of this building is that it is completely covered in glass.

While this skyscraper was being built in 1972 and 1973, a disaster struck—windowpanes started falling out all over the building and crashing to the ground. So many fell out that the Hancock Tower was nicknamed the "plywood palace" due to the boarded-up window holes. Some people said the windows fell out because the building swayed too much in the wind. They thought the problem was caused by the natural harmonic motion of the skyscraper.

Why does a skyscraper sway?

Just like trees, which experience harmonic motion in strong winds, skyscrapers also sway side to side. Skyscrapers, even if made of steel and concrete, begin to vibrate when the wind blows or an earthquake occurs. In fact, all buildings have a fundamental frequency of vibration. The fundamental frequencies of buildings cover a range of values: 5 hertz for two-story buildings, 2 hertz for five-story buildings, 1 to 0.5 hertz for tall buildings (10–20 stories), and 0.2 hertz for skyscrapers.

On the top floor of some skyscrapers, during a strong wind the amplitude of the side-to-side motion ("sway") can be several feet. Therefore, engineers have carefully designed skyscrapers to handle such a swaying motion. They strive to keep the amplitude small so that the people inside will not be disturbed. When the falling windowpanes of the Hancock Tower were blamed on the building's sway, engineers were quick to point out that the building was designed to sway slightly. They did not think the sway of the building was responsible for the falling windows.

Swaying is a form of simple harmonic motion. Swaying starts with a disturbing force, such as the wind pushing on the side of the building. A restoring force keeps the motion accelerating back towards its equilibrium point. In a skyscraper, the equilibrium point is when the building is perfectly vertical with respect to the ground. For a skyscraper, the restoring force is provided by the mass of the skyscraper. The Hancock Tower has a stiff "backbone" in the skyscraper's core, made of steel columns and beams. That backbone allows the building to bend slightly and then ease back towards its center point. Some skyscrapers get their restoring force from hollow, rigid tubes on the perimeter of the structure. The advantage of the tubes is that they are a strong core design, with less weight.

The Citicorp Center in New York City was the first building to have

The Citicorp Center Building

a mechanical means for providing a restoring force to counteract swaying. Housed on the top floors of the building is a 410-ton concrete weight. It slides back and forth in opposition to the sway caused by wind. The restoring force in the Citicorp Center shifts the center of mass of the building so that gravity pulls the building back towards its vertical or equilibrium position. The device used in the Citicorp Center is called a wind-compensating damper or "tuned mass damper."

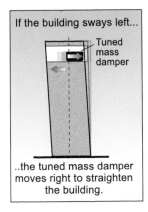

If the building sways left...

Tuned mass damper

..the tuned mass damper moves right to straighten the building.

William LeMessurier (1926–2007), an innovative American structural engineer, installed the tuned mass damper in the Citicorp Center. LeMessurier was also involved in installing a tuned mass damper in the Hancock Tower after the building opened. This device wasn't necessary to stop windows from falling, but was used to keep the building from twisting as it swayed, preventing a nausea-inducing effect felt by some early occupants of the building's top floors.

The world's tallest buildings

- 828 m (2,716.5 ft) — Burj Khalifa Dubai, UAE
- 628.8 m (2,063 ft) — KVLY-TV Mast Blanchard, North Dakota
- 553 m (1,815 ft) — CN Tower Toronto, Canada
- 519 m (1,703 ft) — Sears Tower Chicago, Illinois
- 508 m (1,667 ft) — Taipei 101 Taipei, Taiwan
- 452 m (1,486 ft) — Petronas Towers Kuala Lumpur, Malaysia
- 449 m (1,472 ft) — Empire State Building New York, New York
- 324 m (1,063 ft) — Eiffel Tower Paris, France

What is the world's tallest building?

The 2011 world champion of skyscrapers is the Burj Khalifa in Dubai, United Arab Emirates. Standing 828 meters tall, the building is designed with a hexagon-shaped central core supported by three "wings" that form a y-shape. The y-shape provides more interior space with natural light and outward views. The wings get narrower in alternating "steps" as the building rises, forming a spiral pattern. Each of the wings serves as a brace for the other two, minimizing sway no matter which direction the wind is blowing. Because the building changes shape with height, the wind flow patterns are broken up. This prevents strong vortices, or "whirlpools" of air current from forming. As a result, the wind creates very little periodic force, and the harmonic motion of the building is minimized.

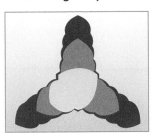

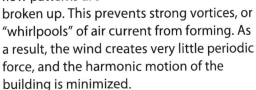

3-wing, y-shaped tower design cross section of Burj Khalifa.

The reason for the falling windows

The windows of the Hancock Tower fell out because of the way the double-paned glass was bonded to the window frame. The bonding prevented the glass from responding to temperature changes and wind forces. Because the windows were held too rigidly by the bonding, the glass fractured easily and fell out. The modern John Hancock Tower sways slightly in the wind just like before, but without twisting thanks to its tuned mass damper. Also, the bonding of the windows has been fixed, and now the windows stay in place.

QUESTIONS

1. Describe the sway of a building. Use the terms *periodic force*, *restoring force*, and *harmonic motion* in your answer.

2. William LeMessurier earned a reputation as an outstanding structural engineer. He is also remembered for the way in which he handled a significant engineering problem with the Citicorp Center. Research and write a brief report about the ethical dilemma LeMessurier faced and what he did to correct the problem.

3. Research the John Hancock Tower to find out what its tuned mass damper looks like and how it works.

Chapter 18 Review

Understanding Vocabulary

Select the correct term to complete the sentences.

amplitude	hertz	periodic force
cycle	natural frequency	phase
damping	oscillation	resonance
frequency	oscillator	restoring force
harmonic motion	period	vibration

Section 18.1

1. One complete turn of a bicycle wheel is one _____ of harmonic motion.

2. The time it takes for one cycle is called the _____.

3. The number of cycles an oscillator makes per second is called the _____.

4. Friction causes _____ in an oscillator.

5. The _____ of an oscillator describes where it is in the cycle.

6. A guitar is tuned by adjusting the _____ of the vibrating string to match a musical note.

Reviewing Concepts

Section 18.1

1. Identify the following as examples of harmonic motion, linear motion, or both. Explain your answer.

   a. a child moving down a playground slide one time
   b. an ocean wave rising and falling
   c. a car moving down the street
   d. a ball bouncing up and down

2. A system with harmonic motion is called an oscillator. Oscillators can be virtually any size. List at least one example each of a very large oscillator and a very small oscillator.

3. Describe a single cycle of harmonic motion for the following situations.

   a. a spinning merry-go-round
   b. Earth orbiting the Sun
   c. a clock pendulum

4. Using a person on a swing as an example of harmonic motion, describe these terms:

   a. period
   b. frequency
   c. cycle
   d. amplitude

5. Your favorite radio station is 106.7. What are the units of this number and what do they mean in terms of harmonic motion?

6. What is the mathematical relationship between frequency and period for a harmonic motion system?

7. Name a unit used to measure the following.

   a. amplitude
   b. frequency
   c. period
   d. mass

Section 18.2

8. Describe how you would determine the period and amplitude of an oscillator from a graph of its harmonic motion. You may use a diagram to help you answer this question.

9. Two players dribble basketballs at the same time. How does the motion of the basketballs compare if they are in phase? out of phase?

10. Explain why circular motion, like the motion of a Ferris wheel, is an example of harmonic motion.

Section 18.3

11. The length of the ropes on a swing are made longer.

   a. What happens to the period of the swing?
   b. What happens to the frequency of the swing?

12. Pushing a child on a playground swing repeatedly at the natural frequency causes resonance, which increases the amplitude of the swing, and the child goes higher. If the pushes provide the periodic force of the system, what provides the restoring force?

13. Identify the equilibrium position for the following situations.

   a. a person on a swing
   b. a person bungee jumping
   c. a guitar string being plucked

14. What is resonance and how is it created? Give an example of a resonant oscillating system in nature.

Solving Problems

Section 18.1

1. The wings of a honeybee move at a frequency of 220 Hz. What is the period for a complete wing-beat cycle?

2. If a pendulum's period is 4 s, what is its frequency?

3. What is the period of Earth spinning on its axis? What is its frequency? (*Hint*: How long does it take for one spin?)

4. Jason's heartbeat is 65 beats per minute.

   a. What is the frequency of his heartbeat in hertz?
   b. What is the period for each heartbeat in seconds?

5. In the table below, fill in the period and frequency for the second hand, minute hand, and hour hand of a clock.

	Period (s)	Frequency (Hz)
Second hand		
Minute hand		
Hour hand		

Section 18.2

6. The graph shows the motion of an oscillator that is a weight hanging from a rubber band. The weight moves up and down. Answer the following questions using the graph.

   a. What is the period?
   b. What is the frequency?
   c. What is the amplitude?
   d. If you count for 5 seconds, how many cycles would you count?

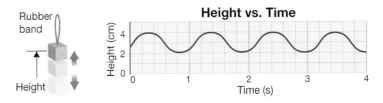

7. Make a graph of three cycles of motion for a pendulum that has a period of 2 s and an amplitude of 5 cm.

8. Which of the following graphs illustrates the harmonic motion of two children on swings, 180° out of phase? What fraction of a 360° cycle are these two graphs out of phase: $\frac{1}{8}$, $\frac{1}{4}$, $\frac{1}{2}$, or $\frac{3}{4}$?

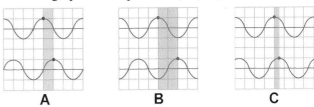

Section 18.3

9. The mass of a pendulum bob is increased by a factor of two. How is the period of the pendulum affected?

10. Describe how you might change the natural frequency of the following oscillating systems.

   a. a guitar string
   b. a playground swing
   c. a paddle ball game with a ball attached to a paddle with an elastic
   d. a diving board

11. How does decreasing the length of a pendulum affect its period?

Test Practice

Section 18.1

1. Which of the following is *not* an example of an oscillating system?

   a. a toy car sliding down a ramp
   b. the human heart and surrounding muscles
   c. Earth's orbit around the Sun
   d. stereo speakers

2. A hummingbird moves its wings up and down 300 times in 5 s. What is the period of this movement?

   a. 60 s
   b. 0.017 Hz
   c. 60 Hz
   d. 0.017 s

3. The graph shows harmonic motion. One cycle is represented by the distance from

   a. W to X.
   b. W to Y.
   c. W to Z.
   d. X to Y.

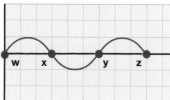

4. A pendulum completes one cycle every 4 s. What is the frequency of this pendulum?

   a. 0.50 Hz
   b. 0.25 Hz
   c. 0.25 s
   d. 0.75 s

Section 18.2

5. The graph represents position versus time for the amplitude of a pendulum. What is the amplitude?

   a. A
   b. B
   c. C
   d. D

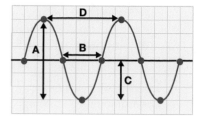

6. The graph shows the harmonic motion of a vibrating string. What is the period of the cycle?

   a. 2
   b. 4
   c. 6
   d. 8

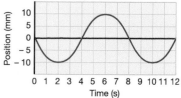

7. One cycle of harmonic motion for a certain spring has a period of 20 s. If a second, identical spring is set in motion 5 s after the first, the phase relationship between the motion of the two springs differs by _____ degrees.

   a. 25
   b. 45
   c. 90
   d. 180

8. The graph shows the motion of two pendulums. What is their phase difference measured in degrees?

   a. 45
   b. 90
   c. 180
   d. 240

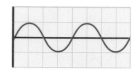
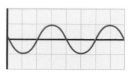

Pendulum #1   Pendulum #2

Section 18.3

9. A restoring force is any force that pulls a system with harmonic motion back toward

   a. equilibrium.
   b. resonance.
   c. oscillation.
   d. gravity.

10. Gravity is the restoring force for

    a. a guitar string.
    b. a mass on a spring.
    c. a stretched rubber band.
    d. a pendulum.

11. The natural frequency of a pendulum can be increased by

    a. increasing the mass of the bob.
    b. decreasing the mass of the bob.
    c. increasing the length of the string.
    d. decreasing the length of the string.

12. A periodic force applied with the same frequency as the natural frequency of a system produces

    a. resonance.
    b. a smaller amplitude.
    c. damping.
    d. equilibrium.

Applying Your Knowledge

Section 18.1

1. The human heart is both strong and reliable. As a demonstration of how reliable the heart is, calculate how many times your heart beats in one day. Start by measuring the frequency of your pulse in beats per minute and use the result for your calculation.

2. Ocean tides rise and fall based on the position of the Moon as it moves around Earth. The ocean's water is pulled in the direction of the Moon by the Moon's gravity. The Sun's gravity also affects the tides, but because of its great distance from Earth, the effect is not as strong as the Moon's. The picture shows different positions of the Moon relative to Earth and the Sun.

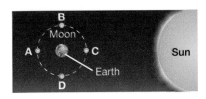

   a. Which two positions of the Moon result in greater tide amplitudes (spring tides)? Which two positions result in smaller tide amplitude (neap tides)? Refer to the picture.

   b. *Challenge*: In many places on Earth, there are two high tides and two low tides each day. Why do you think this happens?

3. The solar system is an oscillator with each of the planets in harmonic motion around the Sun. Give five examples of cycles that relate to the solar system and also give the period and frequency of each example. Use your library or the Internet to find the answers to this question.

4. A sewing machine makes sewing stitches, a repetitive task, easier. As a result, many parts of a sewing machine have harmonic motion. Find a sewing machine to examine, or a video of a sewing machine. List two parts of this machine that use harmonic motion. If you don't know the names of certain parts, make a diagram of the machine to help you explain your answer.

Section 18.2

5. A pirate ship amusement park ride uses harmonic motion. Use what you know about kinetic and potential energy to answer the following questions.

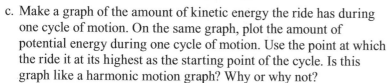

   a. Where in its cycle does the pirate ship have its highest *potential* energy and its lowest *potential* energy?

   b. Where in its cycle does the pirate ship have its highest *kinetic* energy and its lowest *kinetic* energy?

   c. Make a graph of the amount of kinetic energy the ride has during one cycle of motion. On the same graph, plot the amount of potential energy during one cycle of motion. Use the point at which the ride it at its highest as the starting point of the cycle. Is this graph like a harmonic motion graph? Why or why not?

Section 18.3

6. Buildings are not completely stiff. They sway side-to-side at their natural frequency.

   a. What do you think happens if the natural frequency of a building matches the frequency of an earthquake?

   b. How could a building's natural frequency be changed?

7. The cycle of motion of a pendulum is created by the restoring force of the weight of the bob. As with all motion, the harmonic motion of a pendulum must follow Newton's laws of motion.

   a. Newton's first law states that objects tend to keep doing what they are doing. How does the first law apply to a pendulum?

   b. Newton's second law states that $a = F \div m$. Which fact about the motion of a pendulum does the second law explain—that changing the mass does not change the period, or that changing the length does change the period.

   c. Name an action-reaction pair of the pendulum that illustrates Newton's third law.

 *Your Turn* **Answers**

Calculating frequency (Section 18.1, page 429)

a. 0.008 Hz

b. every 5 s

c. 60 s divided by 30 cycles = 2 s per cycle; the period is 2 s and the frequency is 0.5 Hz

Waves

Many sailors know that the Bermuda Triangle is an area of the western part of the North Atlantic Ocean where many ships have been lost. For hundreds of years, sailors believed the area was haunted. Some scientists believe the unusual shape of the sea floor and the ocean currents creates momentary "rogue" waves that can reach 100 feet above the sea surface. An unlucky ship caught in one of those waves may not stand a chance!

Many coastal cities have to worry about waves. Their harbors are designed to reduce the size of water waves that come ashore. A quiet harbor allows for sailboats to sail, for goods to be brought in by big ships, and for coastal buildings to be safe. At beaches, it is also important that waves not be too big so the water is safe for swimmers. Special computer programs help designers of coastal areas determine how to control waves. Usually, underwater structures are built to dampen waves. If you are a surfer, however, you want big waves. The same computer programs can also predict the location of the biggest waves.

What you learn about water waves applies to other waves too—including sound, light, and microwaves. The ideas even apply to gravity waves that occur as masses attract each other in the universe.

VOCABULARY

absorption	harmonics	superposition principle
boundaries	interference	transverse
circular wave	longitudinal	trough
constructive interference	plane wave	wave
crest	propagate	wave fronts
destructive interference	reflection	wave pulse
diffraction	refraction	wavelength
fundamental	standing wave	

KEY QUESTIONS

✓ *How is your cell phone like a traffic light or a drum?*

✓ *Which wave interactions help sunglasses work?*

✓ *What is anti-noise?*

19.1 Waves

A **wave** is an oscillation that travels from one place to another. A musician's instrument creates waves that carry sound to your ears. Calling a friend with a cell phone sends microwaves from your cell phone antenna. Those microwaves carry your voice as a signal to your friend's phone. Similarly, when you throw a stone into a pond, the energy of the falling stone creates a wave in the water that carries the energy to the edge of the pond. In this section you will learn about waves.

Why learn about waves?

What is a wave?   If you poke a ball floating on water, it moves up and down in harmonic motion. But something else happens to the water as the ball oscillates. The surface of the water oscillates in response and the oscillation spreads outward from where it started. An oscillation that travels is a wave.

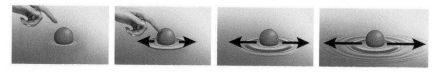

Energy and information   Waves carry the energy of oscillations from one place to another, and can cause oscillations in the matter that carries them. Waves are a moving form of energy. Waves also carry information, such as conversations, pictures, or music. Waves are used in many technologies to quickly carry information over great distances. The sound wave from a violin carries information about the vibration of the strings to your ear. Your ear hears the vibrations as music. Likewise, a radio wave carries sounds from a transmitter to your car radio. Another kind of radio wave carries the pictures and sounds in television signals. All the information you receive with your eyes and ears comes from waves (Figure 19.1).

- The light from the traffic light is a wave.
- The ripples in the puddle of water are waves.
- The electricity flowing in the wires attached to the street lights is a wave.
- Waves carry radio, television, and cell phone transmissions through the air and all around you all day long.

> **wave** - an oscillation that travels from one place to another

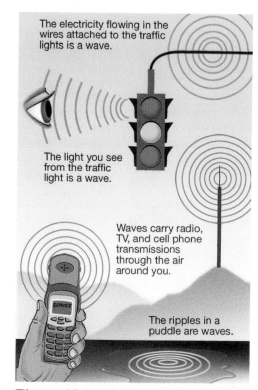

The electricity flowing in the wires attached to the traffic lights is a wave.

The light you see from the traffic light is a wave.

Waves carry radio, TV, and cell phone transmissions through the air around you.

The ripples in a puddle are waves.

Figure 19.1: *Waves are found in real-life situations every day.*

Recognizing waves

How do you recognize a wave? All waves are traveling oscillations that move energy from one place to another. The energy might be in moving matter, or it might be sound, light, or another form of energy. Waves are oscillations that move energy. When you see the things in this list, you should infer that waves are involved.

Waves are present

- when you see a vibration that moves.
  Example: A guitar string after it is plucked
- when something makes or responds to sound.
  Example: A drum for making music or your eardrum
- when something makes or responds to light.
  Example: A light bulb or your eyes
- when technology allows us to "see through" objects.
  Examples: ultrasound, CAT scans, MRI scans, and x-rays (Figure 19.2)
- when information travels through the air (or space) without wires.
  Example: A satellite dish for receiving television signals

Waves transmit information Waves are present whenever information, energy, or motion is transmitted over a distance in a set amount of time. The remote control on a TV is an example. To change the channel, you can use the remote, or you can get up and push the buttons with your finger. Both actions change the channel on the TV. However, one takes more time than the other. One action uses physical motion and the other uses a wave that goes from the remote control to the television. Your knowledge of physics and waves tells you there must be some kind of wave coming from the remote control because information travels from one place to another, and nothing appears to move. The wave from the remote control is infrared light that is invisible to your eyes.

Like all oscillations, waves have the properties of frequency, period, and amplitude. Information in waves is often transmitted in patterns of changing amplitude or frequency. For example, the number 3 might be represented by three wave pulses with an amplitude of 2 centimeters and a period of 1 second (Figure 19.3). Waves also have the properties of *speed* and *wavelength*.

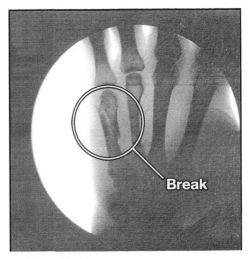

Figure 19.2: *An x-ray is created by passing waves through the body. The calcium in bones absorbs x-rays so bones show up as darker areas in an x-ray photo. This photo clearly shows a broken finger.*

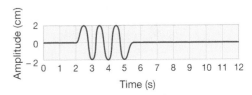

Figure 19.3: *One way to represent numbers using the amplitude of a wave. This graph could represent the number 3.*

Transverse and longitudinal waves

How waves travel How do waves travel through the air or along a rope? For a wave to travel, molecules need to be connected or in contact with each other. Because air molecules collide, waves can travel in the air. A wave can travel along a rope because its molecules are connected. If you cut a rope, a wave would not travel across the break.

Transverse waves A **transverse** wave has its oscillations perpendicular to the direction the wave moves. For example, a wave pulse along a rope attached to a wall moves left to right as shown. The boy's hand moves up and down to cause an oscillation. Water waves are transverse waves because the oscillation of the water's surface is perpendicular to the direction of the wave's motion (Figure 19.4, top).

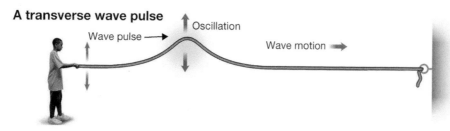

Longitudinal waves A **longitudinal** wave has vibrations in the same direction as the wave moves (Figure 19.4, bottom). A spring with one end fastened to a wall is a good way to demonstrate a longitudinal wave. A sharp push-pull on the end of the spring results in a traveling wave pulse as portions of the spring compress, then relax. The direction of the compressions are in the same direction that the wave moves. Sound waves are longitudinal waves. Like a wave pulse on a spring, air molecules oscillate back and forth as sound travels.

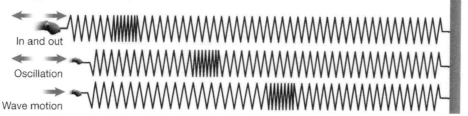

transverse - describes a wave with oscillations that are perpendicular to the direction the wave travels

longitudinal - describes a wave with oscillations that are in the same direction as the wave travels

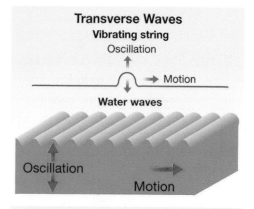

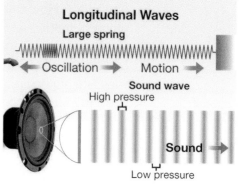

Figure 19.4: *Transverse and longitudinal waves.*

Frequency, amplitude, and wavelength

Waves are oscillators Waves have cycles, frequency, and amplitude. However, unlike other kinds of oscillators, waves travel and have speed. On this page, you will learn how frequency and amplitude are defined and measured for waves.

Frequency The frequency of a wave is a measure of how often it goes up and down (Figure 19.5). The frequency of the motion of one point on the wave is equal to the frequency of the whole wave. Distant points on the wave oscillate up and down *with the same frequency*. A wave's frequency is the same wherever it goes.

Frequency is measured in hertz Wave frequency is measured in *hertz* (Hz). A wave with a frequency of 1 hertz (1 Hz) causes everything it touches to oscillate at one cycle per second. Water waves made in a large pan of water typically have low frequencies, between 0.1 and 10 hertz. Sound waves that we hear have higher frequencies, between 20 hertz and 20,000 hertz.

Amplitude The amplitude of a wave is the maximum amount the wave moves away from equilibrium. Equilibrium is the average, or resting position (Figure 19.6) of the wave. The wave's amplitude is one half the distance between the highest and lowest points.

Wavelength You can think of a wave as a series of high points and low points. A **crest** is a high point of the wave, a **trough** is a low point. **Wavelength** is the distance from any point on a wave to the same point on the next cycle of the wave. One wavelength is the length of one complete cycle of the wave. We use the Greek letter lambda to represent wavelength. A lambda (λ) looks like an upside-down *y*.

> **crest** - the top or highest point on a wave
>
> **trough** - the bottom or lowest point on a wave
>
> **wavelength** - the length of one complete cycle of a wave

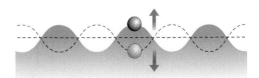

Figure 19.5: *The frequency of a wave is the rate at which every point on the wave moves up and down. The floating ball moves up and down at the frequency of the wave.*

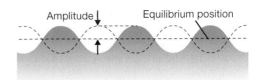

Figure 19.6: *The amplitude of a water wave is the maximum height the wave rises. This is half the distance between its lowest and highest places.*

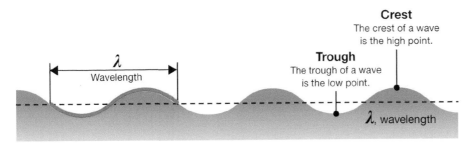

Crest
The crest of a wave is the high point.

Trough
The trough of a wave is the low point.

λ
Wavelength

λ, wavelength

The speed of waves

What is moving? The speed of a wave is different from the speed of a moving object, like a ball. The speed of a ball is the speed at which the ball itself moves. The speed of a wave is the speed at which the wave's oscillations travel through a material. When a wave moves through water, *the water itself stays in about the same place.* The typical speed of a water wave might be a meter per *second.* Light waves are extremely fast—about 300 million meters per second (186,000 mi/s). Sound waves travel at about 340 meters per second (0.21 mi/s), faster than water waves and much slower than light waves.

What is the speed of a wave? The graphic below illustrates how to measure wave speed. You have to start a wave in one place and measure how long it takes it to travel some distance away. The speed of the wave is how fast it gets from one place to the next, *not* how fast the wave surface moves up and down. The up-and-down speed of the water surface determines its frequency.

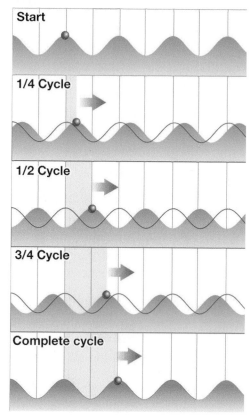

Figure 19.7: *In one complete cycle, a wave moves a distance equal to one wavelength.*

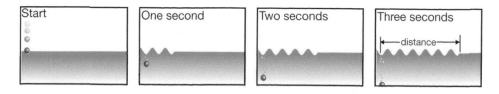

Speed is frequency times wavelength In one complete cycle, a wave moves forward one wavelength (Figure 19.7). The speed of a wave is the distance traveled divided by the time it takes. Since the frequency is the inverse of the period, it is easier to calculate the speed of the wave by multiplying its wavelength and frequency. This result is true for all kinds of waves. Frequency times wavelength is the speed of the wave as shown here.

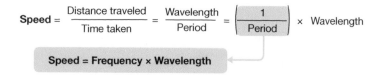

$$\text{Speed} = \frac{\text{Distance traveled}}{\text{Time taken}} = \frac{\text{Wavelength}}{\text{Period}} = \left(\frac{1}{\text{Period}}\right) \times \text{Wavelength}$$

$$\boxed{\text{Speed} = \text{Frequency} \times \text{Wavelength}}$$

Calculating the speed of waves

Units   You can calculate the speed of a wave if you know its frequency and wavelength. Recall that 1 hertz equals 1 cycle per second. The number of cycles is a number with no units. The *units* of hertz are 1 ÷ second (1/s). If wavelength is in meters (m), and frequency has units of 1/s, then the wave speed has units of meters per second (m × 1/s = m/s).

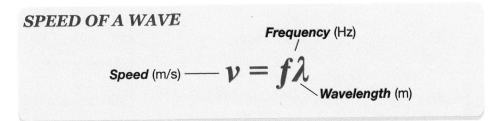

SPEED OF A WAVE

Frequency (Hz)

Speed (m/s) ——— $v = f\lambda$

Wavelength (m)

Cooking with waves

A magnetron is a device in a microwave oven that creates a wave with electricity. The wave vibrates inside the cooking space at 2.5 billion cycles per second (2.5 gigahertz). This frequency is best absorbed by water molecules and some other molecules in food, and to some extent by ceramics, glass, or plastics only in the absence of food or water. A microwave heats food by transferring wave energy to the food. (*Note*: Avoid placing metals in a microwave oven!)

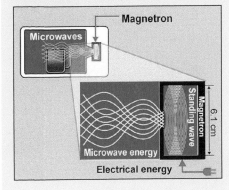

Magnetron

Microwaves

6.1 cm

Magnetron Standing wave

Microwave energy

Electrical energy

 **Finding wave speed**

A wave has a wavelength of 0.5 meters, and its frequency is 40 hertz. What is the speed of the wave?

1. Looking for:	The speed of the wave in meters per second.
2. Given:	Wavelength is 0.5 meters and frequency is 40 hertz.
3. Relationships:	*speed = frequency × wavelength*
4. Solution:	*speed* = 40 Hz × 0.5 m = 40 1/s × 0.5 m
	speed = 20 m/s
	The speed of the wave is 20 m/s.

Your Turn...

a. The frequency of a wave is 50 hertz and its wavelength is 0.001 meters. What is the wave's speed?

b. The period of a wave is 10 seconds and its wavelength is 2 meters. What is the wave's speed?

(Answers are listed at the end of the chapter.)

Standing waves on a string

What is a standing wave A wave that is confined in a space is called a **standing wave**. It is possible to make standing waves of almost any kind, including sound, water, and even light. You can experiment with standing waves using a vibrating string. Vibrating strings are what make music on a guitar or piano.

Harmonics A string with a standing wave is a kind of oscillator. Like all oscillators, a string has natural frequencies.

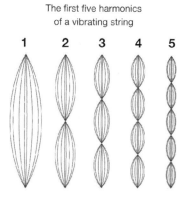

The first five harmonics
of a vibrating string

1   2   3   4   5

The lowest natural frequency is called the **fundamental**. A vibrating string also has other natural frequencies called **harmonics**. The diagram shows the first five harmonics. You can tell the harmonic number by counting the number of "bumps" on the string. The first harmonic has one bump, the second has two, the third has three, and so on. Another name for the "bump" on a wave is *antinode* (Figure 19.8).

Wavelength A vibrating string moves so fast that your eye sees a wave-shaped blur. At any one moment the string is in only one place within the blur. One complete s shape on the string is one wavelength. As frequency increases, wavelength decreases for a specific wave velocity. Higher frequency waves have shorter wavelengths.

> **standing wave** - a resonance created by trapping a wave between boundaries that causes the wave to interfere with its reflections
>
> **fundamental** - the lowest natural frequency of a standing wave
>
> **harmonics** - frequencies that are multiples of a fundamental frequency

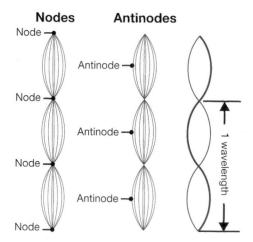

Figure 19.8: *These are nodes and antinodes for the third harmonic of a vibrating string. Nodes are points where the string does not move. Antinodes are points of the greatest amplitude. One complete s shape on the string equals one wavelength.*

19.1 Section Review

1. Does a pair of walkie-talkies work using waves? Justify your answer.
2. Which is the fastest way to send information, using sound, light, or water?
3. Compare and contrast longitudinal and transverse waves in a short paragraph.
4. What is the speed of a wave that has a wavelength of 0.4 meters and a frequency of 10 hertz? Is this wave most likely to be a sound wave, light wave, or water wave?
5. What is the period of a wave that has a wavelength of 1 meter and a speed of 20 hertz?
6. Identify the number of wavelengths shown above for each of the first five harmonics.

19.2 The Motion of Waves

As a wave travels from one place to another, how do we know which direction it moves? What happens when a wave encounters an edge, or moves from one substance into another? In this section, we will explore how waves move and interact with other objects.

Why do waves travel? Waves **propagate**, which means they spread out from where they begin. When you drop a ball into water, some of the water is pushed aside and raised by the ball (A). The higher water pushes the water next to it out of the way as it tries to return to equilibrium (B). The water that has been pushed then pushes on the water in front of *it*, and so on. The wave spreads through the interaction of each bit of water with the bit of water next to it (C).

> **propagate** - to spread out or travel
>
> **plane wave** - a wave with crests that form of a pattern of straight-line wave fronts
>
> **wave fronts** - another term for the crests of a wave
>
> **circular wave** - a wave with crests that forms a pattern of circular wave fronts

Propagation of a water wave

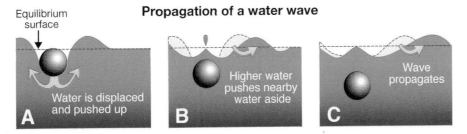

Equilibrium surface

A Water is displaced and pushed up

B Higher water pushes nearby water aside

C Wave propagates

Plane waves and circular waves The easiest waves to make and study are plane waves and circular waves (Figure 19.9). The crests of a **plane wave** form a pattern of parallel straight lines called **wave fronts**. The crests of a **circular wave** form a pattern of circular wave fronts. A plane wave is started by disturbing water in a line. Pushing the water with a ruler makes a plane wave. A circular wave is started by disturbing water at a single point. A fingertip touched to the water's surface makes a circular wave.

The direction a wave moves *The direction a wave moves depends on the shape of the wave front.* Plane waves are straight and move perpendicular to the crest of the wave. Circular waves move outward in a circle from the wave source. Anything that changes the shape of the wave front changes the direction the wave moves.

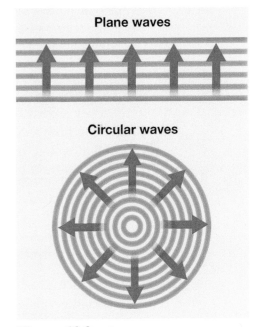

Plane waves

Circular waves

Figure 19.9: *Plane waves move perpendicular to the wave fronts. Circular waves radiate outward from the wave source.*

When a wave encounters objects

The four wave interactions

Have you ever heard a radio station fade out while driving into a tunnel or down into a valley? Radio signals are carried by radio waves. An FM radio wave can only propagate a short distance into a tunnel. Light reflecting off a mirror and x-rays passing through a body also depend on how waves behave when they encounter objects. How a wave responds to an object or a surface is called a wave interaction. Three wave interactions are described and shown on this page (Figure 19.10). A fourth wave interaction, diffraction, is described on the next page.

Boundaries

Waves are affected by **boundaries** where conditions or materials change. A boundary is an edge or surface where the change occurs. The surface of glass is a boundary. A wave traveling in the air is changed by the new material (glass) as it crosses the boundary. Reflection, refraction, and diffraction usually occur at boundaries. Absorption can occur at a boundary, but usually happens when the wave travels *through* a material.

Reflection

When a wave bounces off an object we call it **reflection**. A reflected wave is like the original wave but moves in another direction. The wavelength and frequency are usually unchanged. An echo is an example of a sound wave reflecting from a distant object or wall. People who design concert halls pay careful attention to the reflection of sound from the walls and ceiling.

Refraction

Refraction occurs when a wave bends as it crosses a boundary. We say the wave is *refracted* as it passes through the boundary. Eyeglasses are a good example of a device that uses refraction to bend light waves. Some people have trouble focusing images. Eyeglasses bend incoming light waves so that an image is correctly focused within the eye.

Absorption

Absorption is what happens when the amplitude of a wave gets smaller as it passes through a material. The wave energy is transferred to the absorbing material. A sponge can absorb a water wave while letting the water pass. Theaters often use heavy curtains to absorb sound waves so the audience cannot hear backstage noise. The tinted glass or plastic in the lenses of your sunglasses absorbs some of the energy in light waves. Cutting down the energy makes vision more comfortable on a bright, sunny day.

boundaries - an edge or surface where conditions or materials change

reflection - the bouncing of a wave off of a surface

refraction - the bending of a wave as it crosses a boundary between different materials

absorption - the decrease in amplitude of a wave as it passes through a material and loses energy

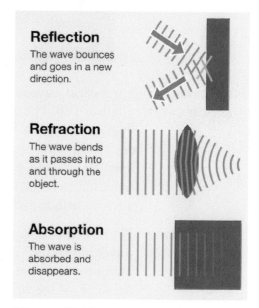

Reflection
The wave bounces and goes in a new direction.

Refraction
The wave bends as it passes into and through the object.

Absorption
The wave is absorbed and disappears.

Figure 19.10: *Reflection, refraction, and absorption.*

Diffraction and absorption

Diffraction   The process of waves bending around corners or passing through openings is called **diffraction**. We say a wave is *diffracted* when it is changed by passing through a hole or around an edge. Diffraction usually changes the direction and shape of the wave. When a plane wave passes through a narrow opening, diffraction turns it into a circular wave. Diffraction explains why you can hear someone even though a door is open only a tiny crack. Diffraction causes the sound wave to spread out from the crack.

> **diffraction** - the change in the shape of a wave as it passes through an opening or bends around an edge

Diffraction

The wave bends around an object or through holes in the object.

Diffraction through a small opening turns plane waves into circular waves.

Waves and earthquakes

An earthquake releases powerful seismic waves that travel along the surface of and through Earth. One type of seismic wave is longitudinal. Another type is transverse. As they travel through Earth, seismic waves might bend, reflect, speed up, slow down, or stop depending on the nature of the rocky material they encounter. By studying what happens to the waves as they travel through Earth, scientists are able to make detailed models of Earth's interior.

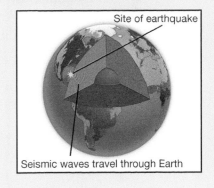

Site of earthquake

Seismic waves travel through Earth

19.2 *Section Review*

1. If you threw a small rock into a pond, would plane waves or circular waves be created? Explain your answer.
2. Does a mirror work by reflection or refraction?
3. How is refraction used in eyeglasses?
4. One of the four wave interactions is very important in how plants use light to grow. Which one do you think it is? Write a couple of sentences justifying your answer.

19.3 **Wave Interference and Energy**

You almost never see or hear a single wave with only one frequency. That would be like seeing only one color or hearing only one note. Instead, you see and hear a complex mixture of waves of many different frequencies and amplitudes, all mixed together. **Interference** happens when two or more waves mix together. Interference mixes waves in ways that are very useful but can also be dangerous. For example, radio stations use interference to carry music to your radio. In contrast, sometimes water waves in the ocean add up to make a gigantic wave that may last only a few moments, but can sink a large ship.

The superposition principle

The superposition principle   It is common for many waves to be in the same system at the same time. For example, if you watch the ocean, you can see small waves on the surface of larger waves. When more than one wave is present, the **superposition principle** states that the total vibration at any point is the sum of the vibrations from each individual wave.

An example   The diagram below illustrates the superposition principle. If there are two waves present (A and B), the total vibration at any point in time (C) is the sum of the vibrations from wave A and wave B. In reality, single waves are quite rare. The sound waves and light waves you experience are the superposition of thousands of waves with different frequencies and amplitudes. Your eyes, ears, and brain separate the waves in order to recognize individual sounds and colors.

interference - the pattern of frequency, brightness, amplitude, or other wave characteristics that comes from adding waves of the same kind

superposition principle - states that when more than one wave of the same type is present in a system, the total vibration at any point is the sum of the vibrations from each individual wave

Active noise reduction

In some environments, people wear headphones to muffle sounds and protect their hearing. Headphones can also create "anti-noise." A microphone in the headphone samples the noise and generates anti-noise, or sound that is 180 degrees out of phase with the noise. The anti-noise uses superposition to cancel out or reduce noise.

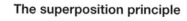

The superposition principle

$$A + B = C$$

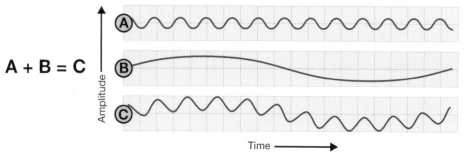

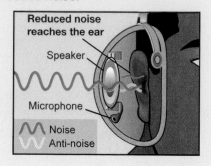

Constructive and destructive interference

Wave pulses A **wave pulse** is a wave of short duration, or maybe just a single oscillation. Imagine stretching an elastic string over the back of a chair as shown. To make a wave pulse, pull down a short length of the string behind the chair and let go. This creates a "bump" in the string that races away from the chair. The moving "bump" is a wave pulse. The wave pulse moves *on* the string, but each section of string returns to the same place after the wave moves past. The speed of the wave pulse is what we mean by the speed of a wave.

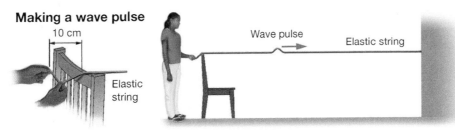

Constructive interference Suppose you make two wave pulses on a stretched string. One comes from the left and the other comes from the right. When the waves meet, they combine to make a single large pulse. After meeting, the waves continue moving as they did before they met. **Constructive interference** occurs when waves add up to make a larger amplitude (Figure 19.11). Constructive interference is useful in working with light and sound. For example, when two sound waves constructively interfere, loudness increases.

Destructive interference There is another way to add two pulses. What happens when one pulse is on top of the string and the other is on the bottom? When the pulses meet in the middle, they cancel each other out (Figure 19.11). One pulse pulls the string up and the other pulls it down. The result is that the string flattens and both pulses vanish for a moment. In **destructive interference**, waves add up to make a wave with smaller or zero amplitude. After interfering, both wave pulses separate and travel on as they did before they met. This is surprising if you think about it. For a moment, the middle of the cord is flat, but a moment later, the two wave pulses reappear and race away from each other. Waves still store energy, even when they interfere. Noise cancelling headphones are based on technology that uses destructive interference.

wave pulse - a short-duration wave or a single oscillation
constructive interference - occurs when waves add up to make a larger amplitude
destructive interference - occurs when waves add up to make a smaller amplitude

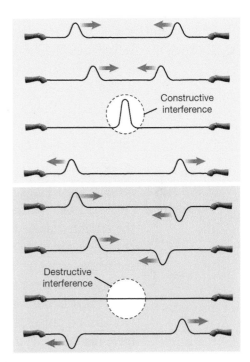

Figure 19.11: *Constructive and destructive interference.*

Natural frequency and resonance

Natural frequency and resonance As you learned in Chapter 18, oscillators have natural *frequency* and *resonance*, and so do waves. But a wave has to be caught in a system with boundaries to show resonance. By itself, light keeps going in a straight line. There is no resonance. But catch the light between two perfect mirrors and you can get resonance of light waves, which is exactly how a *laser* works!

In free space a light wave travels in a straight line.

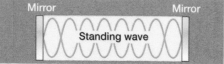
Between mirrors light can form a standing wave.

Mirror   Standing wave   Mirror

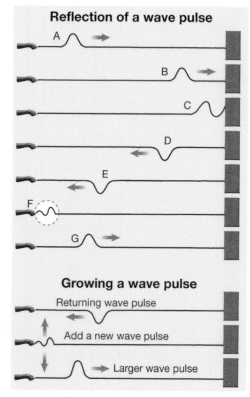

Figure 19.12: *Reflections of a wave pulse on an elastic string.*

Resonance and reflections Resonance in waves comes from the interference of a wave with its own reflections. To see how this works, first think about making a single pulse on an elastic string (Figure 19.12, top). One end of the string is tied to a wall, making a boundary. A pulse launched on the top of the string (A and B) reflects off the wall (C). The pulse comes back *on the bottom* of the string (D and E). When the pulse gets back to where it began, it reflects (F). Then, the pulse is back on top of the string and the cycle repeats (G).

Resonance and constructive interference To build up a larger wave with more energy on a string, you wait until a reflected pulse has returned to your hand before launching a new pulse (Figure 19.12, bottom). By constructive interference, the new pulse adds to the reflected pulse to make a bigger pulse. The bigger pulse moves away and reflects again. You wait until the reflection gets back to your hand and then shake the string to add a third pulse. The total wave pulse is now three times as large as at the start. *Resonance is created by adding new pulses so that each adds to the reflected pulse in constructive interference.* After a dozen well-timed pulses, the string develops a single large wave motion, and you have resonance (Figure 19.13)!

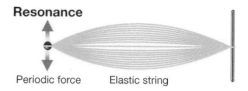

Figure 19.13: *A vibrating string in resonance has a single large wave pattern such as this.*

Why is resonance important The concepts of resonance and natural frequency apply to a huge range of natural and human-made systems. The tides of the oceans, musical instruments, the laser, the way our ears separate sound, and even a microwave oven are all examples of waves and resonance.

Waves and energy

A wave is a form of moving energy
What exactly moves in a wave? In a water wave, the water moves up and down, but stays, on average, in the same place. What moves is *energy*. A wave is an organized form of energy that travels. When you drop a stone into a pool, most of the stone's kinetic energy is converted into water waves. The waves spread, carrying the energy far from the place where the stone fell.

Frequency and energy
The energy of a wave is proportional to its frequency. Higher frequency means higher energy. This is obvious for a jump rope. You have to move the rope up and down twice, doing twice as much work, to make the rope swing at twice the frequency. Figure 19.14 shows three standing waves with the same amplitude and different frequencies. The wave with the higher frequency has more energy. This result is true for almost all waves. The energy of a wave is proportional to its frequency.

Amplitude and energy
The energy of a wave is also proportional to its amplitude. Given two standing waves of the same frequency, the wave with the larger amplitude has more energy. With a vibrating string, the potential energy of the wave comes from the stretching of the string. A larger amplitude means the string has to stretch more and therefore stores more energy.

Why are standing waves useful?
Standing waves are used to store energy at specific frequencies. With a wave on a string, a small input of energy at the natural frequency can accumulate over time to build a wave with much more energy. Musical instruments use standing waves to create sound energy of an exact frequency. Radio transmitters and cell phones also use standing waves to create signals at specific frequencies.

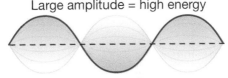

Frequency and energy

Lowest frequency, lowest energy

Double frequency, double energy

Triple frequency, triple energy

Amplitude and energy

Small amplitude = low energy

Large amplitude = high energy

Figure 19.14: *The energy of a wave is proportional to its frequency and amplitude.*

19.3 Section Review

1. Explain the superposition principle in your own words.
2. Two waves combine to make a wave that is larger than either wave by itself. Is this constructive or destructive interference?
3. Two waves experience destructive interference. Is energy lost? Explain your answer.
4. Which has more energy—a vibrating string at 30 hertz or one at 70 hertz?
5. If a wave is absorbed, what would you expect to happen to the amplitude of the wave? Explain your answer using the idea of energy.

Waves that Shake the Ground

On January 12, 2010, a 7.0-magnitude earthquake struck the Caribbean nation of Haiti. Its capital, Port-au-Prince, was nearly destroyed. Many government buildings, schools, hospitals, and businesses collapsed. The International Red Cross estimated that 3 million Haitians lost their homes. The powerful earthquake was caused by waves traveling through Earth.

The National Palace in Port-au-Prince, Haiti, after the earthquake.

You know how to cause water waves and how to make a wave travel along a string. But how do waves get started in the ground? Earthquakes begin in Earth's crust. Twisting or squeezing causes pressure to build up in underground rocks. Like a stretched rubber band or a compressed spring, the rocks store energy. When the rocks break or change shape, stored energy is suddenly converted to ground-shaking energy. As a result, seismic waves radiate from the place where the stored energy was released and an earthquake occurs. During a quake, there is a strong burst of shaking that lasts from a few seconds to several minutes. The longest earthquake ever recorded occurred in 1964 in Alaska. It lasted 4 minutes.

Earthquake waves

Two kinds of waves are released from an earthquake's starting point. Primary waves are longitudinal waves. They are faster and push and pull on rocks as they move through Earth. Secondary waves are transverse waves. They move back and forth. They travel a little slower than primary waves. Because they are faster, primary waves reach Earth's surface first. When primary and secondary waves reach the surface, they become surface waves. These waves move about 10 percent slower than secondary waves, but can still be very damaging. When these waves have a lot of energy, the ground rolls like the surface of the ocean. Surface waves can also move side to side and cause buildings to collapse.

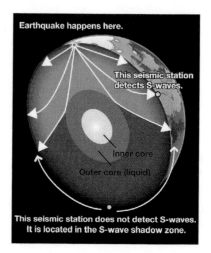

Seeing inside Earth

Seismic waves are recorded and measured by a worldwide network of seismographs. The seismologists who record and interpret seismic waves use the data to study Earth's internal structure. Primary and secondary seismic waves help identify the properties of the layers inside Earth. For example, seismologists have observed that primary waves pass through the outer core of Earth, but secondary waves do not. We know that secondary waves cannot travel through liquids. Therefore, this observation provides evidence that the outer core of Earth is liquid.

Where do earthquakes occur?

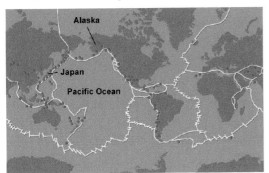

Earth is covered by a thin crust of rock. Rather than being continuous, the crust is broken into pieces called *tectonic plates*. These pieces are constantly moving. As edges of the plates move against each other, pressure builds up and an earthquake can occur. This map shows the edges of Earth's "puzzle pieces" as white lines. The red dots show common earthquake locations.

Dangerous underwater earthquakes

In the middle of the Pacific Ocean, earthquakes can occur on the ocean floor. When this happens, a huge and dangerous water wave called a *tsunami* can occur. A tsunami can travel at about 700 kilometers per hour. In the open sea, a tsunami is very long, but not very tall. You would not notice it as it passed under your boat. However, as the wave reaches a shallow area, it becomes shorter, causing the water to pile up so that its amplitude greatly increases. The wave may get as high as 25 meters! Tsunamis cause serious flooding, and the wave power can wreck buildings and cause loss of life. Tsunamis affect coastal areas and islands that experience earthquakes.

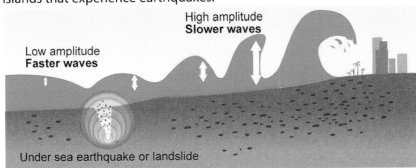

Around the Pacific coastline of Alaska, Hawaii, and the west coast of the continental United States, there are ocean-bound tsunami detectors and seismographs to warn residents about approaching tsunamis. Scientists also use information from the detectors and seismographs to forecast tsunamis. Because scientists know how fast a tsunami can travel after it has been triggered by an earthquake, they can warn people in these coastal locations to evacuate to higher ground.

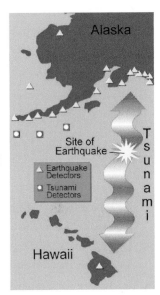

QUESTIONS

1. List and describe the different types of seismic waves.

2. Research the Richter scale. What do the numbers on this scale represent?

3. Where are earthquakes most likely to occur?

4. If an earthquake occurs in the Pacific Ocean about 3,000 kilometers from Hawaii and 1,900 kilometers from Alaska, how much time do Hawaiians have to evacuate from coastal areas? How much time do the Alaskans have? (*Hint*: Use the speed for a tsunami from this connection.)

5. Research and write a report on the cause of the 2004 Indian Ocean Tsunami.

Seismogram image courtesy of Tim Long, Georgia Institute of Technology seismogram archives. Seismograms may also be viewed at www.IRIS.edu. Photo of the National Palace by Logan Abassi, United Nations Development Programme

Chapter 19 Review

Understanding Vocabulary

Select the correct term to complete the sentences.

absorption	diffraction	reflection
circular wave	fundamental	transverse waves
constructive interference	harmonics	trough
destructive interference	longitudinal waves	waves

1. The lowest natural frequency of an object is known as the _____ frequency.

2. Multiples of the natural frequency of a wave are called _____.

3. A wave bending around obstacles and going through openings is called _____.

4. Using a heavy curtain in a theater to keep the audience from hearing backstage sound is an example of the _____ of sound waves.

5. Two waves that combine and cancel each other out is called _____.

Reviewing Concepts

Section 19.1

1. Identify how each of the following situations involves waves. Explain each of your answers.

   a. a person is talking to someone on a cell phone

   b. an earthquake causes the floor of a house to shake

   c. a person listens to her favorite radio station on the car stereo

   d. a doctor takes an x-ray to check for broken bones

   e. you turn on a lamp when you come home in the evening

2. Compare transverse waves and longitudinal waves. Give two examples of each type of wave.

3. Arrange the equation relating wave speed, frequency, and wavelength for each of the following scenarios. Let v = wave speed, f = frequency, and λ = wavelength.

   a. You know frequency and wavelength. Solve for v.

   b. You know frequency and wave speed. Solve for λ.

   c. You know wave speed and wavelength. Solve for f.

4. Write a formula relating the speed of a wave to its period and wavelength.

5. Give one example of a wave with a very short wavelength and one with a very long wavelength.

6. In the diagram, which measurement shows the amplitude? Which measurement shows the wavelength?

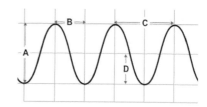

7. What causes a standing wave?

8. How many nodes and antinodes are in a single wavelength of the second harmonic of a vibrating string?

Section 19.2

9. Sketch the wave crests, indicating the direction of motion, for

   a. a circular wave.

   b. a plane wave.

10. The diagrams below represent interactions between waves and boundaries. Identify each interaction by name.

A   B   C   D

11. What happens to the amplitude of a wave when the wave is absorbed?

12. Explain why you can hear a sound through a door that is only open a crack. Use the terms *wave* and *interaction* in your answer.

13. Read the descriptions below and indicate which of the four types of wave interactions—absorption, reflection, refraction, or diffraction—has occurred.

    a. The distortion of your partially-submerged arm that makes it look "broken" when viewed from above the water's surface.

    b. You hear the music even though you are seated behind an obstruction at a concert.

    c. You see yourself in a mirror.

    d. Water ripples become smaller after passing through a sponge.

    e. Heavy curtains are used to help keep a room quiet.

Section 19.3

14. What happens if two waves are in the same place at the same time? Use the term *superposition principle* in your answer.

15. Can two waves interfere with each other so that the new wave formed by their combination has *no* amplitude? What type of interference is this?

16. What happens to the amplitude of two waves as the result of

    a. constructive interference?

    b. destructive interference?

Solving Problems

Section 19.1

1. A wave has a frequency of 10 Hz and a wavelength of 2 m. What is the speed of the wave?

2. A sound wave has a speed of 400 m/s and a frequency of 200 Hz. What is its wavelength?

3. The wavelength of a wave on a string is 1 m and its speed is 5 m/s. Calculate the frequency and the period of the wave.

4. Draw at least one cycle of a transverse wave with an amplitude of 4 cm and a wavelength of 8 cm. If the frequency of this wave is 10 Hz, what is its speed?

5. The standing wave pattern shown in the diagram has a frequency of 30 Hz.

    a. What is the period?

    b. At what frequency will you find the fourth harmonic?

    c. At what frequency will you find the fifth harmonic?

    d. How many nodes are in this wave pattern?

    e. How many antinodes are in this wave pattern?

30 Hz

6. You are doing a vibrating string experiment and observe the sixth harmonic at 48 Hz. At what frequency do you find the third harmonic?

7. How many nodes and antinodes does this standing wave have?

8. An "A" note played on a piano vibrates at a frequency of 440 Hz. Find the frequency for its second harmonic.

Section 19.2

9. The wave in the picture is about to pass through a small hole. Sketch what the wave front will look like after it passes through the hole.

Section 19.3

10. Which graph shows the superposition of the two in-phase waves?

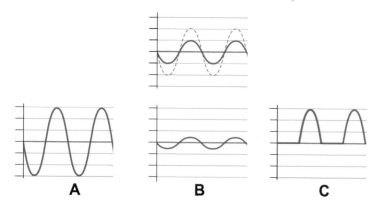

11. Which graph shows the superposition of the two out-of-phase waves?

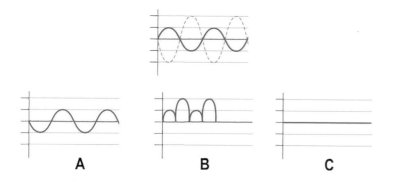

Test Practice

Section 19.1

1. All of the following are true *except*

   a. sound waves are a travelling form of energy.

   b. sound waves have frequency, period, and amplitude.

   c. sound waves have oscillations that are perpendicular to the direction the wave moves.

   d. sound waves have oscillations that are in the same direction as the wave moves.

2. Under normal circumstances, a _____ wave is the fastest wave.

   a. water

   b. microwave

   c. sound

   d. light

3. The distance from point A to point E is 4 cm. If the frequency is 125 Hz, what is the speed?

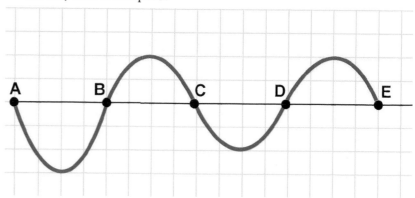

   a. 62.5 cm/s

   b. 125 cm/s

   c. 250 cm/s

   d. 500 cm/s

4. A student does a vibrating string experiment and observes the fifth harmonic at 25 Hz. The length of the string is 5 m. What is the speed?

   a. 25 m/s

   b. 50 m/s

   c. 100 m/s

   d. 125 m/s

Section 19.2

5. Skipping a rock in a pond creates

   a. circular waves.

   b. plane waves.

   c. perpendicular waves.

   d. dimensional waves.

6. The lens in your eye uses _____ to focus light on your retina.

   a. absorption

   b. reflection

   c. refraction

   d. diffraction

7. The process of _____ occurs when the amplitude of a wave gets smaller and smaller as it passes through a material.

   a. absorption

   b. reflection

   c. refraction

   d. diffraction

8. This diagram represents an interaction between a wave and a boundary. What is the name of this type of interaction?

   a. absorption

   b. reflection

   c. refraction

   d. diffraction

Section 19.3

9. Headphones which generate sound waves 180° out of phase with samples of external noise demonstrate the principle of

   a. superposition.

   b. damping.

   c. standing waves.

   d. resonance.

10. Which pair of moving pulses will cause constructive interference to occur?

   a. A

   b. B

   c. C

   d. D

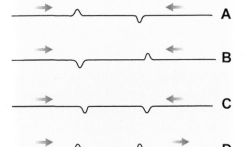

11. Waves with zero amplitude can be created by

   a. resonant interference.

   b. destructive interference.

   c. reflective interference.

   d. constructive interference.

12. Given two standing waves with the same frequency,

   a. both waves must have the same energy.

   b. both waves must have zero energy.

   c. the wave with the smaller amplitude has more energy.

   d. the wave with the larger amplitude has more energy.

Applying Your Knowledge

Section 19.1

1. Tsunami waves are large ocean waves generated by disturbances like underwater earthquakes or landslides. Tsunamis can travel on the open ocean at speeds of 200 m/s, which is comparable to the speed of a jet airplane.

   a. What type of wave is a tsunami, transverse or longitudinal?

   b. If the period of a tsunami is 1 h, what is its frequency? (*Hint*: How many seconds are in 1 h?)

   c. If a tsunami's wave speed is 200 m/s and its period is 3,600 s, what is its wavelength?

2. The "sweet spot" on a baseball bat is related to how the bat vibrates when it hits a baseball. If a ball hits the sweet spot, your hands do not feel the vibrations of the bat. However, if the ball hits a place on the bat that is not the sweet spot, you can feel the vibrations. Find out why this happens. Use your library or go on the Internet to research this phenomenon. Write a short paragraph with a diagram to summarize your findings.

Section 19.2

3. Eye doctors use a refraction test to measure your eyesight for glasses. The test is performed by having you look through a refractor device at an eye chart. The refractor device has different types of lenses for you to look through. When a lens is found that gives you clear vision, the doctor can prescribe the correct set of eyeglasses for you.

   a. Why do you think this is called a refraction test?

   b. What kind of wave is being refracted by the refraction device?

   c. How do eyeglasses help you to see more clearly?

4. The reflection of sound waves leads to echoes, a delayed repetition of the original sound. If a canyon wall is 34 m away and the speed of sound in air is 340 m/s, what would be the time delay of an echo in the canyon?

Section 19.3

5. In 1933, the US Navy steamship *Ramapo* reported seeing a 64-m wave in the open ocean where the sea is 4,000 to 6,000 m deep. How might this wave have been formed? Is this just a sea tale or is a wave of this size possible?

6. Have you ever been in a situation that was too noisy? Choose one of the following research topics on the subject of noise. Research your topic and present your findings in a one- or two-page essay. Include in your essay information about how noise is reduced using an understanding of sound waves.

   a. noise from airports

   b. noise from highways

   c. use of hearing protection by teenagers

   d. health problems related to noise

 *Your Turn* **Answers**

Finding Wave Speed (Section 19.1, page 453)

a. 0.05 m/s

b. 0.2 m/s

Sound

Humans were making musical instruments to produce sounds 20,000 years before the wheel and axle were invented! Among instrument builders, Antonio Stradivari is one of the most famous. Between 1667 and 1730, Stradivari built violins in the small town of Cremona, Italy.

A violin's sound is rich and complex because vibrations of its wooden parts create a unique blend of frequencies. Stradivari worked tirelessly trying different woods and different varnishes, searching for the perfect sound. Over time, he developed a formula for varnish and special ways to carve and treat the all-important vibrating parts of the violin. In the 300 years since Stradivari, no one has completely figured out how he did it. Today, a Stradivarius violin is one of the most highly prized of all musical instruments. Its rich sound has never been duplicated.

VOCABULARY

acoustics	Fourier's theorem	reverberation
beat	frequency spectrum	rhythm
cochlea	musical scale	shock wave
consonance	note	sonogram
decibels	octave	subsonic
dissonance	pitch	supersonic
Doppler effect		

KEY QUESTIONS

✓ *How do atoms make sound happen?*

✓ *Why is your voice unique?*

✓ *How do beats help keep your musical instruments in tune?*

20.1 Properties of Sound

Like other waves, sound has the properties of frequency, wavelength, amplitude, and speed. Because sound is such a big part of human experience, you already know its properties, but by different names. You may never hear anyone complain about amplitude, but you have heard about sound being too *loud*. The loudness of sound comes from the amplitude of a sound wave.

pitch - the perceived frequency of a sound

The frequency of sound

Frequency and pitch
Sound is a wave, and like all waves it has a frequency. Your ear is very sensitive to the frequency of sound. The **pitch** of a sound is how you hear and interpret its frequency. A low-frequency sound has a low pitch, like the rumble of a big truck or a bass guitar. A high-frequency sound has a high pitch, like the scream of a whistle or siren. The range of frequencies humans can hear varies from about 20 hertz to 20,000 hertz.

Most sound has more than one frequency
Most sound that you hear contains many frequencies. In Chapter 19, we talked about the *superposition principle*. Complex sound is created by the superposition of many frequencies. In fact, the sound of the human voice contains thousands of different frequencies—all at once (Figure 20.1).

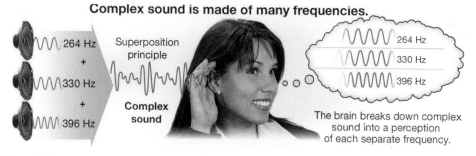

Complex sound is made of many frequencies.

264 Hz + 330 Hz + 396 Hz

Superposition principle

Complex sound

The brain breaks down complex sound into a perception of each separate frequency.

264 Hz
330 Hz
396 Hz

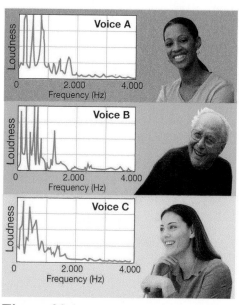

Figure 20.1: *The frequencies in three people's voices as they say the word "hello."*

The frequency spectrum
Why is it easy to recognize one person's voice from another, even when people are saying the same word? The reason is that voices have different mixtures of frequencies. A *frequency spectrum* is a graph showing the different frequencies present in a sound. Loudness is on the vertical axis and frequency is on the horizontal axis. Figure 20.1 shows the frequencies of the voices for three individuals saying "hello."

The loudness of sound

The decibel scale The loudness of sound is measured in **decibels** (dB). Loudness is determined mostly by the amplitude of a sound wave. However, instead of amplitude, we usually use the decibel scale to measure loudness (Figure 20.2). Most sounds fall between 0 and 100 on this scale, which makes it a convenient number to understand and use. Every increase of 20 decibels (dB) means the sound wave has 10 times greater amplitude and it sounds about twice as loud.

> **decibels** - the unit for measuring the loudness of sound
> **acoustics** - the science and technology of how sound behaves

Table 20.1: Common sounds and their loudness in decibels

0 dB	The threshold of human hearing; the quietest sound we can hear
10–15 dB	A quiet whisper 3 feet away
30–40 dB	Background sound level at a house
45–55 dB	The noise level in an average restaurant
65 dB	Ordinary conversation 3 feet away
70 dB	City traffic
90 dB	A jackhammer cutting up the street 10 feet away; louder sounds than 90 dB cause hearing damage
100 dB	A personal audio device turned to its maximum volume
110 dB	The front row of a rock concert
120 dB	The threshold of physical pain from loudness

The sensitivity of the ear How loud you hear a sound depends on both the amplitude of the sound wave and the response of your ear. The human ear is most sensitive to frequencies between 500 and 5,000 Hz. These are the same frequencies found in human voices. An *equal loudness curve* compares how loud you hear sounds of different frequencies (Figure 20.3). For example, a 30 dB sound at 2,000 Hz sounds just as loud as an 70 dB sound at 70 Hz. Sounds near 2,000 Hz seem less loud than sounds of other frequencies, even at the same decibel level. Almost no one can hear sound above 20,000 Hz no matter how large the amplitude is.

Acoustics **Acoustics** is the science and technology of sound. Knowledge of acoustics is important in many situations. For example, reducing the loudness of sound is important in designing libraries so that sounds are absorbed to maintain quiet. Recording studios are designed to block out sound from the outside. Can you name some other places where a knowledge of acoustics is useful?

Comparing Decibels and Amplitude

Decibels (dB)	Amplitude
0	1
20	10
40	100
60	1,000
80	10,000
100	100,000
120	1,000,000

Figure 20.2: *The decibel scale is a measure of the amplitude of sound waves.*

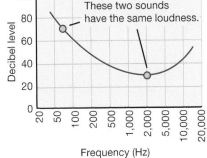

Figure 20.3: *All points on an equal loudness curve have the same loudness.*

The speed of sound

Sound moves at about 340 meters per second
You hear the sound of thunder many seconds after you see lightning. Why? Lighting creates thunder, so these events occur at the same time. You hear a delay because sound travels slower than light. The speed of sound in air is 343 meters per second (about 767 mph) at room temperature (20°C). The speed of sound increases as air temperature increases.

Subsonic and supersonic
Objects that move slower than sound are called **subsonic**. A passenger jet is subsonic because its speed ranges from about 180 to 220 meters per second. Objects that move faster than sound are called **supersonic**. Some military jets fly at supersonic speeds. If you are on the ground watching a supersonic plane fly toward you, there would be silence (Figure 20.4). The sound would be *behind* the plane.

Sonic booms
A supersonic jet "squishes" the sound waves that are created as its nose cuts through the air. A cone-shaped **shock wave** forms where the wave fronts pile up. In front of the shock wave, there is total silence. Behind the shock wave, you can hear the noise from the plane. Right at the shock wave the amplitude changes abruptly, causing a very loud sound called a *sonic boom*.

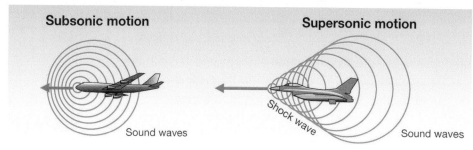

subsonic - motion that is slower than the speed of sound

supersonic - motion that is faster than the speed of sound in air

shock wave - the "piled up" wave fronts that form in front of a supersonic object

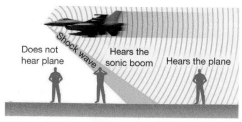

Figure 20.4: *If a supersonic jet flew overhead, you would not hear the sound until the plane was past you. A shock wave is the boundary between sound and silence.*

Material	Sound Speed (m/s)
Air	330
Helium	965
Water	1,530
Wood (average)	2,000
Gold	3,240
Steel	5,940

Figure 20.5: *The speed of sound in various materials (helium and air at 0°C and 1 atmospheric pressure).*

Sound in liquids and solids
The speed of sound in liquid and solid materials is usually faster than in air (Figure 20.5). Compared to air, sound travels about five times faster in water, and about 18 times faster in steel. This is because sound is really a travelling oscillation of the atoms in a material. Like other oscillations, sound depends on restoring forces and inertia, only on an atomic scale. The forces holding steel atoms together in a solid are much stronger than the forces between molecules in air. Stronger restoring forces increase the speed of sound.

The Doppler effect

Definition of the Doppler effect
If a sound-producing object is stationary, listeners on all sides will hear the same frequency. When the object is moving, the sound will *not* be the same to all listeners. People moving with a moving object or to the side of it hear the sound as if the object were stationary. People in front of an object hear sound of higher frequency; those behind it hear sound of lower frequency. The shift in frequency caused by such motion is called the **Doppler effect**. It occurs when a sound source is moving at speeds below the speed of sound.

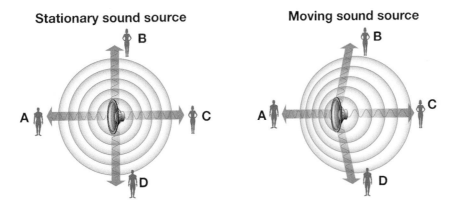

Stationary sound source

Moving sound source

The cause of the Doppler effect
The Doppler effect occurs because an observer hears the frequency at which wave fronts arrive at the observer's ears. Observer A in the graphic above hears a higher frequency. This is because the object's motion causes the crests in front to be closer together. The opposite is true behind a moving object, where the wave crests are farther apart. Observer C hears a lower frequency because the motion of the object makes more space between successive wave fronts. Observers B and D experience the Doppler effect. Also, the greater the speed of the object, the larger the difference in frequency between the front and back positions.

Demonstrating the Doppler effect
You can hear the Doppler effect when you hear the siren of a fire engine coming toward you and then moving past you. You can observe and hear the Doppler effect if someone whirls a small battery-powered beeper around overhead on a string. The frequency shifts up and down with each rotation according to whether the beeper is moving toward you or away from you.

> **Doppler effect** - the shift in frequency caused by the relative motion of a sound source and an observer

Doppler radar

The Doppler effect can happen with reflected waves, including microwaves. With Doppler radar, a transmitter sends a pulse of microwaves. These waves reflect from a moving object, such as a car. The frequency of the reflected waves is increased if the car is moving toward the source and decreases if the car is moving away.

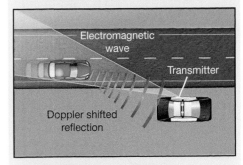

Electromagnetic wave

Transmitter

Doppler shifted reflection

The difference in frequency between the reflected and transmitted wave is called the Doppler shift. Because Doppler shift is proportional to speed, Doppler radar is a way to measure speed at a distance. For this reason, Doppler radar is used to enforce speed limits and to measure the speed of wind in storms.

Recording sound

The importance of recorded sound A hundred years ago, the only way to hear music was to be within hearing range of the musicians as they played. The recording of sound was a breakthrough in technology that changed the human experience.

The microphone To record a sound, you must store the pattern of vibrations in a way that can be replayed and be true to the original sound. A common way to record sound starts with a microphone. A microphone transforms a sound wave into an electrical signal with the same pattern of vibration (top of Figure 20.6).

Analog to digital conversion In modern digital recording, a sensitive circuit called an "analog to digital converter" measures the electrical signal 44,100 times per second. Each measurement consists of a number between 0 and 65,536 corresponding to the amplitude of the signal. One second of compact-disc-quality sound is a list of 44,100 numbers. The numbers are recorded as data on the disc.

Playback of recorded sound To play the sound back, the string of numbers on the CD is read by a laser and converted into electrical signals again by a second circuit. This circuit is a digital-to-analog converter, and it reverses the process of the first circuit. The playback circuit converts the string of numbers back into an electrical signal. The electrical signal is amplified until it is powerful enough to move the coil in a speaker and reproduce the sound (bottom of Figure 20.6).

Stereo sound Most of the music you listen to has been recorded in stereo. A stereo recording is actually two recordings, one to be played from the right speaker, the other from the left. Stereo sound seems almost "live" because it creates slight phase differences between the sounds reaching your left and right ears.

20.1 *Section Review*

1. What is the relationship between pitch and frequency?
2. Do two sound waves that seem equally loud always have the same amplitude? Explain.
3. How do the amplitudes of a 120-decibel sound and a 100-decibel sound compare?
4. Would an object moving at 800 miles per hour be supersonic or subsonic?
5. A paramedic in an ambulance does not experience the Doppler effect of the siren. Why?
6. How many numbers are involved in generating 1 minute of stereo sound on a CD?

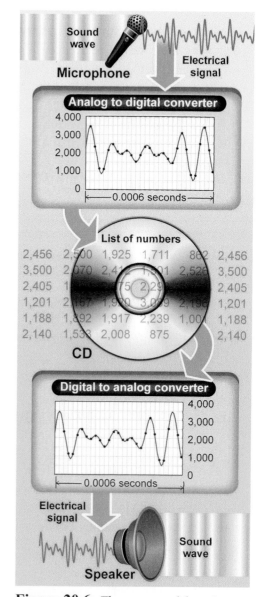

Figure 20.6: *The process of digital sound reproduction.*

20.2 **Sound Waves**

You can see water move in a water wave, but sound waves are invisible. Sound is a wave because it has both frequency and wavelength. We also know sound is a wave because it does all the things other waves do. Sound can be reflected, refracted, and absorbed. Sound also shows interference and diffraction. Resonance occurs with sound waves and is especially important in how instruments work.

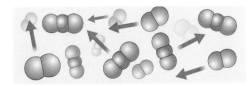

Figure 20.7: *Air is made of molecules in constant random motion, bumping off each other and the walls of their container.*

What is oscillating in a sound wave?

Sound in air and gases Sound is a traveling oscillation of atoms and molecules. In air, atoms are spread far apart and interact by colliding with each other (Figure 20.7). Air pressure is higher where atoms are close together and lower where they are farther apart (Figure 20.8). Imagine pushing the atoms on the left side of the picture below. Your push squeezes atoms together creating a layer of higher pressure. That layer pushes on the next layer, which pushes on the next layer, and so on. The result is a traveling oscillation in pressure, which is a sound wave. Sound is a *longitudinal* wave because atoms are compressed in the same direction the wave travels.

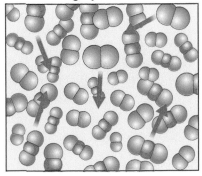

High pressure

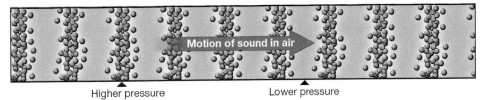

Higher pressure   Lower pressure

Sound in solids and liquids In solids and liquids, the push on one atom causes it to push on its neighbor. Then, that atom pushes on the next atom, and so on. The push causes atoms to oscillate back and forth like tiny masses on springs. The oscillation spreads through the connections between atoms to make a sound wave that travels through the solid or liquid.

Low pressure

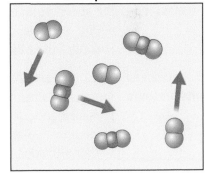

The frequency range of sound waves Anything that vibrates creates sound waves, as long as there is contact with other atoms. The oscillations we call sound waves cover a wide range of frequencies. Whether or not an organism can hear these sounds depends on the abilities of its sound receptors or ears. Humans can hear only the narrow range between 20 Hz and 20,000 Hz. Bats can hear high-frequency sounds between 40,000 and 100,000 Hz, and whales hear low-frequency sounds that are lower than 10 Hz.

Figure 20.8: *At the same temperature, high pressure means more molecules per unit volume. Low pressure means fewer molecules per unit volume.*

Sound and air pressure

Speakers
If you touch the surface of a speaker, you feel the vibration that creates a sound wave. Figure 20.9 shows a speaker as well as an exaggerated sound wave and the oscillation of pressure. When music is playing, the surface of the speaker moves back and forth at the same frequencies as the sound waves. The back-and-forth motion of the speaker creates a traveling sound wave of alternating high and low pressure.

Air pressure
The change in air pressure created by a sound wave is incredibly small. An 80 dB sound, equivalent to a loud stereo, changes the air pressure by only one part in a million. Our ears are very sensitive to such small changes in pressure created by sound waves.

Frequency and pressure change
The frequency of sound indicates how fast air pressure oscillates back and forth. The purr of a cat, for example, might have a frequency of 50 hertz. This means the air pressure alternates 50 times per second. The frequency of a fire truck siren may be 3,000 hertz. This corresponds to 3,000 vibrations per second in the pressure of the air.

Sound speed depends on temperature
In air, the energy of a sound wave is carried by moving atoms and molecules bumping into each other. Anything that affects the motion of atoms affects the speed of sound. Atoms move more slowly in cold air, and the speed of sound decreases. For example, at 0°C, the speed of sound is 330 meters per second, but at 21°C, it is 344 meters per second.

Sound speed and pressure
At higher air pressures, atoms are closer together. The speed of sound increases because collisions between atoms increase. Therefore, if the pressure goes down, the speed of sound decreases. This phenomenon affects airplanes. A plane that is subsonic at low altitudes may become supersonic at higher altitudes where the temperature and pressure are lower.

Sound speed and molecular weight
Lighter atoms and molecules move faster than heavier ones at the same temperature. The speed of sound is higher in helium gas because its atoms are lighter than those of oxygen or nitrogen gas that make up air.

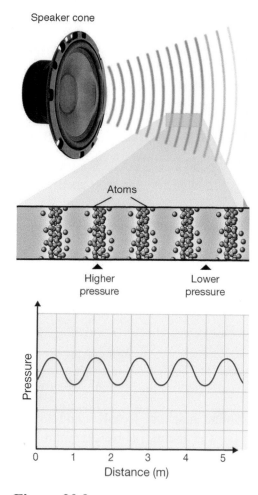

Figure 20.9: *What a sound wave might look like if you could see the atoms. The effect is greatly exaggerated to show the variation.*

The wavelength of sound

Range of wavelengths of sound   The wavelength of sound in air is comparable to the size of everyday objects. The chart below gives some typical frequencies and wavelengths for sound in air. As with other waves, the wavelength of a sound is inversely related to its frequency (Figure 20.10). A low-frequency 20-hertz sound has a wavelength the size of a large classroom. At the upper range of hearing, a 20,000-hertz sound has a wavelength about the width of your thumb.

Table 20.2: Frequency and wavelength for some typical sounds

Frequency (Hz)	Wavelength	Typical Source
20	17 m	rumble of thunder
100	3.4 m	bass guitar
500	70 cm (27")	average male voice
1,000	34 cm (13")	female soprano voice
2,000	17 cm (6.7")	fire truck siren
5,000	7 cm (2.7")	highest note on a piano
10,000	3.4 cm (1.3")	whine of a jet turbine
20,000	1.7 cm (0.67")	highest-pitched sound you can hear

Wavelengths of sounds are important

Valves

Long tube

Long wavelength, low-frequency sound

Short tube

Short wavelength, high-frequency sound

Although we usually think about different sounds in terms of frequency, the wavelength can also be important. If you want to make sound of a certain wavelength, you often need to have a vibrating object that is similar in size to the wavelength. That is why instruments like a French horn have valves. A French horn makes sound by vibrating the air trapped in a long coiled tube. Short tubes only fit short wavelengths and make high-frequency sound. Long tubes fit longer wavelengths and make lower-frequency sounds. Opening and closing the French horn's valves lets the player add and subtract different-length tubes, which changes the sound's frequency.

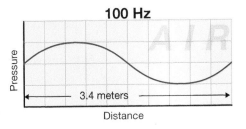

100 Hz

3.4 meters

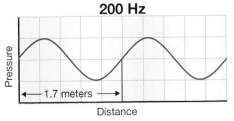

200 Hz

1.7 meters

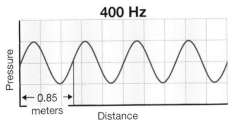

400 Hz

0.85 meters

Figure 20.10: *The frequency and wavelength of sound are inversely related. When the frequency goes up, the wavelength goes down proportionally.*

Interactions between sound waves and boundaries

Interactions of sound and materials
Like other waves, sound waves can be reflected by hard surfaces and refracted as they pass from one material to another. Diffraction causes sound waves to spread out through small openings. Carpet and soft materials can absorb sound waves. Figure 20.11 shows examples of sound interactions.

Reverberation
In a good concert hall, the reflected sound and direct sound from the musicians together create a multiple echo called **reverberation**. The right amount of reverberation makes the sound seem livelier and richer. Too much reverberation and the sound gets "muddy" from too many reflections. Concert hall designers choose the shape and surface of the walls and ceiling to provide the best reverberation. Some concert halls have movable panels that can be raised or lowered from the ceiling to help shape the sound.

Constructing a good concert hall
Direct sound (A) reaches the listener along with reflected sound (B and C) from the walls. The shape of the room and the surfaces of its walls must be designed and constructed so that there is some reflected sound, but not too much.

Absorbent wall panels dampen side reflections

Angled back walls help project sound forward

Interference can also affect sound quality
Reverberation also causes interference of sound waves. When two waves interfere, the total can be louder or softer than either wave alone. The diagram above shows a musician and an audience of one person. The sound reflected from the walls interferes as it reaches the listener. If the distances are just right, one reflected wave might be out of phase with the other. The result is that the sound is quieter at that spot. An acoustic engineer would call it a *dead spot* in the hall. Dead spots are areas where destructive interference causes some of the sound to cancel with its own reflections. It is also possible to make very loud spots where sound interferes constructively. The best concert halls are designed to minimize both dead spots and loud spots.

> **reverberation** - multiple echoes of sound caused by reflections of sound building up and blending together

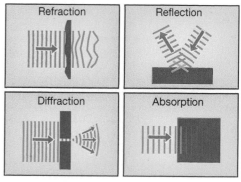

Refraction | Reflection
Diffraction | Absorption

Figure 20.11: *Sound displays all the properties of waves in its interactions with materials and boundaries.*

Ultrasound

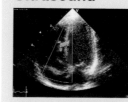

Ultrasound is high-frequency sound, often 100,000 hertz or more. We cannot hear ultrasound, but it passes through the human body easily. Medical ultrasound instruments use the refraction and reflection of ultrasound waves inside the body to create images of the human body's interior. The ultrasound image pictured above is a heart.

Standing waves and resonance

Resonance of sound   Spaces enclosed by boundaries can create *resonance* with sound waves. Almost all musical instruments use resonance to make musical sounds. A panpipe is a good example of resonance in a musical instrument. A panpipe is a simple instrument made of many tubes of different lengths (Figure 20.12). One end of each tube is closed and the other end is open. Blowing across the open end of a tube creates a standing wave inside the tube. The frequency of the standing wave is the frequency of sound given off by the pipe. Longer pipes create longer wavelength standing waves and make lower frequencies of sound. Shorter pipes create shorter-wavelength standing waves and therefore make higher frequencies of sound.

Standing wave patterns   The closed end of a pipe is called a closed boundary. A closed boundary makes a node in the standing wave. The open end of a pipe is an open boundary to a standing wave in the pipe. An open boundary makes an antinode in the standing wave. Figure 20.12 shows a standing wave that has a node at the closed end and an antinode at the open end. One-quarter of a wavelength fits in the pipe. Therefore, the fundamental is four times the length of the pipe. The pipe resonates when its length is one-fourth the wavelength of a sound.

Designing a musical instrument   Suppose you wish to make a pipe that makes a sound with a frequency of 660 hertz (the note E). Using the relationship between speed, frequency, and wavelength, the required wavelength is (343 m/s) ÷ (660 Hz) = 0.52 m. The length of pipe needs to be one-fourth of the wavelength to resonate in the fundamental mode. One-quarter of 52 centimeters is 13 centimeters. If you make a thin pipe that is 13 centimeters long with one closed end, it will have a natural frequency of about 660 hertz. This is the principle on which musical instruments are designed. Sounds of different frequencies are made by standing waves. The length of a vibrating system can be chosen so that it resonates at the frequency you want to hear.

$$Wave\ speed = Frequency \times Wavelength$$
$$Wave\ speed \div Frequency = Wavelength$$

Panpipes

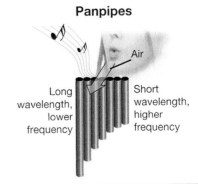

Long wavelength, lower frequency

Short wavelength, higher frequency

Air

Standing wave in a panpipe

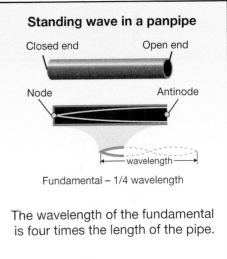

Closed end   Open end

Node   Antinode

wavelength

Fundamental – 1/4 wavelength

The wavelength of the fundamental is four times the length of the pipe.

Figure 20.12: *A panpipe is made from tubes of different length. The diagram shows the fundamental for a standing wave of sound in a panpipe.*

Fourier's theorem

How are multiple frequencies of sound created? To make a single frequency of sound, a speaker vibrates back and forth in a simple pattern with a single wavelength and frequency. However, almost all the sound you hear is a combination of frequencies. What kind of motion should a speaker use to create multiple frequencies of sound at the same time, as there is in music or speech?

> **Fourier's theorem** - the creation of a complex wave by adding single-frequency waves

Fourier's theorem The answer involves **Fourier's theorem**. Fourier's theorem says a wave of any shape can be made by adding up single-frequency waves. Remember that the superposition principle states that many single waves add up to one complex wave. Fourier's theorem works from the other direction. A complex wave can be made from a sum of single-frequency waves, each with its own frequency, amplitude, and phase.

An example Figure 20.13 shows a "square wave" with a frequency of 100 Hz. A square wave does not have a single frequency, but instead contains many frequencies. Fourier's theorem allows you to make a pretty good square wave by adding five waves of different frequencies and amplitudes. To produce multiple frequencies, a speaker vibrates back and forth with a complex motion. If a speaker were to vibrate back and forth with sudden jerks, like the square wave, it would create sound of all the frequencies it takes to make the square wave!

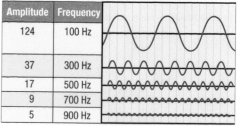

100 Hz square wave

Amplitude	Frequency
100	100 Hz

First five frequencies in a square wave

Amplitude	Frequency
124	100 Hz
37	300 Hz
17	500 Hz
9	700 Hz
5	900 Hz

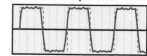

Sum of first five frequencies

Figure 20.13: *Making a square wave by adding up five single-frequency waves.*

20.2 Section Review

1. Is sound a longitudinal or transverse wave?
2. A 200-hertz sound has a wavelength about equal to the height of an adult. Would a sound with a wavelength equal to the height of a 2-year-old child have a higher or lower frequency than 200 Hz?
3. In which situation does sound travel faster: (a) outside on a winter day, or (b) outside on a summer day?
4. Would a full concert hall have a different reverberation from an empty hall? Explain.

20.3 Sound, Perception, and Music

Sound is everywhere in our environment. We use sound to communicate and we listen to sound for information about what is going on around us. Our ears and brain are constantly receiving and processing sound. In this section, you will learn about how we *hear* a sound wave and how the ear and brain construct meaning from sound. This section will also introduce some of the science behind music. Musical sound is a rich language of rhythm and frequency that developed over thousands of years of human culture.

Constructing meaning from patterns

As you read this paragraph, you subconsciously recognize individual letters. However, the *meaning* of the paragraph is not in the letters themselves. The meaning is in the *patterns* of how the letters make words and the words make sentences. The brain does a similar thing with sound. A single frequency of sound is like one letter. It does not have much meaning. The meaning in sound comes from patterns of many frequencies changing together.

The ear hears many frequencies at once

When you hear a sound, the nerves in your ear respond to more than 15,000 different frequencies at the same time. This is like having an alphabet with 15,000 letters! The brain interprets all 15,000 different frequency signals from the ear and creates a "sonic image" of the sound. The meaning in different sounds is derived from the patterns of the different frequencies as they get louder and softer.

Complex sound waves

Imagine listening to live music with a singer and a band. Your ears can easily distinguish the voice from the instruments. How does this occur? The microphone records a single "wave form" of how pressure varies with time. The recorded wave form is very complex, but it contains all the sound from the music and voice (Figure 20.14).

How the brain finds meaning

You ear is a living application of Fourier's theorem. The ear separates the sound into different frequencies. Your brain has learned to recognize certain patterns of how each frequency changes over time. One pattern might be a word. Another might be a musical note. Inside your brain is a "dictionary" that associates a meaning with a pattern of frequency in the same way an ordinary dictionary associates a meaning from a pattern of letters or words.

(see next page)
frequency spectrum - a graph showing the distribution of different frequencies in a complex signal, like a sound wave

sonogram - a graph showing how the loudness of different frequencies of sound changes with time

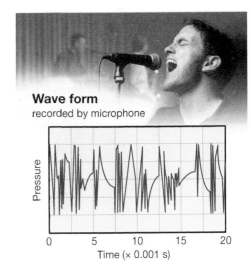

Wave form
recorded by microphone

Figure 20.14: *The recorded wave form from 0.02 seconds of music.*

The frequency spectrum and sonogram

Frequency spectrum
A **frequency spectrum** is a graph showing the different frequencies present in a sound. The vertical axis tells you the loudness (amplitude) and the horizontal axis tells you the frequency. Sound containing many frequencies has a wave form that is jagged and complicated. The wave form in Figure 20.15 (top) is from an acoustic guitar playing the note E. The frequency spectrum (Figure 20.15, bottom) shows that the complex sound of the guitar is made from many frequencies, ranging up to 10,000 Hz and beyond.

The wave form and spectrum change with time
Both the wave form and the spectrum change as the sound changes. The wave form and spectrum represent only a single moment of the sound. Since meaning comes from patterns of changing frequencies, we need another graph that shows the three variables at once: frequency, amplitude, and time.

Sonograms
A **sonogram** shows how loud a sound is at different frequencies over a period of time. Color is used to show variations in loudness. The sonogram shown below is for a male voice saying "hello." The word lasts from 0.1 seconds to about 0.6 seconds. Every person's sonogram for the same word is different.

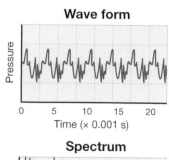

Wave form

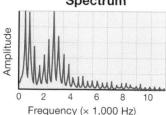

Spectrum

The spectrum shows the frequencies that make up a complex wave form.

Figure 20.15: *Each peak in the spectrum represents the frequency and amplitude of a wave that makes up the wave form.*

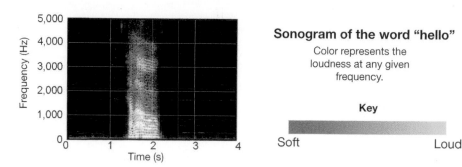

Sonogram of the word "hello"

Color represents the loudness at any given frequency.

Key

Soft   Loud

Reading a sonogram
A sonogram shows frequency on the vertical axis and time on the horizontal axis. The loudness is shown by different colors. The sonogram shown for the word "hello" lasts from 1.4 to 2.2 seconds. You can see that there are many frequencies almost filling up the space between 0 and 5,000 Hz. Figure 20.16 is an example of a simpler sonogram. Which bar—A, B, C, or D—represents a loud sound of 100 Hz lasting from 1 to 3 seconds?

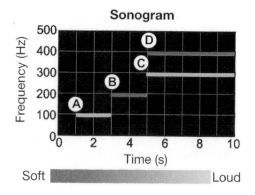

Figure 20.16: *A sonogram shows how the loudness of different frequencies of sound changes with time.*

How we hear sound

Hearing sound We get our sense of hearing from the **cochlea**, a tiny, fluid-filled organ in the inner ear (Figure 20.17). The inner ear has two important functions: providing our sense of hearing and our sense of balance. The three semicircular canals near the cochlea are also filled with fluid. Fluid moving in each of the three canals tells the brain whether the body is moving left-right, up-down, or forward-backward.

How the cochlea works The perception of sound starts with the eardrum. The eardrum vibrates in response to sound waves in the ear canal. The three delicate bones of the inner ear transmit the vibration of the eardrum to the side of the cochlea. Fluid in the spiral of the cochlea vibrates and creates waves that travel up the spiral. The spiral channel starts out large and gets narrower near the end. The nerves near the beginning are in a relatively large channel and respond to longer-wavelength, lower-frequency sound. The nerves at the small end of the channel respond to shorter-wavelength, higher-frequency sound.

The range of human hearing The range of human hearing is between 20 hertz and 20,000 hertz (or 20 kilohertz, abbreviated kHz). The combination of the eardrum, bones, and cochlea all contribute to the limited range of hearing. You could not hear a sound at 50,000 hertz (50 kHz), even at a loudness of 100 decibels. Animals such as cats and dogs can hear higher frequencies because of the design of their outer ears and the more-sensitive structures in their inner ears.

Hearing ability changes with time Hearing varies greatly with people and changes with age. Some people can hear higher-frequency sounds while others cannot. People gradually lose high-frequency hearing with age. Most adults cannot hear frequencies above 15,000 hertz, while children can often hear to 20,000 hertz.

Hearing can be damaged by loud noise Hearing is affected by exposure to loud or high-frequency noise. The nerve signals that carry sound sensation to the brain are created by tiny hairs that shake when the fluid in the cochlea is vibrated. Listening to loud sounds for a long time can cause the hairs to weaken or break off. You can protect your ears by keeping the volume reasonable on audio equipment and by wearing ear protection if you have to stay in a loud place. In concerts, many musicians wear earplugs to protect their hearing.

> **cochlea** - a tiny, fluid-filled structure in the inner ear that contains the nerves that create your sense of hearing

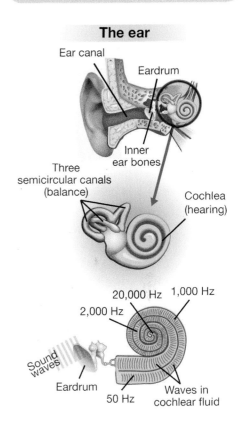

The ear

Figure 20.17: *The structure of the inner ear. When the eardrum vibrates, three small bones transmit the vibration to the cochlea. The vibrations make waves inside the cochlea, which vibrates nerves in the spiral. Each part of the spiral is sensitive to a different frequency.*

Music

Pitch The *pitch* of a sound is how high or low we hear its frequency. A higher-frequency sound is heard as a higher pitch. However, pitch depends on the human ear and brain. The way we hear a sound can be affected by the sounds we hear just before and after the sound.

Rhythm **Rhythm** is a regular time pattern in a sound. Here is a rhythm you can "play" on your desk. Play "TAP" louder than you play "tap": TAP-TAP-tap-tap-TAP-TAP-tap-tap. Rhythm can be made with sound and silence or with different pitches. People respond naturally to rhythm. Cultures are distinguished by their music and the special rhythms used in that music.

The musical scale Music is a combination of sound and rhythm that we find pleasant. Styles of music are vastly different, but all music is created from carefully-chosen frequencies of sound. Most of the music you listen to is created from a pattern of frequencies called a **musical scale**. Each frequency in the scale is called a **note**. The range between any frequency and twice that frequency is called an **octave**. Notes that are an octave apart in frequency share the same letter name. Within the octave, there are eight primary notes in the Western musical scale. Each of the eight notes is related to the first note in the scale by a ratio of frequencies. The scale that starts on the note C (264 Hz) is shown in the diagram below.

rhythm - the organization of sound into regular time patterns
musical scale - a series of frequencies arranged in a special pattern
note - a musical sound such as from a musical scale
octave - the interval between a frequency and twice that frequency

Octaves

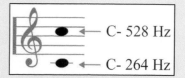

Two notes are an octave apart when the frequency of one note is double the frequency of the other. Notes that are an octave apart are given the same letter name because they sound similar to the ear. For example, the note C has a frequency of 264 Hz. Frequencies of 132 Hz and 528 Hz are also named "C" because they are an octave apart from C at 264 Hz.

C major scale

Note	C	D	E	F	G	A	B	C
Approximate frequency (Hz)	264	297	330	352	396	440	495	528
Ratio to C (264 Hz)	1/1 $\left(\frac{264}{264}\right)$	9/8 $\left(\frac{297}{264}\right)$	5/4 $\left(\frac{330}{264}\right)$	4/3 $\left(\frac{352}{264}\right)$	3/2 $\left(\frac{396}{264}\right)$	5/3 $\left(\frac{440}{264}\right)$	15/8 $\left(\frac{495}{264}\right)$	2/1 $\left(\frac{528}{264}\right)$

Consonance, dissonance, and beats

Harmony *Harmony* is the study of how sounds work together to create effects desired by the composer. From experience, you know that music can have a profound effect on people's moods. For example, the tense, dramatic sound track of a horror movie is a vital part of the audience's experience. Harmony is based on the frequency relationships of the musical scale.

Beats The frequencies in the musical scale are specifically chosen to reduce the occurrence of a sound effect called *beats*. When two frequencies of sound are close but not exactly equal, the loudness of the total sound seems to oscillate or **beat**. At one moment, the two waves are in phase and the total sound is louder than either wave separately. A moment later, the waves are out of phase and they cancel each other out. The rapid alternation in amplitude or loudness is what we hear as beats. Bats use beats to navigate and locate insects. Beats are also useful for determining if a musical instrument is out of tune (see sidebar on the next page).

beat - the oscillation of amplitude that results from the interference of two sound waves with frequencies that are almost but not quite equal

consonance - a combination of sound frequencies that is agreeable or harmonious

dissonance - a combination of sound frequencies that is discordant or unsettling

Adding two waves with different frequency

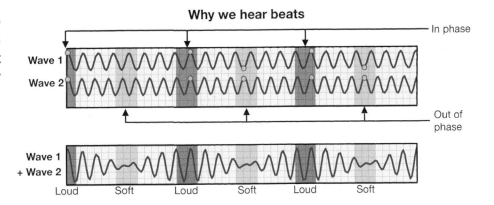

Why we hear beats

Wave 1 — In phase

Wave 2 — Out of phase

Wave 1 + Wave 2

Loud Soft Loud Soft Loud Soft

Echolocation and beats

Bats navigate and find food using echolocation. A bat "chirps" in short bursts of ultrasound waves. When the waves reflect off an insect, the bat's ears receive the echo. The echo returns to the bat with a slightly different frequency than the chirp. The difference between the echo and the chirp makes beats that the bat can hear. The beat frequency is proportional to how far the insect is from the bat. A bat can even determine where the insect is by comparing the echo it hears in the left ear with what it hears in the right ear.

Consonance and dissonance When we hear more than one frequency of sound and the combination sounds good, we call it **consonance**. When the combination sounds bad or unsettling, we call it **dissonance**. Consonance and dissonance are related to beats. When frequencies are far enough apart that there are no beats, we get consonance. When frequencies are too close together, we hear beats that are the cause of dissonance. Dissonance is often used to create tension or drama. Consonance can be used to create feelings of balance and comfort.

Voices and instruments

Voices The human voice is a complex sound that starts in the larynx, a small structure at the top of your windpipe. The term *vocal cords* is a little misleading because the sound-producing structures are not really cords, but folds of expandable tissue that extend across a hollow chamber known as the larynx. The sound that starts in the larynx is changed by passing through openings in the throat and mouth (Figure 20.18). Different sounds are made by changing both the vibrations in the larynx and the shape of the openings.

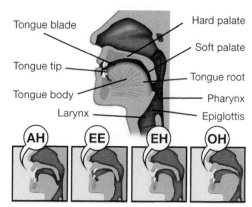

Figure 20.18: *The human voice is created by a combination of vibrating folds of skin in the larynx and the resonant shapes of the throat and mouth.*

The guitar The guitar has become a central instrument in popular music. Guitars come in many types but share the common feature of making sound from vibrating strings. A standard guitar has six strings that are stretched along the neck. The strings have different weights and therefore different natural frequencies.

On many guitars, the heaviest string has a natural frequency of 82 Hz and the lightest a frequency of 330 Hz. Each string is stretched by a tension force of about 125 newtons (28 pounds). The combined force from six strings on a guitar is more than the weight of a person (750 N or 170 lbs). The guitar is tuned by changing the tension in each string. Tightening a string raises its natural frequency and loosening the string lowers it.

Each string can make many notes A typical guitar string is 63 centimeters long. To make different notes, the vibrating length of each string can be shortened by holding it down against the space between metal bars on the neck called *frets*. The frequency goes up as the vibrating length of the string gets shorter. A guitar with 20 frets and six strings can play 126 different notes, some of which are duplicates. Figure 20.19 shows frequency spectra for two guitars' sounds. Often musicians distort notes to change the quality of the sound produced.

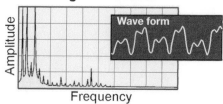

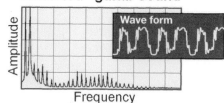

Figure 20.19: *Wave forms from "clean" and "distorted" guitar sounds. Notice that both sounds have the same fundamental frequency, but the distorted sound has more high-frequency harmonic content.*

Harmonics and the sound of instruments

The same note can sound different
The same note sounds different when played on different instruments. As an example, suppose you listen to the note C at 264 Hz played on a guitar and the same C played on a piano. A musician would recognize both notes as being C because they have the same frequency and pitch. But the guitar sounds like a guitar and the piano sounds like a piano. If the frequency of the note is the same, what gives each instrument its characteristic sound?

Instruments make mixtures of frequencies
The answer is that the sound from an instrument is not a single pure frequency. The most important frequency is still the fundamental note (C at 264 Hz, for example). The variation comes from the *harmonics*. Remember, harmonics are frequencies that are multiples of the fundamental note. We have already learned that a string can vibrate at many harmonics. The same is true for all musical instruments. A single C note from a grand piano might include 20 or more different harmonics.

Recipes for sound
A good analogy is that every instrument has its own *recipe* for the frequency content of its sound. Another word for recipe in this context is *timbre*. In Figure 20.20, you can see how the mix of harmonics for a guitar compares to the mix for a piano when both instruments play the note C. This graphic illustrates that the timbre of a guitar is different from that of a piano.

Beat frequency

An "A" tuning fork produces vibrations for the note A at 440 hertz. Let's say the A string on a guitar is out of tune and its natural frequency is 445 hertz. This means that when you play the string and listen to the tuning fork, you will hear a beat frequency of 5 beats per second or 5 hertz. The beat frequency becomes zero when the string is "in tune" with the natural frequency of 440 hertz.

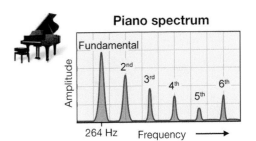

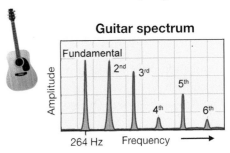

Figure 20.20: *The sound of the note C at 264 Hz on a piano and on a guitar. Notice that the fundamental frequencies are the same but the harmonics have different amplitudes.*

20.3 Section Review

1. Explain how the cochlea allows us to hear both low-frequency and high-frequency sound.
2. What is the range of frequencies for humans?
3. If you were talking to a person who was having trouble hearing you, would it be better to talk in a deeper voice (low-frequency sound) or a higher voice (high-frequency sound)?
4. What is the difference between the pitch of a sound and its frequency?
5. If two sound waves are in phase, do you hear beats? Why or why not?
6. A musician in a group plays a "wrong" note. Would this note disrupt the harmony or the rhythm of the song they are playing? Explain your answer.
7. Why does an A played on a violin sound different from the same note played on a guitar?

Chapter 20 **Connection**

Hearing: An Essay by Dame Evelyn Glennie Reprinted with permission from www.evelyn.co.uk

Music represents life. A particular piece of music may describe a real, fictional or abstract scene from almost any area of human experience or imagination. It is the musicians job to paint a picture which communicates to the audience the scene the composer is trying to describe. I hope that the audience will be stimulated by what I have to say (through the language of music) and will therefore leave the concert hall feeling entertained. If the audience is instead only wondering how a deaf musician can play percussion then I have failed as a musician. For this reason my deafness is not mentioned in any of the information supplied by my office to the press or concert promoters.

J.Wilson/©EG Images

Unfortunately, my deafness makes good headlines. I have learnt from childhood that if I refuse to discuss my deafness with the media they will just make it up. The several hundred articles and reviews written about me every year add up to a total of many thousands, only a handful accurately describe my hearing impairment. More than 90% are so inaccurate that it would seem impossible that I could be a musician. This essay is designed to set the record straight and allow people to enjoy the experience of being entertained by an ever evolving musician rather than some freak or miracle of nature.

Deafness is poorly understood in general. For instance, there is a common misconception that deaf people live in a world of silence. To understand the nature of deafness, first one has to understand the nature of hearing.

Hearing is basically a specialized form of touch. Sound is simply vibrating air which the ear picks up and converts to electrical signals, which are then interpreted by the brain. The sense of hearing is not the only sense that can do this, touch can do this too. If you are standing by the road and a large truck goes by, do you hear or feel the vibration? The answer is both. With very low frequency vibration the ear starts becoming inefficient and the rest of the body's sense of touch starts to take over. For some reason we tend to make a distinction between hearing a sound and feeling a vibration, in reality they are the same thing. It is interesting to note that in the Italian language this distinction does not exist. The verb 'sentire' means to hear and the same verb in the reflexive form 'sentirsi' means to feel. Deafness does not mean that you can't hear, only that there is something wrong with the ears. Even someone who is totally deaf can still hear/feel sounds.

If we can all feel low frequency vibrations why can't we feel higher vibrations? It is my belief that we can, it's just that as the frequency gets higher and our ears become more efficient they drown out the more subtle sense of 'feeling' the vibrations. I spent a lot of time in my youth (with the help of my school Percussion teacher Ron Forbes) refining my ability to detect vibrations. I would stand with my hands against the classroom wall while Ron played notes on the timpani  (timpani produce a lot of vibrations). Eventually I managed to distinguish the rough pitch of notes by associating where on my body I felt the sound with the sense of perfect pitch I had before losing my hearing. The low sounds I feel mainly in my legs and feet and high sounds might be particular places on my face, neck and chest.

It is worth pointing out at this stage that I am not totally deaf, I am profoundly deaf. Profound deafness covers a wide range of symptoms, although it is commonly taken to mean that the quality of the sound heard is not sufficient to be able to understand the spoken word from sound alone. With no other sound interfering, I can usually hear someone speaking although I cannot understand them without the additional input of lip-reading. In my case the amount of volume is reduced compared with normal hearing but more importantly the quality of the sound is very poor. For instance when a phone rings I hear a kind of crackle. However, it is a distinctive type of crackle that I associate with a phone so I know

J.Wilson/©EG Images

when the phone rings. This is basically the same as how normally hearing people detect a phone, the phone has a distinctive type of ring which we associate with a phone. I can in fact communicate over the phone. I do most of the talking whilst the other person can say a few words by striking the transmitter with a pen, I hear this as clicks. I have a code that depends on the number of strikes or the rhythm that I can use to communicate a handful of words.

So far we have the hearing of sounds and the feeling of vibrations. There is one other element to the equation, sight. We can also see items move and vibrate. If I see a drum head or cymbal vibrate or even see the leaves of a tree moving in the wind then subconsciously my brain creates a corresponding sound. A common and ill informed question from interviewers is 'How can you be a musician when you can't hear what you are doing?' The answer is of course that I couldn't be a musician if I were not able to hear. Another often asked question is 'How do you hear what you are playing?' The logical answer to this is; how does anyone hear?. An electrical signal is generated in the ear and various bits of other information from our other senses all get sent to the brain which then processes the data to create a sound picture. The various processes involved in hearing a sound are very complex but we all do it subconsciously so we group all these processes together and call it simply listening. The same is true for me. Some of the processes or original information may be different but to hear sound all I do is to listen. I have no more idea of how I hear than you do.

You will notice that more and more the answers are heading towards areas of philosophy. Who can say that when two normally hearing people hear a sound they hear the same sound? I would suggest that everyone's hearing is different. All we can say is that the sound picture built up by their brain is the same, so that outwardly there is no difference. For me, as for all of us, I am better at certain things with my hearing than others. I need to lip-read to understand speech but my awareness of the acoustics in a concert venue is excellent. For instance, I will sometimes describe an acoustic in terms of how thick the air feels.

To summarize, my hearing is something that bothers other people far more than it bothers me. There are a couple of inconveniences but in general it doesn't affect my life much. For me, my deafness is no more important than the fact I am female with brown eyes. Sure, I sometimes have to find solutions to problems related to my hearing and music but so do all musicians. Most of us know very little about hearing, even though we do it all the time. Likewise, I don't know very much about deafness, what's more I'm not particularly interested. I remember one occasion when uncharacteristically I became upset with a reporter for constantly asking questions only about my deafness. I said: 'If you want to know about deafness, you should interview an audiologist. My speciality is music.'

In this essay I have tried to explain something which I find very difficult to explain. Even so, no one really understands how I do what I do. Please enjoy the music and forget the rest.

QUESTIONS

1. Which two of your senses can convert sound waves to electrical signals? Which do you use more frequently?

2. How did Evelyn Glennie's percussion teacher help her refine her ability to distinguish pitch?

3. Describe an occasion when you have been able to see vibration caused by a sound wave.

Chapter 20 Review

Understanding Vocabulary

Select the correct term to complete the sentences.

beat	Fourier's theorem	reverberation
cochlea	musical scales	rhythm
consonance	note	shock wave
decibels	octave	subsonic
dissonance	pitch	supersonic
Doppler effect		

1. The _____ of a sound is how high or low we hear its frequency.

2. The shift in sound frequency caused by a moving sound source is called the _____.

3. A sonic boom is caused by the pressure change across a(n) _____.

4. Reflected sound waves added to direct sound create a multiple echo called _____.

5. Most music is based on patterns of frequencies called _____.

Reviewing Concepts

Section 20.1

1. Imagine you are cruising in outer space in a spaceship when you notice an asteroid hurtling towards your ship. You fire a missile and score a direct hit. The asteroid explodes into a billion pieces. Would you hear the explosion? Explain your answer.

2. How do we recognize people's voices?

3. What does the decibel scale measure, and what scale does it use?

4. If a fire engine moves toward you, does the pitch of its siren increase or decrease? Explain.

5. How fast does an airplane need to be traveling to create a sonic boom? Is this speed supersonic or subsonic?

6. How is stereo sound recorded, and why does it sound "live"?

Section 20.2

7. Explain how sound is caused at the molecular level. Sketch what a sound wave would look like at the molecular level.

8. What type of waves are sound waves?

9. How does pressure work as a restoring force to create a sound wave?

10. Which of the following sounds has the shortest wavelength?

    a. the rumble of thunder at 20 Hz
    b. a base guitar at 100 Hz
    c. a fire truck siren at 2,000 Hz
    d. the highest note on a piano at 5,000 Hz

11. If the temperature of a material increased, how would the speed of sound through this material be affected? Why?

12. In which space would it be easier to hear a musician and why—outdoors or in your classroom?

Section 20.3

13. What is the difference between a wave-form graph and a sound-spectrum graph for a complex sound? Which graph best illustrates the harmonic motion of sound? Why? Which graph best illustrates which frequencies are the loudest in a complex sound?

14. Some musicians wear earplugs when playing in concerts. What happens when the inner ear is exposed to very loud noises?

15. Which part of the ear vibrates in response to sound in the ear canal?

16. How are the pitch and frequency of a sound related?

17. What gives different instruments their characteristic sound? For example, why does a note played on a piano sound different from the same note played on a guitar?

18. How are beats created?

19. Why can't you hear a dog whistle at 25,000 Hz, but your dog can?

Solving Problems

Section 20.1

1. The sound of ordinary conversation 3 ft away is 65 dB and the sound in a restaurant is 45 dB.

   a. To our ears, how much louder is the ordinary conversation than the restaurant sound?

   b. How much larger is the amplitude of the sound waves in ordinary conversation than in the restaurant?

Section 20.2

2. The speed of sound through air is approximately 340 m/s. What is the wavelength of a sound wave with a frequency of 680 Hz?

3. The range of human hearing is between 20 Hz and 20,000 Hz. If the speed of sound is 340 m/s, what is the longest wavelength you can hear? What is the shortest?

4. Suppose you stand in front of a wall that is 170 m away. If you yell, how long does it take for the echo to get back to you if the speed of sound is 340 m/s?

5. What is the fundamental frequency of an organ pipe that is 1 m long? The pipe has one end that is open and another end that is closed. Use a wave speed of 340 m/s.

Section 20.3

6. If "middle" C on a piano has a frequency of 264 Hz, what is the frequency of the C one octave higher? One octave lower?

7. Describe what you hear when a musical note at 440 Hz is played at the same time as another note played at 443 Hz.

Test Practice

Section 20.1

Source	Loudness
A quiet whisper 3 feet away	15 dB
Ordinary conversation 3 feet away	65 dB
City traffic	70 dB
A jackhammer cutting up the street 10 feet away	90 dB
The front row of a rock concert	110 dB

1. According to the table, which noise sounds twice as loud as city traffic?

   a. a quiet whisper
   b. ordinary conversation
   c. a jackhammer
   d. the front row of a rock concert

2. Sound waves travel fastest in

   a. air.
   b. water.
   c. helium.
   d. steel.

3. A car horn with a frequency of 500 Hz is travelling from a car that is moving toward a stationary person. Which of the following frequencies might be heard by the stationary person?

   a. 600 Hz
   b. 500 Hz
   c. 400 Hz
   d. 250 Hz

4. When comparing sounds, some frequencies must be played at a larger decibel level to be perceived by the human ear as equally loud. All points on the equal loudness curve have the same perceived loudness by the human ear. According to the graph of the equal loudness curve, at which frequency is the human ear most sensitive?

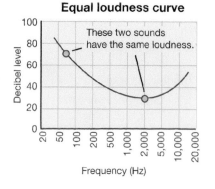

Equal loudness curve

These two sounds have the same loudness.

Frequency (Hz)

a. 20 Hz
b. 200 Hz
c. 2,000 Hz
d. 20,000 Hz

Section 20.2

5. The chart shows wavelengths of some common sounds. Which would have the highest frequency?

Source	Wavelength
bass guitar	3.4 m
average male voice	70 cm
fire truck siren	17 cm
highest note on a piano	7 cm

a. highest note on a piano
b. bass guitar
c. fire truck siren
d. average male voice

6. Sound is a _____ wave because molecules are compressed in the same direction that the wave travels.

a. surface
b. transverse
c. perpendicular
d. longitudinal

7. A person blows a whistle. The sound echoes off a wall and returns to the person after 2 s. Given that the speed of sound in air is 340 m/s, how far away is the wall?

a. 170 m
b. 340 m
c. 680 m
d. 1,360 m

8. Sound waves travelling through air are a travelling oscillation of

a. temperature.
b. mass.
c. pressure.
d. vapor.

Section 20.3

9. Hearing loss can occur due to exposure to loud noise causing

a. the tiny hairs in the cochlea to weaken or break.
b. the tiny bones of the inner ear to weaken or break.
c. the ear canal to become blocked with fluid.
d. punctures in the eardrum.

10. Which of the following frequencies is *not* in the range of human hearing?

a. 50 Hz
b. 200 Hz
c. 4,000 Hz
d. 30,000 Hz

11. Which of the following musical notes would likely cause beats when played at the same time?

a. 220 Hz and 440 Hz
b. 330 Hz and 660 Hz
c. 440 Hz and 443 Hz
d. 132 Hz and 264 Hz

12. The note C at 264 Hz sounds different when played on a piano than when played on a guitar because of the difference in

 a. pitch.
 b. harmonics.
 c. frequency.
 d. rhythm.

Applying Your Knowledge

Section 20.1

1. Some people have perfect pitch. Research in your library or on the Internet what it means to have perfect pitch. What are the pros and cons of having perfect pitch?

2. The Doppler effect is used by astronomers to determine if stars are moving away from or toward Earth. Red light has a lower frequency than blue light. If light from a star is shifted toward the red end of the visible-light spectrum, does that mean the star is moving toward or away from Earth? Explain.

Section 20.2

3. Why is hanging heavy curtains a good way to decrease sound in a room? Use the terms *absorption* and *amplitude* in your answer.

4. Compare the superposition principle to Fourier's theorem.

Section 20.3

5. Compare active noise reduction to traditional hearing protection, such as ear muffs or ear plugs.

6. At what level does sound become unsafe? What are some ways you can protect your hearing? Suggest three places where you might need to use hearing protection.

7. Harmonic synthesizers can mimic almost any sound and allow you to play it as music on a keyboard. A synthesizer can sound like a flute, a bell, or a piano. In a short paragraph, describe how the synthesizer is able to play the same keyboard notes with such different sounds.

8. The human voice is a complex sound that is created by a combination of vibrating folds of skin in the larynx and the resonant shapes of the throat and mouth. Humans can hear sounds at frequencies of 20 to 20,000 Hz. Research the range of human-voice frequencies. How do the voice ranges compare to the hearing ranges?

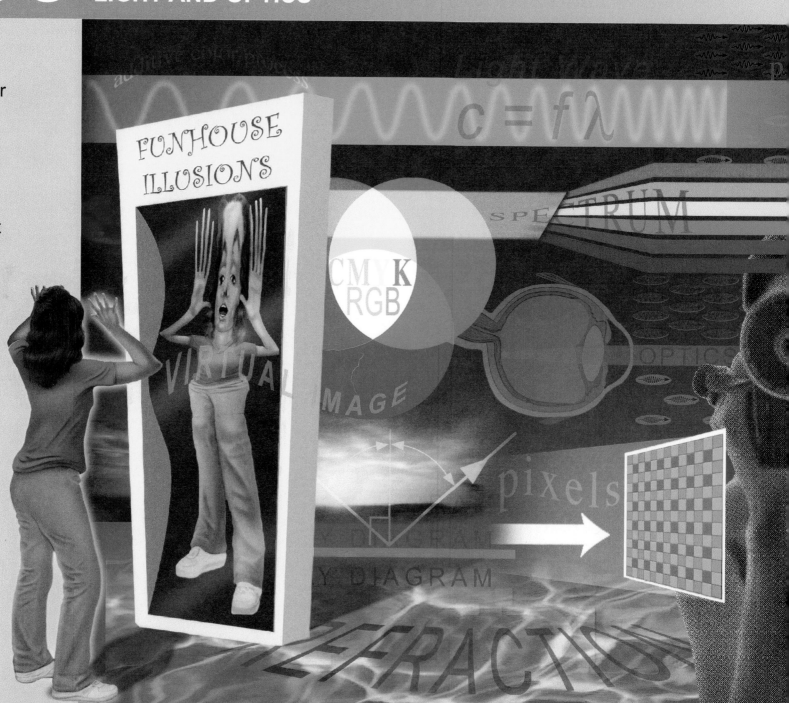

Unit 8 LIGHT AND OPTICS

$$c = f\lambda$$

Light and Color

Television brings you images of objects and places that you may not otherwise have ever seen. What's more, the images move with full sound and color as if you really are there. For example, the color of a blue sky in one part of the world is sent to you at home so that you can see it. The vibrant colors of a flower get from the flower, to the television, to your eyes.

What creates color? Does the flower give off red and orange light like a neon sign? How is color seen by our eyes?

To answer these questions, start with a short experiment. Take a colorful object like a shirt or a toy. Look at the object in the light. Then, look at the same object in a totally dark room. What do you see? How do the colors compare in the light versus in the dark? Your answer and your observations will prepare you for this chapter, where you will learn about light and color.

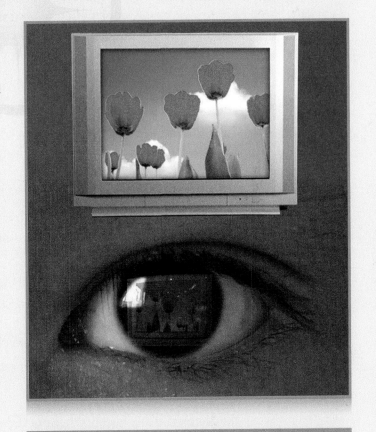

VOCABULARY

additive color process	subtractive primary colors	photoreceptors
incandescence		transparent
subtractive color process	color	fluorescence
	photoelectric effect	rods
additive primary colors	translucent	white light
intensity	cones	

KEY QUESTIONS

✓ *How do computers and DVDs make color using only numbers?*

✓ *What is color and how do our eyes see color?*

✓ *Where does light come from?*

21.1 Properties of Light

Every time you see something, light is involved. Whether you are looking at a light bulb or a car or a book, light brings visual information to your eyes. In fact, the very act of "seeing" means forming images in your mind from the light received by your eyes. In complete darkness, we cannot see anything! In this section, you will learn about some of the properties of light and how it interacts with matter.

What is light?

Light is a form of energy
Like sound and heat, light is a form of energy. It is possible to make light and use it to do all sorts of useful things. Understanding light begins with investigating its properties and learning some important terms (Figure 21.1). We know that:

- light travels extremely fast and over long distances;
- light carries energy and information;
- light travels in straight lines;
- light bounces (reflects) and bends (refracts) when it comes in contact with objects;
- light has color; and
- light has different intensities, and can be bright or dim.

Seeing and reflected light
What physically happens when you see a page from a printed book? Light in the room reflects off the page and into your eyes. The reflected light carries information about the page that allows your brain to construct an image of the page. You see because light in the room reflects from the page into your eyes. If you were inside a perfectly dark room with no light, you would not be able to see the page at all because the page does not give off its own light. We see most of the world by reflected light.

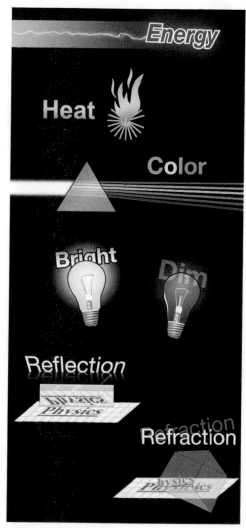

Figure 21.1: *Some words and properties that are associated with light. What words do you use to describe light?*

Light carries energy and power

Light radiates in all directions
You can see a bare light bulb from anywhere in a room because the bulb emits light in all directions. When the rays of light are represented by arrows, the light coming from a bulb looks like the illustration in Figure 21.2. You can see the paper of a book page from different places because the page reflects light in all directions.

Light intensity
From experience, you know that as you move away from a source of light, the amount of light decreases. We use the word **intensity** to describe the amount of light energy per second falling on a surface. For example, on a sunny day, the amount of sunlight falling on a single square meter of surface might be 500 watts. The intensity of this light is 500 watts per square meter (500 W/m^2). Light intensity is the power of light per unit area (Figure 21.3).

Light intensity follows an inverse square law
For a small source of light, the intensity decreases as the square of the distance from the source increases. In other words, light intensity follows an inverse square law: as the distance from a light source increases, the light intensity decreases as the square of the distance from the source.

An example
The diagram below shows the inverse square law. At a radius of one meter, 8 watts of light fall on a one-meter-square area. The light intensity is 8 W/m^2. The intensity at 2 meters is one-fourth the intensity at 1 meter or 2 W/m^2. Increasing the distance by a factor of 2 reduces the intensity by a factor of 2^2 or 4. Tripling the distance from 1 to 3 meters would reduce the intensity by a factor of 3^2 or 9. The intensity at 3 meters would be 8/9 or 0.89 W/m^2.

intensity - a term that describes the amount of light energy per second falling on a surface

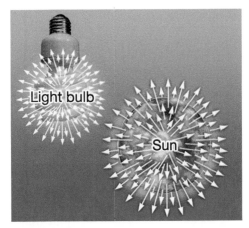

Figure 21.2: *Light emitted from the Sun or from a light bulb travels in straight lines from their surfaces.*

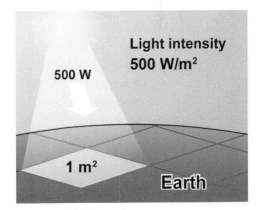

Figure 21.3: *Light intensity is the amount of energy per second falling on one unit of area of a surface.*

The inverse square law for light intensity

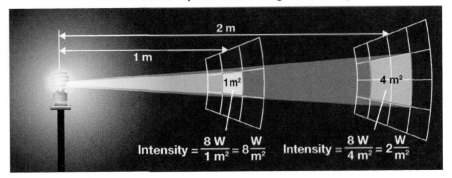

$$\text{Intensity} = \frac{8\ W}{1\ m^2} = 8\frac{W}{m^2} \qquad \text{Intensity} = \frac{8\ W}{4\ m^2} = 2\frac{W}{m^2}$$

The speed of light

Comparing the speeds of sound and light What happens when you shine a flashlight on an object? You do not see the light leave your flashlight, travel to the object, bounce off, and come back to your eyes. But that's exactly what happens. You do not see it because it happens so fast! For example, suppose you shine a flashlight on a mirror 170 meters away. The light travels to the mirror and back in one millionth of a second (0.000001 s). Sound travels much slower than light. If you shout, you will hear an echo 1 second later from the sound bouncing off a wall 170 meters away. Light travels a million times faster than sound.

Light is faster than sound

The speed of light is about 300 million meters per second or 186,000 miles per second. At 15°C, the speed of sound is about 340 m/s or 0.21 miles per second. You can use the speed of sound to determine how far away a lightning strike has occurred. In 1 second, light travels 186,000 miles. Sound travels about one-fifth of a mile in 1 second. When you see lightning, begin counting seconds until you hear thunder. Multiply the number of seconds you count by one fifth. The result is the distance in miles between where you are and where the lightning struck. What value would you need to multiply by to get this distance in kilometers?

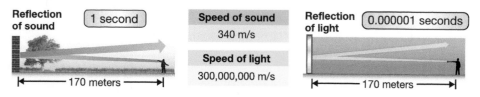

The speed of light, $c = 3 \times 10^8$ m/s The speed at which light travels through air is about 300 million meters per second. Light is so fast it can travel around the entire Earth 7½ times in 1 second. The speed of light is so important in physics that it is given its own symbol, a lowercase c. When you see this symbol in a formula, remember that $c = 3 \times 10^8$ m/s.

Why you hear thunder after you see lightning The speed of light is so fast that when lightning strikes a few miles away, we hear the thunder several seconds after we see the lightning. At the point of the lightning strike, the thunder and lightning are simultaneous. But just a mile away from the lightning strike, the sound of the thunder is already about 5 seconds behind the flash of the lightning. You can use this information to calculate how far you are away from a thunderstorm, as described in the sidebar.

Accurate measurement of c Using very fast electronics, the speed of light can be measured accurately. One technique is to record the time a pulse of light leaves a laser and the time the pulse returns to its starting position after making a round trip. The best accepted experimental measurement for the speed of light in a vacuum is 299,792,458 m/s. For most purposes, we do not need to be this accurate and may use a value for c of 3×10^8 m/s.

Four ways light is affected by matter

The four interactions When light interacts with matter—like glass, wood, or anything else—four things can happen.

- The light can pass through almost unchanged (transparency).
- The light can pass through but be scattered (translucency).
- The light can bounce off (reflection).
- The light can transfer its energy to the material (absorption).

Transparent Materials that allow light to pass through are called **transparent**. Glass is transparent, as are some kinds of plastic. Air is also transparent. You can see an image though a transparent material if the surfaces are smooth, like a glass window.

Translucent An object is **translucent** if some light can pass through but the light is scattered in many directions (Figure 21.4). Tissue paper is translucent, and so is frosted glass. If you hold a sheet of tissue paper up to a light, some light comes through the paper, but you cannot see an image clearly through it.

Reflection and absorption Almost all surfaces reflect some light. A mirror is a very good reflector, but a sheet of white paper is also a reflector. The difference is in how they reflect. When light is absorbed, its energy is transferred to the material. That is why a black road surface gets hot on a sunny day. A perfect absorber looks black because it reflects no light at all. Black paper and black velvet cloth are good absorbers of light.

All interactions at once All four interactions of light with matter almost always happen at the same time. An ordinary glass window is mostly transparent but also absorbs about 10 percent of light. The glass scatters some light (translucency) and reflects (transparency) some light. The same material also behaves differently depending on how well-polished the surface is. Frosted glass has a rough surface and is translucent. Clear glass has a polished surface and is transparent. Colored paper absorbs some light, reflects some light, and is partly translucent.

transparent - describes materials that allow light to pass through them

translucent - describes materials that allow light to pass through, but scatter that light in many directions

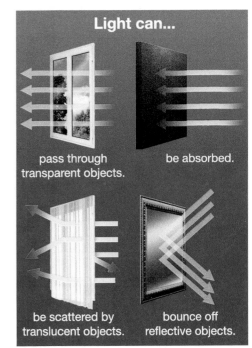

Figure 21.4: *The four interactions of light with matter.*

Light from atoms

The electric light   For most of human history people relied on the Sun, the Moon, and fire to provide light. Thomas Edison's electric light bulb (1879) changed our dependence on fire and daylight forever. The electric light is one of the most important inventions in the progress of human development.

Light is produced by atoms   Whether in an electric bulb or in the Sun, light is mostly produced by atoms. Remember from Chapter 10, atoms absorb and emit energy by rearranging electrons. Eventually, any excess energy that an atom has is released. This energy release or transfer is analogous to a ball rolling downhill. Unlike a ball, an atom releases the extra energy usually—but not always—as light!

incandescence - the process of making light with heat

Figure 21.5: *Incandescent light bulbs are often used in restaurants to illuminate and warm food.*

Incandescent light bulbs

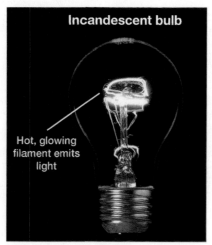

Incandescent bulb

Hot, glowing filament emits light

In order to get light out of an atom, you must put some energy into the atom first. One way to do this is with heat. When atoms get hot enough, some of the thermal energy is released as light. The process of making light with heat is called **incandescence**. In incandescent bulbs, an electric current passes through a thin metal wire called a *filament*. The filament heats up and gives off light. The atoms of the filament convert electrical energy to heat and then to light. Unfortunately, incandescent bulbs are not very efficient. Only a fraction of the energy of electricity is converted into light. Most of the energy becomes heat. In restaurants, this feature of incandescent bulbs is used to both illuminate and warm food (Figure 21.5).

Compact fluorescent light bulbs   Another common kind of electric light is a compact fluorescent light (CFL). CFLs are being used in schools, businesses, and homes because they are much more efficient than incandescent bulbs. Compared with a standard incandescent bulb, you get four or more times as much light from a CFL for the same amount of electrical energy.

Fluorescent lights and LEDs

How do fluroescent lights work? CFLs are a type of fluorescent light. Fluorescent lights consist of a tube filled with a gas. A CFL is actually a thin tube coiled into the shape of a bulb. Other fluorescent lights are formed into straight tubes, rings, or other shapes. A fluorescent light uses high-voltage electricity to energize atoms of gas inside the tube. These atoms release the electrical energy as light (not heat), in a process called **fluorescence**. The atoms in the tube emit high-energy ultraviolet light—the same kind that gives you a sunburn. The ultraviolet light is absorbed by other atoms in a white coating on the inside surface of the tube. The atoms that make up this coating re-emit the energy as white light (Figure 21.6). Even with this two-step process, fluorescent lights are still more efficient at producing light than incandescent bulbs.

LEDs LED stands for light-emitting diode. A diode is an electronic device usually made out of layers of silicon that allow electric current to flow in one direction through a circuit while blocking current flowing in the opposite direction. Diodes are found in almost every electronic device in use today. Since the 1960s, LEDs have been used as indicator lights on appliances and electronic devices as number displays, such as those found on alarm clocks, watches, and calculators (Figure 21.7). If you've ever pushed a button on a device and a little colored light lit up, it was probably an LED. Modern traffic signals also use LEDs. One of the LED's best qualities is that they need very little current to produce light. Recent technological breakthroughs have enabled LEDs to create more light. Designers have assembled arrays of LEDs into bulb shapes, and these new LED bulbs are even more efficient than CFLs. These arrays have allowed LEDs to be used as the video-display surface for computer monitors and television sets.

fluorescence - a process by which atoms release light energy

Compact fluorescent lamp

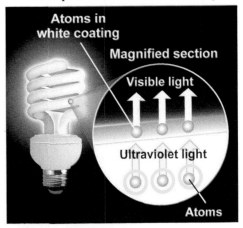

Figure 21.6: *Fluorescent lights generate light by exciting atoms with electricity in a two-step process.*

Figure 21.7: *The display on this alarm clock is made of LEDs.*

21.1 Section Review

1. Why can we see an object in a room from any position?
2. Describe four ways that light interacts with matter.
3. Why can you see lightning before you hear thunder?
4. What has to be done to make an atom produce light?

21.2 **Vision and Color**

Light reaches your eyes in one of two ways. Light can come directly from an object that produces light, such as a light bulb or glow stick. In this case, the color of the light depends on the colors produced by the object. Light can also be reflected from objects that do not produce their own light, such as clothes or plants. With reflected light, the color is produced by selectively "subtracting out" some colors. What exactly is color and how do our eyes perceive light and color?

> **white light** - light that is a combination of all colors of light
>
> **color** - the perception of the energy of light

Color and energy

White light   When all of the colors of the rainbow are combined, we do not see any one color. We see light without any color. We call this combination of all the colors **white light**. White light is a good description of the ordinary light that is all around us most of the time. The light from the Sun and the light from most electric lights is white light. The colors that make up white light are called visible light. There are also other forms of light that we cannot see, such as infrared and ultraviolet light.

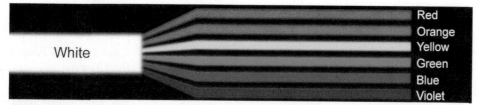

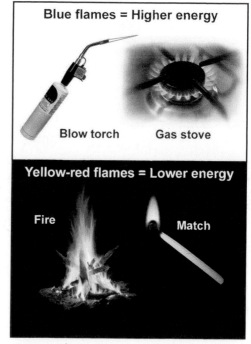

Figure 21.8: *Higher-energy flames, such as the ones from a gas grill, produce blue light. Fire flames are of lower energy and produce reddish-yellow light.*

What is color?   Why does some light appear red and other light appear blue? **Color** is how we perceive the energy of light. This definition of color was proposed by Albert Einstein. All of the colors in the rainbow are light of different energies. Red light has the lowest energy we can see, and violet light the highest energy. As we move through the rainbow from red to yellow to blue to violet, the energy of the light increases.

What do we mean when we talk about the energy of light? Think about the very hot, blue flames from a gas stove or a gas grill. The atoms of gas in the flame have high energy so they give off blue light. The flame from a match or from a burning log in the fireplace is reddish-orange. This color of flame means the atoms have less energy, and is not as hot as a blue, gas flame (Figure 21.8).

How the human eye sees light

How we see color
The energy of light explains how we see colors. Light enters your eye through the lens (Figure 21.9) and strikes the retina. On the surface of the retina are light-sensitive cells called **photoreceptors**. When light hits a photoreceptor cell, the cell releases a chemical signal that travels along the optic nerve to the brain. In the brain, the signal is translated into a perception of color. Which signal is sent depends on how much energy the light has. Some photoreceptors respond only to low energy, others to medium energy and a third to higher energy.

Cone cells respond to color
Our eyes have two types of photoreceptors, called *cones* and *rods*. **Cones** (or *cone cells*) respond to color (Figure 21.10), and there are three types. One type responds best to red light. Another type responds best to green light and the last type responds best to blue light. We see a wide range of light colors depending on how much each kind of cone cell is stimulated. For example, we see white light when all three types of cones—red, green, blue—are equally stimulated.

Rod cells respond to light intensity
The second kind of photoreceptor, **rods** (or *rod cells*), respond only to differences in intensity, and not to color (Figure 21.10). Rod cells detect black, white, and shades of gray. However, rod cells are more sensitive than cone cells, especially at low light levels. At night, colors seem washed out because there is not enough light for cone cells to work best. When the light level is very dim, you see "black and white" images transmitted from the rod cells.

Black and white vision is sharper than color vision
An average human eye contains about 130 million rod cells and 7 million cone cells. Each one contributes a "dot" to the total image assembled by your brain. The brain evaluates all 137 million "dots" about 15 times each second, creating the perception of motion. Because there are more rod cells, fine details are sharpest when there is high contrast between light and dark areas. That is why black print and white print is easier to read than colored print. The cone cells are concentrated near the center of the retina, making color vision best at the center of the eye's field of view. Each cone cell "colors" the signals from the surrounding rod cells. Because there are fewer cone cells, and there are three kinds, our color vision is much less sharp than our black-and-white vision at recognizing fine details.

> **photoreceptors** - light-sensitive cells on the surface of the retina
> **cones** - photoreceptors that respond to color
> **rods** - photoreceptors that respond to light intensity

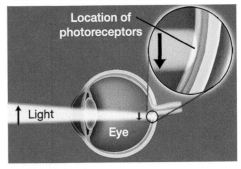

Figure 21.9: *The photoreceptors that send color signals to the brain are in the back of the eye on the retina.*

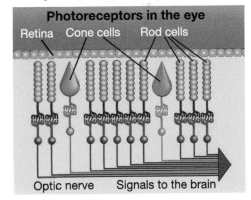

Figure 21.10: *The human eye has two types of photoreceptors—cones and rods. Cones respond to color and rods respond to the intensity of light.*

How we see colors

The additive color process
Our eyes work according to an **additive color process**—three photoreceptors (red, green, blue) in the eye operate together so that we see millions of different colors. The color you "see" depends on how much energy is received by each of the three different types of cone cells. The brain thinks "green" when there is a strong signal from the green cone cells but no signal from the blue or red cone cells (Figure 21.11).

How we perceive color
We perceive different colors as a combination of percentages of the three **additive primary colors**: *red, green,* and *blue*. For example, we see yellow when the brain gets an equally strong signal from both the red and the green cone cells at the same time. Whether the light is actually yellow, or a combination of red and green, the cones respond the same way and we perceive yellow. If the red signal is stronger than the green signal, we see orange (Figure 21.12). If all three cones send an equal signal to the brain, we interpret the light we see as white light.

The additive primary colors

Yellow

Red   Green

White

Magenta   Cyan

Blue

Two ways to see a color
The human eye can see any color by adding different percentages of the three additive primary colors. Mixing red and green light is one way the eye sees the color yellow or orange, for example. Keep in mind that you perceive these colors even though the light itself is still red and green. You can also see pure yellow light or orange light that is not a mixture of red and green.

Do animals see colors?
To the best of our knowledge, primates, such as chimpanzees and gorillas, are the only animals with three-color vision similar to that of humans. Birds and fish—in particular, tropical varieties—have three or more kinds of photoreceptors. Some birds and insects can also see ultraviolet light which humans cannot detect. Dogs, cats, and some squirrels are thought to have at least two color photoreceptors. Although both octopi and squid can *change* color better than any other animal, they cannot *see* color.

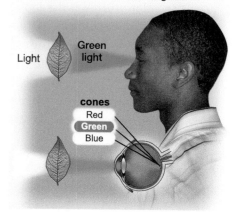

Color signals from only the green cones tell the brain the leaf is green.

Figure 21.11: *If the brain gets a signal from only the green cone, we see green.*

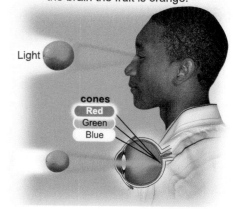

A strong signal from the red cones and a weaker signal from the green cones tell the brain the fruit is orange.

Figure 21.12: *If there is a strong red signal and a weak green signal, we see orange.*

The physics of color and light

Photons Just as matter is made of tiny particles called atoms, light energy comes in tiny bundles called *photons*. In some ways, photons act like jellybeans of different colors. Each photon has its own color, no matter how you mix them up. The lowest energy photons we can see are the ones that appear dark red in color (Figure 21.13). The highest-energy photons we can see are the color of blue, tending to deep violet in color.

Waves Light is also a wave. Like other waves, the frequency of light is proportional to its energy. Red light has lower energy than blue light and also has a lower frequency as shown. The frequency of light waves is very high compared to sound waves. The frequency of light waves is measured in hertz (Hz). Red light has frequencies in the range of 460 trillion (460×10^{12}) Hz and blue light in the range of 640 trillion Hz.

Colors You can think of a photon as a wave with a very short wavelength. Each photon carries the frequency of the light corresponding to its energy. An orange photon has a frequency of 490 trillion Hz, between red and yellow. This energy stimulates the red cone cells strongly and the green cone cells weakly, causing us to see orange. Mixing a little green light with more red light causes the same stimulation of the cone cells. This tricks the brain into "seeing" orange light even though the actual photons are red and green.

> *(from previous page)*
> **additive color process** - a process that creates color by adding proportions of red, green, and blue light together
>
> **additive primary colors** - red, green, and blue

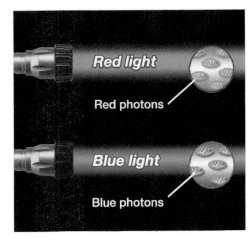

Figure 21.13: *Light is made of tiny bundles of energy called photons.*

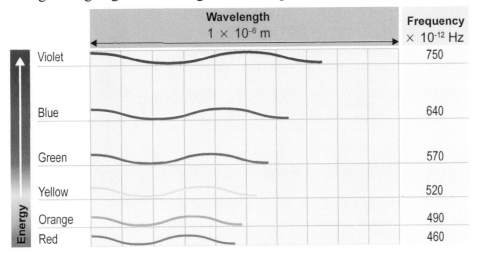

	Wavelength 1×10^{-6} m	Frequency $\times 10^{-12}$ Hz
Violet		750
Blue		640
Green		570
Yellow		520
Orange		490
Red		460

The photoelectric effect

What is the photoelectric effect? In the early 1900s, Albert Einstein was thinking about the photoelectric effect. The **photoelectric effect** is the emission of electrons from a metal surface when light falls on that surface. Einstein and other scientists of his time could not explain why brighter, or more intense light didn't produce emitted electrons with more energy. Scientist knew that brighter light should mean that the metal was absorbing more energy. And if the metal had more energy, the emitted electrons should have greater energy, too. But, this was not what happened during the photoelectric effect.

Results of experiments Experiments on the photoelectric effect showed that the effect was related to frequency. With low frequency (long wavelength) red light, no electrons come off at all, even if the light is very bright. As the frequency increases (shorter wavelength, more blue), electrons start to be emitted. The kinetic energy of the emitted electrons also depends on the frequency of the light. The higher the frequency, the more energy the emitted electrons have.

Einstein explains the photoelectric effect In 1905, Einstein published his explanation of the photoelectric effect. This work led to his Nobel Prize for physics in 1921. Einstein proposed that an atom absorbs only one photon at a time. An electron needs a minimum amount of energy to break free from an atom. If a photon's energy is too low, there is not enough energy to free an electron and no photoelectric effect is observed. Using brighter light does not help. Brighter light has more photons, but none with enough energy to free an electron. If the frequency of light gets higher, at a particular frequency one photon has just enough energy to free an electron. Even if the light is made very dim, you get exactly one electron for each photon of light.

> **photoelectric effect** - the emission of electrons from a metal surface when light falls on that surface

Einstein's explanation

With high-frequency light, there is more than enough energy in each photon to free an electron. Part of the photon energy goes to freeing the electron and the rest becomes kinetic energy of the electron. Einstein's explanation perfectly matched the data collected in experiments and provided strong evidence that the quantum theory of light was correct. The quantum theory states that light is not a continuous wave of energy but comes in bundles of energy called photons that have wave-like properties. In other words, light has a dual nature—it acts as particles and as a wave.

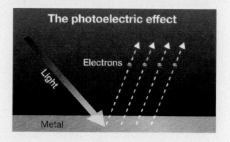

21.2 Section Review

1. How do we know that white light is composed of all visible colors?
2. At a fireworks display on the fourth of July, you see red, green, and blue fireworks. Which fireworks produce the highest light energy?
3. If humans have only three kinds of color photoreceptors, how can we see so many colors?
4. Why can't very bright, red light produce the photoelectric effect?

21.3 **Using Color**

You have learned how we see and interpret color. This section describes how a wide range of colors can be created by using a few colors. With the subtractive and additive color processes, color is created and used in publishing books, in television, and in other video technology.

How things appear to be different colors

What gives objects their color?

Why does a blue shirt look blue? We see blue because chemical dyes in the cloth absorbs the other colors and *reflects only the blue to our eyes* (Figure 21.14). The color blue is not in the cloth! The blue light you see is the blue light that is in the white light that shines on the cloth. You see blue because the other colors in the white light have been absorbed by the cloth.

The subtractive color process

Colored fabrics and paints get color from a **subtractive color process**. Chemicals known as *pigments* in the dyes and paints absorb some colors and reflect others. Pigments work by taking colors from white light, which is a mixture of all the colors.

The subtractive primary colors

To make all colors by the subtractive process, we need three primary pigments. We need one that absorbs blue, and reflects red and green. This pigment is called *yellow*. We need another pigment that absorbs green, and reflects red and blue. This color is called *magenta*. The third pigment is *cyan*, which absorbs red and reflects green and blue. Cyan, magenta, and yellow are the three **subtractive primary colors** (Figure 21.14). By using different proportions of the three pigments, a paint can appear almost any color by varying the amount of reflected red, green, and blue light. For example, to make *black*, add all three and all light is absorbed, reflecting none.

The subtractive primary colors

Red
Magenta   Yellow
Black
Blue   Green
Cyan

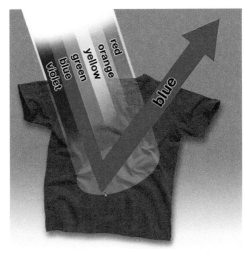

Figure 21.14: *The pigments in a blue cloth absorb all colors except blue. You see blue because blue light is reflected to your eyes.*

The CMYK color process

A subtractive color process

Another name for the subtractive color process is the *CMYK color process* CMYK stands for cyan, magenta, yellow, and black. The letter *K* stands for black because the letter *B* is used to represent the color blue.

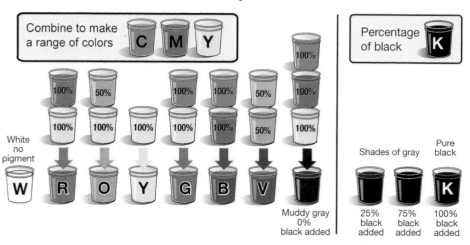

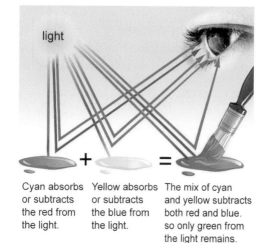

Figure 21.15: *Creating the color green using cyan and yellow.*

CMYK are pigments

The CMYK color process is used for making all colors that are seen in reflected light, including printing inks and fabric dyes. The three pigments—cyan, magenta, and yellow—are combined in various proportions to make any color. Figure 21.15 shows how CMYK pigments can be combined to make green. You might think that mixing cyan, magenta, and yellow would make black, but in reality the result is a muddy gray. This is why a fourth color, pure black, is included in the CMYK process. Figure 21.16 shows how the CMYK process works with an ink-jet printer.

To make	Mix	Because
Red	Magenta and yellow +	Magenta absorbs green Yellow absorbs blue Red is reflected ←
Blue	Magenta and cyan +	Magenta absorbs green Cyan absorbs red Blue is reflected ←
Green	Cyan and yellow +	Cyan absorbs red Yellow absorbs blue Green is reflected ←

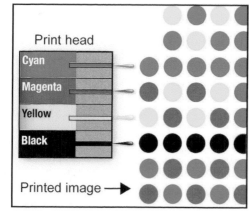

Figure 21.16: *An ink-jet printer makes tiny dots of cyan, magenta, yellow, and black to print a full-color image. The dots are so small that your eye sees only colors. Look at an ink-jet print under a magnifying glass and will see these dots.*

Making a color image

Making a color photograph
Modern printing presses use the CMYK color process to produce vivid colors from only four inks. To print a color photograph, the image is converted into four separate images in cyan, magenta, yellow, and black. Each separate image represents what will be printed with its matching CMYK ink. The cyan separation is printed with cyan ink, the magenta separation with magenta ink, and so on. Figure 21.17 shows the four color separations from a color image.

The RGB color process
Color images are created using the RGB color process, an additive process that uses red, green, and blue light. The RGB process is used by television screens and computer monitors (Figure 21.18). A television makes different colors by lighting red, green, and blue pixels to different percentages. For example, a light brown tone is 88 percent red, 85 percent green, and 70 percent blue. A computer monitor works the same way. Each pixel (or dot) has three numbers that tell how much red, green, and blue to use. A digital video image is 720 dots wide times 480 dots high. If each dot has three numbers (R, G, B) a single image takes 1,036,800 numbers to store!

Video cameras create color images
A video camera-recorder (also called a camcorder) uses the RGB process differently than a TV. Like the rods and cones in your retina, a video camcorder has 300,000–500,000 sensors on a small chip called a CCD (charge-coupled device). The sensors on the CCD measure the light intensity as percentages of red, green, and blue in the light coming through the camera lens. This information is recorded 30 times per second. The CCDs in most video camera-recorders are typically 1 centimeter square or less.

Figure 21.17: *To be printed by a full-color press, an image is separated into separate cyan, magenta, yellow, and black images.*

Figure 21.18: *A television makes colors by using tiny glowing dots of red, green, and blue.*

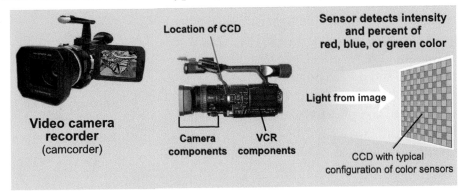

Color blindness

Not everyone sees color the same way You may be surprised to learn that all people do not see color the same way. A condition called *color blindness* affects about 5 to 8 percent of males and 0.5 percent of females. This means that about 1 out of every 12 men has color blindness and about one out of every 200 women has color blindness.

Color blindness is inherited Although color blindness can be caused by eye disease, it is most often an inherited condition. More males than females have color blindness because of how the genes that determine our gender are inherited. Males have a X and a Y chromosome; females have two X chromosomes. The genes that are related to color blindness are on the X chromosome which males receive only from their mothers; they receive the Y chromosome from their fathers. Because females receive two X chromosomes, they have two chances to inherit the genes for normal color vision.

What is color blindness? People who are color-blind have trouble seeing certain colors. Figure 21.19 shows what the colors of visible light look like for people who have two forms of color blindness. People with green-weak color blindness (deuteranopia) lack green cone cells that detect green. Hues of red and green are hard to tell apart. For this reason, this form of color blindness is also called red-green color blindness. People with red-weak color blindness (protanopia) lack cone cells that detect red. Red looks dark or black to these individuals.

Living with color blindness It is easy to lead a normal life with color blindness. Having color blindness just means that an individual must look for ways to adapt to situations where color is involved. For example, how might a color-blind person interpret traffic lights? Fortunately, in most states, the traffic lights are stacked vertically, and the colors are in the same position—red on top, yellow in the center, and green on the bottom. A less-serious situation where color is important is in interpreting maps and purchasing clothes. In these cases, color-blind people rely on other methods to interpret colors. Working with computers requires lots of color. For example, if you are going to make a website, you will want to include color. For a color-blind person this can be tricky. Fortunately, colors are standardized and a color-blind person can chose colors using numbers.

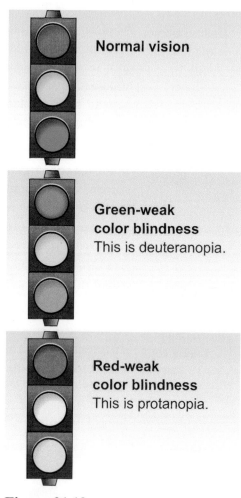

Normal vision

Green-weak color blindness This is deuteranopia.

Red-weak color blindness This is protanopia.

Figure 21.19: *This illustration shows how color blindness affects seeing a traffic light. The top shows what the traffic light looks like with normal color vision. The middle and bottom show what a traffic light looks like with two forms of color blindness.*

Plants use color

Light is necessary for photosynthesis

Plants absorb energy from light and convert it to chemical energy in the form of sugar. The process is called *photosynthesis*. The *y*-axis of the graph in Figure 21.20 shows the percentage of light of different colors absorbed by a plant. The *x*-axis on the graph shows the colors of light. The heavy line shows how much and which colors of visible light are absorbed by plants. Based on this graph, can you explain why plants look green?

Why most plants are green

The important molecule that absorbs light in a plant is called *chlorophyll*. There are several forms of chlorophyll in a plant. They absorb mostly blue and red light, and reflect green light. This is why most plants look green. This graph also shows that plants need red and blue light to grow. A plant will die if placed under only green light!

Plants reflect some light to keep cool

Why don't plants absorb all colors of light? The reason is the same reason you wear light-colored clothes when it's hot outside. Like you, plants must reflect some light to avoid absorbing too much energy and overheating. Plants use visible light because the energy is just enough to change certain chemical bonds, but not enough to completely break them. Ultraviolet light has more energy but would break the chemical bonds. Infrared light has too little energy to change chemical bonds.

Why leaves change color

The leaves of some plants, such as sugar maple trees, turn brilliant red or gold in the fall. Chlorophyll masks other plant pigments during the spring and summer. In the fall when photosynthesis slows down, chlorophyll breaks down and red, orange, and yellow pigments in the leaves are revealed.

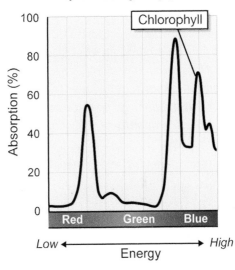

Figure 21.20: *Plants need to absorb light to grow. The plant pigment chlorophyll absorbs red and blue light, and reflects green light. This is why plants look green.* Challenge: *All plants that use sunlight to grow have chlorophyll, but some do not look green. Come up with a hypothesis to explain this observation.*

21.3 *Section Review*

1. Do you think this textbook was printed using the CMYK color process or the RGB color process? Explain your answer.
2. If you were going to design the lighting for a play, would you need to understand the CMYK or the RGB color process? Explain your answer.
3. Why does static on a television set appear white?
4. How is the color black produced in the CMYK color process versus the RGB color process?
5. Why do some plants that grow in shady areas have dark green or even purple leaves?

Sensing the Quantum World

In 1905, Albert Einstein proposed a revolutionary idea: Light can behave not only like a wave but also like a particle–crashing into things (like electrons on a metal plate) and knocking them out of place. Einstein's proposal is known as the quantum theory of light. It opened up an entirely new way of thinking about the nature of matter and the motion of tiny particles. But quantum theory is more than just an idea to ponder in physics class.

If you upload videos to the web, send digital photos, or use your cell phone as a camera, you are using technology made possible by quantum theory. If you've had a torn ligament repaired, you've benefitted from this technology. And someday you may be a journalist, an astronomer, an oceanographer, a surgeon, an engineer, a visual artist, an educator, or someone else whose chosen field utilizes the digital technology made possible by quantum theory.

The CCD: photography's quantum leap

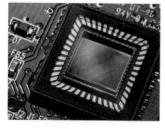

Most of the digital cameras and camcorders on the market today use a charge-coupled device, or CCD, to record visual data. The CCD was invented in 1969 by two researchers at Bell Laboratories in New Jersey. Willard Boyle and George Smith were working on creating a new kind of computer memory when they realized the technology could be used to record images.

1974 - W. S. Boyle (left) and G. E. Smith of Bell Labs are demonstrating an experimental TV camera that contains a CCD substitute for the vacuum tube of a conventional TV camera.

The CCD uses a light-sensitive silicon chip made up of tiny square pixels. When photons of light hit a CCD pixel, they kick electrons off its surface. Sound familiar? This process of photons knocking electrons out of atoms is known as the photoelectric effect. Einstein figured out that light had to be behaving like a particle, not a wave, in order for the photoelectric effect to work.

In a CCD, electrons that are kicked off the pixel are kept in a "holding tank"—the pixel's capacitor. The amount of electrons, or "charge," in each holding tank depends on the amount of light that hits the pixel.

A voltage is then applied which causes the charge to be passed down the row of pixels, one step at a time, like buckets of water passed from hand to hand in an old firefighting technique. At the end of the row, information about the amount of charge on each pixel is turned into a digital value and recorded.

Pictures from pixels

A pixel only records information about the amount of light that hits it. The first digital images produced using a CCD were just shades of gray. Soon, engineers placed a color filter over each pixel—either red, blue, or green. So each pixel in a modern CCD records information about one primary color of light. Since human eyes are most sensitive to green light, a CCD chip contains as many green-sensitive pixels as it does blue and red combined.

Even though each pixel gathers data about only one primary color of light, the image file received by your computer monitor or printer provides information about all three colors of light for each pixel. How is this possible? Let's look at one red pixel.

Arrangement of red, green, and blue filters on CCD pixels.

Data processing software built into your camera reads the light value for the red-filtered pixel. Then, it examines the value of nearby green-filtered and blue-filtered pixels. The software uses this information to estimate the amount of green and blue light that fell on the red-filtered pixel. The software reports all three values for each pixel. If your camera takes high-resolution photos with thousands of pixels, this data processing can take a few seconds. That's why you'll get an error message—or lose your last picture—if you turn off your camera too soon.

A spiral galaxy created with data from the Hubble telescope.

Astronomical images

In the early 1970s, NASA engineers were trying to figure out how best to record images from the Hubble Space Telescope. They even considered putting film in the telescope and sending astronauts to load and retrieve it. The invention of the CCD made it possible to collect Hubble images digitally and beam them back to Earth, no astronauts required!

In addition, a CCD is 100 times more sensitive to light than photographic film, providing astronomers with sharper, clearer images than film could record.

By the year 2000, CCDs were found in digital cameras, cell phones, video recorders, and many medical imaging devices. CCDs enable scientists to record and share detailed images of previously inaccessible places, such as the far reaches of the universe or ocean depths. CCDs enable surgeons to perform "microsurgery," where scalpels are guided by tiny cameras. In 2009, Boyle and Smith were awarded the Nobel Prize in Physics for their invention.

The Eye-in-the-Sea is a specially-designed camera that was left on the sea floor by a submersible for one or two days at a time to record digital images of the surrounding bioluminescence.

QUESTIONS

1. Describe the photoelectric effect. How does a CCD make use of this effect?

2. Why is a filter placed over each pixel in a CCD?

3. Solar cells are another type of technology that utilizes the photoelectric effect. Research how the type of solar cell used to power a hand-held calculator works. Draw a diagram or write a paragraph to explain your findings.

Boyle and Smith photo courtesy of Alcatel-Lucent/Bell Labs.

Spiral galaxy image courtesy of NASA, ESA, and the Hubble Heritage Team (STScI/AURA)

Eye In The Sea photo by Tammy Frank, HBOI
Credit: Islands in the Stream Expedition 2002. NOAA Office of Ocean Exploration

Chapter 21 Review

Understanding Vocabulary

Select the correct term to complete the sentences.

additive primary colors	incandescent	subtractive primary colors
additive process	intensity	subtractive
CMYK color process	photoreceptors	translucent
color	RGB color process	transparent
cones	rods	white light
fluorescent		

1. The _____ of a small light source incident upon a screen is inversely proportional to the square of the distance between the source and the screen.

2. _____ light bulbs produce light by passing electricity through a gas.

3. All colors that are seen as reflected light are formed using the _____ or _____ color process.

4. Although some light incident upon tissue paper will pass through, a clear image of the light is *not* formed because tissue paper is _____.

5. _____ is made up of all the possible colors of light.

Reviewing Concepts

Section 21.1

1. How is an incandescent bulb different from a fluorescent bulb?

2. Why do we see lightning before we hear thunder?

3. Which of the following is *not* a quality of light?

   a. high speed

   b. acceleration

   c. color

   d. intensity

4. Describe the role of atoms in producing light in a fluorescent light bulb.

5. In terms of the absorption and reflection of light, describe the difference between a black piece of cloth and a white piece of cloth.

6. What is the difference between reflection and refraction of light?

Section 21.2

7. What is white light in terms of other colors?

8. What determines the color of an object?

9. What are the three additive primary colors?

10. What color of visible light has the least energy? The most energy?

11. Which photoreceptors in your eye respond the most in dim, evening light? Which photoreceptors respond the least? How does this explain your vision in this type of light?

Section 21.3

12. Answer true or false for each of the following sentences. If the sentence is false, correct the word(s) to make the sentence true.

    a. A green object reflects green light.

    b. A blue object absorbs red and yellow light.

    c. A yellow object reflects red light.

    d. A white object absorbs red light.

13. What are the three subtractive primary colors?

14. If colorants (pigment) are added to a can of white paint, what happens to the light we use to view the paint?

15. Why is mixing pigments called *color subtraction*?

16. What colors of light are reflected by the color magenta?

17. In the CMYK color process, why is black pigment used instead of mixing cyan, magenta, and yellow pigments?

18. How does a color printing press produce all the colors of a printed picture?

19. How does a color television screen produce all the colors you see on the screen?

20. An image of a sunset is displayed on a computer screen. This image is then printed onto a piece of paper by a printer. When the paper is held up next to the screen, the images are almost identical. What is the difference between the processes used to create these two images?

Solving Problems

Section 21.1

1. Rewrite the following false statements so that they are true.

   a. Light intensity is measured in units of power per volume of space.

   b. If the intensity of light at 1 m from a source is 1 W/m^2, it will be 2 W/m^2 at 2 m from the source.

   c. At 1 m from a light source, a 1 m^2 area has a light intensity of 0.8 W/m^2. At 3 m from a light source, a 1 m^2 area will have a light intensity of 0.4 W/m^2.

2. You are reading a book by the light of a lamp. Compare the intensity of the light on your book at 1 m away from the lamp to the intensity of the light on your book at 2 m away from the lamp.

3. If 4 s pass between seeing a lightning strike and hearing thunder, about how far away was the lightning?

4. Arrange the following in order of speed from fastest to slowest: sound waves, light waves, water waves.

Section 21.2

5. Which star would be hotter, a star that produces blue light or a star that produces red light?

6. Your brain perceives color by an additive process. How would you see the following combinations of light colors?

   a. red + blue

   b. blue + green

   c. red + green

   d. red + blue + green

7. For stage lighting for a play in a theater, a magenta spot of light is created and a green spot of light. What happens when these two spots of light combine?

Section 21.3

8. Using what you know about the subtractive color process, fill in the rest of the table.

The three subtractive primary colors		
Color	Absorbs	Reflects
Cyan	Red	
Magenta		
Yellow		Red Green

9. If you wanted to make green paint, what combination of pigments would you use?

10. How would you create the following colors using inks on paper?

   a. red

   b. green

   c. blue

   d. white

11. If a cloth that appears blue in white light is viewed in a room filled with only blue light, what color will it appear to be?

12. Identify the color process—RGB or CMYK—used in each step.

    a. taking a photograph with a digital camera

    b. transferring the image to a computer so that the image appears on a computer monitor

    c. printing the image using a laser printer

    d. seeing the image on the paper with your eyes

13. Answer the following questions using the absorption graph shown here.

    a. Which colors of light are most strongly absorbed by the plants?

    b. Which colors of light are reflected the most by plants?

    c. Based on the information from the absorption graph, explain why a plant will grow more quickly if it is grown in white light rather than green light.

    d. When green pigments in the plant leaves break down in the fall, you can see that leaves have other pigments like red and orange pigments. This effect is very noticeable in many regions of the United States. Come up with a hypothesis to explain why plants might have other pigments in addition to green.

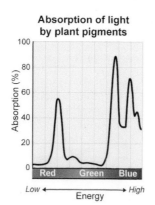

Absorption of light by plant pigments

Absorption (%)

Red   Green   Blue

Low ← Energy → High

Test Practice

Section 21.1

1. The light intensity of a lamp is 6.0 W/m² at a distance of 2.0 m from the source. The light intensity at a distance of 1.0 m from the lamp will be

    a. 3.0 W/m².

    b. 6.0 W/m².

    c. 12 W/m².

    d. 24 W/m².

2. Waxed paper is an example of a(n) _____ material that allows light to pass through it and scatter in different directions.

    a. translucent

    b. transparent

    c. reflecting

    d. absorbing

3. What color is an object that absorbs light with 100% efficiency?

    a. red

    b. green

    c. blue

    d. black

4. The light source which produces the greatest amount of heat per watt of energy consumed is

    a. CFL.

    b. LED.

    c. incandescent.

    d. fluorescent.

Section 21.2

5. Which of the following colors of light has the most energy?

   a. red

   b. yellow

   c. green

   d. violet

6. If the colors of red and green are mixed in the proper proportion a color that may result is

   a. cyan.

   b. magenta.

   c. yellow.

   d. blue.

7. The property of photons most directly related to the photoelectric emission of high energy electrons from a metal surface is

   a. long wavelength.

   b. high intensity.

   c. high frequency.

   d. low velocity.

8. The property that all photons of light have in common is

   a. color.

   b. frequency.

   c. wavelength.

   d. speed.

Section 21.3

9. A blue shirt illuminated by red light would appear

   a. cyan.

   b. magenta.

   c. yellow.

   d. black.

10. If 100% pure pigments of red, yellow, and blue are combined and seen under white light, the resulting color would appear

   a. white.

   b. muddy gray.

   c. pure black.

   d. dark green.

11. The RGB color process is used to produce color images seen in all of the following *except*

   a. magazines.

   b. TVs.

   c. movies.

   d. camcorders.

12. The color of light of *least* importance to the survival of green plants is

   a. red.

   b. green.

   c. blue.

   d. yellow.

Applying Your Knowledge

Section 21.1

1. A common misconception in physics is related to how we see objects. You have learned in this chapter that it is only possible to see an object under two conditions: (1) when light is present, and (2) if an object gives off its own light. To illustrate this misconception, do the following:

   a. Conduct a survey of 20 people you know. Ask them the following question: "If there is no light in a completely dark room, could you see your hand in front of your face?"

   b. What is the correct answer to this question? How many people answered the question correctly? How many people answered it incorrectly?

   c. Make an engaging and creative flyer that would help people understand how we see objects.

2. Even with a two-step process for producing light, fluorescent bulbs are still four times more efficient at producing light than incandescent bulbs. Among the types of incandescent bulbs, the halogen bulbs are most efficient. Find out why, and write a short paragraph about halogen bulbs explaining how they work.

3. Calculate the time it takes light and sound to travel the distance of 1 mi, which is about 1,609 m. Use 340 m/s for the speed of sound.

4. The distances between stars in space are huge compared to distances on Earth. Because of this, scientists have developed units other than kilometers or meters to measure them. A light year is a common measurement unit in astronomy. Even though the name may sound like it, this unit does not measure time. One light year is the distance that light can travel in one year. How far is a light year in meters?

Section 21.2

5. Research which colors of light the human eye is most sensitive to. It has been suggested that fire engines be painted with yellow-green paint instead of red paint. Explain why this might be a good idea.

6. Research the color vision of nocturnal animals. What is different about the photoreceptors in the eyes of nocturnal animals?

Section 21.3

7. A blue filter contains blue pigments. What happens to white light that is shone through a blue filter?

8. Why do clothes that you try on in a store under fluorescent lighting look different when you get home and try them on under incandescent lighting?

9. Design an improvement to a common product that makes it easier for color blind people to use it.

10. A color TV makes colors using just red, green, blue light. The following table illustrates how the colors are made. Using your understanding of the RGB process, fill in the table.

Dot color on TV monitor	The color you see on the TV monitor					
	Black	White	Red	Yellow	Green	Blue
Red						
Green						
Blue						

Optics

Why do people catch colds? For thousands of years, people believed that colds and other illnesses came from evil spirits. The world changed in 1673, when Anton Leeuwenhoek peered through a primitive microscope he had made. To his astonishment, he saw tiny creatures swimming around!

Leeuwenhoek's discoveries revealed a miniature universe no human had ever seen before. He was the first to see that a drop of pond water contains a tiny world of plants and animals.

Once the microscopic world was discovered, the causes of sickness could be investigated. Today, we know that small forms of life—bacteria and viruses—are usually what make you sick. Microscopes and telescopes are based on optics, the science and technology of light. By manipulating light, optical devices greatly enhance our eyesight so that we can see things that are miniscule or astronomically far away.

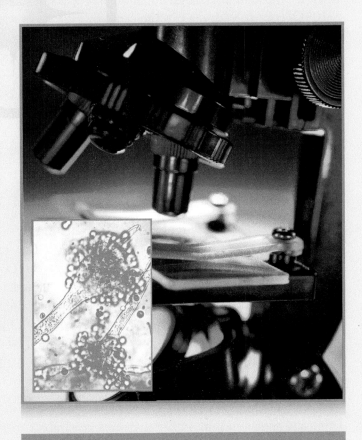

VOCABULARY

angle of incidence	focus	optics
angle of reflection	image	prism
angle of refraction	incident ray	ray diagram
converging lens	index of refraction	real image
critical angle	law of reflection	reflected ray
diffuse reflection	light ray	reflecting telescope
dispersion	magnification	refracting telescope
diverging lens	normal line	specular reflection
fiber optics	object	total internal reflection
focal length	optical axis	virtual image
focal point		

KEY QUESTIONS

✓ *Why can I see myself in a mirror but not when I look at the floor or a bare wall?*

✓ *Is it possible to make an object disappear?*

✓ *How do lenses work?*

22.1 **Optics and Reflection**

Look at your thumb through a magnifying glass. It looks huge! Of course, your hand is the same size it always was, even though what you see is a giant thumb. Explaining how magnification occurs is part of the science of optics. **Optics** is the study of how light behaves. Optics also includes the study of the eye itself because the human eye forms an image with a lens. Devices that rely on optics include mirrors, telescopes, eyeglasses, contact lenses, and magnifying glasses. This section introduces you to optics and how images are formed.

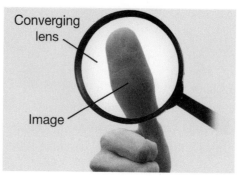

Converging lens

Image

optics - the study of how light behaves

light ray - an imaginary line that represents a light beam's path

ray diagram - an accurately-drawn sketch showing how light rays interact with an optical device

Light rays, reflection, and refraction

Light travels in straight lines   When light moves through a material, it travels in straight lines. Diagrams of light use one or more imaginary lines called **light rays** to show how light travels. Light rays are drawn with an arrowhead to indicate the direction that the light is traveling. When light rays move from one material to another, the rays may bounce or bend. Reflection occurs when light bounces off of a surface. A **ray diagram** is an accurately-drawn sketch showing how light rays interact with mirrors, lenses, and other optical devices.

Light ray

A magnifying glass bends light rays so they *appear* to come from a larger thumb.

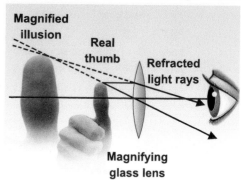

Magnified illusion

Real thumb

Refracted light rays

Magnifying glass lens

Lines and angles describe the path of light   Light does not always go straight from an object to your eyes. For example, light may bend when it crosses the boundary between glass and air. Refraction occurs when light bends crossing a surface or moving through a material. A magnifying glass uses the bending of light (refraction) to make things appear larger, or smaller, than they really are. The curved surface of the magnifying glass bends light so that it appears to come from a much larger thumb. That is the magnified thumb that you see! Figure 22.1 shows a ray diagram of what happens to light in this example.

Figure 22.1: *How a magnifying glass creates the illusion of a giant thumb by bending light rays.*

Lenses, mirrors, and prisms

Optical devices are common — Almost everyone has experience with optical devices. For example, trying on new glasses, checking your appearance in a mirror, or admiring the sparkle from a diamond all involve optics. Through experiences like these, most of us have seen optical effects created by three basic devices: the lens, the mirror, and the prism. Examples of these are shown in the diagram below.

Lenses — A lens bends light in a specific way. A **converging lens** (or convex lens) bends light so that the light rays come together at a point. This is why a magnifying glass makes a hot spot of concentrated light rays (Figure 22.2). The human eye has a single converging lens. A **diverging lens** (or concave lens) bends light so the light waves spread apart instead of coming together. An object viewed through a diverging lens appears smaller than it would look without the lens.

Mirrors — A mirror reflects light and allows you to see yourself. Flat mirrors show a true-size image. Curved mirrors distort images by causing the light rays to come together or spread apart. The curved surface of a fun-house mirror can make you look appear thinner, wider, or even upside down!

Prisms — A **prism** is an optical device used to reflect and refract light in precise ways. It is made of a solid piece of glass with flat, polished surfaces. A common triangular prism is shown in the diagram below. Telescopes, cameras, and supermarket laser scanners use prisms of different shapes to accurately refract and reflect light so the devices work properly. A diamond is a prism with many flat, polished surfaces. The "sparkle" that makes diamonds so attractive comes from light being reflected many times as it bounces around inside of a cut and polished diamond.

> **converging lens** - a lens that is thickest in the middle causing parallel light rays to come together to a point
> **diverging lens** - a lens that is thinnest in the middle causing light rays to spread apart
> **prism** - an optical device used to reflect and refract light in precise ways

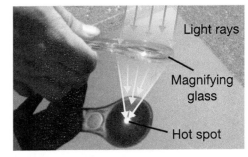

Figure 22.2: *A magnifying glass is a converging lens. This is why a magnifying glass can be used to make a hot spot of concentrated light waves.*

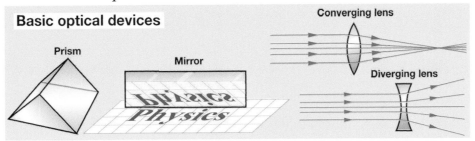

Reflection

The image in a mirror When you look at yourself in a mirror, you see your own image as if your exact twin is standing in front of you. The image appears to be the same distance from the other side of the mirror as you are on your side of the mirror (Figure 22.3). If you step back, so does your image. Images appear in mirrors because of how light is reflected by mirrors.

Specular reflection Light is reflected from all surfaces, not just mirrors. But not all surfaces form images. This is true because there are two types of reflections. A ray of light that strikes a shiny surface like a mirror creates a single reflected ray. This type of reflection is called **specular reflection**. In specular reflection, each light ray bounces off in a single direction (Figure 22.4, top). Images are produced in polished surfaces that create specular reflection, such as on the surface of a mirror. If you look closely at a mirror illuminated by a light bulb, somewhere the reflected light forms an image of the light bulb itself. In fact, a surface which has perfect specular reflection is invisible. If you look at that surface, you see reflections of other things, *but you don't see the surface itself.*

Diffuse reflection A surface that is not shiny creates **diffuse reflection**. In diffuse reflection, a single ray of light scatters into many directions (Figure 22.4, bottom). Diffuse reflection is caused by the roughness of a surface. Even if a surface feels smooth to the touch, on a microscopic level it may be rough. For example, the surface of a wooden board creates a diffuse reflection. In a lighted room, you see the board by reflected light, but you cannot see an image of a light bulb in the board. When you look at a diffuse reflecting surface *you see the surface.*

One surface can show both types of reflection Many surfaces are in between rough and smooth. These kinds of surfaces create both kinds of reflection. For example, a polished-wood tabletop can reflect some light waves as specular reflection and the rest of the light waves as diffuse reflection. The specular reflection creates a faint reflected image on the table surface. You also see the table surface itself by light from diffuse reflection.

> **specular reflection** - reflection in which each incident ray creates only one reflected ray
> **diffuse reflection** - the scattering of a light ray into many directions off of a non-shiny surface

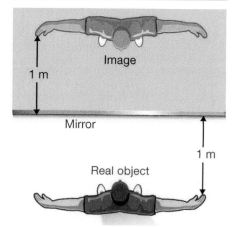

Figure 22.3: *Seeing an image in a mirror.*

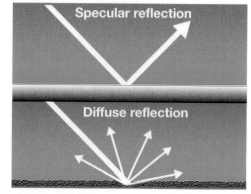

Figure 22.4: *Specular and diffuse reflections.*

The law of reflection

Incident and reflected rays Consider a ray of light coming from a light bulb and striking a mirror. The **incident ray** is the light ray that strikes the mirror. The **reflected ray** is the light ray that bounces off the mirror (Figure 22.5).

The normal line Between the incident and reflected rays, there is an imaginary line called the **normal line** which is perpendicular to the surface of the mirror (Figure 22.5). The angle between the incident ray and the normal line is called the **angle of incidence**. The **angle of reflection** is the angle between the normal line and the reflected ray.

The law of reflection The **law of reflection** states that *the angle of incidence equals the angle of reflection.* Light rays reflect from a mirror at the same angle at which they arrive. Angles are always measured relative to the normal line. The law of reflection applies to any surface with specular reflection.

An example Imagine that a light ray strikes a flat mirror at a 30-degree angle of incidence (Figure 22.5). What would be the angle of reflection? According to the law of reflection, the angle of reflection is also 30 degrees.

Drawing a ray diagram Incident and reflected rays are drawn as arrows on a ray diagram. A mirror is drawn as a solid line. The normal line is drawn as a dashed line perpendicular to the mirror surface; this line starts where the incident ray strikes the mirror. The angle of incidence and angle of reflection are measured between the light rays and the normal line as shown in Figure 22.5.

incident ray - the light ray that strikes a reflective surface

reflected ray - the light ray that bounces off a reflective surface

normal line - the line that is perpendicular to a surface

angle of incidence - the angle between the incident ray and the normal line

angle of reflection - the angle between the reflected ray and the normal line

law of reflection - the angle of incidence equals the angle of reflection

22.1 Section Review

1. Make a list of the optical devices you use on an average day.
2. Why can you see your reflected image in a mirror but not on dry, painted wall?
3. A light ray leaving a mirror has a 15-degree angle of reflection. What is the angle of incidence?

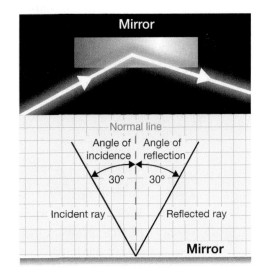

Figure 22.5: *This ray diagram illustrates the law of reflection.*

22.2 **Refraction**

Light rays may bend as they cross a boundary from one material to another. Refraction is the bending of light rays. Optical devices such as eyeglasses, telescopes, binoculars, and fiber optics technology, use the refraction of light to perform their functions.

An example of refraction   A straw in a glass of water makes a good example of refraction (Figure 22.6). The straw appears to break where it crosses the surface of the water. It is obvious that the straw has not *actually* broken. The illusion is caused by refracted light rays. The light rays from the straw are refracted, or "bent," when they cross from water back into air before reaching your eyes.

The index of refraction   The ability of a material to bend rays of light is described by a number called the index of refraction. The **index of refraction** (n) for a material measures its ability to bend light. The index of refraction is represented by a lowercase letter n. The index of refraction for air is approximately 1.00. A value of 1.00 means that a material does not refract light. Water has an index of refraction of 1.33. A diamond has an index of refraction of 2.42. Diamonds sparkle because of their high index of refraction. Table 22.1 lists the index of refraction for some common materials.

Table 22.1: The index of refraction for some common materials

Material	Index of refraction
Vacuum	1.0
Air	1.0001
Water	1.33
Ice	1.31
Glass	1.5
Diamond	2.42

Why refraction occurs   Refraction occurs when light rays cross a surface between two materials that have a different index of refraction. The "broken straw" illusion described above happens because the index of refraction of water and air are different.

index of refraction - a value that describes the ability of a material to bend light

(on next page)
angle of refraction - the angle between the refracted light ray and the normal line

Figure 22.6: *A straw appears to be broken at the point it enters the water. This illusion is created because light is refracted as it travels from air to water.*

How much does refraction bend light rays?

The angles of incidence and refraction
As we did with reflection, we will look at angles that light rays make as they are refracted by a surface. The angle of incidence is the angle between the incident ray and the normal line, the same as for a mirror. The **angle of refraction** is the angle between the refracted ray and the normal line.

The direction a light ray bends
The direction in which a light ray bends depends on whether it is moving from a material with a high index of refraction to one with a lower index or vice versa. A light ray going from a low index of refraction into a higher index bends *toward the normal line*. A light ray going from a high index of refraction to a low index bends *away from the normal line.*

Light path	How light is refracted
High *n* to low *n*	Bends away from normal line
Low *n* to high *n*	Bends toward normal line

The index of refraction in both materials
The angle that light is refracted depends on the index of refraction on both sides of a surface. The diagram below shows light crossing a piece of glass. When light goes from air into glass (A) it bends toward the normal line because glass has a higher index of refraction than air. When the light goes from glass into air again (B) it bends away from the normal line. As it comes out of the glass, the light ray is going into air with a lower index of refraction than glass.

Refraction from air into glass

Angle of incidence
Light ray
A
Normal line
Angle of refraction
Air | Glass

Refraction from glass into air

Angle of incidence
Light ray
Normal line
B
Angle of refraction
Glass | Air

Refraction can make objects seem invisible

When light travels from one material to another, the light rays may bend. If so, it is because the two materials have different indices of refraction.

However, if two materials have the same index of refraction, the light doesn't bend at all. This makes for a neat trick you can do with a glass rod. Glass is transparent, so you only see the edges of the rod because of refraction. The edge appears dark because light is refracted away from your eyes.

Vegetable oil and glass have almost the same index of refraction. If you put a glass rod into a cup of vegetable oil, the rod seems to disappear! Light travels through the oil and glass as if the two materials are the same!

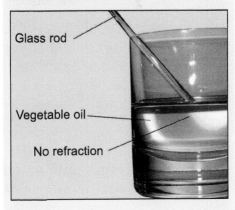

Glass rod

Vegetable oil

No refraction

Total internal reflection

When light goes from one material to another
When light goes from one material into another that has a lower refractive index, it bends away from the normal line. The angle of refraction that occurs when the light bends from the normal line is always greater than the angle of incidence. For example, in water when the angle of incidence is 45 degrees, the angle of refraction in air is 70 degrees. The refractive index of water is 1.33, for air it is 1.00.

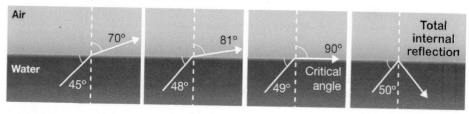

> **total internal reflection** - a phenomenon that happens when the angle of refraction becomes greater than 90 degrees
>
> **critical angle** - the angle of incidence at which the angle of refraction is 90 degrees
>
> **fiber optics** - thin glass fibers that use total internal reflection to carry light

Total internal reflection
As the angle of incidence increases, there is a point at which the light will not enter the air but will reflect back into the water. This effect is called **total internal reflection**. Total internal reflection happens when the angle of refraction becomes greater than 90 degrees. As you can see in the diagram above, when the angle of refraction reaches 90 degrees, the refracted ray is traveling straight along the surface of the water. In water, this happens when the angle of incidence is 49 degrees. At angles greater than 49 degrees, *there is no refracted ray*. All of the light is reflected back into the water.

The critical angle
The angle of incidence at which the angle of refraction is 90 degrees is called the **critical angle**. The critical angle depends on the index of refraction of the material. The critical angle for water is about 49 degrees. The critical angle for glass is about 42 degrees. At angles of incidence greater than the critical angle for a material, total internal reflection occurs.

Fiber optics are pipes for light
Figure 22.7 shows how a glass rod can be used as a *light pipe*. If glass rods are made very thin, they are flexible and trap light by total internal reflection. **Fiber optics** are thin glass fibers that use total internal reflection to carry light, even around bends and corners. Light can also be used to transmit images or data. In an *image pipe*, a bundle of optical fibers can transmit the dots that make up an image, such as a numeral, letter, or picture.

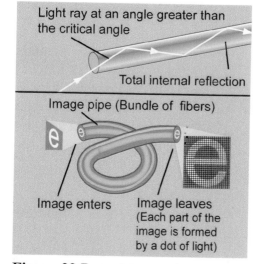

Figure 22.7: *A solid glass rod can become a pipe that carries light. This happens if light enters the rod at an angle of incidence greater than the critical angle. Inside the rod, light reflects off of the inside walls and bounces back into the rod because of total internal reflection.*

Refraction and colors of light

Index of refraction varies for different colors of light
The index of refraction for most materials varies by a small amount depending on the color of light. For example, glass has an index of refraction slightly greater for blue light than for red light. A glass prism splits white light into its spectrum of colors because each color is bent slightly differently. For example, blue light is bent more than red (Figure 22.8). Colors between blue and red are bent proportional to their position in the spectrum. Remember, the order of colors in the visible light spectrum is red, orange, yellow, green, blue, violet (or ROY-G-BV). Yellow rays, in the middle of the spectrum, are bent about halfway between red and blue rays.

Dispersion
The "rainbow" you see when light passes through a prism and a real rainbow in the sky are examples of dispersion. **Dispersion** describes how refractive index varies depending on the color of light. The refractive index values listed in Table 22.1 are based on the bending of yellow light. Yellow light was chosen because it is the at the center of the visible light spectrum.

Rainbows
Rainbows occur when white light from the Sun passes through water droplets in the atmosphere. Like a prism, each drop splits white light into the spectrum of colors. However, we see bands of colors in the sky because each color of light that reaches your eyes come from droplets at different heights (Figure 22.9). This is because of how the light is bent by the curved surface of each droplet. The colors you see follow ROY-G-BV from top to bottom.

> **dispersion** - describes how refractive index varies depending on the color of light

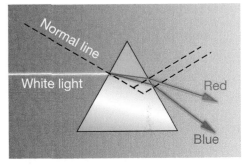

Figure 22.8: *A prism splits white light into its spectrum of colors.*

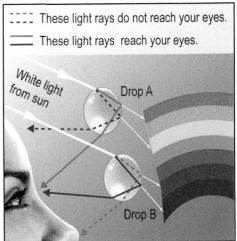

Figure 22.9: *Water droplets in the sky act as prisms. However, we see bands of color because red light reaches your eyes from higher in the atmosphere and blue light reaches your eyes from lower in the atmosphere.*

22.2 *Section Review*

1. A glass rod seems to disappear when placed in a container of vegetable oil. Based on this observation and Table 22.1, predict the index of refraction for vegetable oil.
2. Fill in the blank: When light travels from water into the air, the refracted light ray bends _____ (away or toward) the normal line.
3. Describe the refracted ray when the angle of incidence is at the critical angle. What happens to an incident light ray when the angle of incidence is *greater* than the critical angle?
4. In which situation might dispersion be a problem in focusing a camera lens: (a) taking a color photograph, or (b) taking a black and white photograph? Explain your answer.

22.3 Mirrors, Lenses, and Images

An *image* is a picture that represents the way light is organized to produce something that is useful or something that we recognize. For example, the image of an ice cream cone created by your eye or a camera matches the pattern of light from a real ice cream cone. In this section, you will learn how images are created. You will learn how to use lenses and mirrors to make images larger or smaller, upright or upside down, and near or far away.

object - a real, physical thing that gives off or reflects light

image - a picture of an object that is formed in space where light rays meet

Objects and images It is helpful to think about optics in terms of objects and images. An **object** is a real physical thing that gives off or reflects light. An **image** is a "picture" of an object that is formed in space where light rays meet (Figure 22.10). Images are formed by our eyes, and by mirrors, lenses, prisms, and other optical devices. Images are not objects you can touch; they are illusions created by organizing light *collected* from objects.

Rays come together in an image Each point on an object gives off or reflects light in all directions. That is why you can see an object from different directions. Images are created by collecting many light rays from each point on the object and bringing them back together again to form the image. For example, a camera works by collecting the rays from an object so they form an image that can be printed. The diagram below shows how multiple light rays from an object are *focused* to a single point by the camera lens, forming the image of that object. A camera captures some but not all the rays. This is why a photograph only shows one side of an object—you can't turn a photograph over and see the back of any object!

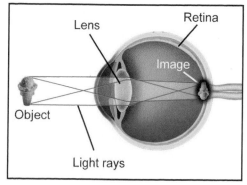

Figure 22.10: *The lens of your eye forms an image of the ice cream cone that is projected onto the back of your eye (the retina), upside down and backwards! Your brain interprets the image back to its original orientation as the actual object.*

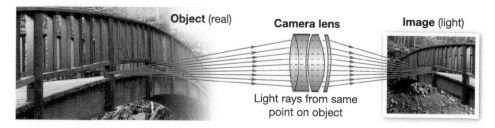

Light rays from same point on object

The image in a mirror

Seeing your reflection   If you stand in front of a flat mirror, your image appears the same distance behind the mirror as you are in front of the mirror. If you move back the image seems to move back too. If you raise your left hand, the hand on the left side of the image is raised. How does this happen?

The image of an arrow in a mirror   The photograph in Figure 22.11 shows a mirror in front of a piece of graph paper that has an arrow drawn on it. The arrow on the graph paper is an *object* because it is a physical source of reflected light. The image of the arrow appears in the mirror. Look carefully and you see that the image of the arrow appears the same number of squares *behind* the mirror as the paper arrow is *in front* of the mirror.

A ray diagram of an image in a mirror   Figure 22.12 shows a ray diagram of the arrow and mirror. The head of the arrow is a source of light rays. The ray diagram traces three light rays that leave the tip of the arrow and reflect from the mirror. These rays obey the law of reflection. We see an image of the arrow in the mirror because the reflected rays *appear* to come from behind the mirror. To see where the rays appear to come from, you extend the actual rays using dashed lines. The image of the tip of the arrow is formed at the point where the dashed lines meet. Remember, an image forms when many rays on an object come together again, *or appear to come together again*. The diagram shows the image appears the same distance behind the mirror as the arrow is in front of the mirror.

Virtual images   The image in a mirror is called a **virtual image** because the light rays do not *actually* come together to form the image. They only *appear* to come together. The virtual image in a flat mirror is created by your eyes and brain. Your brain "sees" the arrow where it would be if the light rays reaching the eye had come in a single straight line.

Real and virtual images   Because the light rays do not actually meet, a virtual image cannot be projected onto a screen or on film. Virtual images are illusions created by your eye and brain. To show a picture on a screen or record an image on film you need a *real image*. Real images form where light rays actually come together again. The images formed by a camera lens or a projector lens are real images.

virtual image - an image formed when light rays are bent so they appear to come from a point in space different from where they originated

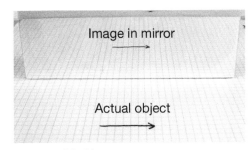

Figure 22.11: *The image in a flat mirror.*

Ray diagram

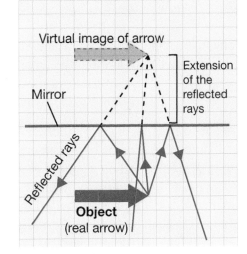

Figure 22.12: *A ray diagram of the arrow in the mirror which shows the location of the virtual image.*

Lenses

A lens and its optical axis   A lens is made of transparent material with an index of refraction different from air. The surfaces of a lens are curved to refract light in a specific way. The exact shape of a lens's surface depends on how strongly and in what way the lens needs to bend light. Nearly all lenses are designed with an **optical axis**, an imaginary line that goes through the center of the lens. Light traveling along the optical axis is not bent by the lens.

Focal point and focal length   Light rays that enter a converging lens parallel to its axis bend to meet at a point called the **focal point** after they leave the lens. Light can go through a lens in either direction so there are always two focal points, one on either side of the lens. The distance from the center of the lens to the focal point is the **focal length**. The focal length is usually (but not always) the same for both focal points of a lens.

> **optical axis** - an imaginary line that runs through the center of a lens
> **focal point** - the point in an optical system at which light rays meet or appear to meet
> **focal length** - the distance from the center of a lens to the focal point

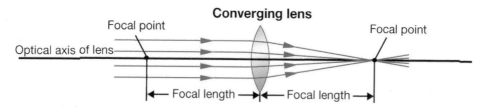

Converging lens

Converging and diverging lenses   Figure 22.13 and Figure 22.14 show how light rays enter and exit two types of lenses. The entering rays are parallel to the optical axis. A converging lens bends the rays inward, toward the focal point. A diverging lens bends the rays outward, away from the focal point.

How light travels through a converging lens   Converging lenses have surfaces that are shaped like part of a sphere. A radius of the sphere is also a normal line to the surface. When light rays fall on a spherical surface from air, they bend *toward* the normal line (Figure 22.13). For a converging lens, the first surface (air to glass) bends light rays toward the normal. At the second surface (glass to air), the rays bend *away* from the normal line. Because the second surface curves away from the normal line where the rays exit, it bends the rays *toward* the focal point. In contrast, both surfaces of a diverging lens bend light *away* from the optical axis (Figure 22.14).

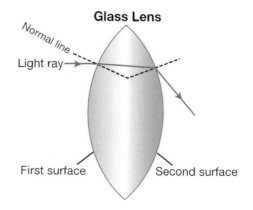

Figure 22.13: *Most lenses have spherically-shaped surfaces.*

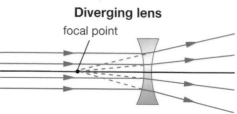

Figure 22.14: *A diverging lens.*

Drawing a ray diagram for a converging lens

What a ray diagram tells you A ray diagram is the best way to understand what type of image is formed by a lens. To draw a ray diagram for a lens, you need to know the focal length and the distance of the object from the lens. If the lenses are not too thick, then three particular rays of light follow rules that make them easy to draw.

1. A ray passing though the center of the lens, which is not bent at all.
2. A ray parallel to the axis bends to pass through the *far* focal point.
3. A ray passing through the *near* focal point comes out of the lens parallel to the axis.

Setting up to make a ray diagram The first step in making an accurate ray diagram is to set up a sheet of graph paper by drawing a straight horizontal line to be the optical axis. The lens itself is drawn as a vertical line crossing the axis. The last step in setting up is to draw the two focal points on the axis. The focal points should be the same distance, *f*, on either side of the lens. It is important that the ray diagram be drawn to *scale*. For example, a scale often used with graph paper is one box equals 1 centimeter.

Drawing the object An upward arrow is used to represent the object, usually on the left side of the lens. The distance from the arrow to the lens must be correctly scaled. For example, an object 20 centimeters away from a lens is drawn 20 boxes to the left of the lens in a ray diagram if on the scale one box is 1 centimeter.

To find the location of the image, draw the three rays listed above, starting each from the tip of the arrow. Figure 22.15 shows how to draw each ray.

Step 1: Draw a light ray passing through the center of the lens (A).

Step 2: Draw a light ray that starts parallel to the axis and bends at the lens to pass through the far focal point (B).

Step 3: Draw a light ray passing through the near focal point. This light ray bends so it is parallel to the axis on the far side of the lens (C).

The three principal rays The point where these three rays intersect on the far side of the lens is where the image of the tip of the arrow will be. Remember, an image forms where many rays from an object come together again. Notice that the image is smaller than the original object and "upside down."

Setting up

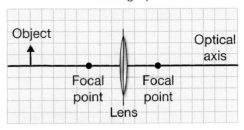

A. Drawing the first ray

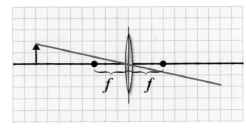

B. Drawing the second ray

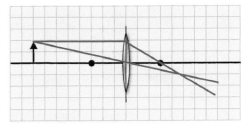

C. Drawing the third ray

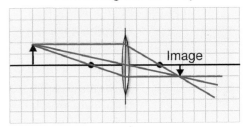

Figure 22.15: *The process of drawing a ray diagram.*

The image formed by a lens

Real images   A converging lens can form a **real image**. In a real image, light from each single point on an object comes back together again at a single point in another place to make an image. The place where the light comes back together again is called the **focus**. The focus is where you see the image clearly.

real image - an image formed by light rays coming together

focus - the point where light rays from each point on an object come together to form an image

Experiment

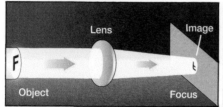

Ray diagram

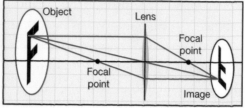

Projecting an image on a screen   The ray diagram next to the experiment shows how the real image is formed. Following the rules on the preceding page, three light rays are drawn starting from the same point, the upper corner of the *F*. Notice that these three rays all meet together again at a single point on the other side of the lens. That point is the *image* of the upper corner of the *F*. You can see the image on a screen at that distance from the lens. Each point on the *F* is "mapped" to its location on the image (Figure 22.16).

Single lenses invert images   Notice that the image of the *F* is upside down. The lens in a movie projector also makes an upside-down image. To make the image right side up, the film is put in the projector upside down!

How a lens makes an image   To make an image of any object, a lens collects rays from every point on an object. Rays from *each point* on the object are brought back together again to make *each point* of the image. Even when you cover half the lens, you still see the whole image. Light from the uncovered half still passes through the lens, but the image is dimmer since less light from the object is used to form each point of the image. Your eye does the same thing in bright light: The pupil gets smaller, and the iris covers more of the lens (Figure 22.17).

Ray diagrams

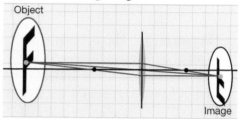

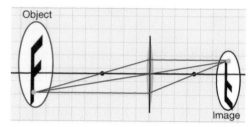

Figure 22.16: *Each point of the F in the image is formed by collecting light from a single point on the real F.*

Figure 22.17: *The pupil of your eye gets smaller, and the iris blocks more of the lens in bright light. However, your field of vision does not get smaller.*

Magnification and telescopes

Lenses can form virtual images
Both converging and diverging lenses can form virtual images. For example, a converging lens used as a magnifying glass creates an image that is virtual and larger than life (magnified). Light is bent by the lens so that it appears to come from a much larger object (Figure 22.18).

Magnification
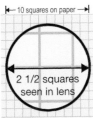

Images can be smaller than life size, too, or equal to or larger than life size. The **magnification** of an image is the ratio of the size of the image divided by the size of the object. For example, a lens with a magnification of 4 creates an image that appears four times larger than the real-life object. A magnifying glass is a single converging lens. A magnified virtual image forms when you look at an object that is *less than* one focal length from the lens. If the object is *greater than* one focal length you see a real image that is smaller than actual size and upside down. The focal-length limit is why magnifying glasses should be held fairly close to the objects you want to observe.

The refracting telescope
To get higher magnification, microscopes and telescopes use more than one lens. A **refracting telescope** has two converging lenses with different focal lengths. The lens with the shorter focal length is nearer to the eye.

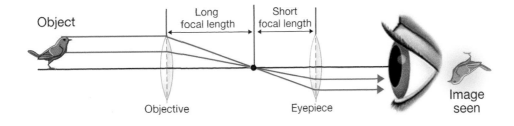

Reflecting telescope
Because high-quality, large lenses are difficult to make, **reflecting telescopes** use a concave mirror instead of one lens. The diagram shows a reflecting telescope, much like the one used by the Hubble Space Telescope and almost all astronomical observatories (Figure 22.19).

magnification - the ratio of the size of the image divided by the size of the object
refracting telescope - a device that uses two converging lenses to magnify objects
reflecting telescope - a device that uses a concave mirror and a converging lens to magnify objects

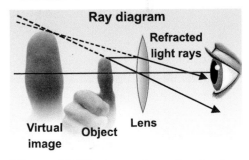

Figure 22.18: *A magnifying glass is a lens that forms a virtual image that is larger than life and appears behind the lens.*

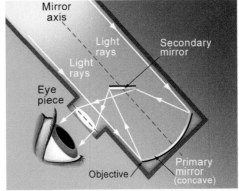

Figure 22.19: *A reflecting telescope.*

Optical systems

Optical systems Optical systems are built from lenses, mirrors, and prisms. Optical systems do two things. First, an optical system collects light rays. Second, the system changes the light rays to form an image, or processes light in other ways. A camera is an optical system that collects light to record an image. Your eye is also an optical system. A photocopying machine is another optical system. The more light an optical system collects, the brighter the image it can form.

The image from a pinhole camera A simple optical system can be made with a pinhole in a box (Figure 22.20). No image forms on the front of the box because rays from many points of the object reach the same point on the box. An image *does* form inside the box, however. The image inside the box forms because light rays that reach a point on the box surface are restricted by the pinhole to come from only a pinhole-sized point on the object.

A lens makes a brighter image than a pinhole The image formed by a pinhole is very dim because the pinhole is small and does not allow much light to come through. The image formed by a lens is brighter because a lens is larger and collects more light (Figure 22.20). Each point on the image is formed by a cone of light collected by the lens. With a pinhole, the cone is much smaller and therefore the image has a much lower light intensity.

The larger the lens, the brighter the image. This is because a larger lens collects more light rays. Compared to smaller lenses, larger lenses can make good images with less light. That is why inexpensive cameras with small lenses need a flash to take pictures indoors. The small lens does not capture enough light by itself.

Why multiple lenses are useful Multiple lenses are useful because they allow an optical system to change the size of an image. The size of the image from a single lens depends on the distance between the object and the lens. If you are looking at a bird through a lens, you can't easily change the distance between you and the bird (see the previous page)! It is much easier to change the optical system. A telephoto camera lens uses two or more lenses that move relative to one another. When you zoom in and out, the camera changes the separation between the lenses. As the separation changes, the magnification also changes.

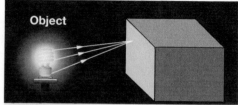

No image forms on the face of the box because light from many points on the object fall on the same point on the box.

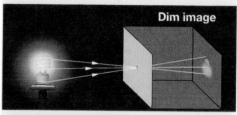

A pinhole forms a dim image by restricting light from each point on the object to a spot the size of the pinhole on the back surface of the box.

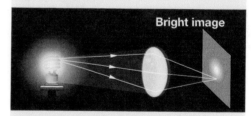

A lens forms a bright image by focusing more light from each point on the object to the equivalent point on the image.

Figure 22.20: *The images formed by a pinhole camera and a lens are different in brightness because different amounts of light are collected to form each point of the image.*

Recording images

Recording images on film   One technique for recording images uses film. Film uses special inks that respond to light. For a black-and-white photograph, the ink darkens in response to the intensity of light. Where light on the image is intense, the ink becomes dark. Where the image is dark, the ink remains light. Because dark and light are inverted, this image is known as a *negative* (Figure 22.21). A positive image is created by shining light through the negative onto photographic paper that is also coated with light-sensitive ink. Light areas on the negative allow light through and darken corresponding areas on the photographic paper. Color film uses three colors of light-sensitive ink.

Recording images electronically   Another technique for recording an image is electronic. A digital camera, like a video camera-recorder, uses a sensor called a CCD, which is located at the focal plane of the camera lens. The surface of the CCD is covered by thousands of tiny light sensors. There are separate light sensors for red, blue, and green (Figure 22.22). For each sensor, the amount of light is recorded as a number from 0 to 255. For example, if the red sensor records 255, it is seeing the most red light it can handle. A recording of 0 means the sensor sees no light. A color image is recorded as a table of numbers. Each point on the image has three numbers corresponding to the amount of red, blue, and green light. The *resolution* of a digital camera is the number of points, called *pixels*, that can be recorded by the CCDs. A *2 megapixel* camera stores 2 million pixels per image. Since each pixel is three numbers, a 2 megapixel image actually requires 6 million stored numbers.

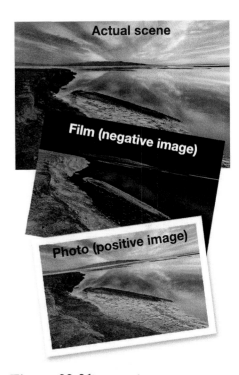

Figure 22.21: *Recording an image on film is a two-step process.*

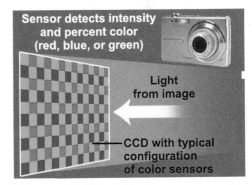

Figure 22.22: *A digital camera records an image as intensity of red, green, and blue light.*

22.3 Section Review

1. If an object is 1 foot away from a mirror, how far behind the mirror surface does the image appear to be? Is this image a real or virtual image? Explain.
2. What is the difference between a real and virtual image?
3. Is a pair of binoculars a simple optical device or an optical system? Explain your answer. (*Hint*: Research how binoculars work by going to the library or by using the Internet.)
4. Compare how images are recorded on film to how they are made using a digital camera.

Retinal Implants: Hope for the Blind

Mike, a 28-year-old blind man, lies awake on an operating table, while surgeons place a three-millimeter square electrode panel on the retina of his anesthetized eye. Soon, a medical research team will stimulate the electrodes, in hopes that these electrical impulses will do what the rods and cone cells in his eye once did: send a message from the ganglion cells through the optic nerve to the visual cortex of his brain, forming an image.

Legally blind since age 17, Mike volunteered for this study knowing that he may not see anything, and even if he does, the electrode panel will have to be removed at the end of the four hour operation, since engineers are still working to develop materials that will protect the delicate electronics from the salty, wet environment of the eye for a long time.

Ready? asks the head surgeon. Mike gives a "thumbs-up" and the room falls quiet. The electrical stimulation machine emits a tone and then activates one of the electrodes on the panel. "I can see something...a pea-sized circle of light, at about arm's length!" Mike's voice crackles with excitement. After the next tone, two electrodes are activated. "This time it's about the size of a dime, and twice as bright." The experiments continue, varying the amount of current and the placement of the activated electrodes. Mike sees a banana-shaped curve when four electrodes in a row are activated. He cannot yet distinguish the patterns that form an "L" and a "T" however. He sees blobs of light, but not distinct shapes. Mike was one of six participants in this first human trial of the Boston Retinal Implant Project. The project's team of doctors, biologists, engineers, and rehabilitation specialists has been working since 1988, with the goal of producing a safe, long-lasting method to stimulate the retina. They want to generate images detailed enough to enable a blind person to, for example, walk by herself in an unfamiliar place.

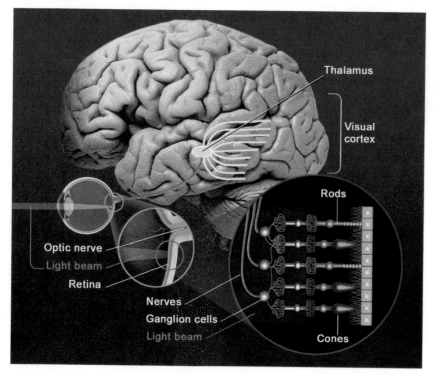

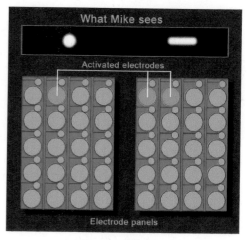

How artificial vision works

The vision system consists of a special pair of glasses with a tiny video camera attached. The camera sends information about an image via wireless transmission to a chip surgically implanted on the outside of the eye. The chip in turn decodes the image and activates electrodes in order to stimulate the ganglion cells that normally send messages to the visual cortex of the brain.

This technology will most likely help people who have damaged photoreceptors (rod and cone cells) but whose ganglion cells and optic nerves are still functioning. Researchers expect that people with adult-onset blindness will adjust most easily to the vision system, because the visual cortex of their brain is used to organizing information about light, dark, and colors into recognizable pictures.

While the vision system won't be a cure for every type of blindness, it does hold promise for people affected by two of the most common causes of adult onset blindness, retinitis pigmentosa and macular degeneration. Both of these diseases damage the eye's photoreceptors but usually leave the other parts unharmed.

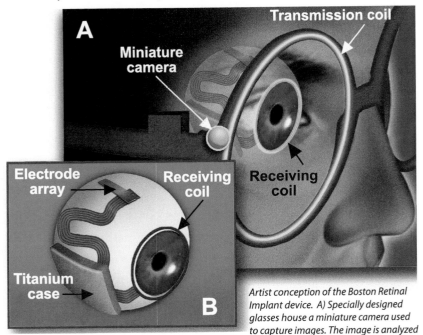

Artist conception of the Boston Retinal Implant device. A) Specially designed glasses house a miniature camera used to capture images. The image is analyzed by an image processing unit (a small microcomputer worn on the person's belt) and appropriate electrical pattern information and power are sent via a transmission coil. A secondary receiving coil (sutured around the iris of the eye) captures the wireless information transmitted. B) the transmitted information is relayed through a series of electronic components (sealed in a titanium case) and then ultimately to the stimulating electrode array that is inserted into the retina through a flap created behind the outside of the eye.

A look ahead

The Boston Retinal Implant Project team knows that there is much work to be done in order to create a vision system that can improve the quality of life for blind patients. Biologists are researching how to lower the amount of electrical current needed to get ganglion cells to send messages, while engineers are exploring different ways to transmit information to the eye's interior and protect the implant from corrosion. However, they have proven that electrical stimulus of the ganglion cells does activate the body's remaining intact visual system and allows the patient to perceive light. This is a crucial first step toward the formation of images, which is the ultimate goal of the project.

And as the technology develops there is hope that one day this artificial vision system may be so fine-tuned that the video camera could serve as a pair of binoculars or even a microscope. Someday, perhaps, this system will not only restore Mike's ability to see, but even extend his range of vision beyond the normal capabilities of the human eye.

QUESTIONS

1. Why do you think the team's biologists are seeking the lowest effective amount of current?
2. Explain a significant breakthrough the Boston Retinal Implant project team has accomplished.
3. Describe at least two challenges that the team faces.

Chapter 22 Review

Understanding Vocabulary

Select the correct term to complete the sentences.

dispersion	fiber optics	incident ray
reflected ray	diffuse reflection	focal length
law of reflection	virtual image	specular reflection
converging lens	index of refraction	normal line

1. In _____, each light ray bounces off in a single direction. In _____, a single light ray scatters in many directions.

2. The _____ is an imaginary line drawn perpendicular to the surface of a mirror or any surface.

3. The _____ can be calculated for a material by dividing the speed of light in a vacuum by the speed of light in the material.

4. Total internal reflection occurs in a substance when the angle of an incidence light ray exceeds the _____.

Reviewing Concepts

Section 22.1

1. What are light rays and what are they used for?

2. Can you predict how far away the image of an object will appear in a mirror?

3. How does the size of your image in a flat mirror compare to your actual size?

4. Describe the four interactions light can have with matter. Give an example of a situation where more than one interaction happens at the same time.

5. Glare from headlights can make it harder to see when driving at night. Glare is worse when roads are wet from rain versus when roads are dry. Explain why this happens in terms of the two types of reflection.

6. What happens to light when it travels through a prism or a lens?

7. When drawing a ray diagram, what is the normal line?

8. State the law of reflection in your own words.

9. Describe how you measure the incident angle.

Section 22.2

10. What happens to light as it moves from one material to another that has a different index of refraction?

11. Refer to Table 22.1 in the chapter. For light moving from air, which material has a greater ability to bend light toward the normal line: ice or glass? How do you know?

12. A glass rod appears to disappear when placed in vegetable oil. Why?

13. Explain total internal reflection using an application or example.

14. Fiber optics are glass fibers that carry light. You know from experience that light shines through glass. Why doesn't light escape from these glass fibers?

Section 22.3

15. Mirrors and lenses both produce images that your eye can see. How are mirrors and lenses alike and different?

16. Describe how objects, real images, and virtual images are different.

17. What happens to light traveling along the optical axis of a lens?

18. What happens to light rays entering a converging lens parallel to its optical axis?

19. When you've used a camera, you may have noticed that you can't have both a close object and a far away object in focus at the same time. Why?

20. An optical system has a magnification of 100. What does 100 mean in this context? Use the terms object and image in your answer.

21. Explain the differences between a converging lens and a diverging lens. For each lens: discuss the shape, how each bends parallel light rays, and how the images are formed.

Solving Problems

Section 22.1

1. A ray of light strikes a mirror. Which of the following rays (a, b, c, or d) best describes the path of the light ray leaving the mirror?

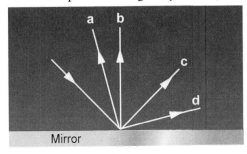

Mirror

2. A light ray strikes a mirror and is reflected. The angle between the incident ray and the reflected ray is 60°. What is the angle of reflection for this ray?

3. If you stand 2 m in front of a mirror, what is the apparent distance between you and your image?

4. A light ray strikes a mirror and is reflected as shown.

a. Copy the sketch and draw the normal line to the mirror.

b. On your sketch, label the angle of incidence and the angle of reflection.

c. If the angle of incidence is 45°, what is the angle of reflection?

Section 22.2

5. The graphic shows a ray of light travels from air into water.

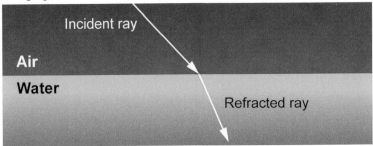

a. Copy the sketch and draw the normal line at the boundary between the air and water.

b. On your sketch, label the angle of incidence and the angle of refraction.

c. Find and label the index of refraction for each material.

6. A light ray crosses from a piece of glass into a liquid. You observe that the light ray bends closer to the normal passing from the glass to the liquid. Based on this observation, how does the index of refraction for the liquid compare to the index of refraction for the glass?

Section 22.3

7. A 2-cm tall object is positioned 10 cm from a converging lens with a focal length of 5 cm.

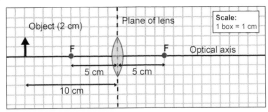

a. Copy the graphic to scale on your own graph paper. Trace the rays and predict where the image will form.

b. Is the image real or virtual?

c. What is the image size compared to the object size?

d. Is the image upright or inverted?

8. A 2-cm tall object is positioned 4 cm from a converging lens. The focal length of the lens is 5 cm.

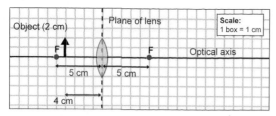

a. Copy the graphic to scale on your own graph paper. Trace the rays and predict where the image will form

b. Is the image real or virtual?

c. What is the image size compared to the object size?

d. Is the image upright or inverted?

9. If a 1-cm-diameter coin is viewed under a lens with a magnification of 2.4, what will the diameter of the image be?

Test Practice

Section 22.1

1. The diagram below represents a light ray reflected from a plane mirror. From the data given in the diagram, what is the value of the angle of reflection?

a. 35°

b. 55°

c. 80°

d. 110°

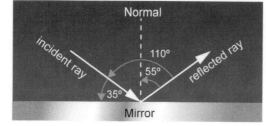

2. Which of the following optical devices is able to produce both real and virtual images?

a. a plane mirror

b. a converging lens

c. a diverging lens

d. all of the above

3. A light ray strikes a surface at an acute angle. The line drawn perpendicular to the surface at the point where the light ray strikes is the

a. normal.

b. incident ray.

c. refracted ray.

d. reflected ray.

4. Which of the diagrams represents light rays reflecting from a surface that shows diffuse reflection?

a. A

b. B

c. C

d. D

5. When light traveling in a material strikes the boundary of a different material, the energy of the light will be

a. completely absorbed by the boundary.

b. entirely transmitted into the new material.

c. entirely reflected back into the original material.

d. partly reflected back into the original material, partly absorbed, and partly transmitted by the new material.

Section 22.2

6. The diagram below shows a light ray entering air from water. Through which point is the light ray most likely to pass?

a. A

b. B

c. C

d. D

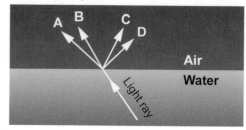

7. The diagram below represents a light ray passing from ice into an unknown material. Using Table 22.1 on page 524, determine which of the following is the unknown material.

   a. water

   b. diamond

   c. glass

   d. air

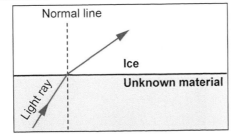

8. Which choice best describes the phenomenon shown in the diagram?

   a. scattering and diffuse reflection

   b. absorption and specular reflection

   c. refraction and dispersion

   d. transmission and regular diffusion

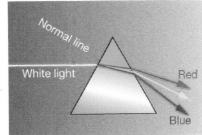

9. A light ray traveling through a piece of glass meets a boundary with air at the critical angle for glass. Which diagram best shows the path of this light ray?

   a. A

   b. B

   c. C

   d. D

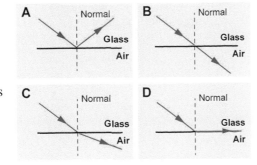

Section 22.3

10. Which diagram best represents a light ray passing through a diverging lens?

    a. A

    b. B

    c. C

    d. D

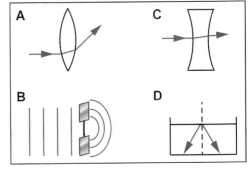

11. Which graph shows the relationship between image size and object size for an object reflected in a plane mirror?

    a. A

    b. B

    c. C

    d. D

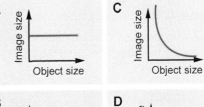
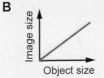

12. A converging lens having an optical center O and focal length F is used to produce an image of a rabbit. The lens is being used to produce an image of the rabbit that is

    a. virtual and upright.

    b. real and upright.

    c. virtual and inverted.

    d. real and inverted.

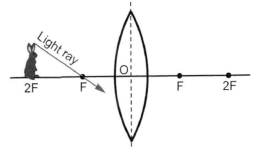

13. A converging lens can be used to produce an image that is

  a. smaller and real.

  b. larger and real.

  c. larger and virtual.

  d. all of the above

14. A diverging lens can be used to produce an image that is

  a. smaller and real.

  b. larger and real.

  c. smaller and virtual.

  d. all of the above

Applying Your Knowledge

Section 22.1

1. The phrase "MY MOM" is held in front of a flat mirror. When you read it in the mirror, what do you read? Try it and find out. Make sure you use capital letters.

2. Why do ambulances often have the reversed lettering for "AMBULANCE" on the front of their vehicles?

Section 22.2

3. In Section 22.2, you learned that it is possible for objects to appear invisible. Write a short story that includes this phenomenon in the plot. Be sure to explain accurately the science behind why and how this can happen.

4. *Chromatic aberration* is a common optical flaw found in simple lenses. It causes colored images to appear blurred instead of in sharp focus. Use what you know about prisms and rainbows to explain why chromatic aberration occurs. Research how chromatic aberration can be corrected.

5. A microscope is a tool used to magnify cells and very small objects. Find and study a labeled diagram of a microscope. Magnification for this tool depends on the eyepiece and objective lenses. Describe these parts and explain where they are located on a microscope. How do you calculate the magnification of a microscope?

Section 22.3

6. Your eye is an entire optical system that works together with the optic nerve and your brain to help you see images. Research the human eye and write a report that answers the following questions.

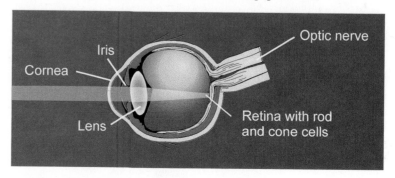

  a. What is the purpose of the iris in the eye?

  b. What is the purpose of the optic nerve?

  c. What is the purpose of rod and cone cells?

  d. What is the purpose of the lens?

  e. How does the flexibility of the lens affect your ability to see?

7. A telescope can be used for looking at objects on Earth as well as in the sky. What do the following words mean when used to describe the working of a telescope: aperture, magnification, reflector, and refractor?

The Physical Nature of Light

How is a radio like a flashlight? How can microwaves act like rays of light? While these may seem like strange questions, they are not. Radio, microwaves, and light are all three forms of the same kind of wave. They just have different frequencies—like chocolate, vanilla, and strawberry are different flavors of ice cream. The same processes of reflection and refraction work with microwaves as with ordinary light. That is why cell phone towers have funny-shaped dishes on them. The dishes act like mirrors and lenses for microwaves that carry cell phone transmissions. Human technology has found uses for almost every frequency of "light," including frequencies we cannot see.

Light is a form of energy. In this chapter, you will learn about the electromagnetic spectrum and how electromagnetic radiation, including visible light, behaves. Microwave ovens, laptop computer screens, sunglasses, and lasers are all different types of technology that take advantage of the unique properties of the electromagnetic spectrum.

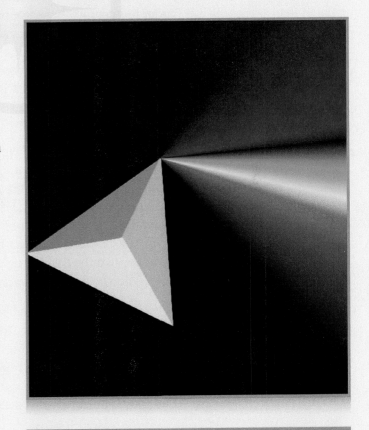

VOCABULARY

electromagnetic spectrum	nanometer	radio waves
electromagnetic wave	photoluminescence	ultraviolet light
gamma rays	polarization	visible light
infrared waves	polarizer	x-rays
microwaves		

KEY QUESTIONS

✓ *What does the acronym "ROY-G-BV" refer to?*

✓ *Why do radio broadcast towers have to be so tall?*

✓ *How does glow-in-the-dark plastic work?*

23.1 Electromagnetic Spectrum

Common objects can vary in size. For example, a rock can be bigger than your fingernail but smaller than a truck. While harder to imagine, the whole range of rock sizes actually includes objects as big as the Moon and smaller than a grain of sand. Wavelengths of light also come in a range of sizes. We see the range of wavelengths from red to violet (ROY-G-BV), but this visible light is just a small part of a much larger range of light waves called the electromagnetic spectrum. This section explores the whole spectrum, most of which is used by humans in one way or another.

Light is an electromagnetic wave

What is an electromagnetic wave? Light is a wave, like sound and the ripples on a pond. What is oscillating in a light wave? Imagine you have two magnets. One hangs from a string and the other is in your hand. If you wave the magnet in your hand back and forth close to the other one, you can make the magnet on the string sway back and forth. How does the oscillation of one magnet move the other one? In Chapter 17, you learned that magnets have an invisible magnetic field around them. When you move the magnet up and down, you make a wave in the magnetic field. The wave in the magnetic field makes the other magnet move.

The frequency of the wave However, the wave in the magnetic field also keeps travelling outward at the speed of light as an **electromagnetic wave**. If you could shake your magnet up and down 100 million times per second (100 MHz) you would make an FM radio wave. If you could shake the magnet up and down 450 trillion times per second, you would make waves of red light (Figure 23.1). Light and radio waves are waves of electromagnetism.

Oscillations create electromagnetic waves Anything that creates an oscillation of electricity or magnetism also creates electromagnetic waves. If you switch electricity on and off repeatedly, the oscillating electricity makes an electromagnetic wave. This is exactly how radio towers make radio waves. Electric currents oscillate up and down the metal towers and create electromagnetic waves of the right frequency to carry radio signals. Tapping a stick up and down in a puddle makes ripples that spread out from where you tap. Oscillating electric current in a radio tower makes ripples of electric and magnetic fields that spread out from the tower at the speed of light as electromagnetic waves (Figure 23.2).

> **electromagnetic wave** - a wave of oscillating electric and magnetic fields that moves at the speed of light

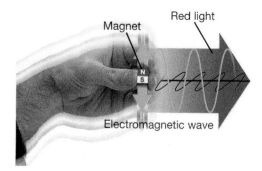

Figure 23.1: *If you could shake a magnet up and down 450 trillion times per second, you could make an electromagnetic wave that you would see as red light.*

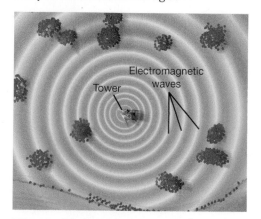

Figure 23.2: *Ripples of electric and magnetic fields spread out from the radio tower at the speed of light.*

The electromagnetic spectrum

Properties of electromagnetic waves
Like all waves, electromagnetic waves have frequency, wavelength, amplitude, and speed. Also, like other waves, electromagnetic waves carry energy in proportion to their frequency. Shaking a magnet 1 million times per second (1 MHz) takes more energy than shaking it once per second (1 Hz). That is why a 1 MHz electromagnetic wave has a million times more energy than a 1 Hz electromagnetic wave of the same amplitude.

Why visible light is different
Almost all electromagnetic waves are invisible for the same reason you cannot see the magnetic field between two magnets. The exception is visible light. Visible light includes only the electromagnetic waves with the range of energy that can be detected by the human eye.

The electromagnetic spectrum
The entire range of electromagnetic waves, including all possible frequencies, is called the **electromagnetic spectrum**. The electromagnetic spectrum includes radio waves, microwaves, infrared light, ultraviolet light, x-rays, and gamma rays. Visible light is a small part of the spectrum in between infrared and ultraviolet light.

> **electromagnetic spectrum** - the entire range of electromagnetic waves, including all possible frequencies

How does an electromagnetic wave spread?

Electromagnetic waves have both magnetic and electrical qualities. The two qualities exchange energy back and forth like a pendulum exchanges potential and kinetic energy back and forth. In Chapter 16 you learned about induction; a changing magnetic field induces an electric field and vice versa. Induction is how electromagnetic waves propagate and spread. Each cycle of the electric part of the wave creates a magnetic wave as it changes. Each cycle of the magnetic wave in turn creates a new cycle of the electric wave. The electric and magnetic parts of the wave keep regenerating each other as the wave propagates.

The electromagnetic spectrum

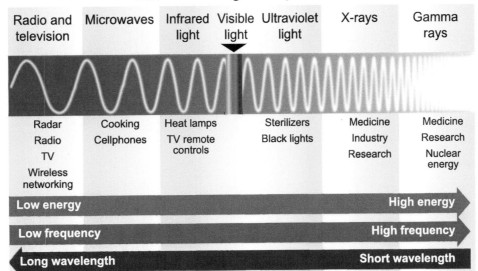

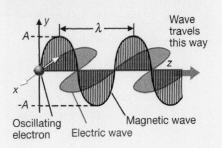

The wavelength and frequency of visible light

Wavelength of light   The wavelength of visible light is very small. For example, waves of orange light have a length of only 0.0000006 meters (6×10^{-7} m). Because wavelengths of light are so small, wavelengths are given in nanometers. One **nanometer** (nm) is one billionth of a meter (10^{-9} m). Figure 23.3 shows the size of a light wave relative to other small things. Thousands of wavelengths of red light would fit in the width of a single hair on your head!

Frequency of light   The frequency of light waves is very high. For example, red light has a frequency of 460 trillion, or 460,000,000,000,000 cycles per second. To manage these large numbers, units of terahertz (THz) are used to measure light waves. One THz is a trillion hertz (10^{12} Hz), or a million megahertz.

Wavelength and frequency are inversely related   Wavelength and frequency are inversely related to each other. As frequency increases, wavelength decreases. Red light has a lower frequency and longer wavelength than blue light. Blue light has a higher frequency and shorter wavelength than red light.

Energy and color of light   The energy of waves is proportional to frequency. Higher-frequency waves have more energy than lower-frequency waves. The same is true of light. The higher the frequency of the light, the higher the energy. Since color is related to energy, there is a direct relationship between color (energy) and frequency and an inverse relationship between color (energy) and wavelength. Table 23.1 shows the color, frequency, and wavelength of visible light.

Table 23.1: Frequencies and wavelengths of light

Energy (relative)	Color	Wavelength (nm)	Frequency (THz)
Low ↑ ↓ High	Red	650	462
	Yellow	580	517
	Green	530	566
	Blue	470	638
	Violet	400	750

> **nanometer** - one billionth of a meter (10^{-9} m)

Size

Bee 1×10^{-2} m
Visible to the human eye

Pollen 3×10^{-5} m
Microscopic

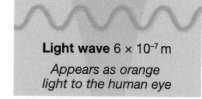

Light wave 6×10^{-7} m
Appears as orange light to the human eye

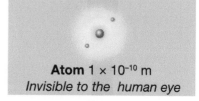

Atom 1×10^{-10} m
Invisible to the human eye

Figure 23.3: *Comparing the sizes of objects to the wavelength of light.*

The speed of electromagnetic waves

The speed of light   All electromagnetic waves travel at the same speed in a vacuum, the speed of light—3×10^8 m/s. As with other waves, the speed of light is the frequency multiplied by the wavelength.

THE SPEED OF LIGHT (Relationship between frequency and wavelength)

Speed of light (3×10^8 m/s) $c = f\lambda$ — Wavelength (m)
Frequency (Hz)

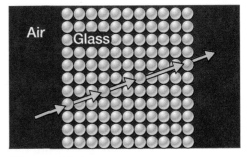

Figure 23.4: *It takes light more time to pass through a material because the light is absorbed and re-emitted by each atom in the material.*

Light travels slower through materials where n > 1   When passing through a material, light is continuously absorbed and re-emitted by the atoms that make up the material (Figure 23.4). Light moves at 3×10^8 m/s *between* the atoms. However, the process of absorption and emission by the atoms causes a delay that makes the light take longer to move through the material. The speed of light in a material is equal to the speed of light in a vacuum divided by the refractive index (n) of the material. For example, the speed of light in water ($n = 1.33$) is 2.3×10^8 m/s (3×10^8 m/s ÷ 1.33). The refractive index of a material is the speed of light in a vacuum divided by the speed of light in the material (see sidebar at right).

Wavelengths are shorter in refractive materials   When moving through a material, the frequency of light stays the same. Because the frequency stays the same, the wavelength of light is reduced in proportion to how much the speed changes. That means the wavelength of red light is shorter in water than in air.

Finding the wavelength of light   You can find the wavelength of light from its frequency and speed. For example, the frequency of red light is 4.6×10^{14} hertz (Hz). If you used the speed of light in a vacuum, 3×10^8 m/s, the wavelength is 6.5×10^{-7} m (3×10^8 m/s ÷ 4.6×10^{14} Hz). Use this calculation to find the wavelength of blue-green light in a vacuum. The frequency of blue-green light is 6.0×10^{14} hertz. The answer is that blue-green light has a wavelength of 5×10^{-7} meters.

Index of refraction

The index of refraction (n) for a material is the ratio of the speed of light in a vacuum to the speed of light in that material.

INDEX OF REFRACTION (n) FOR A MATERIAL

$$n = \frac{\text{speed of light in a vacuum}}{\text{speed of light in the material}}$$

Low-energy electromagnetic waves

What does "low-energy" mean? We classify the energy of electromagnetic waves by comparing it to the energy it takes to remove an electron from an atom. Energy great enough to remove an electron can break the chemical bonds that hold molecules together. Low energy waves, like visible light, do not have enough energy to break most chemical bonds.

Radio waves **Radio waves** are the lowest-frequency waves. They have wavelengths that range from kilometers down to about 30 centimeters (Figure 23.5). Radio broadcast towers are tall because they need to be one-quarter of a wavelength high to efficiently create the large wavelengths of radio waves.

Microwaves 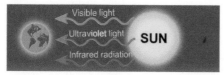 **Microwaves** range in length from approximately 30 cm (about 12 inches) to about 1 mm (the thickness of a pencil lead). Cell phones and microwave ovens use microwaves. The waves in a microwave oven are tuned to the natural frequency of liquid water molecules. The high intensity of microwaves inside an oven rapidly transfers energy to water molecules in food. Microwaves heat up and cook food by heating water molecules.

Infrared waves **Infrared waves** include wavelengths from 1 millimeter to about 700 nanometers. Infrared waves are often referred to as radiant heat. Although we cannot see infrared waves, we can feel them with our skin. Heat from the Sun comes from infrared waves in sunlight.

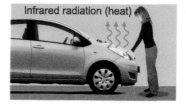
Infrared radiation (heat)

Visible light 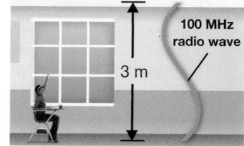 **Visible light** has wavelengths between 700 nanometers and 400 nanometers and includes all the colors of light (ROY-G-BV) we see when white light is split by a prism. The term *light* commonly refers to this part of the spectrum. However, any part of the electromagnetic spectrum—from radio waves to gamma rays—can be considered as "light." The Sun emits the whole spectrum of electromagnetic waves, including infrared, ultraviolet, and visible light.

Visible light
Ultraviolet light SUN
Infrared radiation

radio waves - the lowest frequency electromagnetic waves with wavelengths greater than about 30 cm
microwaves - electromagnetic waves with wavelengths between 30 cm and 1 mm
infrared waves - a type of electromagnetic wave with wavelengths between 1 mm and 700 nm
visible light - a type of electromagnetic wave with wavelengths between 700 nm and 400 nm

100 MHz radio wave

3 m

Figure 23.5: *A 100-megahertz radio wave, 100 FM on your radio dial, has a wavelength of 3 meters, about the height of a classroom.*

High-energy electromagnetic waves

Ultraviolet light **Ultraviolet light** has a range of wavelengths from 10 to 400 nanometers. Like other forms of high energy electromagnetic waves, ultraviolet light has enough energy to remove electrons and to break chemical bonds. Sunlight contains ultraviolet waves (Figure 23.6). A small amount of ultraviolet radiation is beneficial to humans, but larger amounts cause sunburn, skin cancer, and cataracts. Most ultraviolet light is blocked by ozone in Earth's upper atmosphere (Figure 23.6). A hole in Earth's ozone layer over its poles allows more ultraviolet light to reach the surface of the planet, which creates problems for humans, plants, and animals.

X-rays **X-rays** are high-frequency waves that are used extensively in medical and manufacturing applications. Their wavelength range is from about 10 nanometers to about 0.001 nm (or 10-trillionths of a meter). When you get a medical x-ray, the film darkens where bones are because calcium and other elements in your bones absorb the x-rays before they reach the film. X-rays show the extent of an injury such as a broken bone.

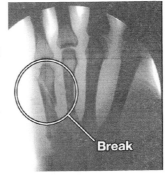

Break

Gamma rays **Gamma rays** have wavelengths of less than about ten-trillionths of a meter. Gamma rays are generated in nuclear reactions, and are used in many medical applications. Gamma rays are very energetic and can strip the innermost electrons out of an atom and disrupt chemical bonds. You do not want to be around strong gamma rays without heavy shielding material that blocks gamma rays.

> **ultraviolet light** - a type of electromagnetic wave with a range of wavelengths from 10 nm to 400 nm
>
> **x-rays** - high-frequency electromagnetic waves with wavelengths ranging from about 10 nm to about 0.001 nm
>
> **gamma rays** - electromagnetic waves with wavelengths of less than ten-trillionths of a meter

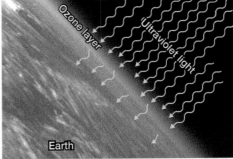

Ozone layer

Ultraviolet light

Earth

Earth image courtesy NASA/JPL/UCSD/JSC

Figure 23.6: *Ultraviolet light from the Sun is absorbed by Earth's ozone layer.*

23.1 *Section Review*

1. Describe an electromagnetic wave. How is one made?
2. What is the relationship between the frequency of light and its wavelength?
3. What is the speed of light in air (n = 1.0001)? What could you do to make light slow down?
4. Compare and contrast a radio wave and ultraviolet light.
5. Why might an infrared camera be able to "see" a person in the dark?

23.2 Interference, Diffraction, and Polarization

The wave-like properties of light cannot be observed directly. In this section, you will learn about experimental evidence that demonstrates how we know light is a wave. Like sound and water waves, light shows interference and diffraction. Light also has the property of polarization. Many inventions use the properties of light. Lasers use interference of light waves. We separate colors with a diffraction grating. Sunglasses and LCD screens use polarization.

Diffraction and shadows

Shadows   Imagine shining a flashlight on a wall though a slot in a piece of cardboard. On the wall, you see bright light where the light rays pass through the slot. You see shadow where the cardboard blocks the light rays. If the light bulb is very small, there is a sharp edge to the shadow, showing you that light rays travel in straight lines (Figure 23.7).

Thin slits can cause diffraction   If the slot is very narrow, the light on the screen looks very different. The light spreads out after passing through the opening. The spreading is caused by diffraction. Recall that diffraction is a wave behavior. We saw the same spreading of water waves when they passed through a small opening. Diffraction occurs when a wave passes through an opening not too much wider than the wavelength of the wave. The small opening acts like the center of a new circular wave. Observing diffraction with light is evidence that light is a wave.

The fuzzy edge of a shadow   An ordinary shadow often has a fuzzy edge for a different reason. When light comes from a light bulb, light rays from many points on the bulb cast shadows in slightly different places. The width of the fuzzy edge depends on how far away the light bulb is, how large the bulb is, and how far away the screen is (Figure 23.8, left).

Diffraction in a shadow   You can see diffraction in a shadow cast by a sharp edge with light from a laser. The edge of the shadow has ripples in it (Figure 23.8, right)! The ripples are caused by diffraction. You do not see this in white light because of the mixture of its wavelengths. A laser makes light of one color with a single wavelength.

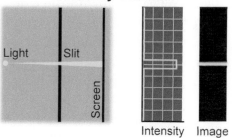

Ordinary shadow

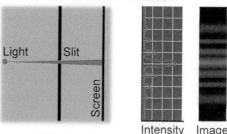

Diffraction shadow

Figure 23.7: *Light and an ordinary shadow compared to diffraction.*

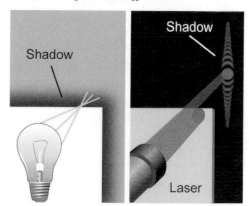

Figure 23.8: *The difference between a shadow caused by light from a light bulb (left) and light from a laser (right).*

The interference of light waves

Young's double-slit experiment
Interference is a property of waves. In 1807, Thomas Young proved light was a wave when he showed that two beams of light could interfere with each other. In a famous experiment, Young let a beam of light pass through two very thin slits. After passing through the slits, the light fell on a screen.

Interpreting the experiment
If light was *not* a wave, then the pattern should look like the diagram seen below on the left. The light at any point on the screen is simply the light from one slit plus the light from the other. However, when the experiment is done, the pattern looks like the diagram on the right. There are bright and dark bands across the screen caused by the interference of the two light beams

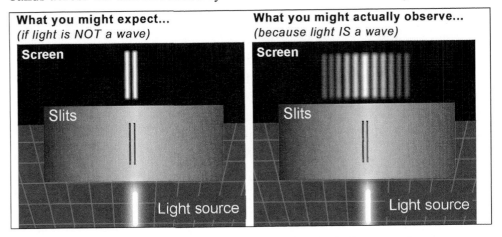

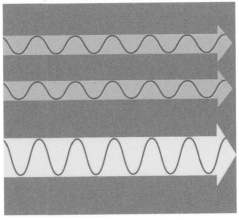

Constructive interference

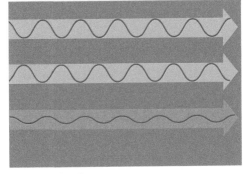

Destructive interference

Interference of light waves
The double-slit experiment is strong evidence that light is a wave because an interference pattern can only be created by the addition of waves. Think of each slit as the source of a circular wave. The waves from both slits are exactly in phase when they leave the slit, because light from both slits is from the same wave front. Straight ahead of the slits, the waves reach the screen in phase and there is a bright area on the screen. Next to this bright area, the light from each slit hits the screen out of phase because one of the two waves has to go a longer distance than the other. The bright bands in an interference pattern are where the light waves from both slits are in phase at the screen (constructive interference, Figure 23.9, top). The dark bands appear where the light waves reach the screen out of phase (destructive interference, Figure 23.9, bottom).

Figure 23.9: *The interference pattern (bands) comes from the interference of light as waves from each slit add up at each point on the screen. Constructive interference creates brighter light. Destructive interference creates dimmer light.*

Diffraction gratings and spectrometers

Diffraction grating
A **diffraction grating** creates an interference pattern similar to the pattern for the double slit. A grating is actually a series of thin parallel grooves on a piece of glass or plastic. When light goes through a diffraction grating, each groove scatters the light so the grating acts like many parallel slits.

The central spot
When you shine a laser beam through a diffraction grating, most of the light goes straight through. A bright spot called the *central spot* appears directly in front of the grating where the light passes straight through (Figure 23.10). Some light is also scattered off of the grooves. The interference of the light scattered from the grooves is what causes the additional bright bands on either side of the central bright spot.

The diffraction pattern
The **diffraction pattern** is the series of bright spots on either side of the central bright spot. The closest bright spots to the center are called the *first order*. The light waves that produce the first order spots are one whole wavelength different in phase from each other. The second closest set of bright spots are called second order spots because they are made by the constructive interference of light waves that are two wavelengths different. You can often see third order, and even fourth order spots as well.

The location of bright spots is related to wavelength
Like the double slit, a bright spot forms when the light waves from two adjacent grooves arrive in phase at the screen. The two waves travel a slightly different distance. They arrive in phase when the difference in distance between the two waves is exactly one wavelength. Because the location of the bright spots depends on wavelength, different wavelengths of light make bright spots at different distances from the central spot (Figure 23.11).

The spectrometer
When light with a mixture of wavelengths passes through a diffraction grating, each wavelength makes a bright spot at a different place on the screen. As a result, the grating spreads the light out into its separate wavelengths. That is why you see a rainbow when looking at a bright white light through a diffraction grating. A spectrometer is a device that uses a diffraction grating to create a spectrum (Figure 23.12). The spectrometer has a scale that allows you to read different wavelengths of light directly from the pattern of light made by the grating.

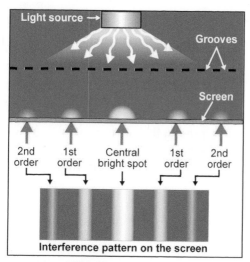

Figure 23.10: *The interference pattern from a diffraction grating.*

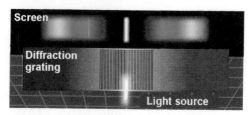

Figure 23.11: *Different wavelengths of light make bright spots at different distances from the central spot.*

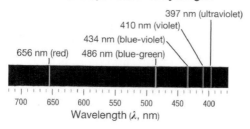

Figure 23.12: *The spectrum of light from hydrogen gas as seen in a spectrometer.*

Polarization

Polarization of a wave on a spring
The orientation of light is called its **polarization**. An easy way to think about polarization is to think about shaking a spring back and forth. Waves move *along* the spring in its long direction. The oscillation of the *transverse* wave is perpendicular to the direction the wave travels. If the spring is shaken up and down, it is *vertically polarized*. If the spring is shaken back and forth, it is *horizontally polarized*. The polarization is in the direction of the wave's oscillation, and is perpendicular to the direction the wave moves. Only transverse waves can have polarization. Longitudinal waves, like sound waves, cannot have polarization since they oscillate in only one direction—along the direction the wave moves.

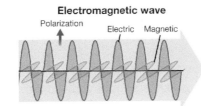

polarization - the direction of the oscillation of a wave that is perpendicular to the direction the wave travels

polarizer - a material that allows light of only one polarization (horizontal or vertical) to pass through

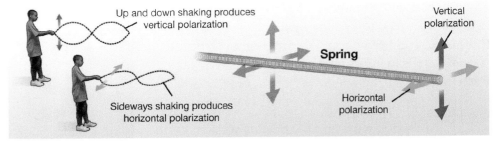

Figure 23.13: *The orientation of a light wave is its polarization. The polarization of light always refers to its electrical component.*

Polarization of light waves
Polarization is another wave property of light. The polarization of a light wave is the direction of the electric part of the wave oscillation (Figure 23.13). The fact that light shows polarization tells us that light is a *transverse wave*. Like a spring, the polarization of a light wave may be resolved into two perpendicular directions, *horizontal* and *vertical*.

Unpolarized light
Most of the light that you see is *unpolarized*. That does not mean the light has no polarization. Unpolarized light is really just an equal mixture of all polarizations. We call ordinary light unpolarized because no single polarization dominates the mixture.

Polarizers
A **polarizer** is a material that allows light of only one polarization to pass through it. Light that comes through a polarizer has only one polarization—along the *transmission axis* of the polarizer. Light with a single polarization is called *polarized light*. (Figure 23.14).

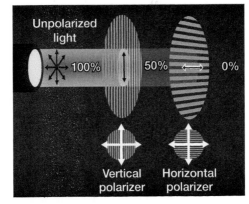

Figure 23.14: *The light that passes through a polarizer will be horizontally or vertically polarized, depending on the polarizer.*

Applications of polarization

Polarized sunglasses   Light that reflects at low angles from horizontal surfaces is polarized mostly horizontally. Polarized sunglasses reduce glare because they selectively absorb light with horizontal polarization (Figure 23.15) while letting other light through. Using polarized sunglasses, you can still see the light reflected from other objects, but the glare off of a surface such as water is blocked.

LCD computer screens   Images on a laptop computer's LCD (liquid crystal display) screen are made using polarized light, as seen below. Unpolarized light comes from a lamp and passes through a polarizer. The resulting polarized light then passes through numerous pixels of liquid crystal that act like windows.

Dark dots are made by crossing polarizers   Each liquid crystal window can be electronically controlled to act like a polarizer, or not. When a pixel is *not* a polarizer, the light comes through and you see a bright dot. When a pixel becomes a polarizer, light is blocked and you see a dark dot. The picture is made of light and dark dots. To make a color picture, there are separate polarizing windows for red, blue, and green pixels.

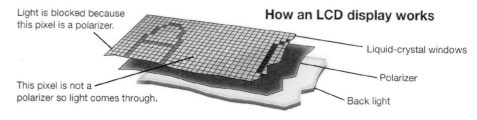

Light is blocked because this pixel is a polarizer.

How an LCD display works

Liquid-crystal windows

This pixel is not a polarizer so light comes through.

Polarizer

Back light

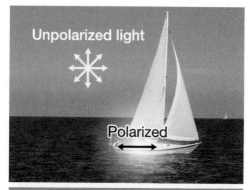

Unpolarized light

Polarized

Regular sunglasses

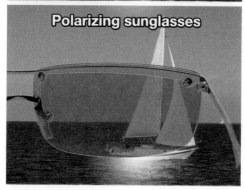

Polarizing sunglasses

Figure 23.15: *Unpolarized light from the Sun is polarized horizontally when it reflects off the water. Polarized sunglasses block out this light; regular sunglasses do not.*

23.2 Section Review

1. Why do sound waves spread out after passing through a partly-open door while light waves make a beam of light that does not spread nearly as much?

2. Suppose you shine white light through a filter that absorbs a certain color of green. What will the spectrum of this light look like after passing through a diffraction grating?

3. Look at an LCD screen through polarizing sunglasses. Explain what you see when you rotate the sunglasses to change the angle of the transmission axis of the polarizing lenses.

23.3 **The Dual Nature of Light**

Light has both wave-like and particle-like properties. By "particle-like" we mean that the energy of a light wave is divided up into little bundles called *photons*. Each atom that makes light gives off one photon at a time. Each atom that absorbs light absorbs one photon at a time. A beam of light consists of trillions of photons travelling at the speed of light.

The photon theory of light

Photons
The energy of a light wave is divided up in tiny bundles called *photons*. Each photon has its own color, no matter how you mix them up. Orange light is made of orange photons, red light of red photons, and so on. You can almost think of photons as colored jelly beans, except they have no mass.

Color and photons
The lowest-energy photons we can see are the ones that appear red to our eyes (Figure 23.16). The highest-energy photons we can see appear blue. Low-energy atoms make low-energy photons and high-energy atoms make high-energy photons. As atoms gain energy, the color of the light they produce changes from red, to yellow, to blue, and violet.

White light
White light is a mixture of photons with a range of energy. This is because white light is created by atoms that also have a range of energy. For example, when a dimmer switch is set very low, the filament of an incandescent bulb is relatively cool (low energy) and the light is red. As you turn up the switch, the filament gets hotter and makes more green and blue light. At full power, the filament is bright white, which means it is producing photons of all colors.

Temperature and energy
The atoms in a material have a range of energy depending on temperature. At room temperature (20°C), a rock gives off no visible light. At 600°C, some atoms produce red light. At 2,600°C, atoms can make all colors of light, which is why the hot filament of a light bulb appears white (Figure 23.17).

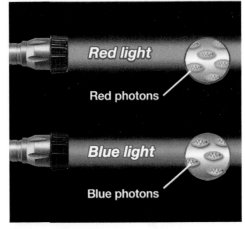

Figure 23.16: *Blue photons have a higher energy than red photons.*

Figure 23.17: *The range of light produced by an object depends on its temperature.*

The energy and intensity of light

Energy, color, and intensity

The intensity of light is a combination of both the number of photons and the energy per photon. There are two ways to make light of high intensity. One way is to have high-energy photons. A second way is to have a lot of photons even if they are low-energy (Figure 23.18). In practical terms, to make a red light with an intensity of 100 watts per meter squared (W/m^2) takes a lot more photons then it does to make the same intensity with blue light.

Glow-in-the-dark plastic

If glow-in-the-dark plastic is exposed to light, it stores some energy and releases the energy later by giving off light. The plastic can only make light if it is "charged up" by absorbing energy from other sources of light. You can test this theory by holding your hand on some "uncharged" glow-in-the-dark plastic and then exposing it to bright light. If you then bring the plastic into a dark area and remove your hand, you can see that the areas that were covered by your hand are dark while the rest of the plastic glows (Figure 23.19).

Photo-luminescence

The glow-in-the-dark effect comes from phosphorus atoms that are in the plastic. When photons of light collide with phosphorus atoms, the energy from the photons is stored in the atoms. Slowly, the stored energy is released as pale green light. The process of releasing stored light energy is called **photoluminescence**.

An experiment with photon energy

Glow-in-the-dark plastic demonstrates that *a single atom only absorbs a single photon at a time*. Let's say we want a phosphorus atom to give off a green photon. To give off green light, the atom must absorb equal or greater energy. If one red photon is absorbed, the atom does not get enough energy to make a green photon and cannot glow. However, if a single atom could absorb two or more red photons, it might get enough energy to emit a green photon. If you try the experiment, you find that even very bright red light does not make the atoms of phosphorus glow. However, even dim blue light causes the atoms to glow. This is because one blue photon has more than enough energy to cause a phosphorus atom to release a green photon. If you try different colors, you find that only photons with more energy than those of green light will cause the glow-in-the-dark plastic to glow.

> **photoluminescence** - the process of releasing stored light energy

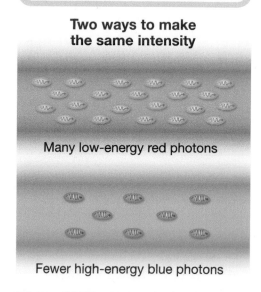

Two ways to make the same intensity

Many low-energy red photons

Fewer high-energy blue photons

Figure 23.18: *The number and energy of photons determine the intensity of the light.*

In a dark room

Area around shadow glows

Glow in the dark plastic   Shadow

Figure 23.19: *The light from the flashlight cannot energize the phosphorus atoms that your hand blocks. These atoms will not glow because they did not receive any energy from the flashlight's photons.*

Absorbing, reflecting, and creating light

Light reflects off surfaces Light reflected off a wall in a room started at a light source like a light bulb. Atoms in the wall first absorb and then re-emit the light energy. This process of absorbing and re-emitting light happens so fast that we may accurately describe the light as reflecting off the surfaces.

The process of how light is reflected The atoms on the surface of this paper in the white areas absorb the light from the room and immediately emit almost all of the light back in all directions. You see a white page because the atoms on the surface of the paper absorb and re-emit light of all colors equally (Figure 23.20). The black letters are visible because light falling on black ink is almost completely absorbed and no light is re-emitted.

Most atoms absorb and emit light Almost all atoms absorb and emit light. For most atoms, the absorption and emission of light happens in less than one millionth of a second. This is so fast that only the most sensitive instruments can detect the time delay. However, a phosphorus atom in glow-in-the-dark plastic is different. Phosphorus atoms have a special ability to delay the emission of a photon for a relatively long time after they have absorbed light.

Light from chemical reactions Many chemical changes release energy. Some of the energy is absorbed within atoms and re-emitted as light. For example, the warm flickering glow from a candle comes from trillions of atoms in the wick giving up photons as they combine with oxygen atoms in the air (Figure 23.21). The light that comes from a glow stick is also made through chemical changes.

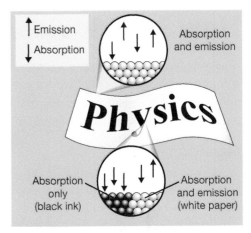

Figure 23.20: *White paper absorbs and immediately re-emits photons of all colors in all directions. Black ink absorbs photons of all colors and emits none, which is why it looks black.*

Figure 23.21: *The light from a candle flame comes from energy released by chemical changes.*

23.3 *Section Review*

1. Give one example where light acts like a wave and one example where light acts like a particle.
2. Is it possible for two beams of light to have the same number of photons per second yet have different amounts of intensity? Explain.
3. List at least three differences between a photon and an atom.
4. A piece of wood does not produce light. However, a log on a fire glows with a reddish light. Explain this observation.

How 3-D Movies Work

Have you ever wondered how a 3-D movie creates the illusion that creatures are jumping right out of the screen? Cinematographers, ophthalmologists, optical engineers, and computer graphic designers all play a role in the development of modern 3-D movie technology.

Stereoscopic Vision

In order to understand how 3-D technology works, you need to know how your eyes and brain work together to see a real-life object in three dimensions. Try this: Place an object on a table about an arm's length away from you. Close one eye and look at the object. Repeat with the other eye closed. Did you notice that you get a slightly different view of the object from each eye? Now look at the object with both eyes open. Your brain merges the separate image from each eye into one 3-D image. This is called *stereoscopic vision*.

3-D cinema technology

What is special about 3-D movie technology? To create the illusion of three-dimensions on a flat screen, each eye must receive its own separate image of the movie from a slightly different perspective, mimicking the way your eyes take in a real three-dimensional scene. In most 3-D cinema, the two separate images are shown simultaneously, superimposed on the screen.

Anaglyph 3-D imaging

Early 3-D movies, popular in the 1950s, used the anaglyph method. It separated the images by color. Two separate projectors ran simultaneously. One showed the movie in blue and the other one layered red images onto the same screen. Viewers wore 3-D glasses with one red and one blue lens, so that each eye saw a separate image. The viewer's brain combined the images, producing the illusion of depth. However, anaglyph 3-D movies had a couple of drawbacks: the coloration wasn't natural, and details were often hard to see. If one of the filmstrips had to be repaired, it might get out of synch with the other filmstrip after that point. This was a real headache for the projector operator!

Cinema technology has come a long way since the 1950s. Now, 3-D movies are produced in digital format, eliminating filmstrip repair issues. Some modern 3-D projectors have two lenses and display the images for the left and right eye simultaneously. Another type has just one lens. It alternates the left and right eye images very quickly so that each eye seems to be receiving a constant stream of visual information.

Polarization technology

Modern 3-D movies separate the images for the left and right eye by polarization rather than color. Polarized movies project one image using only vertically-polarized light rays, and the other image using only horizontally-polarized rays. The viewer wears glasses with two different lenses--one that filters out each of those two polarizations. While the color is perfectly natural in these films—a big improvement over the early anaglyph technology—there is still a downside. If you tilt your head, the lenses in your glasses will be rotated at an angle to the screen and will no longer filter out the vertical and horizontally polarized light, destroying the 3-D illusion.

To overcome this problem, most 3-D movies now use circular polarization. This technology uses a filter over the projector that converts linear-polarized light into circular-polarized light.

You can see the linear-polarized light coming into the filter. The filter contains a crystal structure that slows down the vertical component of the light but not the horizontal component. As a result, the vertical and horizontal components are out of phase when they emerge from the filter. The resulting wave appears to rotate like a corkscrew rather than moving up and down. The filters can produce circularly-polarized light with a counterclockwise or a clockwise rotation.

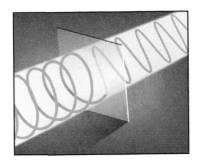

When you watch a 3-D movie that uses circular polarization, two images are superimposed on the screen. One image is produced with light polarized in the clockwise direction and the other in the counterclockwise polarization. You wear glasses with one lens that filters out each of these polarizations. With this system, you can tilt your head without losing the perception of 3-D.

High-tech "active 3-D" glasses

Circular polarization is the most common 3-D imaging system used in the commercial movie industry. That's largely because the glasses are inexpensive to make so each moviegoer can be given a disposable pair. However, there are also more expensive options.

Active 3-D glasses don't just sit passively on your head. One type contains lenses made of a material like that in LCDs that darkens only when a current is applied. Current is briefly applied to darken the left lens, and then the right lens. This process alternates at least 30 times per second. On the screen, the display alternates between left- and right-eye views, in sync with the glasses. This system eliminates "ghosting," a problem that sometimes occurs when the images for each eye are shown simultaneously.

Scientific 3-D imaging

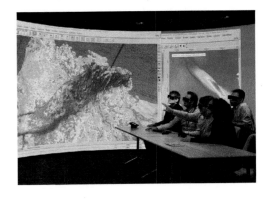

While most people are familiar with 3-D imaging technology as an entertainment tool, it has important uses in the scientific community, as well. Surgeons use 3-D–imaging to locate and remove tumors, open blocked blood vessels, and perform other life-saving operations. Geophysicists use 3-D imaging technology to search for underground oil without disturbing the land. Can you imagine other ways to use 3-D–imaging technology?

Questions

1. Some people experience headaches or nausea while viewing 3-D movies. Search the Internet with the phrase "vergence accommodation conflict" to find out why.

2. What is the advantage of viewing a 3-D movie with circular polarization technology instead of with linear polarization technology?

3. Use the Internet to find an additional scientific application of 3-D–imaging technology. Write a paragraph that describes how the technology is used.

Photo of engineers and geophysicists in screening room courtesy of Shell Oil Company.

Chapter 23 Review

Understanding Vocabulary

Select the correct term to complete the sentences.

diffraction grating	microwaves	polarizer
diffraction pattern	nanometer	radio waves
electromagnetic spectrum	photoluminescence	ultraviolet light
electromagnetic wave	photons	visible light
gamma rays	polarization	x-rays
infrared waves		

1. A shaking magnet or an oscillating charged particle will create a(n) _____.

2. The range of the electromagnetic spectrum with the highest energy but the shortest wavelengths is the section containing _____.

3. Cell phones transmit and receive electromagnetic energy in the range of waves known as _____.

4. The phenomenon that causes light to vibrate in one direction is called _____.

5. When light passes through a(n) _____, interference causes a series of bright spots to appear on either side of a central bright point.

Reviewing Concepts

Section 23.1

1. Compare red light and blue light in terms of the energy, wavelength, and frequency.

2. The speed of light changes as it passes through different materials due to the absorption and emission of the light by atoms. As the speed changes, does its frequency, wavelength, or both change? Explain.

3. How is the index of refraction for a material dependent upon the speed of light? Is it possible for a material to have an index of refraction less than 1? Why or why not?

4. Write the equation for the speed of light that you would use in each of the following situations. Let c = the speed of light, f = frequency, and λ = wavelength.

    a. You know frequency and wavelength.

    b. You know the speed of light and frequency.

    c. You know the speed of light and wavelength.

5. List two different ways that microwaves are used.

6. When a beam of x-rays passes through a person's body and onto a special film, a radiograph (or x-ray photograph) is created. How do radiographs enable a doctor to "see" a broken arm?

Section 23.2

7. List four pieces of evidence that light is a wave.

8. How is an interference pattern of light created? In your answer, use the terms *constructive interference* and *destructive interference*.

9. Thomas Young demonstrated that light is a wave. What experiment did he use and what evidence did his experiment create?

10. What is a spectrometer used for?

11. What causes the central spot when light goes through a diffraction grating? What causes the first-order bright spots?

12. Is an electromagnetic wave a transverse or a longitudinal wave?

13. What does it mean to say a light wave is polarized?

14. Explain what a polarizer does to unpolarized light.

Section 23.3

15. How is the intensity of light related to photons?

16. How is a photon's color related to its energy?

17. What "charges up" glow-in-the-dark plastic? Does it matter what color light you use to charge up the plastic?

18. In the subtractive color process, pigments absorb some colors of light and reflect others. Explain the absorption and reflection of colors of an object in terms of atoms and electrons.

Solving Problems

Section 23.1

1. The following are different types of electromagnetic waves: gamma rays, visible light, x-rays, microwaves, radio waves, infrared light, ultraviolet light. Arrange these waves in order from

   a. *lowest* energy to *highest* energy.

   b. *shortest* to *longest* wavelength.

2. For the electromagnetic waves in the question above, does it make sense to order them by their speed? Why or why not?

3. Calculate the wavelength of violet light that has a frequency of 7.5×10^{14} Hz.

4. What is the frequency of a microwave with a 30-cm wavelength?

5. The speed of light in a vacuum is 3×10^8 m/s. What is the speed of light in flint glass which has an index of refraction is 1.65?

6. Light travels at 1.56×10^8 m/s through zircon. What is the index of refraction of zircon?

Section 23.2

7. A polarizer transmits 50% of a light's intensity, and the transmitted light is oriented horizontally. How much of the light intensity is absorbed, and what is the orientation of this light?

8. A red laser with a wavelength of 650 nm is passed through a diffraction grating. What would you expect to see?

Section 23.3

9. Photographers use a special scale called color temperature for comparing the colors of light sources when they take pictures. Color temperature is the temperature in Kelvins at which a particular color of light would be emitted. Which would have the higher color temperature, a sunset or a blue flashbulb?

10. At 600°C, a heating element produces red light. Is red light also present when a light bulb filament makes white light at 2,000°C?

11. A blacksmith can tell the temperature of a metal piece by looking by its color. You know that the order of colors in a rainbow is ROY-G-BV. Which color would a blacksmith see first, red or white, as the metal is heated to a temperature of 2,600°C?

Test Practice

Section 23.1

1. A typical microwave produces radiation with a frequency of 1.0×10^{10} Hz. What is the wavelength of this microwave radiation?

   a. 3.0×10^{-1} m

   b. 3.0×10^{-2} m

   c. 3.0×10^{10} m

   d. 3.0×10^{18} m

2. Which formula represents a constant for light waves of different frequencies in a vacuum?

   a. $f \times \lambda$

   b. $f + \lambda$

   c. $\lambda \div f$

   d. $f \div \lambda$

3. Which of the following electromagnetic waves has the lowest energy?

   a. gamma ray

   b. infrared wave

   c. visible light wave

   d. microwave

4. Diamond has a refractive index of $n = 2.42$. If the speed of light in a vacuum is given as 3.00×10^8 m/s, the speed of light in a diamond is

   a. 8.07×10^{-9} m/s.

   b. 7.26×10^7 m/s.

   c. 1.24×10^8 m/s.

   d. 7.26×10^8 m/s.

Section 23.2

5. Only the wave theory of light offers an explanation for the ability of light to exhibit

   a. interference.

   b. reflection.

   c. photoluminescence.

   d. illumination.

6. Light waves can be polarized because they

   a. have high frequencies.

   b. have short wavelengths.

   c. are transverse.

   d. can be reflected.

7. Which diagram best illustrates diffraction?

A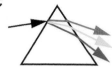

B

C

D

   a. A

   b. B

   c. C

   d. D

8. The diagram shows the side view of part of an interference pattern produced by light passing through a double-slit barrier.

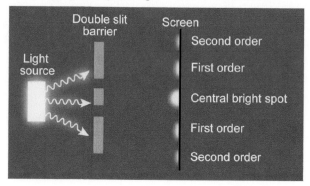

The first-order bright spots are caused by light waves that are

   a. destructively interfering.

   b. in phase.

   c. out of phase.

   d. reflecting off the central bright spot.

9. The diagram below shows sunglasses being used to eliminate glare. Which phenomenon of light is represented in the diagram?

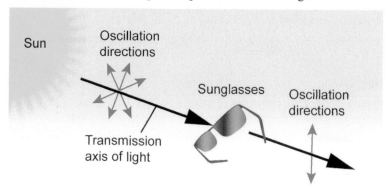

   a. dispersion

   b. diffraction

   c. internal reflection

   d. polarization

Section 23.3

10. Which graph best represents the relationship between the energy of a photon and its wavelength?

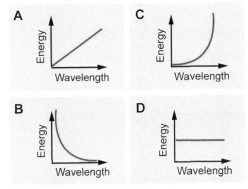

a. A

b. B

c. C

d. D

11. A metal surface emits photons when illuminated by green light. The surface must also emit photons when illuminated by

a. blue light.

b. yellow light.

c. orange light.

d. red light.

Applying Your Knowledge

Section 23.1

1. What would the world look like if your eyes could see all the different wavelengths of the electromagnetic spectrum—from radio waves to gamma waves—and not just visible light? What would your experience be like if you were able to see all kinds of electromagnetic waves? Write a short essay that answers these questions.

Section 23.2

2. Unlike humans, who sense only brightness and color, some animals use polarized vision for a variety of uses. Research an animal that uses polarized vision and, in a poster, describe how this animal uses polarized vision to its advantage. What is special about the eyes of animals with polarized vision?

3. Edwin Land (1909–1991), a physicist, invented the first filters to polarize light and held many patents in the fields of optics and photography. Research his life and inventions. Write a short paper or give a presentation that summarizes your findings about this inventor.

Section 23.3

4. The trick in building fireworks is to find materials that release light at the specific color you want to see. Research which materials are used to produce the different colors of fireworks. Make a table of the materials and the frequency and color they produce.

Glossary

A

absolute zero - the lowest possible temperature—0 K on the Kelvin temperature scale—where molecules have the lowest energy they can have   *223*

absorption - the decrease in amplitude of a wave as it passes through a material and loses energy   *456*

acceleration - a change in velocity over time   *35*

acceleration due to gravity - the acceleration of an object due to Earth's gravity that is equal to 9.8 m/s² and represented by g *63*

accuracy - how close a measurement is to an accepted or "true" value   *15*

acoustics - the science and technology of how sound behaves   *471*

additive color process - a process that creates color by adding proportions of red, green, and blue light together   *505*

additive primary colors - red, green, and blue   *505*

air resistance - a force that acts against the force of gravity on an object in free fall   *69*

alpha decay - radioactive decay that results in an alpha particle—a helium nucleus—being emitted from the nucleus of an atom   *260*

alternating current - electric current that reverses its direction at regular intervals   *329*

ampere - the unit of electric current   *298*

amplitude - the maximum distance from the equilibrium position in harmonic motion   *430*

angle of incidence - the angle between the incident ray and the normal line   *523*

angle of reflection - the angle between the reflected ray and the normal line   *523*

angle of refraction - the angle between the refracted light ray and the normal line   *524*

angular speed - the amount an object spins per unit of time in circular motion   *142*

antimatter - matter which has the opposite charge and other properties from normal matter   *276*

armature - the rotating part of an electric motor that includes the rotor and electromagnets   *390*

atomic number - the number of protons in an atom   *249*

atomic theory - a theory which states that all matter is composed of tiny particles called atoms   *244*

atom - the smallest particle of an element that exists alone or in combination with other atoms   *217*

average velocity - found by dividing total displacement by total time taken   *33*

axis of rotation - the point or line around which an object rotates   *122*

B

battery - a device that transforms chemical energy into electrical energy and moves the current in a circuit   *300*

beat - the oscillation of amplitude that results from the interference of two sound waves with frequencies that are almost but not quite equal   *485*

beta decay - radioactive decay that results in a beta particle—an electron—being emitted from the nucleus of an atom   *260*

Big Bang - a theory of the origin of the universe in which the universe was once smaller than an atom and began to expand after a huge explosion *285*

black hole - a compact, astronomical object with such strong gravity that its escape velocity is equal to or exceeds the speed of light *284*

boiling point - the temperature at which a substance changes from liquid to gas (boiling) or from gas to liquid (condensing) *221*

boundaries - an edge or surface where conditions or materials change *456*

brushes - allow current to flow into the coil of an electric motor *390*

C

calorie - a unit of energy equal to 4.184 joules, which is the amount of heat energy required to raise the temperature of 1 gram of water by 1°C *227*

capacitance - a measure of a capacitor's ability to store charge *352*

capacitor - a device that stores electric charge by keeping positive and negative charges separated *350*

Celsius scale - a temperature scale on which 0 equals the temperature at which water freezes (0°C) and 100 is the temperature at which water boils (100°C) *222*

center of gravity - the average position of an object's weight *156*

center of mass - the point about which an object naturally spins *155*

centrifugal force - the effect of inertia on an object moving in a curve *150*

centripetal force - any force that causes an object to move in a circle *147*

chain reaction - occurs when the fission reaction of a single atom triggers more nuclear reactions and results in an increasing release of nuclear energy *259*

charge - a fundamental electrical property of matter that can be positive, negative, or zero *246*

chemical energy - energy that is stored in the chemical bonds that join atoms *195*

circuit diagram - a drawing that uses symbols to represent each part of an electrical circuit *296*

circular motion - motion that results when a force causes an object to curve in a full circle *142*

circular wave - a wave with crests that forms a pattern of circular wave fronts *455*

circumference - the distance traveled during one revolution *144*

closed circuit - a circuit with no breaks in which charge flows *297*

cochlea - a tiny, fluid-filled structure in the inner ear that contains the nerves that create your sense of hearing *483*

coil - a current-carrying wire made into loops *386*

collision - occurs when two or more objects hit each other *91*

color - the perception of the energy of light *502*

commutator - the device that switches the direction of electrical current in the electromagnets of an electric motor *389*

compass - a device containing a magnet that interacts with Earth's magnetic field to indicate direction *371*

components - the two vectors, at right angles to each other, that add up to a given vector *108*

compound - a substance made of two or more elements that cannot be separated by physical means *218*

conductor - a material with low electrical resistance such as copper or aluminum *306*

cones - photoreceptors that respond to color *503*

consonance - a combination of sound frequencies that is agreeable or harmonious *485*

constant speed - an unchanging speed of a moving object that covers the same distance each second *17*

constant velocity - an unchanging velocity; both speed and direction remain the same *32*

constructive interference - occurs when waves add up to make a larger amplitude *459*

contact force - a force between two objects that are in contact, or between an object and a surface *111*

control variable - a variable in an experiment that is kept the same throughout the experiment *8*

convection - the transfer of thermal energy by the motion of a fluid *233*

converging lens - a lens that is thickest in the middle causing parallel light rays to come together to a point *521*

Coulomb's law - states that the attraction or repulsion between two electric charges is inversely related to the square of the distance between them *342*

coulomb - the unit of electric charge *340*

crest - the top or highest point on a wave *451*

critical angle - the angle of incidence at which the angle of refraction is 90 degrees *526*

cycle - a unit of oscillation that repeats *426*

D

damping - the gradual loss of amplitude of an oscillator *430*

decibels - the unit for measuring the loudness of sound *471*

dependent variable - the variable in an experiment that changes in response to choices made by the experimenter *8*

destructive interference - occurs when waves add up to make a smaller amplitude *459*

diffraction - the change in the shape of a wave as it passes through an opening or bends around an edge *457*

diffuse reflection - the scattering of a light ray into many directions off of a non-shiny surface *522*

direct current - electric current that flows in one direction only *329*

dispersion - describes how refractive index varies depending on the color of light *527*

displacement - a change in position *31*

dissonance - a combination of sound frequencies that is discordant or unsettling *485*

distance - a measure of the space between two points *11*

diverging lens - a lens that is thinnest in the middle causing light rays to spread apart *521*

Doppler effect - the shift in frequency caused by the relative motion of a sound source and an observer *473*

E

efficiency - the ratio of a machine's output work to its input work *184*

elastic collision - occurs when objects collide so that the total kinetic energy remains the same before and after the collision *91*

electrical energy - energy resulting from electric currents *195*

electrical power - the rate at which electrical energy is changed into other forms of energy *326*

electrical symbol - a symbol used for the parts of an electrical circuit in circuit diagrams *296*

electric circuit - a complete path through which electricity travels *295*

electric current - the flow of electric charge *294*

electric field - a force field created by the forces between electric charges *414*

electric motor - a machine that converts electrical energy into mechanical energy *388*

electromagnet - a magnet created by electric current flowing in wires *366*

electromagnetic force - a force created by electric charge or magnetism or both *247*

electromagnetic induction - the process of using a moving magnet to create a current in a conductor *391*

electromagnetic spectrum - the entire range of electromagnetic waves, including all possible frequencies *545*

electromagnetic wave - a wave of oscillating electric and magnetic fields that moves at the speed of light *544*

electron - a low-mass particle with a negative charge that occupies energy levels in space around an atom's nucleus *246*

electroscope - an instrument used to detect charged objects *344*

element - a pure substance that contains only atoms with the same number of protons in each atom's nucleus *217*

energy - a measure of a system's ability to change or create change in other systems *4*

energy conversion - the transformation of or changing from one kind of energy to one or more other kinds of energy *203*

energy flow diagram - a diagram showing the transformations and conversions of energy in a system *197*

energy of pressure - energy stored in and resulting from the pressure of a fluid *195*

English System - the measurement system used for everyday measurements in the United States *12*

entropy - a measure of the energy in a system that is not available to do work *201*

equilibrium - occurs when the forces on an object are balanced so the net force on the object is zero *111*

evaporation - the process by which atoms or molecules leave a liquid and become a gas at a temperature below the boiling point *221*

experimental variable - a variable in an experiment that is changed by the experimenter *8*

experiment - a situation created to test or investigate a hypothesis *6*

F

Fahrenheit scale - a temperature scale on which water freezes at 32 degrees Fahrenheit (or 32°F) and water boils at 212°F *222*

farad - a unit of capacitance *352*

Faraday's law of induction - the voltage induced in a coil is directly proportional to the rate of change of the magnetic field through the coil *392*

fiber optics - thin glass fibers that use total internal reflection to carry light *526*

field - the physical phenomena responsible for how forces are transmitted from one object to another everywhere in space *408*

first law of thermodynamics - the law of conservation of energy: Energy cannot be created or destroyed, only converted from one form into another *201*

fluorescence - a process by which atoms release light energy *501*

focal length - the distance from the center of a lens to the focal point *530*

focal point - the point in an optical system at which light rays meet or appear to meet *530*

focus - the point where light rays from each point on an object come together to form an image *532*

food chain - a series of steps through which energy and nutrients are transferred from organism to organism in an ecosystem *207*

force - a push, pull, or other action that has the ability to change motion *54*

force field - a distribution of energy in space that exerts a force on objects in it, including magnetic fields, gravitational fields, and electrical fields *412*

fossil fuel - substances found in Earth's crust that were formed over millions of years from the remains of dead organisms *395*

Fourier's theorem - the creation of a complex wave by adding single-frequency waves *480*

frame of reference - an object or system assumed to be at rest *34*

free-body diagram - a diagram showing all of the forces acting on an object *110*

free fall - the acceleration of a falling object due to Earth's gravity *63*

frequency spectrum - a graph showing the distribution of different frequencies in a complex signal, like a sound wave *481*

frequency - the number of cycles per second *428*

friction - a force that results from relative motion between objects *117*

fulcrum - a fixed point on a lever about which the lever rotates *178*

fundamental - the lowest natural frequency of a standing wave *454*

G

gamma decay - a process by which the nucleus of an atom emits a gamma-ray radiation *260*

gamma rays - electromagnetic waves with wavelengths of less than ten-trillionths of a meter *549*

gas - a phase of matter that flows and can expand or contract to fill its container *220*

gauss - a unit used to measure the strength of a magnetic field *374*

general relativity - Einstein's theory in which gravity is an effect created by the curvature of space-time *282*

generator - a device that converts kinetic energy into electrical energy using Faraday's law of induction *393*

gravitational constant - the constant in the law of universal gravitation that is equal to $6.67 \times 10^{-11} \, \mathrm{N \cdot m^2/kg^2}$ *153*

gravitational field - a force field created by mass and acting on mass *412*

H

half-life - the length of time it takes for half of any sample of a radioactive isotope to change into other isotopes (or elements) *262*

hard magnet - a material in which the magnetic domains remain aligned after being magnetized, making them more difficult to demagnetize *369*

harmonic motion - repeating motion; also called oscillatory motion *426*

harmonics - frequencies that are multiples of a fundamental frequency *454*

heat conduction - the transfer of thermal energy by the direct contact of particles of matter *231*

heat - the movement of thermal energy from one object to another object due to a temperature difference *226*

hertz - the unit of one cycle per second *428*

Hooke's law - states that the force exerted by a spring is proportional to its change in length *115*

horsepower - a unit of power equal to 746 watts *171*

hypothesis - a tentative statement that can be tested by comparison with scientific evidence *6*

I

image - a picture of an object that is formed in space where light rays meet *528*

impulse - the product of force and time that causes a change in momentum *80*

incandescence - the process of making light with heat *500*

incident ray - the light ray that strikes a reflective surface *523*

independent variable - the variable in an experiment that is manipulated by the experimenter and that causes changes in the dependent variable in the experiment *8*

index of refraction - a value that describes the ability of a material to bend light *524*

inelastic collision - a type of collision in which the total kinetic energy after the collision is less than it was before the collision and which usually involves objects sticking together or changing shape *91*

inertia - the property of an object that resists changes in motion *55*

infrared waves - a type of electromagnetic wave with wavelengths between 1 mm and 700 nm *548*

input arm - the side of a lever between the fulcrum and the input force *178*

input - the force, work, energy, or power applied to a machine *173*

instantaneous velocity - describes an object's velocity at one moment in time or at one specific point in the object's path *33*

insulator - a material with high electrical resistance such as plastic or rubber *306*

intensity - a term that describes the amount of light energy per second falling on a surface *497*

intensity - the field strength at a certain point in space *410*

interference - the pattern of frequency, brightness, amplitude, or other wave characteristics that comes from adding waves of the same kind *458*

intermolecular forces - the forces between atoms or molecules that determine their phase—solid, liquid, or gas—at any given temperature *220*

inverse square law - describes a quantity that varies inversely with the square of the distance *410*

irreversible - a process that can only run in one direction and which is less than 100 percent efficient *185*

isotopes - forms of the same element that have diffewrent numbers of neutrons and different mass numbers *249*

J

joule - a unit of energy and work that is equal to 1 newton of force times 1 meter of distance *83*

K

Kelvin - the temperature scale that starts at absolute zero and measures the actual energy of atoms *223*

kilowatt-hour - 1 kilowatt or 1,000 watts of power used per hour *328*

kinetic energy - energy that comes from motion and is related to mass and velocity *86*

Kirchoff's current law - the total current entering a circuit branch must equal the current leaving the branch *321*

Kirchoff's voltage law - the sum of the voltage drops in a series circuit must equal the circuit's total voltage *319*

L

law of conservation of energy - energy cannot be created or destroyed, although it can be changed from one form to another; also called the first law of thermodynamics *88*

law of conservation of momentum - in the absence of external forces, the total momentum of a system remains constant *81*

law of reflection - the angle of incidence equals the angle of reflection *523*

law of universal gravitation - the relationship between gravitational force, mass, and distance *153*

length - a measured distance that uses a specific measurement system's units *11*

lever arm - the perpendicular distance between the line of action of a force and the axis of rotation *123*

light ray - an imaginary line that represents a light beam's path *520*

linear speed - distance traveled per unit of time *144*

line of action - an imaginary line in the direction of the force and passing through the point where the force is applied *122*

liquid - a phase of matter that has definite volume but can change its shape and flow *220*

longitudinal - describes a wave with oscillations that are in the same direction as the wave travels *450*

lubricant - a fluid used to reduce friction *120*

M

machine - a mechanical system capable of performing work *173*

magnetic declination - the difference between the direction a compass points and the direction of true (geographic) north *373*

magnetic domain - a region of a material in which atoms align in the same direction, increasing the magnetic field strength *369*

magnetic field line - one of many lines with arrows used to show the direction of the forces in a magnetic field; magnetic field lines always point away from a magnet's north pole and toward a magnet's south pole *365*

magnetic field - the magnetic forces that surround an object at all points in space *364*

magnetic pole - north or south; one of the two opposite places on a magnet where the magnetic field is the strongest; all magnets have at least one north pole and one south pole *362*

magnetic - the ability to exert forces on magnets or other magnetic materials *362*

magnification - the ratio of the size of the image divided by the size of the object *533*

magnitude - a quantity's size or amount without regard to its direction or other factors   *106*

mass number - the total number of protons and neutrons in the nucleus of an atom   *249*

mass - the amount of matter an object has and a measure of its inertia   *4*

mechanical advantage - the ratio of output force to input force   *175*

mechanical energy - the energy an object or system has due to motion or position   *195*

melting point - the temperature at which a substance changes from solid to liquid (melting) or liquid to solid (freezing)   *221*

microwaves - electromagnetic waves with wavelengths between 30 cm and 1 mm   *548*

mixture - a substance that contains more than one kind of atom, molecule, or compound   *218*

model - a method of representing a relationship between variables   *10*

molecule - the smallest particle of a compound that has the identity of the compound   *218*

momentum - the mass of an object multiplied by its velocity   *79*

multimeter - an instrument that measures current, voltage, and resistance   *299*

musical scale - a series of frequencies arranged in a special pattern   *484*

N

nanometer - one billionth of a meter (10^{-9} m)   *546*

natural frequency - the frequency at which a system naturally oscillates   *437*

natural law - a rule that describes an action or set of actions in the universe   *4*

net force - the total of all forces acting on an object   *57*

neutron - an uncharged particle found in the nucleus of an atom which has a mass about equal to the mass of a proton   *246*

Newton's first law - an object at rest will stay at rest and an object in motion will continue in motion with the same velocity unless acted on by an outside force   *55*

Newton's second law - relates the net force acting on an object to its mass and acceleration   *59*

Newton's third law - whenever one object exerts a force on another, the second object exerts an equal and opposite force on the first   *76*

newton - the SI unit of force   *56*

nonrenewable resource - a natural resource that is not replaced as it is used   *395*

normal force - a support force exerted on an object by another object that is perpendicular to the objects' contact surfaces   *111*

normal line - the line that is perpendicular to a surface   *523*

note - a musical sound such as from a musical scale   *484*

nuclear energy - energy that is stored in the nucleus of an atom which can be absorbed or released by nuclear reactions   *195*

nuclear reaction - a reaction that changes the nucleus of an atom and which may change the element into another element or into an isotope of the same element   *256*

nucleus - the mass at the center of an atom that contains protons and neutrons   *246*

O

object - a real, physical thing that gives off or reflects light **528**

objective - describes evidence that documents only what actually happens and is observed as exactly as possible **9**

octave - the interval between a frequency and twice that frequency **484**

Ohm's law - states that the current is *directly* related to the voltage and *inversely* related to the resistance **304**

open circuit - a circuit with a break in which charge can't flow **297**

optical axis - an imaginary line that runs through the center of a lens **530**

optics - the study of how light behaves **520**

orbit - a regular, repeating path that an object in space follows around another object **154**

origin - a place where the position has been given a value of zero **30**

oscillation - a motion that repeats regularly **427**

oscillator - a system that shows harmonic motion **427**

output arm - the side of a lever between the fulcrum and the output force **178**

output - the force, work, energy, or power produced by a machine **173**

P

parabola - the curved path a projectile follows **137**

parallel circuit - an electric circuit with more than one path or branch **321**

periodic force - an oscillating (repetitive) force **437**

period - the amount of time it takes for one cycle **428**

permanent magnet - a material that retains its magnetic properties even when no external energy is supplied **362**

phase - where an oscillator is in its cycle **433**

photoelectric effect - the emission of electrons from a metal surface when light falls on that surface **506**

photoluminescence - the process of releasing stored light energy **556**

photon - the smallest quantity of light energy **254**

photoreceptors - light-sensitive cells on the surface of the retina **503**

physics - a branch of science concerned with understanding the natural laws that relate to matter and energy **4**

pitch - the perceived frequency of a sound **470**

plane wave - a wave with crests that form of a pattern of straight-line wave fronts **455**

plasma - an ionized gas phase of matter such as found in stars, lightning, and some kinds of electric lights **223**

polarization - the direction of the oscillation of a wave that is perpendicular to the direction the wave travels **553**

polarized - describes the separation of positive and negative charge in an object's atoms **345**

polarizer - a material that allows light of only one polarization (horizontal or vertical) to pass through **553**

position - a variable that tells location relative to an origin **30**

potential energy - stored energy that comes from position **85**

power - the rate at which work is done and which is measured in watts or joules per second **171**

precision - describes how close together or reproducible repeated measurements are **15**

pressure - the force exerted per unit area by particles of matter in a fluid and which acts in all directions in a container **225**

prism - an optical device used to reflect and refract light in precise ways *521*

probability - the science of describing the chance of an event or events to occur *255*

projectile - an object moving through the air and affected only by the force due to gravity *137*

propagate - to spread out or travel *455*

proton- a positively-charged particle found with neutrons in the nucleus of an atom *246*

Q

quantum state - the specific values of energy and momentum which are allowed for a particle as described by quantum theory *253*

quantum theory - the theory that describes the behavior of matter and energy on the atomic scale *252*

R

radiant energy - another term for electromagnetic energy *195*

radioactive decay - the spontaneous changing of the nucleus of atoms through the release of radiation *260*

radioactive - describes atoms which are unstable and spontaneously change into other atoms by the emission of particles and/or energy from the nucleus *259*

radio waves - the lowest frequency electromagnetic waves with wavelengths greater than about 30 cm *548*

range - the horizontal distance a projectile travels before touching the ground *137*

ray diagram - an accurately-drawn sketch showing how light rays interact with an optical device *520*

real image - an image formed by light rays coming together *532*

reference frame - a perspective from which the position and motion of a system can be described *282*

reflected ray - the light ray that bounces off a reflective surface *523*

reflecting telescope - a device that uses a concave mirror and a converging lens to magnify objects *533*

reflection - the bouncing of a wave off of a surface *456*

refracting telescope - a device that uses two converging lenses to magnify objects *533*

refraction - the bending of a wave as it crosses a boundary between different materials *456*

relative velocity - describes the velocity of an object with respect to a frame of reference *34*

renewable resource - a natural resource that can be replaced *395*

repeatable - describes evidence that can be seen independently by others if they repeat the same experiment or observation in the same way *9*

resistance - a measure of how much current flows in a circuit for a given voltage *302*

resistor - a device that controls or uses the energy carried by an electric current *296*

resolution - refers to the smallest interval that can be measured *15*

resonance - occurs when a periodic force has the same frequency as the natural frequency *438*

restoring force - a force that pulls an oscillating system back toward equilibrium *435*

resultant - a vector that is the vector sum of two or more individual vectors *112*

reverberation - multiple echoes of sound caused by reflections of sound building up and blending together *478*

reversible - an ideal process that can run forward or backward *185*

revolve - to move around, or orbit, an external axis *142*

rhythm - the organization of sound into regular time patterns *484*

right-hand rule - a method used to identify the direction of a magnetic field *366*

rods - photoreceptors that respond to light intensity *503*

rotational equilibrium - occurs when an object's net torque is zero *125*

rotor - a rotating disk found in an electric motor or generator *388*

S

satellite - an object that circles around another object with gravity providing the centripetal force *154*

scalar - a quantity that is completely described by its magnitude and measurement units *106*

scientific method - a process of learning that begins with a hypothesis and proceeds to prove or change a hypothesis by comparing it with scientific evidence *6*

second law of thermodynamics - when work is done by heat flowing, the output work must be less than the amount of heat flowing *201*

second - the basic unit of time in both the English and SI systems of measurement *14*

semiconductor - a material with electrical conductivity between that of conductors and insulators *306*

series circuit - an electric circuit that has only one path for the current *316*

shielding - materials that reduce or block electric fields *417*

shock wave - the "piled up" wave fronts that form in front of a supersonic object *472*

short circuit - occurs when a circuit branch has a very low resistance, creating a large current *325*

significant digits - meaningful digits in a measured quantity *16*

simple machine - an unpowered mechanical device, such as a lever, that works by a single movement *174*

SI - the International System of Units (SI) used by most countries for everyday measurement and used by the scientific community worldwide *12*

sliding friction - resistance created when two surfaces slide across one another *117*

slope - ratio of rise to run *38*

soft magnet - a magnetic material that is relatively easily magnetized or demagnetized, such as iron *369*

solenoid - a coil of wire that acts as an electromagnet when current passes through it *386*

solid - a phase of matter that holds its volume and shape and does not flow *220*

sonogram - a graph showing how the loudness of different frequencies of sound changes with time *481*

source charge - the charge that creates an electric field *415*

specific heat - a property of a substance that tells us how much heat is needed to raise the temperature of 1 kg by 1°C *228*

spectral line - each individual line of color appearing in a spectrometer *251*

spectrometer - a device that breaks light into its component colors *251*

spectrum - the characteristic pattern of colors emitted by a pure substance *251*

specular reflection - reflection in which each incident ray creates only one reflected ray *522*

speed of light - a universal constant equal to 300 million m/s in a vacuum *275*

speed - the rate at which an object's distance changes over time *17*

spring constant - a constant that represents the relationship between the force exerted by a spring and its change in length *115*

standing wave - a resonance created by trapping a wave between boundaries that causes the wave to interfere with its reflections *454*

static electricity - a buildup of positive or negative charge consisting of isolated motionless charges, such as those produced by friction *341*

static friction - a type of friction that keeps two surfaces from sliding across each other *117*

steady state - a condition in which the variables describing a system remain constant over time and relative to each other *205*

strong nuclear force - the force that holds protons and neutrons together in the nucleus of an atom *247*

subsonic - motion that is slower than the speed of sound *472*

subtractive color process - a process that uses absorption to create color by subtracting colors from white light *507*

subtractive primary colors - cyan, magenta, and yellow *507*

superconductor - a material that becomes a conductor with zero resistance at very low temperatures *348*

superposition principle - states that when more than one wave of the same type is present in a system, the total vibration at any point is the sum of the vibrations from each individual wave *458*

supersonic - motion that is faster than the speed of sound in air *472*

switch - a device used to open and close a circuit *297*

system - a collection of related factors that you identify to help answer a question or solve a problem *5*

T

temperature - a measure of the average kinetic energy of the particles in a sample of matter *219*

tension - a force that causes a stretching or pulling of a material or object *180*

terminal velocity - the maximum velocity reached by an object in free fall in which the forces of gravity and air resistance are equal *69*

theory - a scientific explanation supported by a lot of evidence collected over a long period of time *7*

theory of special relativity - a theory by Albert Einstein describing what happens to matter, energy, time, and space at speeds close to the speed of light *278*

thermal conductor - a material that conducts heat easily *232*

thermal energy - the sum of the kinetic energies of *all* of the atoms and molecules in a mass *226*

thermal insulator - a material that conducts heat poorly *232*

thermal radiation - heat transfer in the form of electromagnetic waves, including light *234*

thermodynamics - the branch of physics that deals with heat, energy, and work *201*

time dilation - an outcome of Einstein's theory of special relativity, whereby time runs slower for objects in motion than for objects at rest *278*

time interval - a quantity of time separating two events *13*

torque - a measure of how much a force acting on an object causes the object to rotate *122*

total internal reflection - a phenomenon that happens when the angle of refraction becomes greater than 90 degrees *526*

trajectory - the path followed by a projectile *137*

transformer - a device that increases or decreases the voltage from a power source *398*

translucent - describes materials that allow light to pass through, but scatter that light in many directions *499*

transparent - describes materials that allow light to pass through them *499*

transverse - describes a wave with oscillations that are perpendicular to the direction the wave travels *450*

trough - the bottom or lowest point on a wave *451*

U

ultraviolet light - a type of electromagnetic wave with a range of wavelengths from 10 nm to 400 nm *549*

uncertainty principle - it is impossible to precisely know a particle's position, momentum, energy, and time in a quantum system all at the same time *254*

V

variable - a factor that affects the results of an experiment and which can have different values under different conditions *5*

vector - a quantity that includes both magnitude and direction *106*

velocity - describes an object's change of position over time; can also be defined as speed in a given direction *32*

vibration - a rapid oscillation *427*

virtual image - an image formed when light rays are bent so they appear to come from a point in space different from where they originated *529*

visible light - a type of electromagnetic wave with wavelengths between 700 nm and 400 nm *548*

voltage - a measure of electric potential energy *299*

voltage drop - a reduction of electrical energy by an electrical device as current passes through it *318*

volt - the unit of voltage *299*

W

watt - the metric unit of power that is equal to 1 joule per second *171*

wave - an oscillation that travels from one place to another *448*

wave fronts - another term for the crests of a wave *455*

wavelength - the length of one complete cycle of a wave *451*

wave pulse - a short-duration wave or a single oscillation *459*

weight - the force of gravity acting on an object *67*

white light - light that is a combination of all colors of light *502*

work - a form of energy that is the product of force and distance when both force and distance are in the same direction *84*

work-energy theorem - the work done by a system equals the change in kinetic energy of that system *170*

X

x-rays - high-frequency electromagnetic waves with wavelengths ranging from about 10 nm to about 0.001 nm *549*

Index

index

W

X

Y

Z